DATE DUE

Feb 13 '67			
Sep 27 '68			
Oct 7 '71			
Dec 15 '71			
Oct 25 '72			
Feb 573			
Nov 5 '73			
Feb 2c '76			
Mar 8 '76			
Dec 7 '76			
GAYLORD			PRINTED IN U.S.A.

Precocious metamorphosis of the frog tadpole (*Rana pipiens*) by adding thyroid hormone (thyroxine) to the aquarium water. The mother (large frog) was caused to ovulate in September, some seven months before the normal breeding period, by subcutaneously implanting six pituitary glands from adult female donors. The eggs were artificially inseminated. When the tadpoles had developed hindlimb buds, minute amounts of thyroxine were added to the water. In about three weeks, the treated tadpoles resorbed their swimming tails, grew hindlimbs and then forelimbs, lost their horny teeth (used for plant feeding), shortened their intestinal tracts in preparation for carnivorous feeding, modified their respiratory and integumentary systems for terrestrial environments, and emerged as normal, but miniature, air-breathing adults. This experiment was first performed by Gudernatsch (1912), who fed bits of horse thyroid to young tadpoles.

Since thyroxine initiates the metamorphic changes long before they would normally occur, the resulting froglets are about one-third the size of those metamorphosing in nature. Thyroidectomized tadpoles never metamorphose, but grow to "giant" size. Drawn to scale from photographs of the living specimens.

4TH EDITION   ILLUSTRATED

GENERAL

ENDOCRINOLOGY

C. DONNELL TURNER, Ph.D.
PROFESSOR OF BIOLOGY,
DUQUESNE UNIVERSITY, PITTSBURGH

W. B. SAUNDERS COMPANY · Philadelphia · London · 1966

General Endocrinology

To

DR. HIROSHI ASAKAWA
and
MISS MAUDE L. BURRIS

in appreciation of their aid and encouragement

Preface to the
Fourth Edition

The objective of the first edition, appearing in 1948, was to present the general and comparative aspects of endocrinology in a manner which would meet the needs of students specializing in the biological sciences, and this was the first attempt to do so. This original aim has not changed.

During the past twenty years, there has been a steady accumulation of information on the neuroendocrine mechanisms of invertebrates and poikilothermic vertebrates, and this has served to bring the goal into a clearer perspective and to expedite its achievement. The exploration of integrative mechanisms among organisms of phylogenetically different levels of complexity has been rewarding, and the results are being applied to such basic problems as metabolism, reproduction, development, ecologic adaptation, and organic evolution. The chemical coordination of individuals and groups of individuals is recognized as a pervasive theme throughout the world of life, and the subject is inextricably incorporated into contemporary biology. Our knowledge of the mechanisms whereby major functions of the body are integrated through the diffusible products of the nervous and endocrine systems has assumed such proportions that endocrinology can no longer be adequately taught as part of another course.

Profound alterations in the conceptual fabric of endocrinology have occurred during recent decades: perhaps of greatest importance are the many instances of reciprocal interrelationships prevailing between the nervous and endocrine systems. Indeed, it has been established that certain neurons, like endocrine glands, synthesize and release chemical messengers into the body fluids. These neurosecretory centers are endocrine devices that link the central nervous system with the ductless glands, thus facilitating adjustments which are essentially neuroendocrine in nature. Since the great majority of integrative changes are effected through chemical agents derived from both the nervous system and the ductless glands, endocrinology can no longer be restricted to the conventional complement of ductless glands. The subject must be broadened to encompass neurosecretory centers and the term "neuroendocrinology" is rapidly gaining acceptance. Neuroendocrine integration constitutes the central theme of this edition, and selected examples are mentioned in nearly every chapter.

Some important changes have been made in the present edition. All chapters have been revised or rewritten in order to include current concepts, and several new ones have been added. Chapter 2 on The Science of Endocrinology includes a brief account of the historical development of the subject and provides an introductory résumé of the endocrine system with particular reference to vertebrates. It was decided to place the chapter on invertebrate neuroendocrinology near the beginning of the book, instead of at the end as has traditionally been the case. It seems pedagogically sound to begin with an exploration of the invertebrates where many, if not all, of the chemical messengers are derived from glandlike neurons (neurosecretory cells) rather than from typical ductless glands. In endocrinology, as in other areas of biology, the clues which lead to an understanding of complex systems are often found in simpler ones from which the former have evolved.

The author has felt for a long time that more attention should be devoted to vertebrate chromatophores and the mechanisms involved in their regulation, and a new chapter is introduced to cover this topic. Another new chapter deals with the neurohypophysial peptides, particularly their chemistry and phyletic distribution. There are indications that the pineal body functions as an endocrine organ in the mediation of certain environmental stimuli, and the latest studies on this elusive structure are discussed in appropriate chapters. The mechanisms of hormone action have been considered as fully as present information permits. Interesting and perhaps phylogenetically significant species differences in certain protein, peptide, and steroid hormones have been pointed out.

It has been necessary to redraw some of the old figures in order to bring them up to date, and a number of new ones have been prepared. The author acknowledges with gratitude the skill and patience of the following artists: Miss Margaret Croup, Children's Hospital of Pittsburgh; Mrs. Ann Retaichak, The University of Pittsburgh Medical School; Mr. Stephen Shapiro, Albany Medical College of Union University; and Mrs. Sheryl Smiler, Duquesne University. The assistance of the librarians at Scaife Medical Library of the University of Pittsburgh is deeply appreciated and gratefully acknowledged.

Many constructive criticisms of previous editions have come to the author from both professors and students, and some of their suggestions have found their way into this edition. This friendly sharing of knowledge and experience is invaluable, and continuation of the practice is invited.

C. DONNELL TURNER

Pittsburgh, Pa.

Contents

1 _____

INTRODUCTION

It is not likely that endocrinology could be defined in a manner entirely acceptable to all biologists since there are many points of view and many gaps in our information. There are some who regard it as the aspect of biology dealing broadly with the chemical integration of the individual. Following the classic definition of Bayliss and Starling, others prefer to confine its scope to the circumscribed ductless glands and the adjustments that their special products facilitate. It is probable that the first position is too flexible and the second too rigid. As the field is more critically explored and more becomes known about reactions at the cellular level, unifying principles will probably emerge. At present, it seems desirable not to close the door by formulating strict definitions, and to recognize that there are many deviating types of chemical integrations to be found throughout the animal and plant kingdoms.

The term *hormone* has probably been applied too loosely to a great variety of unrelated substances. Agents emanating from injured tissues have been called "wound hormones" and growth substances in plants "phytohormones"; agents released from nerve terminals have been classed as "neurohormones"; even carbon dioxide has been referred to as a "hormone of respiration." Some have used the term "social hormone" to designate chemical agents that are released into the external environment and serve to influence the behavior of other individuals of the same species. In termites, for example, the reproductive and soldier castes prevent others from becoming members of their own castes by secreting materials that are ingested and act through the corpus allatum, an endocrine gland influencing differentiation.

1

Some of these agents, although they perform integrative functions, probably do not fall within the scope of endocrinology. However, it must be recognized that ductless glands are present in certain invertebrates and in all vertebrates. Moreover, one would be hard pressed to give a precise definition of an endocrine gland because all cells possess some secretory capacity and contribute to the internal environment of the organism.

As research broadens and deepens our knowledge of coordinatory systems, it becomes increasingly apparent that their products participate in every bodily function, and even have profound influences upon the mental states and behavioral patterns of individuals. Studies on the invertebrates and lower vertebrates suggest that chemical integration by hormones and similar agents is an over-all phenomenon prevailing throughout the animal kingdom, and that important actions may be exerted during developmental stages as well as in mature organisms. Further information is urgently needed on the evolutionary history of endocrine mechanisms. Comparative endocrinologists will probably discover more clues that will be of value in helping to interpret adjustments that must be operating at the human level. The general picture is far from complete, and it is imperative to remember that present interpretations and theories are tentative.

Biologists are beginning to realize that the nervous and endocrine systems, both functioning to integrate the organism, are not so divergent and sharply delimited as was formerly supposed. A common physiologic attribute of these two systems is their ability to synthesize and release special chemical agents that are capable of spreading for varying distances. Nerve cells produce materials that act as chemical messengers either locally (*e.g.*, acetylcholine) or at a distance (*e.g.*, oxytocin). Many endocrine glands, through their hormones, act on the nervous system; on the other hand, endocrine organs are frequently stimulated or inhibited by products of the nervous system.[9] Seldom does one encounter biologic phenomena that are controlled exclusively by either the nervous system or the endocrine system; most are under the overlapping authority of both systems. Furthermore, studies on neurosecretion leave no doubt that the nervous system has its own endocrine specializations for the release of hormones.[3] The functional interlocking is so remarkable that nervous and endocrine elements are coming to be regarded as constituting a *neuroendocrine* system.

The hormones act upon *target* tissues and organs by regulating the rates of specific metabolic reactions without contributing much matter to the constituent cells. These biochemical adjustments are accomplished at the cellular level by virtue of their power to augment or restrain special enzyme systems. Hormones are released at the right time and in proper amounts in the normal organism, and maladjustments of severe consequence may be precipitated if the timing is wrong or if they are deficient or present in superabundance. Obviously, hormones are without effect unless the target cells and tissues are capable of responding to them. The competence of a particular hormone within the living body may be altered by a multitude of autopharmacologic substances always present with it in the body fluids.

The rapid coordinations of the body are controlled by the nervous system. Since hormones are generally conveyed by the circulation and must be transmitted through intercellular tissue fluids in order to reach their *target organs,* we find that they regulate processes such as growth, regeneration, reproduction, blood chemistry, molting, metabolic rate, pigmentation, etc. These are adjustments that require duration rather than speed.

TYPES OF CHEMICAL MESSENGERS

Admittedly, many biologic phenomena cannot be confined within the framework of formal definitions, but some agreement on terminology is essential. The suggestion of Parkes and Bruce that the term *chemical messengers* be used broadly to include both internal secretions involved in integration of the individual and external secretions concerned with the integration of populations has some merit.[22] The following categories of chemical messengers may be recognized at this time, though the demarcations are not sharp in all instances. Norepinephrine, for example, is released by adrenergic nerve terminals, where it serves as a transmitter substance, but it is also a normal product of the adrenal medulla. This secretion therefore might be viewed either as a neurohumor or as a true hormone. The chromaffin cells of the adrenal medulla are derived from the neural crests, the embryonic tissue that also forms the sympathetic ganglia. Since the medullary cells are the equivalents of postganglionic neurons, but have specialized as endocrine glands, both epinephrine and norepinephrine might be considered either as hormones or as neurohormones.

Hormones

According to the original use of the word, hormones are chemical agents which are synthesized by circumscribed parts of the body, generally specialized ductless glands, and are carried by the circulating blood to another part of the body where they evoke systemic adjustments by acting on rather specific target tissues or organs. In the course of time, there has been a tendency to restrict the term *hormone* to the products of endocrine glands, and to resist broadening its meaning to include such regulatory metabolites as carbon dioxide and the large category of substances (*e.g.*, embryonic inductors) that exert localized actions. In any case, hormones facilitate integrative adjustments within the individual and must be distinguished from a growing list of exocrine gland products (pheromones) that play important roles in integrating groups of individuals.[11, 12]

Though it is often difficult or impossible to separate the neural and hormonal components of regulatory processes, the complex of endocrine glands in the vertebrates is quite clear-cut. This system includes the pituitary, thyroids, parathyroids, adrenals, gonads, pancreatic islets, and the hormone-producing part of the gastro-intestinal tract. In certain mammals, the placenta would have to be regarded as an endocrine organ since it is the source of various steroidal and protein hormones. During vertebrate evolution, there has not been much change in the position of these structures within the body. Each of the endocrine glands will be considered according to structure, synthesis of hormones, regulation of function, action of hormones, and interrelationships with other components of the regulatory system. All these glands are comparatively small, are devoid of ducts, and have access to a rich vascular supply.

The most thoroughly studied endocrine glands are multicellular, but it is quite probable that unicellular types, sometimes capable of migrating through tissues, must be recognized. Instead of releasing their products upon a free surface, as exocrine glands do, these would discharge regulatory chemicals into the body fluids.

Regarding embryonic origin, the endocrine glands differentiate from all of the germ layers. Those derived from mesoderm (adrenal cortex, gonads) produce steroidal hormones; those coming from ectoderm or endoderm secrete hormones which are either modified amino acids, peptides, or proteins.

Clusters of neurosecretory cells have been identified in a variety of invertebrates, beginning with the Turbellaria. While most internal regulations among the higher invertebrates are *neuroendocrine* in nature, circumscribed ductless glands do exist. In the latter category may be mentioned the androgenic glands of crustaceans and insects, the corpora allata and prothoracic (ecdysial) glands of insects, and the Y organs of crustaceans.

Neurohormones

Within the central nervous systems of all animals from flat-worms to human beings, there are groups of nerve cells that show cytologic indications of being capable of functioning as glands. Granules of a secretory nature originate in the nerve cell bodies (perikarya) and are moved along the axons to bulblike terminals. These neurosecretory cells do not innervate effector organs; their axonal terminals typically end near blood vessels, often within storage and release centers (neurohemal organs) such as the neural lobe of the pituitary, the median eminence of certain birds,[21] the insect corpus cardiacum, and the crustacean sinus gland. The chemical messengers released by neurosecretory cells are called *neurohormones*. These are conveyed by the body fluids and exert prolonged action upon targets at a distance from their site of origin. The possibility that some may be transmitted from cell to cell, in the manner of "tissue hormones," has not been ruled out. It must be emphasized that the stainable granules observed within neurosecretory cells or within neurohemal organs are not necessarily the neurohormone itself: in some instances, at least, the tinctorial responses are due to carrier substances or other materials.

Both invertebrates and vertebrates possess neuroendocrine systems of basically similar design. The neurohormones of the vertebrate neurohypophysis (oxytocin and vasopressin) are well known as to chemistry and action, but most of the others await isolation and identification. The various release factors of the vertebrate median eminence are presumed to be neurohormones, probably peptide in nature, that are delivered to the adenohypophysis via a portal blood flow where they regulate the output of hormones. Among invertebrates, neurohormones are known to be involved in such processes as color change (crustaceans), molting and metamorphosis (insects),[29] the initiation of regeneration (annelids), gametogenesis, and metabolism (certain annelids and arthropods).

Neurohormones may regulate vital processes (a) by acting directly on target organs or (b) by acting indirectly on endocrine glands, which in turn bring about adjustments by virtue of their own secretions (Fig. 1–1). Since most endocrine organs are deficient or lacking in secretory nerve terminals, the latter arrangement is one of great importance. The neurosecretory cells serve as links between the central nervous system and the endocrine system. Being interpolated between the two coordinatory systems, these dual cells are capable of receiving impulses from the central nervous system and of responding to them by releasing neurosecretions which stimulate or inhibit the endocrine glands. With neurosecretory cells acting as "go-betweens," the central nervous system undoubtedly controls the functional activity of many endocrine glands and adjusts their activity in accordance with the requirements of varying internal and external environments. The reverse relationship by which endocrine glands influence the central nervous system is equally important.[9] The concept that nervous and endocrine systems are reciprocally interrelated is well documented and generally accepted.

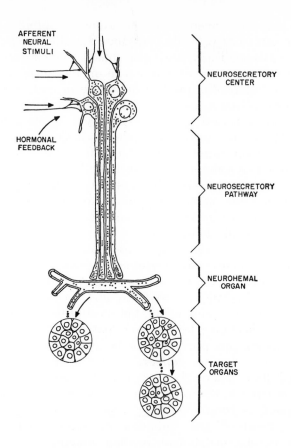

AFFERENT
NEURAL
STIMULI

HORMONAL
FEEDBACK

NEUROSECRETORY
CENTER

NEUROSECRETORY
PATHWAY

NEUROHEMAL
ORGAN

TARGET
ORGANS

Figure 1-1. Generalized diagram of a typical neurosecretory system. Secretory neurons synthesize neurohormones which are freed from their axonic terminals, often within storage and release centers called neurohemal organs. The secretions enter the circulation and affect distant targets. The neurosecretory cells receive nervous impulses from several sources as is indicated by arrows and synapses. Such neurosecretory systems form important links between the nervous and endocrine organs of both invertebrates and vertebrates. (From Scharrer, E., and Scharrer, B.: Neuroendocrinology. New York, Columbia University Press, 1963.)

Neurohumors

The ingenious experiments of Loewi (1921) helped explain why sympathetic and parasympathetic nerves usually have opposite effects upon the effector organs they supply.[16] He used isolated frog hearts, with nerves intact, and arranged them so that Ringer's solution perfused through one heart could be introduced into another completely separated heart. Stimulation of the vagus nerve (parasympathetic) to the first heart caused the contraction rates of both hearts to slow down; stimulation of the sympathetic nerves caused the rates of both hearts to increase. The two kinds of nerves were apparently releasing different materials into the perfusate as it irrigated the first heart. Further studies have shown that the parasympathetic terminals release acetylcholine, whereas the post-ganglionic terminals of the sympathetics release norepinephrine with traces of related compounds.[13] The sympathetic transmitters were formerly called "sympathin." Depending upon the kind of neurohumor released, it is customary to classify the fibers of the autonomic system as "cholinergic" or "adrenergic."

These chemical agents released at axonal endings are products of the nerve cell and are called *neurohumors;* they have often been thought of as "local hormones" or "diffusion hormones." Neuro-humors diffuse over the minute distances separating one neuron from another (synapses) and the junctions between neurons and effector cells (muscles or glands). While they are essential for the transmission of nerve impulses, their actions are transient and localized; they appear to be inactivated at the nerve endings and hence do not build up effective concentrations in the circulation. Studies on neurohumoralism provide further support for the concept that secretion is a fundamental property of nerve cells.

Studies on invertebrates (*e.g.,* the clam *Venus*) have shown that 5-hydroxytryptamine, also called serotonin, serves as a chemical transmitter.[27, 28] This compound has been found in various invertebrate organs and is known to be present in the central nervous system of vertebrates, in thrombocytes, and in mast cells (rat and mouse), where it is present with histamine and heparin. Several of these neurohumors give a positive chromaffin staining reaction and it is certain that this test is not specific for epinephrine, as was formerly supposed.

The mode of transmission of impulses within the central nervous system is largely unknown, but it is probable that a whole family of neurohumors may be involved. The concept that nerve impulses are transmitted across synapses and neuroeffector junctions by agents released from the nerve cells does not rule out the involvement of electrial events at these points. The two phenomena are probably inseparable.

Parahormones

This is a convenient category in which to place the large variety of chemical messengers which fail in one or more ways to satisfy the requirements generally implied by the term *hormone.* The cells of all organisms, whether unicellular or multicellular, produce and release substances of some kind which change the chemistry of internal and external environments. In this sense, no cell has completely lost its glandular properties even though it has differentiated highly in another direction. Many compounds such as carbon dioxide and urea have general origins within the body, in contrast to the specific sources of endocrine gland secretions, and perform integrative roles of great importance.

Products of dead or injured tissues, like histamine and leukocyte-attractants, are known to participate in inflammatory processes. Erythropoietin is an integrative substance released by the kidneys and perhaps other organs in response to anoxia; its action is to promote proliferation of red blood cells by the bone marrow. A hormone-like factor from the thymus is essential for the initiation of immune reactions in response to certain particulate antigens and to skin homografts. Melatonin, a tryptamine derivative, is extractable from the pineal organ and is very potent in causing pigment concentration in frog melanophores. It also inhibits ovarian growth and the in-cidence of estrus in rats. *Secretagogues* are extrinsic factors present in food and, after absorption into the blood, act to stimulate the glands of the gastrointestinal tract. Inductive substances are of great importance during embryonic life; they are rather restricted in their origin and are not effective at great distances from their source.

Renin is a proteolytic enzyme released by the kidneys into the blood stream under certain conditions, where it initiates a series of reactions leading to the formation of angiotensin II, a peptide which causes arteriolar constriction, increased cardiac output, and a consequent elevation of blood pressure. Diminished blood pressure resulting from hemorrhage or shock promotes an increased output of renin, and the value of this renal mechanism in homeostasis is apparent. Whether or not to regard such kidney functions as endo-crine would be a matter of personal opinion.

Many other coordinatory materials acting like hormones in some respects, but not completely satisfying the accepted definition, could be enumerated. It is important to recognize all of these deviant chemical messengers without diluting the classic connotations generally conveyed by the term *hormone.*

Phytohormones

Since plants are devoid of nervous systems, it is clear that their biologic adjustments are accomplished largely through the synthesis and dispersal of chemical messengers. Great advancements have been made by plant physiologists and biochemists in elucidating such regulatory substances as auxins, gibberellins, the so-called "wound hormone" (traumatic acid), leaf-growth substances, root-growth regulators, kinins, florigens, etc.[26] These plant agents are principally growth regulators, and many practical applications of economic importance have been found. The hormones of plants and animals are similar in many ways, but there are certain differences with respect to source and method of transmission. The plant cells that synthesize and release phytohormones are not sufficiently differentiated to be considered circumscribed glands of internal secretion. Moreover, the plant hormones are moved mainly from cell to cell instead of being dependent upon vascular channels for transport to distant targets. It may be discovered, however, that certain animal hormones are disseminated to a greater extent by cell to cell transmission than is presently appreciated.

Raper showed that the development of sex organs in the fungus *Achlya* consists of a series of steps, each being governed by particular *ectohormones* released by other individuals and passed through the aqueous environment.[23]

Pheromones

While endocrinology stresses the integration of the individual through the internal release of chemical messengers, there is an enlarging mass of evidence indicating that individuals also discharge materials externally which may be perceived by other individuals of the group and initiate behavioral or developmental responses in the recipients. The term *pheromone* has been applied to such external secretions that serve to integrate conspecific individuals of a group.[12] Even symbiotic relationships[8] involving animals of different species may be influenced by similar materials, and perhaps the term *ectohormone* could be given a broader connotation to include these.

Parkes and Bruce suggested that a new area of biology, appropriately called *exocrinology*, may be in the process of unfolding.[22] Consideration of these phenomena by endocrinologists might not be justified were it not for the fact that, in certain instances, the same endocrine gland product may be active both within an individual (hormone) and between individuals of a colony (pheromone). According to Lüscher, hormones from the corpora allata of termites probably function in this dual manner.[17] There are instances of host hormones influencing reproductive processes in parasites inhabiting their tissues and organs. In such instances, one and the same substance apparently serves as a hormone for the host and as an ectohormone for the parasite. Furthermore, the production of pheromones by exocrine glands may be under endocrine control, as has been demonstrated in the cockroach by Barth[2] and in the guinea pig (supracaudal gland) by Martan.[18] The activity of human sebaceous glands is regulated by androgenic substances.[25]

Pheromones may exert their influence (a) by directly affecting the recipient's central nervous system to produce rapid and reversible changes in behavior ("releaser" effect) or (b) by acting upon the recipient to trigger a chain of physiologic adjustments which eventually modifies behavioral patterns ("primer" effect).[30] Sex attractants, trail substances and alarm substances of insects are examples of pheromones exerting releaser effects. Reproductive life of the honeybee colony is regulated by a pheromone from the queen's mandibular glands, and this has been chemically identified as 9-ketodecanoic acid. This secretion has a primer effect since it is ingested by the workers and acts to inhibit the development of their ovaries, and also prevents them from constructing royal cells for the rearing of new queens. The queen substance can also produce releaser effects since it serves as a sex attractant during the nuptial flight.

While their exact roles have never been established by rigorously controlled experiments on living individuals, musklike compounds of mammals are thought to be involved in such processes as identification of sexes, the delimitation of home ranges, the defense of territories, and population densities. Because of their use in the manufacture of perfumes, much chemical work has been done on the secretions from preputial glands of the musk deer and muskrat and the perineal glands of the civet cat.

It has been determined that the caging together of female mice leads to mutual disturbance of the estrous cycles: the regular periods of estrus (sexual receptivity) are interrupted by pseudopregnancies if the groups are small, or by extended periods of anestrus if the groups are large (Lee-Boot effect). Since these changes could be prevented by excision of the olfactory bulbs or by caging each female separately, it is reasonably certain that olfactory stimulation is involved. It is also known that the introduction of a male mouse into a group of female mice shortens the cycle and synchronizes estrus (Whitten effect). The odor of a strange male mouse brings about a series of endocrine disturbances (Fig. 1–2) that terminates pregnancy in a newly impregnated female mouse (Bruce effect).[5] The source and chemical identity of the pheromones that produce these effects in the mouse have not been determined. If objective studies of this type were extended to primates, including man, they might lead to some interesting and surprising facts.

NEUROENDOCRINE INTEGRATION

One of the first things learned by a beginning biology student is that living cells are surrounded by a fluid medium (tissue fluid) which provides them with the various chemicals they need for growth, maintenance and repair and into which they discharge materials of many kinds. This means that a mixture of hormones and other chemical messengers is disseminated to all tissues of the organism, but it does not mean that all tissues respond alike to the same chemical agent. Much depends upon the specific chemistry of the internal environment and upon the competence of target cells and tissues to respond. Some components of the body, such as most skeletal muscles, depend heavily upon direct nervous stimulation; others, such as the blood-forming organs, are relatively independent of nervous control and are integrated mainly by chemical messengers reaching them via the tissue fluids. Circulating blood cells and discharged gametes are completely devoid of nervous control. Most functional adjustments within the animal organism are accomplished, to some degree at least, by both nervous and endocrine factors working together.

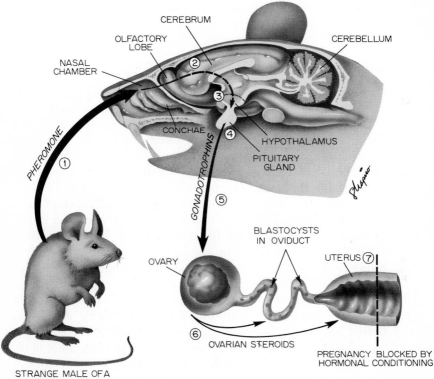

Figure 1–2. A chain of neuroendocrine reactions triggered by pheromones. Pregnancy may be blocked in a newly impregnated mouse by exposure to a strange male of a different strain (Bruce effect). 1, The volatile pheromone is perceived by the olfactory epithelium; 2, impulses are relayed through the olfactory lobes and cerebrum to the hypothalamus; 3, gonadotrophin-releasing factors in the median eminence are conveyed over the hypophysial portal veins to the anterior lobe of the pituitary; 4, the release factors regulate the output of pituitary gonadotrophins; 5, gonadotrophins condition the production of steroid hormones by the ovaries; 6, the ovarian hormones are deficient or of the wrong kind and a pregnancy-type uterus cannot be developed and maintained; 7, young embryos fail to implant, thus terminating pregnancy. (The size and shape of the pituitary gland are exaggerated in this figure for the sake of clarity.)

With the exception of the adrenal medulla and the posterior pituitary complex, the endocrine glands are not under direct nervous control. The consensus is that their activities are regulated by chemical means, often through the products of neurosecretory cells. Studies upon both invertebrates and vertebrates leave no doubt that a multitude of exteroceptive and interoceptive stimuli can affect endocrine gland functions through the intermediation of the central nervous system. Exteroceptive stimuli may be perceived through any sensory modality (auditory, visual, olfactory, thermal, tactile, etc.); interoceptive stimuli include many physical and chemical changes in the body fluids such as pH, temperature, hormones, water, glucose, salt, oxygen, etc. Emotional states clearly influence certain endocrine glands, but little can be said of these except that they are mediated by the higher brain centers.

Neuroendocrine Reflex Arcs

In adjustments of this type, chains of neural and endocrine events are consecutively brought into action. The afferent and efferent components of the arcs may be either hormonal or nervous. Only a few examples, illustrating slightly different situations, can be mentioned here. In certain birds (*e.g.*, Junco finches) and mammals (*e.g.*, ferret), exposure to increasing periods of illumination during the winter months, when the day length is naturally decreasing, stimulates the gonads and brings the animals prematurely into breeding conditions. In some animals such as sheep and goats, normally breeding during the autumn, exposure to light has the reverse effect: breeding activity may be stimulated prematurely by exposing the animals artificially to diminishing periods of light during the early summer when the days are naturally lengthening. Light falling upon the retina sets up impulses which are channeled to hypothalamic centers that control the release of gonadotrophins from the anterior pituitary gland; the latter hormones stimulate the gonads to proliferate gametes and to secrete steroid hormones, which in turn promote development of the accessory sex organs and secondary sex characters and condition breeding behavior. Sexual activity and quiescence appear to be regulated by an inherent rhythm, but the timing of these events can be modified in certain species by light.[10]

Exposure of rats to low environmental temperatures increases the output of thyroid stimulating hormone from the anterior pituitary; this augments the synthesis of thyroid hormones, which enable the body to oxidize more food and maintain the body temperature. This effect is mediated by centers in the hypothalamic portion of the brain.

It is well known that nymphal molting in the hemipteran *Rhodnius* is dependent upon the consumption of a heavy meal of blood.

Stretching of the abdominal wall causes impulses to be relayed to the brain over afferent pathways and these elicit the secretion of hormones which are essential for molting.

Ovulation in the rabbit occurs 10 hours after copulation, and this timing is remarkably constant. Stimulation of the cervix by the penis, perhaps coupled with the act of mating, sets up impulses that reach the spinal cord and travel up the cord to the hypothalamic portion of the brain lying above the pituitary gland. Neurosecretory neurons to the median eminence apparently discharge neurohormones (release factors) which are carried to the anterior pituitary via a system of portal veins. These release factors stimulate the pituitary to discharge gonadotrophins into the systemic circulation. The gonadotrophins stimulate ovarian changes and make the release of eggs (ovulation) possible.

It has been known for years that in many mammals (cow, goat, rabbit, dog, human, and others) the first half minute of milking or suckling yields little milk, but by the end of this period milk begins to flow suddenly and freely. This is known as the "let-down" or "draught," and the mechanism involved is now understood. It is a neuroendocrine reflex, the afferent limb of the arc being formed by sensory nerves and pathways and the efferent limb by the release of oxytocin from the neurohypophysis into the circulating blood. This hormone acts specifically to cause contraction of the myoepithelial cells surrounding the mammary alveoli, squeezing out the milk that is contained in the alveolar cells. Many sensory modalities other than tactile stimulation of the teats may induce the milk-ejection reaction. In cattle, the sound of milking equipment, sight of the calf, manipulation of the external genitalia, the presence of a male, the act of copulation, the arrival of the scheduled time for milking, and many other situations may initiate this neuroendocrine chain of events.

The adrenal glands of socially subordinate mice, repeatedly defeated in combat, are heavier than those of dominant members of the group. It has been shown that exposure of mice to a trained fighter results in hyperactivity of the adrenal cortices of the untrained, attacked subjects. Mice that had suffered previous defeats showed a much greater adrenal response to the fighter's presence than did animals that never before had experienced this social stress.[4] In situations of this type, cues derived from the external environment are received and integrated by the central nervous system; impulses are funneled into neurosecretory cells in the hypothalamus and these release a neurohormone (ACTH releasing-factor) which is carried by portal veins to the anterior lobe of the pituitary gland. The latter responds by releasing ACTH into the blood and this stimulates the adrenal cortices to augment their production of steroid hormones. There is evidence that the growth of mammalian populations may be regulated to an appreciable degree by social pressures operating through neuroendocrine mechanisms.[7] At the human level, clinicians have known for many years that emotional stimuli of many sorts may produce dramatic changes in endocrine glands and other organs.

The introduction of a strange male mouse into the cage of a female, mated less than 24 hours previously with another male, often results in failure of the young embryos to implant in the uterus.[5] The female returns to estrus within 3 or 4 days as though coitus had not occurred. This pregnancy block is not induced by introduction of the original stud male into the cage or by the introduction of other females. Olfactory stimuli are obviously involved since direct physical contact with the alien male is not essential and since it does not occur in females rendered anosmic by excision of the olfactory bulbs. The source of the pheromone operating in this social situation is unknown. It is probable that the pheromone stimulates the olfactory epithelium of the newly impregnated female and that impulses are funneled through the brain to the hypothalamus. Release factors from the median eminence are impaired in some manner and the adenohypophysis does not secrete enough prolactin to maintain functional corpora lutea.[22] The pituitary begins to produce kinds of gonadotrophins that cause the female to return to estrus, and a uterine lining capable of supporting implanting embryos is not developed. (Fig. 1–2).

Egg laying in many birds ceases after a customary number of eggs has accumulated. The house sparrow generally lays four or five eggs, but if the eggs are removed, oviposition may be continued until the ovaries are exhausted and as many as 50 eggs have been laid in succession. Female pigeons do not lay if they are kept in complete isolation, but laying is induced by the presence of males or other females. Ovulation will eventually occur if the isolated female is permitted to observe herself in a mirror. Brooding behavior in pigeons is normally associated with the presence of at least one egg in the nest. Medway found that denervation of that part of the pigeon's breast which covers the eggs does not terminate broodiness.[19] This suggests that the maintenance of broodiness does not depend upon tactile stimuli alone; multiple sensory receptors apparently are involved. Social factors, operating through neuroendocrine pathways, are extremely important in avian reproduction, and many other examples could be mentioned.

It is common knowledge that many wild animals kept in captivity fail to reproduce even though they are well cared for and are in apparent good health. Under captive conditions, reproduction probably fails to occur because the stimuli derived from the physical environment or from social contacts with other individuals of the same species do not duplicate those normally met in the wild.

In mammals, an excessive loss of water (dehydration) increases the osmotic pressure of the blood. As the blood circulates through the capillaries of the brain, certain osmoreceptors in the hypothalamus are stimulated and the neural division of the pituitary gland releases increasing amounts of vasopressin (antidiuretic principle). This neurohormone, a product of neurosecretory cells, acts directly upon the kidney tubules to promote the return of water to the circulation. Consequently, the organism eliminates a small volume of concentrated urine. Excessive hydration decreases the osmotic pressure of the blood and has the opposite effect.

Afferent pathways may be hormonal instead of nervous. For example, it has been shown that in certain crustaceans a male sex hormone is secreted by special *androgenic glands* which are spatially separate from the testes.[6] Male sex behavior is abolished by surgical removal of these glands or is induced in females by transplanting androgenic glands into them. The hormone apparently influences behavior through its action on the nervous system.

The feedback mechanisms which control the functioning of certain anterior pituitary target organs in vertebrates will be discussed in Chapter 2. In many instances, at least, these self-controlling systems involve both hormonal and nervous components.

The Evolution of Regulatory Mechanisms

Invertebrate zoologists played an important role in the elucidation of neurosecretory mechanisms. The functional significance of secretory neurons became apparent in insects and crustaceans long before studies on the vertebrates had yielded positive results. The ligation experiments of Kopeč (1917) demonstrated that the brain of the insect is the source of materials which regulate the onset of pupation, and this suggested for the first time that the central nervous system might function in a secretory capacity.[14] Speidel (1919) described giant cells in the spinal cord of the skate and, on the basis of structure, suggested that these might be the source of internal secretions.[24] Largely through the work of E. and B. Scharrer, B. Hanström and W. Bargmann, it was gradually recognized that vertebrates possess neurosecretory systems analogous to those of the invertebrates.[1]

During the course of phylogeny, the number of cells comprising the bodies of organisms increased and cells specialized in different directions to produce tissues, organs, and organ systems. As a consequence of these advances, integration of divergent parts of the body into a unified organism was a necessity and a problem of increasing importance. Growth and development in time and space had to be regulated to prevent structural malformations; functional mechanisms had to be established to enable the body to adjust to ever-changing environmental conditions that would imperil survival.

Plants are devoid of nervous systems and glands of internal

secretion and, from this, it may be assumed that their integrations are accomplished largely through the dispersal of chemical messengers, these perhaps being formed and released by all living cells of the plant body. From an evolutionary point of view, it is clear that two approaches were employed among animals: (a) the differentiation of nerve cells for the transmission of impulses at high speeds and with point-to-point precision and (b) the release of chemical messengers dispatched without direction through the tissue fluids and blood channels. Nervous regulation is essentially chemical since the neurons release locally acting transmitter substances (neurohumors) at synapses and at junctions between terminal neurons and effector organs. If neurohumors are released by all neurons, and if these products are regarded as secretions, secretion becomes as fundamental an attribute of nerve cells as the transmission of impulses. The main accomplishment of the nervous system is that it enables specific adjustments to be brought about rapidly, but it is not suitable for the regulation of processes that must endure for long periods.

The sequence in the evolution of coordinatory systems seems to have been: nerve cells (neurohumors) $\longrightarrow$ neurosecretory cells (neurohormones) $\longrightarrow$ endocrine glands (hormones). Examination of the lower invertebrate orders suggests that the nervous system was originally the sole agency of integration, and the beginnings of this system are already present in some of the protozoans. The prevalence of neurosecretory cells among the coelenterates has not been accurately determined, but there is evidence that such elements exist in *Hydra*.[15] They are present in most of the higher invertebrates, beginning with the turbellarians, and in all vertebrates from cyclostomes to mammals. Through the differentiation of neurosecretory cells from ordinary nerve cells,[20] the nervous system may be regarded as evolving its own endocrine apparatus for the discharge of regulatory substances which could be transmitted for great distances through the tissue fluids. Neurohemal organs, such as the avian median eminence, the neural lobe of the posterior pituitary in vertebrates, the corpus cardiacum of insects, and the sinus glands of crustaceans, evolved for the storage and final release of neurohormones.

The neurosecretory cells, being capable of receiving impulses from a great variety of neural circuits and of discharging chemical messengers, form a link between the central nervous system and many kinds of effectors. It appears that ductless glands are not present in the lower invertebrates and that most, if not all, of the major functions such as reproduction, metabolism, and behavior are directly controlled by neurosecretions. It may be inferred from this that the neurosecretory system antedated the circumscribed ductless glands. When endocrine glands did appear, most of them came under the regulatory control of neurosecretory cells. This arrangement makes it possible for various kinds of external and internal stimuli, impinging upon the nervous system, to act via neurosecretory cells and endocrine glands to exert amplified and prolonged effects within the organism.

The study of neuroendocrine systems in the invertebrates has sufficed to dispel the old concept of the separateness of nervous and endocrine systems. From the standpoint of comparative anatomy, the endocrine glands have not undergone any very striking structural changes in the various vertebrate classes, but there have been important phylogenic changes in the chemistry and actions of the hormones within the bodies of vertebrates. Among the higher vertebrates, particularly in mammals, neurosecretory centers have concentrated in one small area of the ventral diencephalon, namely, the *hypothalamus*. One would not want to imply, however, that no other centers remain to be discovered among vertebrates.

There is no longer any doubt that many vital processes in both invertebrates and vertebrates are controlled by neurosecretory complexes of basically similar design. Cues that have been received and integrated by the central nervous system are passed to neurosecretory cells which respond by releasing neurohormones into the body fluids. These chemical messengers, unlike the neurohumoral transmitters, can bring about relatively prolonged adjustments by acting upon endocrine glands and other targets. The neurosecretory cells, being of dual nature, perform the important function of tying together the nervous and endocrine systems. The time has come, perhaps, when it is more correct to speak of one coordinatory system (neuroendocrine) than to speak of two (nervous and endocrine).

SOME USEFUL BOOKS ON ENDOCRINOLOGY

Armstrong, C. N., and Marshall, A. J. (eds.): Intersexuality in Vertebrates Including Man. New York, Academic Press, 1964.

Barrington, E. J. W.: General and Comparative Endocrinology. Oxford, Clarendon Press, 1963.

Cantarow, A., and Schepartz, B.: Biochemistry. 3rd ed. Philadelphia, W. B. Saunders Co., 1962. (An excellent textbook recommended for students who may find themselves deficient in biochemistry.)

Cole, H. H. (ed.): Gonadotropins. San Francisco, W. H. Freeman & Co., 1963.

Dorfman, R. I. (ed.): Methods in Hormone Research. Vols. 1 and 2. New York, Academic Press, 1962.

Eckstein, P., and Knowles, F. (eds.): Techniques in Endocrine Research. New York, Academic Press, 1963.

von Euler, U. S., and Heller, H. (eds.): Comparative Endocrinology. Vols. 1 and 2. New York, Academic Press, 1963.

Fingerman, M.: The Control of Chromatophores. New York, The Macmillan Co., 1963.

Gorbman, A. (ed.): Comparative Endocrinology. New York, John Wiley & Sons, 1959.

Gorbman, A., and Bern, H. A.: A Textbook of Comparative Endocrinology. New York, John Wiley & Sons, 1962.

Gordon, M. (ed.): Pigment Cell Biology. New York, Academic Press, 1959.

Greep, R. O., and Talmage, R. V. (eds.): The Parathyroids. Springfield, Ill. Charles C Thomas, 1961.

Hafez, E. S. E. (ed.): Reproduction in Farm Animals. Philadelphia, Lea & Febiger, 1962.

Harris, G. W.: Neural Control of the Pituitary Gland. London, Edward Arnold, 1955.
Heller, H., and Clark, R. B. (eds.): Neurosecretion. Memoirs Soc. Endocrinol., No. 12. New York, Academic Press, 1962.
Hillman, W. S.: The Physiology of Flowering. New York, Holt, Rinehart & Winston, 1962.
Karlson, P. (ed.): Mechanisms of Hormone Action. New York, Academic Press, 1965.
Kon, S. K., and Cowie, A. T. (eds.): Milk: the Mammary Gland and Its Secretion. New York, Academic Press, 1961.
Litwack, G., and Kritchevsky, D. (eds.): Actions of Hormones on Molecular Processes. New York, John Wiley & Sons, 1964.
Lloyd, C. W. (ed.): Recent Progress in the Endocrinology of Reproduction. New York, Academic Press, 1959.
Long, J. A., and Evans, H. M.: The Oestrous Cycle in the Rat and Its Associated Phenomena. Mem. University Calif., 6:1–148, 1922.
Martini, L., and Pecile, A. (eds.): Hormonal Steroids. Vols. 1 and 2. Proc. First Internat. Congr. on Hormonal Steroids. New York, Academic Press, 1964.
Nalbandov, A. V.: Reproductive Physiology. 2nd ed. San Francisco, W. H. Freeman & Co., 1964.
Nalbandov, A. V. (ed.): Advances in Neuroendocrinology. Urbana, University of Illinois Press, 1963.
Pickford, G. E., and Atz, J. W.: Physiology of the Pituitary Gland of Fishes. New York, New York Zoological Society, 1957.
Pincus, G., Thimann, K. V., and Astwood, E. B. (eds.): The Hormones. Vols. 4 and 5. New York, Academic Press, 1964.
Pitt-Rivers, R., and Trotter, W. R. (eds.): The Thyroid Gland. Vols. 1 and 2. Washington, D. C., Butterworth Inc., 1964.
Roeder, K. D.: Nerve Cells and Insect Behavior. Cambridge, Mass., Harvard University Press, 1963.
Scharrer, E., and Scharrer, B.: Neuroendocrinology. New York, Columbia University Press, 1963.
Thimann, K. V. (ed.): The Action of Hormones in Plants and Invertebrates. New York, Academic Press, 1952.
Velardo, J. T. (ed.): Endocrinology of Reproduction. New York, Oxford University Press, 1958.
Waring, H.: Color Change Mechanisms of Cold-Blooded Vertebrates. New York, Academic Press, 1963.
Williams, P. C. (ed.): Hormones and the Kidney. Memoirs Soc. Endocrinol., No. 13. New York, Academic Press, 1963.
Williams, P. C., and Austin, C. R. (eds.): Cell Mechanisms in Hormone Production and Action. Memoirs Soc. Endocrinol., No. 11. Cambridge, Cambridge University Press, 1961.
Young, W. C. (ed.): Sex and Internal Secretions. 3rd ed. Vols. 1 and 2. Baltimore, Williams & Wilkins Co., 1961.
Zarrow, M. X., Yochim, J. M., and McCarthy, J. L.: Experimental Endocrinology. New York, Academic Press, 1964.
Zuckerman, S. (ed.): The Ovary. Vols. 1 and 2. New York, Academic Press, 1962.

REFERENCES

1. Bargmann, W., Hanström, B., and Scharrer, E. and B. (eds.): Zweites Internationales Symposium über Neurosekretion (Lund, Sweden, 1957). Springer-Verlag, Berlin-Göttingen-Heidelberg, 1958.
2. Barth, R. H., Jr.: The endocrine control of mating behavior in the cockroach *Byrsotria fumigata* (Guerin). Gen. & Comp. Endocrinol., 2:53, 1962.
3. Bern, H. A.: The properties of neurosecretory cells. Gen. & Comp. Endocrinol., Suppl. 1:117, 1962.
4. Bronson, F. H., and Eleftheriou, B. E.: Adrenal responses to fighting in mice: Separation of physical and psychological causes. Science, 147:627, 1965.

extreme muscular weakness, gastrointestinal upsets, discoloration of the skin and eventual death. Although some information had accumulated by this time concerning thyroid deficiencies and excesses, Addison's disease appears to be the first clinical defect of an endocrine gland to be accurately described.

In 1889, Brown-Séquard, a French physician, aroused the scientific world by attempting self-rejuvenation, at the age of 72, by taking subcutaneous injections of aqueous extracts of dog testes. He described in intimate detail the astonishing improvement that he experienced after this treatment. Although his attempts at endocrine substitution therapy stimulated much interest, it is now known that his claims of rejuvenation were due to autosuggestion rather than to any male hormone present in the aqueous extracts. Furthermore, the year 1889 stands out in endocrinology because it saw the report by von Mering and Minkowski on the production of diabetes mellitus in the dog through surgical removal of the pancreas.

Murray (1891), an English physician, prepared a glycerin emulsion of sheep's thyroids and demonstrated that the parenteral administration of it provided a helpful replacement therapy in human subjects suffering from hypothyroidism. The parathyroid glands were regarded as small masses of accessory thyroid tissue until Gley, in the same year, demonstrated that the two tissues have separate functions.

Baumann (1895) observed an extraordinarily high concentration of iodine in the thyroid gland, the concentration being hundreds of times higher than that of other tissues. He reported that thyroid glands from persons inhabiting the seacoast contained more iodine than those from persons living farther inland. Magnus-Levy (1896) discovered that thyroid deficiency leads to a marked fall in the basal metabolic rate.

The experiments of Oliver and Schäfer (1895), demonstrating the vasopressor effects of adrenal extracts, led to the isolation, purification, identification, and final synthesis of epinephrine. They also prepared extracts of the pituitary gland and found that these, upon intravenous injection, produced a rapid rise of blood pressure. A few years later, it was shown by others that this vasopressor effect could be obtained only from the "posterior lobe" of the pituitary, and that such extracts also produced powerful contractions of the uterus.

At this period the concept of internal secretion was not well established, and there was much discussion concerning the significance of iodine storage by the thyroid. Many workers alleged that the extraction of iodine from the blood by the thyroid could be interpreted as a detoxicating function. The view that iodine is an essential atom of a molecule synthesized by the thyroid began to take shape before 1900; a period of intensive interest in thyroid biochemistry was initiated and this has continued down to the present time.

The Twentieth Century

Around the turn of the century the impact of Darwin's theory of evolution and Mendel's theory of inheritance began to be felt in all compartments of human life and thought. The rapid strides made by the biologic sciences since that time are due in large measure to the adoption of a mechanistic point of view. Investigators began to proceed on the assumption that the phenomena of living organisms — inheritance, growth, reproduction, and the like — follow the terms of natural laws that can be discovered and explained. Organic evolution, implying a genetic kinship among all organisms, suggested that the biology of the human body is best viewed in the light of its animal ancestry. It is not surprising to find that enzymic systems appear to be similar throughout the whole biologic kingdom. The chemistry of energy exchange in bacteria and in yeast cells is not so different from that in mammalian muscles, which suggests that all living organisms are constructed according to a fundamental pattern that varies only a little from species to species. Since 1900 comparative endocrinology has slowly taken shape, and the results have already indicated that it is a fruitful avenue of approach to human problems.

THE BIRTH OF ENDOCRINOLOGY. The real science of endocrinology was probably born through the experiments of Bayliss and Starling (1902 to 1905). Their work showed the existence and manner of action, at the level of the whole organism, of the hormone *secretin*.[6] This secretion is released from cells of the duodenal mucosa when acidified food enters from the stomach; it is conveyed by the circulation to the pancreas where it stimulates the rapid discharge of pancreatic juice through the pancreatic duct. Although it had been recognized before this time that a variety of endocrine glands exert influences on the body, this discovery was epoch-making because it proved unequivocally for the first time that chemical integrations could occur without assistance from the nervous system. It clearly confirmed the idea that special glands elaborate chemical agents that are freed into the blood and exert regulatory effects upon distant target organs and tissues.

Starling first used the word "hormone" (Greek *hormōn*, exciting, setting in motion) in 1905 with reference to *secretin*. Although the term is not entirely satisfactory, if its meaning is taken literally, it is still in common use. It is now well know that hormones may inhibit as well as excite and they do not initiate metabolic transformations but merely alter the rate at which these changes occur. Pende introduced the term "endocrinology" (Greek *endon*, within; *krinein*, to separate) a few years later.

The twentieth century has seen the isolation and structural identification of a large number of hormones. The biochemical epoch in endocrinology began with Takamine and Aldrich (1901), who, working independently, succeeded in crystallizing epinephrine, one of the hormones from the adrenal medulla.

THE SLOW GROWTH IN INFANCY. Gudernatsch (1912) found thyroid tissue to be an extremely potent substance in accelerating the metamorphosis of frogs and salamanders.[38] This response of the tadpole provided a sensitive test for assaying the potency of thyroid preparations. Kendall (1919) obtained pure thyroxine from the thyroid glands of swine; Harington showed it to be an amino acid related to tyrosine and established its chemical constitution in 1926.

The isolation of insulin was a difficult undertaking because the proteolytic enzymes of the acinar portion of the pancreas destroyed its activity in the process of extraction. Banting and Best (1921), using pancreatic tissue from dogs whose acinar tissue had been caused to degenerate by ligation of the pancreatic duct, succeeded in preparing highly potent extracts.[4] The potency of the extracts was assayed on the basis of their capacity to reduce the blood sugar of experimental animals. Abel (1926) prepared insulin in crystalline form and demonstrated the protein nature of the purified hormone.

That the ovaries play a more subtle role in reproduction than the mere production of eggs had been obvious for many years. No real progress was made until it became possible to relate the cyclic changes in the ovary with those that occur in the accessory sex organs. Of paramount importance in reproductive physiology were the studies of Stockard and Papanicolaou (1917) on the estrous cycle of the guinea pig,[80] and similar studies on the mouse and rat by Edgar Allen (1922).[2] E. Allen and Doisy, in their classic studies during the 1920's, reported that the liquor folliculi from the large follicles of swine ovaries or lipoid-soluble extracts of this fluid contained an agent that induced estrous changes in the vaginae of castrated mice. All attempts at this stage to crystallize the *estrogen* met with failure. ("Estrogen" is a generic term for estrus-producing compounds.)

Aschheim and Zondek (1927) made an astonishing discovery that changed the whole face of research in this field: they reported that the urine from many pregnant animals contained two hitherto unsuspected hormones.[3] One of these was similar to the estrus-producing agent in the fluid of the graafian follicle, whereas the other caused marked growth of ovarian follicles. The latter substance is now known to be chorionic gonadotrophin (of placental origin), which forms the basis of the well-known Aschheim-Zondek test for pregnancy. Doisy (1929) and Butenandt (1929) succeeded in crystallizing the estrogenic substance from human pregnancy urine, and it is now known as *estrone*. Thus, estrogens were the first steroid hormones to be isolated. The actual isolation of estrogens directly from ovarian tissue was accomplished by Doisy (1935) and MacCorquodale (1936).[60] From four tons of sows' ovaries, the latter worker obtained some 12 mg. of estradiol-17β, and this accounted for about half of the estrogenic activity present.

Corner and W. M. Allen (1929) prepared extracts of corpora lutea that effectively maintained pregnancy in ovariectomized rabbits and worked together with estrogen to produce a proliferated uterus suitable for implantation of the blastocyst.[18] They found that the proliferative effect on the rabbit's uterus could be used as a bioassay for the hormone. Pregnanediol, a urinary metabolite of the corpus luteum hormone (progesterone), was chemically determined by Butenandt in 1932. Since pregnanediol was quite inactive biologically, no indication of the identity of progesterone was forthcoming until it was actually isolated from ovarian tissue. Four groups of workers in 1934 obtained progesterone almost simultaneously by extraction of sows' ovaries, and its structure was determined in the same year.

Hisaw (1926) presented evidence for a hormone of pregnancy which, among other effects, causes relaxation of the pelvic ligaments in guinea pigs, thus facilitating parturition.[44] This substance, called *relaxin*, seems to be a nonsteroid, water-soluble protein or polypeptide, but its exact role in reproduction has not yet been revealed completely.

The first effective extracts of testicular tissue were probably prepared by Pézard in 1911. His extracts caused renewed growth of the capon's comb, and he pointed out that this effect provided a suitable bioassay for testicular secretion. Knowing that the hormone of the ovarian follicle is fat-soluble, McGee (1927) extracted bull testes and obtained a material that was relatively potent in stimulating growth of the capon's comb.

It was discovered that, like the estrogens, androgens (substances producing masculinizing effects) are present in the urine. Butenandt (1931) extracted crystals of male sex hormone from urine and called the compound "androsterone." David *et al.* (1935) isolated pure crystalline hormone from testicular material and named it "testosterone." It was correctly assumed that androsterone is a degradation product of testosterone, and it is interesting to note that two groups of workers (Butenandt and Ruzicka) had practically synthesized testosterone before it had been obtained from testicular tissue. It was feasible to prepare testosterone synthetically from cholesterol, and large amounts promptly became available for experimental and clinical uses.

Practically no progress was made in elucidating the hormones of the adrenal cortex until a satisfactory method of adrenalectomy had been perfected, and until the fat-soluble nature of these substances became apparent during the early 1930's. Moreover, satisfactory endpoints for bioassay had to be established. The first potent extracts were made by Swingle and Pfiffner in 1930. Between the years 1936 and 1942, four groups of workers in the United States and Europe succeeded in isolating approximately 30 different steroids from the adrenal cortices of slaughterhouse animals, including six compounds that were biologically potent. The magnitude of the task is indicated by calculations from Reichstein's laboratory: it took about 20,000 cattle to give 1000 kg. of adrenal glands from which 26 grams of highly fractionated material (containing all biologic activity) could be obtained; this gave a yield of approximately 300 mg. each of the 29 steroid compounds obtained.

Endocrine studies on the pituitary gland were hampered for many years because of the surgical difficulties attendant upon removing the organ without injury to the brain. Aschner (1910) worked out a technique for performing hypophysectomies in dogs, and P. E. Smith (1926) developed a similar method for ablating the gland in rats and other laboratory rodents.[77] A notable landmark with reference to the neural lobe was achieved by Kamm and Aldrich (1928), who succeeded in separating the oxytocic and vasopressor hormones in forms sufficiently pure for therapeutic purposes.[48]

Since all of the pituitary hormones are proteins or peptides, their chemical elucidation has been understandably slow. The excellent studies of Stricker and Grueter (1928) indicated clearly that the anterior pituitary is essential for the initiation and maintenance of milk secretion.[81] Riddle (1933) noted that the pituitary principle that induced lactation in mammals was the same as that causing growth of the pigeon's crop gland.[70] This discovery provided a very sensitive and useful bioassay method for this particular hormone and did much to hasten its chemical isolation. Prolactin (lactogenic hormone) was obtained in crystalline form by White *et al.* (1937); it was the first pituitary hormone to be isolated as a pure or nearly pure protein.[91]

The student of endocrinology should always keep in mind that vertebrates are not the only organisms that have ductless glands and employ hormones in their integrative processes. Kopeč (1917) showed that a hormone from the brain controlled pupation in certain insects, thereby demonstrating for the first time that central nervous structures could perform endocrine roles. Since then various species of insects and crustaceans have been investigated intensively, and it is certain that many of the growth and differentiation, reproductive, and metabolic processes, as well as color adaptations, are under endocrine control. The functional significance of neurosecretory centers became apparent in the invertebrates before it was recognized that secretion by nerve cells might be an important phenomenon in vertebrates. Clues derived from the invertebrates and lower vertebrates have appreciably influenced our interpretation of the manner in which the hypothalamic portion of the brain regulates the secretions of the mammalian pituitary gland.

The field of plant hormones began to take shape after the experiments of Boysen-Jensen (1910) on the responses of the oat coleoptile (leaf sheath) to light.[11] The term "auxin" is applied to organic compounds that, in low concentration, cause the longitudinal growth of shoots by cell elongation, rather than by cell division. A variety of hormone-like substances have been found to influence growth, cell division and flower formation. Indole-3-acetic acid, probably derived from tryptophan, is the best known auxin. The interesting observation has been made that a particular auxin may stimulate growth of the shoot by cell elongation, induce cell division at the site of a wound, and inhibit the growth of roots and lateral buds.[55, 72]

AN ERA OF SPECTACULAR GROWTH. The 1940's ushered in a period of biochemical expansion and inquiry that was unprecedented in the history of endocrinology. In 1949, Hench *et al.* cautiously announced that a hormone of the adrenal cortex, cortisone or compound E, improved some of the clinical and biochemical symptoms of rheumatoid arthritis.[43] This study was possible because cortisone had been partially synthesized and was available in sufficient quantities for testing, whereas the other adrenal steroids could be produced only in milligram amounts. Even though this clinical announcement was followed by what now seems to have been an unwarranted outburst of enthusiasm, it immediately precipitated a period of feverish research in the field of steroid biochemistry. In attempts to manufacture large amounts of cortisone as cheaply as possible, it was found that certain micro-organisms (molds such as *Rhizopus, Aspergillus,* etc.) could effect enzymatic changes in the steroid molecule. Some species of yam provided an organic compound from which progesterone (corpus luteum hormone) could be prepared; the latter provides a satisfactory substrate for the production of cortisone by microbial oxygenation. The manufacture of cortisone is one of the most complicated and difficult procedures ever attempted by the pharmaceutical industry.[16]

Scientific progress depends materially upon the introduction of new tools and methods. The phase microscope enables us to visualize many structures in the living cell that cannot be seen with the ordinary microscope; the electron microscope gives us high magnification and has contributed much to our analysis of protoplasmic structures, large chemical molecules, and viruses. Tissue culture techniques have been improved, and methods have been perfected for the perfusion of whole organs. Perhaps of greatest importance in endocrinology has been the widespread use of radioactive isotopes in investigations of intermediary metabolism. Coupled with this has been the development of excellent microanalytic methods such as paper and partition chromatography, infrared spectrophotometry and microwave analysis. Through the use of isotopically labeled compounds our understanding of the biosynthesis, transport, and metabolism of hormones has been broadened.

Hechter and his co-workers have studied steroid biosynthesis by means of isolated perfused adrenals of cows, pigs, dogs, and human beings.[41] After adding appropriate steroid precursors to the perfusion medium, they could study the transformation products that the adrenal tissue released into the perfusate. By perfusing C^{14}-labeled cholesterol or radioacetate they obtained radioactive cortical steroids in the perfusate, indicating that these two substances could act as parent compounds. Many workers have contributed to this field, and the biosynthetic sequences in the adrenal cortex proposed by Hechter *et al.* have been confirmed as the preferred, though not obligatory, pathway. Characterization of the enzyme systems that operate in these adrenal steroid transformations have been fairly well worked out.

Biochemical methods are available for the quantitative determination of steroid hormones in the blood and urine. The testes and ovaries, as well as the adrenal cortices, secrete steroids into the circulation; these are metabolized along certain pathways and are excreted as urinary metabolites or degradation products. These patterns of steroid degradation are so constant that it is possible to determine the type of steroid that the adrenal is actually secreting by analysis of the metabolites found in the urine. From studies on the types of urinary metabolites released by patients suffering from certain adrenal defects, Dorfman and others have postulated that enzymatic defects at points along the biosynthetic pathway in the adrenal are the underlying mechanisms of the diseases.[10, 21, 47]

More than 40 steroids have been isolated from adrenocortical tissue; approximately eight of these are potent in maintaining the life of adrenalectomized animals. Some may be stages in the synthesis of the active ones; others may represent extraction artifacts.

Prior to 1953 it was known that the amorphous fraction of adrenocortical extracts remaining after the then known steroids had been removed, was particularly potent in maintaining the lives of adrenalectomized animals. It was suspected that the amorphous fraction contained a hormone that was highly active in regulation of water and electrolyte metabolism. The isolation and crystallization of a new adrenal steroid, called "aldosterone," by Simpson and Tait and their co-workers in 1953 was a brilliant chapter in steroid research.[75]

During the 1930's, when so many of the natural steroid hormones were being characterized, some investigators regarded them as compounds of the highest order of physiologic effectiveness, upon which man could make no further improvements. Nevertheless, we have entered an era of striking success in synthesizing compounds that not only are more potent than the natural hormones but also are skillfully altered in molecular structure to produce desired effects.

All of the known hormones of the pituitary gland, pancreatic islets, and parathyroids are proteins or polypeptides. Sanger and his colleagues (1954), using the method of partition chromatography, elucidated the full chemical structure of insulin; this is the first protein for which a complete amino acid sequence was established.[86] Du Vigneaud and his co-workers (1953) first determined the structure of oxytocin and vasopressin, polypeptide hormones of the posterior pituitary gland. Though these polypeptides are small molecules as compared with insulin, their organic synthesis by du Vigneaud was a monumental achievement in this phase of chemistry.[22, 23]

During the 1920's it became apparent that most insulin extracts contained a contaminant that antagonized the action of insulin, raising the blood sugar instead of lowering it as insulin does.[20] This hyperglycemic factor is called *glucagon* and appears to be elaborated by the α-cells of the islet tissue. Glucagon was obtained in crystalline form by Staub (1955), and the amino acid sequence in the polypeptide molecule was determined by Bromer (1957).[14, 79]

Since insulin is destroyed by the proteolytic enzymes of the intestinal tract, it is inactive by mouth. For many years, clinicians have been looking for oral substitutes for insulin that would not produce undesirable side effects. There were suggestions as early as 1918 that some of the sulfonamides were effective in reducing blood sugar when taken orally. In 1941 it was rediscovered that some of the compounds having antibacterial properties would reduce blood sugar levels. Loubatières, working in France, showed that this type of compound would reduce the blood sugar of human diabetics whose pancreas could produce *some* insulin.[59] However, the compounds used then were found to be quite toxic and further exploration was abandoned. In 1954 some new sulfonamide derivatives were produced, originally as chemotherapeutic agents, and it was again rediscovered, largely by accident, that they could be used in diabetic patients; the newer compounds were not so toxic as those tested earlier in France. Since 1954 large numbers of publications have appeared from the world's laboratories, and it is now generally believed that some of the sulfonamide compounds are valuable adjuncts to insulin in treating *selected* types of diabetic patients.

Applying the techniques of chromatography and radioautography of compounds labeled with I^{131}, the radioactive isotope of iodine, great progress has been made in our understanding of thyroid metabolism. Using radioiodide, Pitt-Rivers, Roche, Gross, Leblond, and others (1948 to 1953) demonstrated the presence of hitherto unknown compounds in thyroid tissue, blood serum, and other tissues. Gross and Pitt-Rivers (1952) identified 3,5,3'-triiodothyronine, a compound that generally exhibits more biologic potency than thyroxine. Much information has accumulated on the biochemical sequences by which thyroid compounds are formed, their transportation in the blood, and their degradation and elimination from the system. Moreover, we have learned some of the mechanisms whereby the various anti-thyroid drugs interfere with thyroid functions.

Principally through the work of von Euler, it has been shown that the transmitter substance released by sympathetic nerve terminals, and long referred to as "sympathin," is norepinephrine.[26] Tuller (1949) isolated crystalline L-norepinephrine from adrenal medullary tissue and gave evidence that it is normally secreted by this part of the adrenal along with epinephrine.[87] The predominant role of epinephrine as an emergency substance, as postulated by Cannon and Rosenblueth (1937), has been sustained.

One of the most tantalizing problems in endocrinology has been that of the site of origin of the posterior pituitary hormones, and the consensus has shifted several times since 1900. As an outgrowth of studies on neurosecretion, evidence has accumulated that these hormones are synthesized by modified neurons in certain brain nuclei. After movement along the nerve fibers the hormonal substances are thought to be freed into the posterior lobe, where they are stored, possibly altered, and released into the blood as needed.[5] This concept is now well documented and generally accepted.

Another problem receiving much attention, but remaining unsolved, is the mechanism of release of the anterior pituitary hormones. It is generally agreed that, if the cells of the anterior pituitary receive any secretory nerve fibers, they are sparse indeed. Thus it has become apparent that the gland must be regulated by agents that reach it through the circulation. The hypothesis has gained ground that nerve impulses delivered to certain brain nuclei (in the hypothalamus) cause neurosecretory cells to release transmitter agents which are delivered to the anterior lobe via the portal vessels that course through the pituitary stalk. While the three lobes of the pituitary gland differ markedly in their anatomic relationships with the brain, it appears that the functions of the whole gland are under direct or indirect neural control.[39]

THE SCOPE AND POSITION OF ENDOCRINOLOGY

From the foregoing account it is clear that endocrinology, to a greater extent than most biologic studies, grew directly out of the observations and experiments of practicing physicians. In retrospect, it seems unfortunate that the hormones were studied for such a long time only from the standpoint of disease and the cure of disease. It appears that in the 1920's many investigators felt that the hormones were fully understood when one became able to catalogue the signs and symptoms of their excess or deficiency. This purely clinical approach to the hormones made the subject particularly susceptible to quackery and led to considerable confusion. Not being fully aware that endocrinology is concerned with the multitude of chemical integrations occurring in health as well as with the maladjustments characterizing disease, most persons believed that endocrinologists restricted their interests to midgets, giants, bearded women, hermaphrodites, and other side-show freaks.

Happily, the tremendous impact of biochemistry on endocrinology, felt with increasing strength during the past few decades, has done much to rectify this trend of thought. With the perfusion of pure-science techniques and concepts into all phases of the subject, endocrinology has become a respected science and a dignified field of research specialization.

The Comparative Approach

There are certain parallelisms between endocrinology and anatomy. Both began at the mammalian level and progressed backward down the evolutionary tree.[15] As comparative anatomy developed, largely to support or refute the theory of organic evolution, many aspects of human anatomy came to be interpreted in a new light. Advances in comparative endocrinology have necessitated the revision or deletion of numerous traditional concepts which took form when knowledge of coordinatory mechanisms was largely restricted to those of the higher vertebrates.

Endocrine studies have been extended to all vertebrate groups, and while these do not permit any final conclusions relative to the evolution of endocrine organs, they do reveal a variety of unique specializations. Evaluation of the information available on the lower vertebrates (poikilotherms) makes it clear that the endocrine phenomena prevailing among mammals are far from being typical of the whole vertebrate subphylum. Invertebrate endocrinology has developed rapidly since Wigglesworth (1940), studying growth and metamorphosis in *Rhodnius* (Hemiptera), first assigned a functional role to specific groups of neurosecretory cells.[92] Studies of this type have emphasized the interrelationships of the nervous system and endocrine organs, and there is no longer any doubt that many bodily processes are regulated through the release of neurohormones by modified neurons present in the central nervous system. By evoking or suppressing activities that are latent in the gene system, the internal secretions control many aspects of reproduction, diapause, growth, metabolism, and behavior. The concept of neurosecretion is a direct outgrowth of studies on arthropod invertebrates and is known to find application in many different phyla ranging in complexity from worms to mammals. The investigation of neurosecretory mechanisms in the invertebrates has had a direct and tremendous impact on views regarding pituitary functions in vertebrates. This organ is no longer regarded as a "master gland," enjoying a high degree of autonomy, but as a structure whose output of hormones may be controlled by the products of neurosecretory elements present within the central nervous system.

Endocrinology Among the Sciences

Endocrinology is a many-faced subject and, in this respect, it does not differ from most other branches of science. Its "roots" extend into various disciplines, but these "roots" are not one-way streets; they *give* as well as *take*. It contributes to and draws from a large number of special fields such as chemistry, genetics, neurology, embryology, psychology, and clinical medicine — to mention only a few. Endocrinology has both pure and applied aspects; hence, in addition to being a medical specialty, it may be properly pursued in the basic science departments.

Crystalline hormone in a test tube might hold a certain fascination for the pure chemist, but it takes on fullest meaning when studied operating inside an organism. Although there is a large measure of overlap, biochemists and physiologists make their attacks on living protoplasm at two different levels: The biochemist studies biologic systems principally at the molecular and atomic levels, whereas the physiologist is primarily concerned with the whole organism. However different these methods of attack may seem to be, application of the results to the organism itself brings unity. Investigations at each level were necessary before endocrinology could become a science.

All scientists recognize that human knowledge is an entity and that sharp lines of demarcation cannot be drawn between the various disciplines. We have departments of biology, chemistry, physics, etc., simply for the practical reason that the whole is too voluminous to treat effectively. While some degree of specialization is necessary and desirable, modern science students should make every attempt to cross these departmental barriers.

Cooperative Research

The sciences have developed so rapidly that it is impossible for one person to become expert in all of the complicated techniques involved in a research project. It may require years to learn special surgical methods, tissue culture techniques, microchemical procedures, or the operation of modern laboratory machines.

Precise knowledge of the hormonal regulation of reproductive cycles began with the classic experiments of Edgar Allen and E. A. Doisy in the early 1920's. This was an advantageous combination of investigators from different disciplines, one a biologist and the other a biochemist. Allen had a thorough knowledge of estrous cycles as determined by the vaginal smear method of Papanicolaou, whereas Doisy contributed his expert knowledge as a biochemist. By pooling their efforts, they solved problems and laid foundations that neither could have accomplished separately.

Today, in laboratories over the world, physiologists, anatomists, chemists, physicists, geneticists, ecologists, psychologists, and clinicians are working together in attempts to solve basic problems of fundamental importance. Some of the greatest advancements in scientific thought have resulted from this type of cooperative enterprise, and much more exchange of information among specialists is needed.

METHODS OF STUDY

Ablation by Surgery or Disease

Removal of a gland would deprive the organism of its normal source of hormone, so that measurable abnormalities should appear in the individual during its life history. Varying degrees of hypofunction may be produced by subtotal ablations.

Because many, if not all, processes are regulated by multiple hormones working in unison, defects resulting from the extirpation of one kind of gland may be due to the unopposed action of secretions from another gland. Experiments involving multiple ablations may be performed to assess the relative significance of several glands in a particular process. For example, removal of the pancreas elevates the blood sugar and produces other symptoms of diabetes mellitus; if the pituitary is removed from the same animal, the diabetic symptoms are ameliorated (Houssay preparations). Long and Lukens discovered that removal of the adrenals has a similar effect in clearing up some of the impairments resulting from ablation of the pancreas.

Permissive actions may be determined by removing the gland in question and maintaining the animal in a responsive state by a constant intake of hormones from that gland while another hormone is being tested. Large doses of estrogen increase the liver glycogen of intact fasting rats, but do not exert this effect after the adrenals are removed. However, if adrenalectomized rats are maintained on adrenal cortical extracts, estrogen raises the liver glycogen; this effect could not have been mediated by the adrenal cortex. The cortical hormones in the extract are said to have a "permissive" role, inasmuch as they normalize the functions of organs and thereby condition the animal's capacity to adapt and respond to the estrogen.[46]

Many physiologic responses can occur in the absence of the adrenal glands if the animal is maintained by the administration of cortical steroids.

Through disease, accident, or defective heredity, Nature sometimes produces glandular abnormalities that would be difficult to simulate experimentally. Spontaneous lesions of the endocrine system are occasionally detected in large colonies of laboratory animals, and these may be analyzed morphologically and physiologically with profit.

Chemical Ablation or Impairment[36]

When radioactive iodine is administered, it collects principally in the thyroid. The ionization within the thyroid destroys the organ partially or completely, without appreciably damaging other parts of the body. A large number of chemical agents are known to block the secretion of thyroid hormones by interfering at some level with their biosynthesis in the gland. Animals receiving adequate treatment with the antithyroid agents (*e.g.*, thiouracil, sulfonamides, etc.) cannot manufacture thyroid hormones and hence are equivalent to thyroidectomized subjects.

Alloxan is a chemical agent that selectively destroys the β-cells of the pancreatic islets, apparently without permanent injury to other parts of the organism. Since the β-cells are the source of insulin, alloxan provides a convenient method of reducing the output of insulin sufficiently to produce diabetes mellitus. It is doubtful whether alloxan completely prevents the secretion of insulin by the islets.

Amphenone is a drug that depresses the adrenal cortex and causes a marked reduction in the output of cortical steroids. Although too toxic for clinical use, it appears to be a useful tool in studying adrenal function. The nitrofuran Furadroxyl arrests spermatogenesis at the primary spermatocyte stage and has been employed to elucidate certain testicular functions. Some of the tranquilizing agents (*e.g.*, reserpine) block ovulation in laboratory rodents and have been useful in investigating neurogenic control of the anterior pituitary gland.

Replacement Therapy

The physiologic maladjustments resulting from ablation of an endocrine gland should be ameliorated or corrected entirely by transplanting the gland, by injecting appropriate extracts of the gland, or by administering chemically pure hormones extracted from the organ or prepared synthetically in the laboratory. Most of the natural hormones are relatively ineffective when given by mouth; however, considerable progress has been made in preparing orally effective compounds by modifying the hormone molecule or by synthesizing related compounds.

Sometimes the administration of one hormone stimulates or suppresses the release of hormones from other glands. This being the case, one must be careful to distinguish between the primary effects of the injected hormone and the secondary effects it may have produced by altering other members of the endocrine system.

Chemical Extraction

It should be possible to extract the hormone from the particular gland that produces it and also from the blood stream, which conveys it. This has been accomplished in many instances. The urine is sometimes a better source of hormones than is the blood, but the excreted metabolites may be quite different chemically and physiologically from the compounds obtained directly from glandular tissues. Within the circulation, many of the hormones are bound to blood proteins and hence do not filter through the renal glomeruli. Consequently, the urine generally contains only traces of the hormone in its original form.

Although much progress has already been made, improved methods for the qualitative and quantitative determination of hormones and their metabolites in the body fluids are needed. Careful studies on the urinary metabolites may provide clues of defective synthesis of hormones by the endocrine gland. In certain diseases of the adrenal cortex, the abnormal metabolites of the steroid hormones appearing in the urine are thought to reflect enzymatic blocks in the biosynthetic pathway within the adrenal itself.

Isotopic Tracer Methods

Isotopes are of two general kinds: *stable* and *radioactive*. The stable isotopes differ from ordinary atoms only in their mass and may be prepared by fractionation from natural sources. The radioactive isotopes, besides differing in mass, possess unstable nuclei and undergo spontaneous decomposition with the emission of radiation. Most of the radioactive isotopes that are used in biochemical work do not occur in nature but are prepared by bombardment in the cyclotron. The reacting uranium pile, used for the production of atomic weapons, is the best source of neutrons for the preparation of isotopes. The stable isotopes, not being radioactive, are determined with the mass spectrometer; the radioactive ones are determined by instruments such as the Lauritsen electroscope and the Geiger-

Müller radiation counter. Since the analytical methods for the measurement of radioactive isotopes are extremely sensitive, they are
used more commonly in biochemical studies than are the stable
isotopes.

The rate of decomposition of radioactive isotopes is commonly
expressed as their *half-life*; this is the time required for the isotope
in any given sample to diminish to half its original value. The half-
life of I^{131} is 8.1 days, whereas that of C^{14} is 5570 years.

The isotopic method makes it possible to label an element or
compound and to follow the fate of the substance *in vivo* under
conditions that cause a minimum of physiologic disturbance to the
experimental organism. For example, if we administered elemental
iodine (I) to an organism, it would become mixed with like atoms
already in the "metabolic pool"; hence it would be impossible to
trace its metabolic pathway within the body. On the other hand,
when we administer the radioactive isotope of iodine (I^{131}), the
administered atoms can be distinguished from those already in the
body. Their uptake by the different tissues, their incorporation into
compounds, and the breakdown of the compounds can be followed.
Even in those cases in which there is no net increase, or an actual
decrease, in the concentration of the product, isotopic labeling
provides a method for proving the transformation of one compound
to another. Special procedures make it possible to demonstrate
unstable metabolic intermediates that cannot be isolated by ordinary
methods.

In some kinds of work, it may become desirable to know in what
tissues or cells a radioactive isotope has localized. This can be done
by taking two adjacent microtome sections, staining one in the usual
way, and leaving the other in contact with a photographic plate or
film for an appropriate time. The areas of high isotopic concentration
can then be determined by comparing the stained section with the
"radioautograph."

The use of labeled elements and compounds, supplemented by
other techniques, is the most important procedure yet devised for
the study of metabolic pathways and the rates of turnover of substances in the organism. Today the isotopes not only are used in
laboratory experimentation but have found an important place in
clinical diagnosis and treatment.

In Vitro Techniques

The perfusion of whole organs, such as adrenals, testes, and
ovaries, has been a useful procedure in determining the biosynthetic
pathways of the steroid hormones. The endocrine gland is carefully
removed and placed in a closed system that allows it to be perfused

either with the animal's own blood or with a physiologic solution of approximately the same electrolyte content as that of the blood. The excised organs survive for a considerable period of time; hence, isotopically labeled materials may be introduced and samples of the perfusate withdrawn for analysis. One advantage of this method is that metabolic products may be removed as they are formed, instead of accumulating and interfering with the speed of chemical reactions.

In some types of biochemical studies, very thin slices of living organs are suspended in appropriate physiologic solutions and kept alive for hours or days. Various test materials may be added to the suspension fluid and the transformations determined by analytical procedures.

Tissue minces and homogenates are often employed in studying enzymatic transformations. In such preparations the cellular organization is disturbed, and many or all of the individual cells are destroyed. A cell-free homogenate actually consists of a liquid in which the soluble components of protoplasm have been dissolved, and suspended in this liquid are the solid components of cells such as microsomes, mitochondria, nucleoli, etc. The insoluble components of homogenates may be separated from the suspension medium by centrifugation. It appears that many of the important cellular enzymes are bound to the organelles found in homogenates; extracts containing only the soluble constituents may carry some of the enzymes in solution, but their natural relationships in the intact cell have been completely destroyed. Until there is absolute proof, it should not be assumed that the results of *in vitro* procedures are identical with those that normally operate within the whole organism.

It is obvious that no single method of study is uniquely sufficient for the elucidation of every aspect of endocrine function. All of the techniques mentioned have contributed importantly to our understanding, and data obtained by different techniques often reinforce one another and thus become increasingly significant.

THE ASSAY OF HORMONES[25]

Progress in endocrinology depends upon the development of techniques which enable the investigator to know what hormone he is dealing with and to determine how much of the hormone is present in the material being considered. Until a hormone becomes available in pure form, its assay must depend upon some relatively unique biologic alteration that it produces. To mention only a few examples, insulin lowers the level of blood sugar, androgens promote growth of the capon's comb, estrogens cornify the vaginal epithelium of rodents, MSH peptides cause dispersion of melanin granules in the melanophores of the frog's skin, gonadotrophins induce specific alterations in the gonads, and thyrotrophin brings about structural and functional changes in the thyroid gland. The most valid bioassays are based upon changes which are produced exclusively by a particular hormone under rigidly controlled conditions. Elevation of the blood sugar, for example, is not a specific indicator of epinephrine action because pancreatic glucagon, pituitary ACTH, and adrenocortical steroids produce the same end result by acting in different ways.

Perhaps all hormones produce a multitude of responses within the body and different responses among different species. In view of such divergent actions, selection of the best biologic indicator must depend upon the degree of objectivity, accuracy, sensitivity, specificity, reproducibility, and convenience afforded by the test.

It is always desirable to base assay techniques upon structural or functional changes that can be measured objectively by instruments, instead of relying upon subjective estimations. Bodily configuration and hair distribution are reliable indicators of gonadal steroids in human beings, but both parameters are difficult to standardize and measure objectively. Hormones within the organism are typically effective in minute amounts, and indicators that are sensitive enough to respond to physiologic quantities of the hormone are the most preferable. If sensitivity is lacking, and tremendous amounts of hormone are required, the response is likely to be pharmacologic rather than physiologic. The response must be reproducible, and a dose-response relationship should be evident.

Many factors may alter responses to hormones and thus influence bioassays. Important variables are the route of administration, the vehicle in which the hormone is dissolved or suspended, the species and strain of animal, sex, age, and general health. Since most of the natural hormones are not effective orally, they are generally given parenterally, *i.e.*, subcutaneously or intramuscularly. The intravenous route is employed only when a prompt response is desired, or when it is advantageous to have high, but transient, titers present in the blood. Steroid hormones are generally not given intravenously. Hormones in oil vehicles are absorbed more slowly than those in aqueous ones, thus giving relatively constant and prolonged effects. Modifications of the hormone molecule may alter its rate of absorption, degradation, or excretion, without changing its characteristic type of action. On the other hand, even slight changes in chemistry of the molecule may render it ineffective or may alter its effect within the organism.

Once the structure of a hormone molecule is known, physical and chemical procedures may be developed for its detection and quantitative determination. Highly sensitive and specific physiochemical methods are available for the assay of certain steroid hormones. Since it is desirable to assay occasionally on the basis of a biologic indicator to make sure that the molecule is active, it is not likely that the physicochemical or immunologic procedures will entirely replace bioassays. The available assays for protein and peptide hormones are largely biologic, though there is hope that valid immunologic methods may be found for the determination of such molecules in the blood plasma. The difficulty is that the immunologic methods are not absolutely valid unless the antigenic site and the active center of the protein molecule coincide. When antigenicity and activity are located at different levels in the molecule, the immunologic information must be verified by some bioassay procedure.

GENERAL ORGANIZATION OF THE VERTEBRATE ENDOCRINE SYSTEM

The approximate positions of the best known endocrine glands of the human body are indicated in Figure 2–1. Since little positional change has occurred in these structures during evolution, this diagram would serve for almost any vertebrate. The source and action of the pituitary hormones are summarized in Table 2–1.

At the center of the endocrine system is the hypophysis, or pituitary gland, a relatively small, unpaired organ attached by a slender stalk to the floor of the brain. The pituitary consists of an *adenohypophysis* and a *neurohypophysis*, and these two subdivisions are distinctly different in embryonic origin and in histologic composition.* The adenohypophysis includes the anterior lobe (pars distalis) with its pars tuberalis, and the intermediate lobe (pars intermedia). The so-called "posterior lobe" is only part of a unit that should be termed the neurohypophysis. The latter consists of the median eminence of the tuber cinereum; certain nuclei in the hypothalamus; their axons, which descend along the stalk; and the neural lobe, in which many of the axons terminate. The hypophysial portal venules are of great functional importance since they convey blood from the primary capillary plexus of the median eminence to the

---

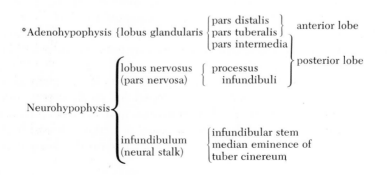

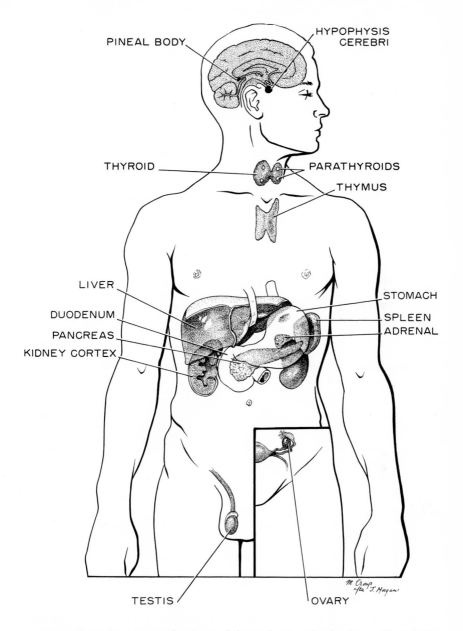

Figure 2–1. Approximate locations of the endocrine glands of man. Though the liver, kidneys, and spleen add important materials to the blood they are not definitely known to be organs of internal secretion.

Table 2–1.   Hormones of the Pituitary Gland

Hormones	*Cellular Source*	*Principal Actions*
1. Pars distalis		
Somatotrophin (STH, growth hormone)	Acidophils	Growth of bone and muscle; promotes protein synthesis; effects on lipid and carbohydrate metabolism.
Adrenocorticotrophin (ACTH)	Basophils (?)	Stimulates secretion of adrenal cortical steroids by the adrenal cortex; certain extra-adrenal actions.
Thyrotrophin (TSH)	Basophils	Stimulates the thyroid gland to form and release thyroid hormones.
Gonadotrophins		
(a) Luteinizing or interstitial cell-stimulating hormone (LH or ICSH)	Basophils	Ovary: formation of corpora lutea; secretion of progesterone; probably acts in conjunction with FSH. Testis: stimulates the interstitial cells of Leydig, thus promoting the secretion of androgen.
(b) Follicle-stimulating hormone (FSH)	Basophils	Ovary: growth of ovarian follicles; functions with LH to cause estrogen secretion and ovulation. Testis: possible action on seminiferous tubules to promote spermatogenesis.
(c) Prolactin (lactogenic hormone, luteotrophin)	Acidophils	Proliferation of mammary gland and initiation of milk secretion; prolongs the functional life of the corpus luteum—secretion of progesterone.
2. Pars intermedia		
Melanophore-stimulating hormone (intermedin, MSH)		Dispersion of pigment granules in the melanophores; darkening of the skin.
3. Neurohypophysis		
Vasopressin (ADH, antidiuretic hormone)	Hypothalamic neurons	Elevates blood pressure through action on arterioles; promotes reabsorption of water by kidney tubules.
Oxytocin	Hypothalamic neurons	Affects postpartum mammary gland, causing ejection of milk; promotes contraction of uterine muscle; possible action in parturition and in sperm transport in female tract.

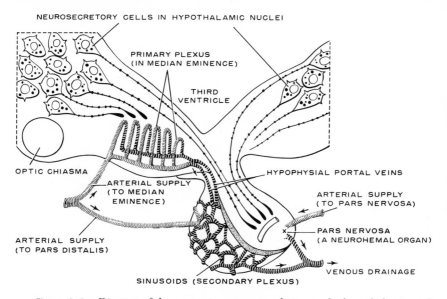

NEUROSECRETORY CELLS IN HYPOTHALAMIC NUCLEI

PRIMARY PLEXUS
(IN MEDIAN EMINENCE)

THIRD
VENTRICLE

OPTIC CHIASMA

HYPOPHYSIAL PORTAL VEINS

ARTERIAL SUPPLY
(TO MEDIAN
EMINENCE)

ARTERIAL SUPPLY
(TO PARS NERVOSA)

ARTERIAL SUPPLY
(TO PARS DISTALIS)

PARS NERVOSA
(A NEUROHEMAL ORGAN)

VENOUS DRAINAGE

SINUSOIDS (SECONDARY PLEXUS)

Figure 2–2. Diagram of the anatomic connections between the hypothalamus and the pituitary gland. Neurosecretory cells are present in certain hypothalamic nuclei: some of the secretory axons pass down the infundibular stalk and terminate near blood vessels in the pars nervosa; others terminate in close proximity to the capillary loops of the median eminence. The hormones of the neurohypophysis (vasopressin and oxytocin) are the products of hypothalamic neurosecretory cells and are stored and released from the pars nervosa (a neurohemal organ). The hypophysial portal venules start as the primary plexus of the median eminence and convey blood downward to the sinusoids of the anterior lobe. There are strong indications that the hypothalamic axons of the median eminence liberate multiple releasing factors (probably peptide in nature) into the portal vessels and that these neural factors are concerned with the regulation of anterior pituitary functions. It is apparent that the whole pituitary gland is predominantly subservient to and partly evolved from the hypothalamic portion of the brain.

sinusoidal spaces (secondary plexus) of the anterior lobe. An awareness of these vascular and neural connections is essential to an understanding of current concepts regarding the manner in which the hypothalamus controls the release of pituitary hormones (Fig. 2–2). There is substantial evidence that neurosecretory products (release factors) are discharged around the capillary loops of the median eminence and that these factors condition the release of anterior pituitary hormones by virtue of the final common path of the hypophysial portal venules. Ectopic pituitary grafts, persisting without direct hypothalamic connections, function very abnormally.

The pituitary is the source of at least nine hormones, all being protein or peptide in nature; six hormones arise from the pars distalis, at least one from the intermediate lobe, and two from the neurohypophysis (Table 2–1). Some of the anterior lobe hormones exert their effects indirectly by stimulating the functional activities of other endocrine glands; these are called *trophic* hormones. The main

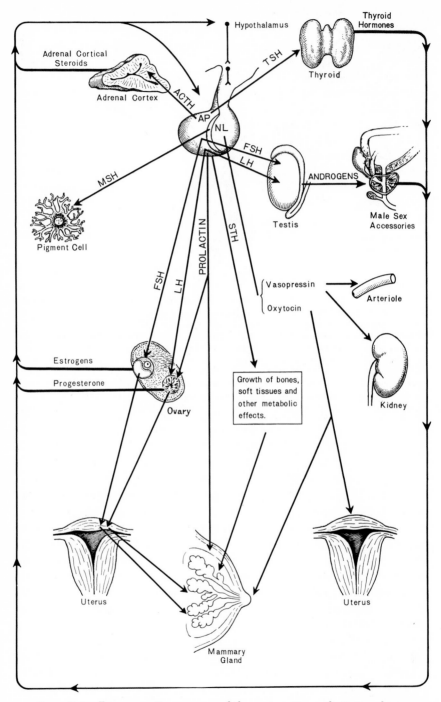

Figure 2–3. Diagrammatic summary of the main actions of pituitary hormones. AP, anterior pituitary; NL, neural lobe; ACTH, adrenocorticotrophic hormone; TSH, thyroid-stimulating hormone; FSH, follicle-stimulating hormone; LH, luteinizing hormone; STH, somatotrophin (growth hormone); MSH, melanophore-stimulating hormone.

target organs affected by the trophic hormones are the thyroid gland, adrenal cortex, testis, and ovary (Fig. 2–3). Somatotrophin (growth hormone) is a general metabolic hormone and has a variety of actions, no single endocrine organ serving as its target.[57] The MSH peptides (intermedin) of the pars intermedia have pigment cells as their main targets. The neurohypophysial hormones exert their main actions upon blood vessels, kidneys, mammary glands, and uterus. Certain endocrine organs, such as the gastrointestinal mucosa, pancreatic islets, parathyroid glands, and adrenal medulla, seem to function with little, if any, dependence upon pituitary hormones. It is well to remember, however, that the tissue fluids contain multiple hormones at all times and none acts by itself within the living body.

ENDOCRINE CONTROL OF NEURAL FUNCTIONS

It has been emphasized that the relationship of the nervous and endocrine systems is one of reciprocity. Examples were given in Chapter 1 of neuroendocrine reflexes in which the nervous system exerts regulatory control over the endocrine glands. Of equal importance is the fact that hormones present in the blood act back upon the central nervous system to influence its development in fetal and neonatal animals and, in adults, to affect the psychologic and behavioral characteristics of the species.

There are great variations in the patterns of breeding activity among different species. Among vertebrates, the reproductive cycle is controlled by pituitary and gonadal hormones present in the blood. The production of these hormones, and hence the rhythmic alteration of sexual receptivity and nonreceptivity, is set by some inherent "biologic clock" which assures a relatively constant pattern of activity for any one species. With the onset of the breeding season, the circulating hormones act not only to induce full anatomic development of the reproductive organs, but also upon the nervous system to assure a behavioral repertoire commensurate with the fully developed genital organs. The behavior of the estrous rat, for example, is strikingly different from that of the same animal during diestrus or following ovariectomy. These behavioral differences are explainable on the basis of the types of hormones which act back upon the central nervous system.

Gonadal Hormones and Hypothalamic Differentiation

In female mammals, the hypothalamus exerts rhythmic influences upon the anterior pituitary, probably by neurosecretions, so that there is a rhythmic release of gonadotrophins. In the male, on the other hand, the hypothalamus is relatively arrhythmic and this accounts for the continuous production of gonadotrophins and the steady state pattern of male activity. Studies upon fetal or neonatal mammals indicate that circulating gonadal hormones have an organizing action upon certain brain areas, particularly the hypothalamus. There are critical periods in development during which the immature hypothalamus is sensitive to gonadal hormones: In rats and mice, this critical period extends from birth to about the tenth day of postnatal life; in mammals with a longer gestation period, such as the guinea pig and monkey, the sensitive period occurs before birth. Whether the hypothalamus causes the anterior pituitary of the adult to produce gonadotrophins rhythmically (female type brain) or continuously (male type brain) depends upon the kind of gonadal hormone to which the central nervous system is exposed during early life.[37, 83, 84] The important factor in hypothalamic differentiation seems to be the presence or absence of testicular hormone; indications are that ovarian hormones (estrogen and progesterone) have no important action in organizing the immature brain structures.[40]

When the ovaries or testes are surgically removed before the hypothalamus is fully differentiated, it matures as a female type organ in both genetic males and genetic females. Two criteria have been used in assessing hypothalamic functions: (1) whether the hypothalamus stimulates the anterior pituitary to release follicle-stimulating hormone (FSH) and luteinizing hormone (LH) rhythmically as in normal females, or arrhythmically as in normal males; (2) the type of sexual behavior that the animal displays after attaining adulthood.[40] Genetic female rats, given a small dose of testosterone shortly after birth, show marked masculine behavioral patterns when they become adults, instead of normal female behavior. When the ovaries or testes are removed from newborn rats, they both grow up to display female behavior.[40]

It appears from observations on the rat, guinea pig, and monkey that the pattern of gonadotrophic secretion, as well as the pattern of sexual behavior in the adult,[93] depends upon whether or not the hypothalamus differentiates under the influence of testicular secretions. It is quite obvious that in laboratory mammals permanent reproductive impairments may result from hormonal imbalances prevailing before the brain areas have fully matured. Since human fetuses cannot be used for experimental purposes, it is not known to what extent these principles apply to human beings. At the human level, however, there is no doubt that abnormal hormone levels during embryonic life are responsible for a variety of genitourinary deformities, and some of these may not become apparent until after puberty.[88]

Feedback Regulation

It was originally proposed by Moore and Price (1932) that gonadal steroids in the blood acted *directly* upon the anterior pituitary to regulate the output of gonadotrophins.[65] That circulating steroids may directly influence pituitary functions has by no means been disproved, but it is apparent now that many of the pituitary adjustments must involve brain centers which are sensitive to hormones in the blood. Otherwise, the reproductive timetable could not be affected by such environmental factors as social contacts, photoperiods, temperature, and food supply. The hypothalamus, that portion of the brain which is attached to the pituitary by vascular and neural pathways, seems to control anterior pituitary functions by producing neurohormones (release factors) and adding these to the hypophysial portal circulation.[29] Pituitary functions in the vertebrates can be altered by a variety of brain areas such as the amygdala, the hippocampus, and the reticular formation of the brain stem; these are in all probability affected through the channeling of impulses into the hypothalamus and median eminence. Irregularities of menstruation in women are often correlated with such psychologic factors as shock, worry, or fear, and these are apparently mediated by higher brain centers. The gonadal feedback includes, therefore, an effect of gonadal steroids in the blood upon certain brain areas which act via the hypothalamus and portal vessels to accelerate or inhibit the release of pituitary gonadotrophins. Comparable self-balancing arrangements, with the central nervous system as an intermediary, are found among the lower vertebrates and even among such invertebrates as insects.

Endocrine glands such as the testes, ovaries, thyroid, and adrenal cortices depend to a large extent upon the circulating levels of pituitary trophic hormones and have, at best, only limited powers of autonomous regulation. Target gland hormones in the circulation, by a feedback mechanism that usually involves central nervous structures, increase or decrease the production of anterior pituitary trophic hormones (Fig. 2–4). When the titers of ovarian steroids in the blood are high, some chemoreceptive mechanism in the hypothalamus acts to reduce the release of pituitary gonadotrophins, and, consequently, the output of steroids by the ovary is diminished. Low titers of ovarian steroids in the blood affect the feedback mechanism in the reverse manner.

Adrenocorticotrophin (ACTH) maintains the functional status of the adrenal cortex; if ACTH is absent, the cortex shrinks and releases only meager amounts of its steroids. Profound functional hypertrophy of the cortex results from administering large amounts of ACTH. When certain cortical steroids are given in excess, the adrenal cortex involutes and becomes comparable to that of a hypophysectomized animal lacking ACTH.[67, 68] Therefore, it is believed that the elaboration and release of ACTH from the anterior pituitary are conditioned by the levels of cortical steroids in the blood. The pituitary increases its secretion of ACTH when there are low titers of

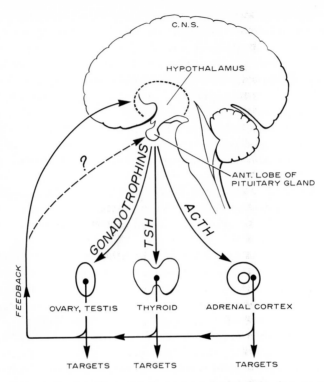

Figure 2–4. A diagram illustrating the reciprocal relationship between the central nervous system and certain endocrine organs. Ovarian, testicular, thyroidal, and adrenocortical hormones in the blood act back upon the anterior pituitary, with the hypothalamus as a probable intermediary, to adjust the output of hormones in accordance with the needs of the organism. This forms a self-balancing system often referred to as *feedback* action. (Modified from Harris, G. W.: Neural Control of the Pituitary Gland. London, Edward Arnold, 1955.)

cortical steroids in the blood, and it diminishes the release of ACTH when the blood steroids are high.[30] While a direct action of cortical hormones on the anterior pituitary gland has not been ruled out, there is convincing evidence that they often act indirectly via the hypothalamus (Fig. 2–4).

The administration of natural or synthetic estrogens to laboratory rodents produces a striking enlargement of the adrenal cortices, but this seems to be an indirect action. A current interpretation is that the estrogens actually interfere with the biosynthesis of steroids by the cortex; thus, there is a deficiency of cortical hormones in the blood, and the anterior pituitary responds by releasing increased amounts of ACTH, which induce the nonfunctional enlargement of the adrenal.[90]

The functional status of the thyroid is regulated to a large extent by thyroid-stimulating hormone (TSH) from the anterior hypophysis. High levels of thyroid hormones in the blood, operating through a feedback effect, inhibit the release of TSH (Fig. 2–4). It appears that the thyroid hormones can affect the anterior pituitary directly, without hypothalamic intervention.[9] However, some of the adjustments in TSH release, especially those occurring in response to changing environments, are mediated through the central nervous system. Clinicians have known for a long time that hyperthyroidism in human subjects (*e.g.,* Graves' disease) is often preceded by emotional shock. Furthermore, excesses of thyroid hormones in the circulation act back upon the nervous system to modify the psychologic and behavioral characteristics of the patient. This is illustrated by the emotional instability, nervousness, muscular tremors, and even dementia not infrequently observed in thyrotoxic subjects.

Factors other than pituitary TSH may function in thyroid regulation, at least in pathologic conditions. There is evidence, for example, that a long-acting thyroid stimulator (LATS) may be involved in the pathogenesis of Graves' disease. The identity and source of LATS remain to be determined conclusively.[61]

The normal level of serum calcium is about 10 mg. per 100 ml. This seems to be maintained through the operation of a dual mechanism. The first is a diffusion equilibrium between the blood serum and the labile fraction of bone mineral; this can hold the serum calcium at approximately 7 mg. per 100 ml. It operates after removal of the parathyroid glands as well as in normal animals. The second part of the mechanism operates in the manner of a feedback. A fall in serum calcium causes an increased output of parathyroid hormone, which mobilizes calcium from the skeleton, thereby raising the serum calcium to about 10 mg. per 100 ml.[62] There is no conclusive evidence indicating either nervous or hormonal control of parathyroid secretion.

The level of blood sugar is the chief factor that regulates the production of insulin by the pancreatic islets. The over-all effect of this hormone is to lower the blood sugar. Elevation of the blood glucose stimulates the production of insulin, whereas decreased titers of blood glucose diminish the output of insulin. This seems to be the only physiologic mechanism governing the production of insulin; however, it must be remembered that a great variety of factors can affect the blood glucose concentration and indirectly modify the production of insulin. Since the carbohydrate-active steroids of the adrenal cortex, as well as certain anterior pituitary hormones, are potent factors in regulating blood sugar levels, they can indirectly exert effects on insulin secretion. This is a kind of feedback mechanism wherein the concentration of a constituent of the blood (glucose, in this case) regulates the production of hormones by an endocrine gland.

The gastrointestinal hormones are exceptional inasmuch as they are produced in response to secretagogues present in food, and each appears to function quite independently of all other endocrine secretions present in the body.

SOME MODERN CONCEPTS AND PROBLEMS

General Characteristics of Hormones

The endocrine glands are among the most highly vascularized organs of the body, and their secretions are typically distributed via the circulation. It appears that in a few instances hormones may not reach the blood stream, but diffuse through tissues and thus give rise to local field effects. They possess a high degree of chemical specificity, and even small alterations in molecular composition may render them inert or modify their physiologic properties.

When hormones are administered, a certain latent period must elapse before the systemic effects become apparent. This may mean that the hormones must undergo chemical alterations in the blood or in the target tissues before they are capable of exerting their actions. Although an impressive number of hormonal substances have been prepared in chemically pure form from glandular tissues, there is no absolute assurance that these compounds are in precisely the same form as those that initiate metabolic alterations in the target organs. Hormones are known to be effective in trace quantities, but it is not clear why specific tissues of an organism respond to a particular hormone, whereas others do not.

Hormone Binding

It is an established fact that many of the hormones in the blood are normally bound to plasma proteins, and this has a great influence on their ability to reach the tissues where they produce their actions.[63] Estrogenic steroids are bound to blood protein (estroprotein complex) in the liver, and this coupling seems to be of great importance in the transport and activity of the hormones. Liver disease or subtotal hepatectomy, either situation preventing the formation of estroprotein complexes, results in the loss of estrogenic activity.[82]

The thyroid hormones of the blood are bound to certain serum proteins, principally α-globulin and serum albumin. A common test for circulating thyroid hormones is based on the determination of protein-bound iodine (PBI). The strength of the protein-hormone union is an important factor in regulating the passage of hormones from the blood into the tissues. To mention one example, a striking increase in PBI is observed during human pregnancy, but the basal metabolic rate remains within normal limits because the bound hormones are held in the blood. Studies have shown that the particular serum proteins that bind the thyroid hormones are increased during pregnancy.

All hormones appear to show a predilection for certain effector tissues, and there is growing realization that these tissues possess selective mechanisms that enable them to trap particular hormones quickly and bind them firmly. We do not know how generally this is true, but it has been clearly demonstrated in the case of insulin, a hormone of the pancreatic islets.[78] Muscle, adipose, and mammary tissues of the rat quickly take up insulin from solution and bind it with such force that repeated washing does not remove it. For instance, if a normal rat diaphragm is dipped for only 10 seconds into a solution of radioactive insulin, the muscle cells will bind sufficient hormone to alter their metabolism. There are strong indications that the gonads are capable of binding the gonadotrophins that affect them.

If the hormones act by modifying enzyme systems, and there is convincing evidence that some of them do, they could hardly be effective without being bound in some manner to the enzyme.

The Problem of Hormone Effectors

During the early days of endocrinology, the idea gained momentum that the hormones acted upon very specific effectors; it appears now that this concept may have been somewhat misleading. The *trophic* hormones of the anterior pituitary were once supposed to stimulate only certain targets (*e.g.*, thyroid, adrenal cortex, gonads), but it now seems probable that all of them exert physiologic effects that are not mediated by stimulation of their conventional target organs. Pituitary "growth hormone" (somatotrophin) was originally thought, as its name implies, to possess only growth-promoting properties, but it is now certain that it has a variety of other actions as well. Moreover, it should be emphasized that this pituitary hormone is only one of the many agents operating to determine the size and form of the animal body.[57]

While the female sex hormones from the ovarian follicles (estrogens) produce striking changes in the female accessory organs such as the uterus and vagina, they also alter a great many other physiologic states. To mention only a few, they stimulate mitotic activity in the skin, change the pattern of behavior, influence antibody formation, exert an influence on body weight and growth, increase the incidence of some kinds of cancer, modify the production of insulin, influence the growth of hair, and affect blood calcium levels and bone deposition. Since the hormones do not act alone but form interlocking complexes in the body, many of these actions are known to be secondary effects mediated by other hormones. Nevertheless, we fall into error when we visualize the hormones as limiting their actions too specifically to one or two target organs.

All the hormones that are necessary for milk secretion are present during pregnancy, but milk production does not normally begin until after the birth of young. The mammary glands appear to be unresponsive to prolactin during pregnancy. *In vitro* experiments have shown that this anterior lobe hormone increases the respiratory activity of mammary slices from lactating rats, but slices of the glands from pregnant rats do not respond.[74]

Studies on insects have shown in an especially clear way that postembryonic development is cyclic and that hormonal activity is restricted to certain critical periods. Immature organs (*e.g.*, leg discs or ovaries of *Drosophila*) are unable to metamorphose when subjected prematurely to large quantities of hormones that normally call forth developmental changes.[8] Apparently in both insects and vertebrates the competence of target organs is dependent upon a certain degree of maturation. It may be that the genes of the immature cell have not yet provided it with the enzymic equipment or other factors required for hormonal responsiveness.

Erroneous conclusions regarding the responsiveness of endocrine targets may arise from a failure to consider important species differences. The metabolic pathways affected by hormones may vary from one species to another.[64] External environmental temperatures are an important consideration when hormones are being tested on poikilotherms. These vertebrates may respond much more slowly than birds and mammals (homoiotherms), and this could be expected because of their relatively low metabolic rates. Corticosterone is the main glucocorticoid produced by the adrenal glands of the rat, but the hamster secretes cortisol instead of corticosterone. One would expect physiologic quantities of cortisol to be more effective in the hamster than comparable amounts of corticosterone, and vice versa.

Removal of the pancreas of some birds (ducks) results in a transient or permanent lowering of the blood sugar, but the same operation in such animals as the dog produces a marked increase in blood sugar and other symptoms of diabetes. Wild and domesticated Norway rats may respond quite differently to factors that influence the functional activity of the adrenal cortex.[66]

In certain species of birds, testicular development can be evoked prematurely by subjecting the animals to increasing daily periods of light, but this activation cannot be sustained indefinitely. Each cycle of testicular recrudescence is followed by a refractory period during which the increased photoperiods are ineffective.[27]

Age and nutritional status of the animal are important variables with respect to hormonal actions. For example, a single injection of estrogen or androgen to the 5-day-old mouse causes infertility for life, but at 20 days of age the same amounts of these hormones have no such effects.[54] Certain hormones can produce marked effects if the body protein stores are filled and labile proteins are available, but little or no response is possible if labile proteins are not available.[53]

Stimulation and Inhibition

The hormones do not produce any new cellular reactions or metabolic transformations. The latter are intrinsic properties of the cells, and the hormones merely regulate the rate at which the cellular machinery operates. This is apparent from the fact that under proper conditions isolated enzyme systems can catalyze their characteristic reactions in the complete absence of hormones. In some instances, the hormones produce very slight accelerations or inhibitions, but these small displacements, maintained for long periods, can produce profound cumulative effects.

Target organs can function to a minimum extent in the complete absence of their regulatory hormones. Living thyroid epithelium, grown in tissue culture, has some secretory capacity in the absence of thyroid-stimulating hormone from the anterior hypophysis.[71] Even after ablation of the pituitary gland, the adrenal cortices, gonads, and thyroid continue to function at a very meager rate. In the complete absence of insulin the cells can utilize some carbohydrate.

The same hormonal compound may inhibit, as well as stimulate, depending upon the nature of the effectors, the amount of hormone present, and the physiologic status of the organism. It is well known that auxins, or plant hormones, stimulate the growth of shoots, but the same substance inhibits the growth of roots and lateral buds.[85]

The thyroidectomized mammal is in negative nitrogen balance and growth is depressed. The thyroidless subject grows normally when given optimum quantities of thyroid hormone. However, if too much thyroid hormone is given, it again goes into negative nitrogen balance and growth is retarded. Adrenal cortical steroids (*e.g.*, cortisol) may cause either sodium retention or sodium diuresis, depending upon the physiologic environment that prevails in the test animal. While the estrogens, acting with other hormones, stimulate uterine growth, they inhibit secretion by the adrenal cortex and depress the gonadotrophic function of the anterior hypophysis. Estriol inhibits the action of other natural estrogens upon the rat's uterus.[45]

In the intact organism, any one process is likely to be influenced by a large number of metabolic systems, some promoting and some inhibiting. Cell physiologists are aware of many instances in which promotion or inhibition by a particular agent depends upon the substrate or energy source supplied.

Hormonal Interrelations

It must be stressed that the hormones within the body form interlocking systems, one hormone never acting in isolation. When we work at the organismic level, the determination of hormonal balance and interaction is undoubtedly the most important and difficult aspect of endocrinology. Multiple hormones are known to control the dispersion and concentration of pigment granules in the chromatophores of crustaceans; the color of the animal at any particular time depends upon the interaction of these hormones.[31] The uterine changes that occur during the menstrual cycle are extremely complicated phenomena and cannot be explained on the basis of one or two hormones only. It is probable that all the hormones and many of their metabolites that are present in the uterine tissues at specific times act *in concert* to produce the observed changes.[45]

Endocrine coordinations are much more complex than was formerly visualized. It appears now that almost every physiologic adjustment with which the endocrinologist deals is effected by a balance between hormones acting together or in sequence. Complete and normal functioning of the mammary glands requires estrogens, progesterone, prolactin, somatotrophin, adrenal cortical hormones, and perhaps others. Insulin is not the only hormone involved in the regulation of carbohydrate metabolism; in the whole organism, glucagon, pituitary, adrenal, thyroid, and even gonadal hormones all function in concert to control it.

The action of one hormone may be modified (potentiated or limited) by others that are present with it.[24] There is evidence that progesterone, emanating from the placenta, prevents premature expulsion of the fetus by blocking the response of the uterine musculature to other hormones.[19] Traumatic injury in the normal rat results in an increased urinary elimination of nitrogen, but this reaction to injury does not occur unless the tissues are maintained in a responsive condition by secretions from the adrenal cortex. Likewise, the administration of estrogens to rats inhibits the growth of hair, but this action can occur only in the presence of adrenal steroids. When adrenocorticotrophin (ACTH) and somatotrophin (STH) are administered to rats, they exert antagonistic actions upon body weight and the width of the epiphyseal cartilages.

It has been established that the adrenal cortex, testis, ovary, and placenta produce steroid hormones, and the biosynthetic pathways employed are remarkably similar. Therefore, it is not surprising to find that compounds considered characteristic of the gonads are present also in the adrenal cortices, or that masculinizing hormones are present in ovarian tissue and feminizing hormones in testicular tissue. Triiodothyronine, a thyroid hormone, has been reported to regulate the metabolic degradation of testosterone (testicular hormone).[12] Since testosterone is a precursor of the natural estrogens, it may be that thyroid hormones can exert an indirect effect on the female reproductive system by conditioning the biosynthesis of estrogens. That hormones produce physiologic effects by operating in unison, rather than in isolation, is an important modern concept.[1]

Synergisms have received a great deal of attention from experimental endocrinologists. Some hormones increase the effectiveness of other hormones that are present with them in low concentrations. The synergistic interaction of progesterone and estrogens in inducing uterine changes is well known. If the two types of hormones are administered together, they produce effects that neither could produce alone when given in the same concentration. Some of the estrogens are known to synergize with each other.

Progesterone augments the action of estrogen on female mating behavior in the chicken, although it has no effect alone. When an estrogen and an androgen are administered together to the pullet, greater oviduct growth ensues than either of the two hormones can produce when given separately. It thus appears that androgens and estrogens cooperate in regulating the reproductive system of the female bird.

Somatotrophin enhances the effectiveness of a large number of other hormones. Perhaps it does this by producing in target tissues the kind of environment that is essential for other hormones to exert their fullest activities. When the pituitary gland and ovaries are removed in the rat, the mammary glands undergo prompt involution and become inactive. No changes are produced in the mammary glands of these animals after the administration of STH or estrogen alone. When the two hormones are injected at the same time, the mammary alveoli begin to proliferate. Acting as a biologic synergist, STH seems to make it possible for estrogen to exert its characteristic effects fully. Without mentioning more specific examples at this time, it may be stated that STH alone has little effect on some of the target organs (*e.g.*, thyroid, gonads, adrenal cortex), but it markedly enhances the effectiveness of the hormones that are specific for those targets when administered together with them.

Mechanisms of Hormone Action

Considering how much is known about the chemistry of hormones and their *in vivo* and *in vitro* effects, it is surprising that there is not sufficient information to disclose fully how any hormone actually performs at a molecular level. The voluminous literature that has accumulated on this subject attests to the magnitude of the task. Enough evidence is at hand to convince everyone that hormones, in one way or another, do modify enzymatic reactions within the target cells. The question remaining to be answered is *how* the hormones influence the enzymes that control metabolic sequences.

Since natural hormone molecules come in many sizes and shapes, ranging in chemical complexity from modified amino acids through steroids to complex proteins, it is not likely that all would employ identical mechanisms in evoking their actions. Moreover, it is possible that the same hormone molecule might be involved in multiple mechanisms, depending upon the nature of the target. For example, thyroxine influences such diverse processes as amphibian metamorphosis, metabolic rate in homoiotherms, maze-learning ability in rats, deposition of guanine in fish scales and of melanin in bird feathers, eruption of teeth in young rats, schooling behavior in fishes, growth of antlers in deer, the rate of glucose absorption from the intestine of mammals, and water diuresis in mammals. It would be difficult to envisage all of these widespread effects of thyroxine as the resultants of a single, uniform mode of action. Three general points of view, each with varying modifications, have been proposed to explain the mechanism of hormone action:

1. Hormones exert a direct effect upon intracellular enzyme systems. After it became known that many vitamins function as coenzymes, impetus was given to the concept that hormones might also interact with enzymes. The main argument was that such activation or inhibition of enzyme systems could account for the large influence produced by minute quantities of hormones. In some instances it has been possible to demonstrate a hormone effect upon cell-free systems, and these reports have been received with much interest. Epinephrine and glucagon have been shown to act upon enzyme protein, in the absence of intact cell structure, to convert the inactive phosphorylase *b* into the active form. Estradiol, an ovarian steroid, is reported to serve in placental and endometrial homogenates as a coenzyme for a transhydrogenation reaction.[89] There are indications that gonadotrophins stimulate the gonads to synthesize steroid hormones by acting directly upon enzyme systems at a step between cholesterol and pregnenolone. This reaction has been demonstrated in tissue homogenates lacking intact cells.[35] Such examples of hormone-enzyme interactions are contrary to the widely held belief that the integrity of the target cells is a prerequisite for hormone action.

2. Hormones act to control permeability relationships at the cell surface or elsewhere and hence indirectly condition enzymic reactions. A considerable body of evidence supports the view that certain hormones exert effects upon cell permeability. Insulin has been shown to promote the transfer of glucose into the cells of certain tissues, such as muscle and fat.[56, 76] The cell membrane acts as a barrier and prevents the free entry of sugar, but insulin molecules act in some manner to make the membrane permeable. Insulin is also capable of altering the transport of amino acids into cells. The molecular basis whereby insulin brings about permeability changes has not been elucidated. After the sugar has entered the cell, it can be acted upon by the intracellular enzymatic machinery. It should be emphasized that many investigators feel that an alteration in membrane permeability is not the only mode of action of insulin. In the liver, its site of action appears to be upon enzymes in the interior of the cell.

Vasopressin, the antidiuretic hormone of the neurohypophysis, seems to react at cell surfaces. The antidiuretic activity of this peptide hormone depends upon the presence of a disulfide ring in the hormone molecule. Evidence has been obtained that the action of this hormone on the toad bladder involves interchange between thiol groups on the receptor cells and the disulfide ring of the hormone. According to this idea, the sulfhydryl-disulfide exchange serves to open the membrane and facilitate the movement of water.[32, 69, 73]

It is an established fact that one important action of somatotrophin is to promote the synthesis of protein from amino acids. An extensive literature suggests that one point of action of this hormone is at the cell surface, where it facilitates the entrance of amino acids into the intracellular pool.[51, 52]

Many variations of the membrane theory have been proposed. Techniques of electron microscopy reveal that the cell contains a large number of membranous structures, such as the plasma membrane, nuclear and mitochondrial membranes, endoplasmic reticulum, Golgi complex, secretion granules, etc. Specific enzyme systems are visualized as being largely confined to these intracellular compartments, the membranous enclosures forming barriers to free communication. Thus the mitochondria contain the tricarboxylic acid cycle–electron transport system; the enzymes concerned in protein and cholesterol synthesis are found in association with the endoplasmic reticulum; and certain systems are concentrated in the nucleus. The view has been proposed that hormones may be concerned with permeability changes in these cytostructural barriers, thus making substrate or other products available to the semi-isolated, multienzyme systems. This appears to be an attractive working hypothesis and is supported by some evidence, but it is not known to what extent it will be able to account for the facts. There is very little information on the specific physical and chemical alterations which occur in cell membranes as they change in permeability.

3. Hormones may produce their effects directly by activating or suppressing particular genes.[49, 50] This hypothesis is an outgrowth of studies on insect development, particularly the effect of ecdysone upon the large chromosomes of the salivary glands. These chromosomes are actually bundles of chromosomal threads arranged in a regular manner; the transverse bands are due to the accumulation of deoxyribonucleic acid (DNA). Studies on the midge *Chironomus* indicated that the transverse bands tend to loosen, or puff up, sequentially during the course of development.[17] The puffs, as they are called, have been identified as sites where ribonucleic acid (RNA) and protein are being synthesized. Since development is regarded as the temporal realization of the potentialities stored within the genes (DNA), it seemed probable that the puffs were the sites where the genes were being activated by specific hormones.

Molting and metamorphosis in insects are known to be controlled

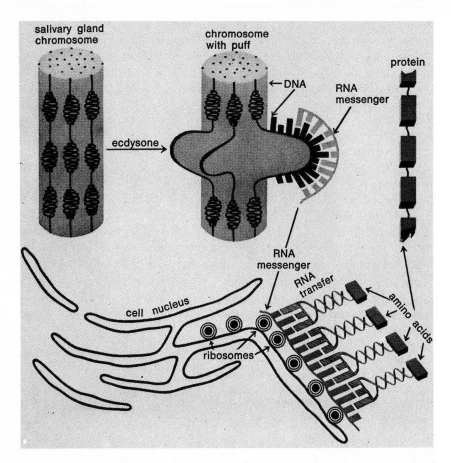

Figure 2-5. Mechanism of action of ecdysone upon the giant salivary gland chromosomes of certain insects. The hormone is believed to act first on the DNA to produce a puff which is the site of RNA synthesis. The messenger RNA carries the information necessary for the alignment of amino acids in the synthesis of specific proteins (*e.g.*, certain enzymes). These enzymes presumably evoke within the target cells the biochemical changes involved in the molting process. (From Karlson, P.: New concepts on the mode of action of hormones. Rassegna, *42*:7, 1965.)

by hormones from three endocrine structures: one or more neuro-hormones produced by neurosecretory cells in the brain, ecdysone (molting hormone) secreted by the prothoracic glands, and juvenile hormone (JH) coming from the corpora allata. Brain hormone causes the prothoracic glands to release ecdysone, which acts to initiate molting. The effectiveness of ecdysone, however, depends upon the quantities of JH that are present with it. If JH is present in abundance, the molt will be a larval molt; if it is present in small amounts, or absent, the result will be a pupal or imaginal molt (Fig. 3-8).

Microscopic inspection of the giant chromosomes in *Chironomus* larvae has shown that the administration of ecdysone causes the puffing of certain genes. The inference is that the activated genes

(DNA) begin to synthesize specific RNA, which is transferred to the cytoplasm, where it acts as template for the synthesis of particular proteins (*e.g.*, enzymes). This concept is schematically represented in Figure 2–5. The literature contains scattered suggestions that certain vertebrate hormones may act in a similar manner.[58] It will be interesting to see how far this concept can be substantiated in processes other than development and in groups other than insects.

REFERENCES

1. Adams, J. L., and Herrick, R. B.: Interactions of the gonadal hormones in the chicken. Poultry Sci., *34*:117, 1955.
2. Allen, E.: The oestrous cycle of the mouse. Amer. J. Anat., *30*:297, 1922.
3. Aschleim, S., and Zondek, B.: Hypophysenvorderlappenhormon und Ovarialhormon in Harn von Schwangeren. Klin. Wchnschr., 6:1322, 1927.
4. Banting, F., and Best, C. H.: The internal secretion of the pancreas. J. Lab. & Clin. Med., 7:251, 1922.
5. Bargmann, W., and Scharrer, E.: The site of origin of the hormones of the posterior pituitary. Amer. Scientist, 39:255, 1951.
6. Bayliss, W. M., and Starling, E. H.: The mechanism of pancreatic secretion. J. Physiol., 28:325, 1902.
7. Berthold, A. A.: Transplantation der Hoden. Arch. Anat. Physiol. u. wiss. Med., 16:42, 1849.
8. Bodenstein, D.: Endocrine mechanisms in the life of insects. Recent Progr. Horm. Res., *10*:157, 1954.
9. Bogdanove, E. M., and Crabill, E. V.: Thyroid-pituitary feedback: direct thyroid hormone inhibition of the pituitary-thyroidectomy reaction in the rat. Memoirs Soc. Endocrinol., No. 9, 54, 1960.
10. Bongiovanni, A. M., and Eberlein, W. R.: Clinical and metabolic variations in adrenogenital syndrome. Pediatrics, *16*:628, 1955.
11. Boysen-Jensen, P.: Über die Leitung des phototropischen Reizes in *Avena* Keimpflanzen. Ber. d. bot. Gesellsch., 28:118, 1910.
12. Bradlow, H. L., Hellman, L., Zumoff, B., and Gallagher, T. F.: Interaction of hormonal effects: Influence of triiodothyronine on androgen metabolism. Science, *124*:1206, 1956.
13. Breneman, W. R.: Steroid hormones and the development of the reproductive system in the pullet. Endocrinology, 58:262, 1956.
14. Bromer, W. W., Sinn, L. G., and Behrens, O. K.: The amino acid sequence of glucagon. J. Amer. Chem. Soc., 79:2807, 1957.
15. Bullough, W. S.: The history of hormones. An inaugural lecture delivered at Birkbeck College, London, 1953.
16. Callow, R. K.: The source of cortisone. Medical World, 84:477, 1956.
17. Clever, U., and Karlson, P.: Induktion von Puff-Veränderungen in den Speicheldrüsenchromosomen von *Chironomus tentans* durch Ecdyson. Exp. Cell Research, *20*:623, 1960.
18. Corner, G. W., and Allen, W. M.: Physiology of the corpus luteum: Production of a special uterine reaction (progestational proliferation) by extracts of the corpus luteum. Amer. J. Physiol., 88:326, 1929.
19. Csapo, A.: Function and regulation of the myometrium. Ann. New York Acad. Sci., 75:790, 1959.
20. De Duve, C.: Glucagon: The hyperglycaemic glycogenolytic factor of the pancreas. Lancet, 2:99, 1953.
21. Dorfman, R. I.: Biosynthesis of adrenocortical steroids. Cancer, *10*:741, 1957.
22. Du Vigneaud, V., Lawler, C., and Popenoe, E.: Enzymatic cleavage of glycinamide from vasopressin and a proposed structure for this pressor-antidiuretic hormone of the posterior pituitary. J. Amer. Chem. Soc., 75:4880, 1953.

23. Du Vigneaud, V., Ressler, C., and Trippett, S.: The sequence of amino-acids in oxytocin, with a proposal for the structure of oxytocin. J. Biol. Chem., *205:* 949, 1953.
24. Edgren, R. A., Elton, R. L., and Calhoun, D. W.: Studies on the interactions of oestriol and progesterone. J. Reprod. & Fertil., 2:98, 1961.
25. Escamilla, R. F. (ed.): Laboratory Tests in Diagnosis and Investigation of Endocrine Functions. Philadelphia, F. A. Davis Co., 1962.
26. von Euler, U. S.: Adrenergic neurohormones. *In* von Euler and Heller (eds.): Comparative Endocrinology, Vol. 2. New York, Academic Press, 1963, p. 209.
27. Farner, D. S.: Photoperiodic control of annual gonadal cycles in birds. *In* Photoperiodism and Related Phenomena in Plants and Animals. Washington, D.C., American Association for the Advancement of Science (Publ. No. 55), 1959, p. 717.
28. Farner, D. S.: Comparative physiology: Photoperiodicity. Ann. Rev. Physiol., *23:*71, 1961.
29. Farner, D. S., and Oksche, A.: Neurosecretion in birds. Gen. & Comp. Endocrinol., 2:113, 1962.
30. Farrell, G. L., and Laqueur, G.: Reduction of pituitary content of ACTH by cortisone. Endocrinology, 56:471, 1955.
31. Fingerman, M.: The Control of Chromatophores. New York, The Macmillan Co., 1963.
32. Fong, C. T. O., Silver, L., Christman, D. R., and Schwartz, I. L.: On the mechanism of action of the antidiuretic hormone (vasopressin). Proc. Nat. Acad. Sci., U.S.A., 46:1273, 1960.
33. Forbes, T. R.: Testis transplantations performed by John Hunter. Endocrinology, *41:*329, 1947.
34. Forbes, T. R.: A. A. Berthold and the first endocrine experiment: Some speculation as to its origin. Bull. Hist. Med., 23:263, 1949.
35. Forchielli, E., Ichii, S., and Dorfman, R. I.: A mechanism of action of gonadotrophins. Research on Steroids, Trans. Internat. Study Group for Steroid Hormones, Rome, December, 1963, p. 43.
36. Gaunt, R., Chart, J. J., and Renzi, A. A.: Endocrine pharmacology. Science, *133:* 613, 1961.
37. Gorski, R. A., and Wagner, J. W.: Gonadal activity and sexual differentiation of the hypothalamus. Endocrinology, 76:226, 1965.
38. Gudernatsch, J. F.: Feeding experiments on tadpoles. Arch. Entwicklungsmech. Organ., 35:457, 1912.
39. Harris, G. W.: Neural Control of the Pituitary Gland. London, Edward Arnold, 1955.
40. Harris, G. W.: The central nervous system and the endocrine glands. Triangle, 6:242, 1964.
41. Hechter, O., *et al.*: Chemical transformation of steroids by adrenal perfusion: Perfusion methods. Endocrinology, 52:679, 1953.
42. Hechter, O., and Halkerston, I. D. K.: On the action of mammalian hormones. *In* Pincus, Thimann, and Astwood (eds.): The Hormones, Vol. 5. New York, Academic Press, 1964, p. 697.
43. Hench, P. S., Kendall, E. C., Slocumb, C. H., and Polley, H. F.: The effect of a hormone of the adrenal cortex (17-hydroxy-11-dehydrocorticosterone: compound E) and of pituitary adrenocorticotrophic hormone on rheumatoid arthritis: Preliminary report. Proc. Staff Meet., Mayo Clin., 24:181, 1949.
44. Hisaw, F. L.: Experimental relaxation of the pubic ligament of the guinea pig. Proc. Soc. Exper. Biol. & Med., 23:661, 1926.
45. Hisaw, F. L., Velardo, J. T., and Goolsby, C. M.: Interactions of estrogens on uterine growth. J. Clin. Endocrinol., *14:*1134, 1954.
46. Ingle, D. J.: Effect of estrogen on liver glycogen in adrenalectomized rats. Proc. Soc. Exper. Biol. & Med., *100:*439, 1959.
47. Jailer, J. W., Gold, J. J., Vande Wiele, R., and Lieberman, S.: 17 α-hydroxyprogesterone and 21-desoxyhydrocortisone; their metabolism and possible role in congenital adrenal virilism. J. Clin. Invest., 34:1639, 1955.

48. Kamm, O., Aldrich, T. B., Grote, I. W., Rowe, L. W., and Bugbee, E. P.: The active principles of the posterior lobe of the pituitary gland. The separation of two principles and their concentration in the form of potent solid preparations. J. Amer. Chem. Soc., 50:573, 1928.
49. Karlson, P.: On the chemistry and mode of action of insect hormones. Gen. & Comp. Endocrinol., Suppl. 1:1, 1962.
50. Karlson, P.: New concepts on the mode of action of hormones. Perspect. Biol. & Med., 6:203, 1963.
51. Knobil, E.: The pituitary growth hormone: Some physiological considerations. *In* M. X. Zarrow (ed.): Growth in Living Systems. New York, Basic Books, 1961, p. 353.
52. Knobil, E., and Hotchkiss, J.: Growth hormone. Ann. Rev. Physiol., 26:47, 1964.
53. Leathem, J. H.: Hormones and protein metabolism. Recent Progr. Horm. Res., 14:141, 1958.
54. Leathem, J. H., and Wolf, R. C.: The varying effects of sex hormones in mammals. Memoirs Soc. Endocrinol., No. 4, 220, 1955.
55. Leopold, A. C.: Plant hormones. *In* Pincus, Thimann, and Astwood (eds.): The Hormones, Vol. 4. New York, Academic Press, 1964, p. 1.
56. Levine, R., and Goldstein, M. S.: On the mechanism of action of insulin. Recent Progr. Horm. Res., 11:343, 1955.
57. Li, C. H.: Pituitary growth hormone as a metabolic hormone. Science, 123:617, 1956.
58. Liao, S., and Williams-Ashman, H. G.: An effect of testosterone on amino acid incorporation by prostatic ribonucleoprotein particles. Proc. Nat. Acad. Sci., U.S.A., 48:1956, 1962.
59. Loubatières, A.: The hypoglycemic sulfonamides: History and development of the problem from 1942 to 1955. Ann. New York Acad. Sci., 71:4, 1957.
60. MacCorquodale, D. W., Thayer, S. A., and Doisy, E. A.: The isolation of the principal estrogenic substance of liquor folliculi. J. Biol. Chem., 115:435, 1936.
61. McKenzie, J. M.: Review: Pathogenesis of Graves' disease: Role of the long-acting thyroid stimulator. J. Clin. Endocrinol., 25:424, 1965.
62. McLean, F. C., and Urist, M. R.: An Introduction to the Physiology of Skeletal Tissue. Chicago, University of Chicago Press, 1955.
63. Mellen, W. J.: Duration of effect of thyroxine and thiouracil in young chickens. Poultry Sci., 37:672, 1958.
64. Miller, M. R.: *In* A. W. Martin (ed.): Comparative Physiology of Carbohydrate Metabolism in Heterothermic Animals. Seattle, University of Washington Press, 1961, p. 125.
65. Moore, C. R., and Price, D.: Gonad hormone functions, and the reciprocal influence between gonads and hypophysis with its bearing on the problem of sex hormone antagonism. Amer. J. Anat., 50:13, 1932.
66. Mosier, H. D., and Richter, C. P.: Response of the glomerulosa layer of the adrenal gland of wild and domesticated Norway rats on low and high salt diets. Endocrinology, 62:268, 1958.
67. Péron, F. G., and Dorfman, R. I.: A method for the evaluation of adrenocorticotropic hormone suppressing action of corticoids. Endocrinology, 64:431, 1959.
68. Péron, F. G., Moncloa, F., and Dorfman, R. I.: Studies on the possible inhibitory effect of corticosterone on corticosteroidogenesis at the adrenal level in the rat. Endocrinology, 67:379, 1960.
69. Rasmussen, H., Schwartz, I. L., Schoessler, M. A., and Hochster, G.: Studies on the mechanism of action of vasopressin. Proc. Nat. Acad. Sci., U.S.A., 46:1278, 1960.
70. Riddle, O., Bates, R. W., and Dykshorn, S. W.: The preparation, identification and assay of prolactin: A hormone of the anterior pituitary. Amer. J. Physiol., 105:191, 1933.
71. Rose, G. G., and Trunnell, J. B.: Thyroid epithelium in tissue cultures: Observations on the morphology and functional capacities of embryo chick thyroids. Endocrinology, 64:344, 1959.
72. Salisbury, F. B.: Plant growth substances. Sci. Amer., 196(4):125, 1957.
73. Schwartz, I. L., Rasmussen, H., Schoessler, M. A., Silver, L., and Fong, C. T. O.:

Relation of chemical attachment to physiological action of vasopressin. Proc. Nat. Acad. Sci., U.S.A., 46:1288, 1960.

74. Sgouris, J. T., and Meites, J.: Differential inactivation of prolactin by mammary tissue from pregnant and parturient rats. Amer. J. Physiol., 175:319, 1953.

75. Simpson, S. A., Tait, J. F., Wettstein, A., Neher, R., v.Euw, J., and Reichstein, T.: Isolierung eines neuen Kristallisierten Hormons aus Nebennieren mit besonders hoher Wirksamkeit auf den Mineralstoffwechsel. Experientia, 9:333, 1953.

76. Smith, G. H., Randle, P. J., and Battaglia, F. C.: The mechanism of action of insulin in muscle. Memoirs Soc. Endocrinol., No. 11, 124, 1961.

77. Smith, P. E.: Ablation and transplantation of the hypophysis in the rat. Anat. Rec., 32:221, 1926.

78. Stadie, W. C.: Recent advances in insulin research. Diabetes, 5:263, 1956.

79. Staub, A., Sinn, L., and Behrens, O. K.: Purification and crystallization of glucagon. J. Biol. Chem., 214:619, 1955.

80. Stockard, C. R., and Papanicolaou, G. N.: The existence of a typical oestrous cycle in the guinea-pig with a study of its histological and physiological changes. Amer. J. Anat., 22:225, 1917.

81. Stricker, P., and Grueter, F.: Action du lobe antérieur de l'hypophyse sur la montée laiteuse. Compt. rend. Soc. de biol., 99:1978, 1928.

82. Szego, C. M.: The loss of estrogen-protein binding capacity in rat hepatoma. Endocrinology, 57:541, 1955.

83. Takewaki, K.: Some aspects of hormonal mechanism involved in persistent estrus in the rat. Experientia, 18:1, 1962.

84. Takewaki, K.: Some experiments on the control of hypophyseal-gonadal system in the rat. Gen. & Comp. Endocrinol., Suppl. 1:309, 1962.

85. Thimann, K. V.: Promotion and inhibition: Twin themes of physiology. Amer. Naturalist, 90:145, 1956.

86. Thompson, E. O. P.: The insulin molecule. Sci. Amer. 192(5):36, 1955.

87. Tuller, B. F.: The separation of L-arterenol from natural U.S.P. epinephrine. Science, 109:536, 1949.

88. Turner, C. D.: Special mechanisms in anomalies of sex differentiation. Amer. J. Obst. & Gynec., 90:1208, 1964.

89. Villee, C. A.: Some current speculations on the action of estrogens. Perspect. Biol. & Med., 2:290, 1959.

90. Vogt, M.: Morphological changes in the adrenal cortex in relation to concentration of steroids in adrenal vein blood. Ciba Found. Colloq. Endocrinol., 11:193, 1957.

91. White, A., Catchpole, H. B., and Long, C. N. H.: A crystalline protein with high lactogenic activity. Science, 86:82, 1937.

92. Wigglesworth, V. B.: The determination of characters at metamorphosis in *Rhodnius prolixus* (Hemiptera). J. Exper. Biol., 17:201, 1940.

93. Young, W. C., Goy, R. W., and Phoenix, C. H.: Hormones and sexual behavior. Science, 143:212, 1964.

3

NEUROSECRETION AND NEUROENDOCRINE MECHANISMS IN THE INVERTEBRATES

Remarkable progress has been made in elucidating the neuro-endocrine systems of invertebrates and lower vertebrates, and certain concepts of great importance have emerged. While members of the animal kingdom are widely divergent in genetic endowments, body structure, and living habits, they are all forced to adjust to the same general environmental conditions in order to thrive as individuals and as species. Since protoplasm is fundamentally the same, irrespective of the species in which it is found, all organisms must obtain from their surroundings about the same materials for growth, maintenance, and repair of their bodies. In other words, all organisms have about the same needs and face very similar problems in their efforts to survive. It is not surprising, therefore, to find that invertebrates and vertebrates often employ comparable functional (analogous) arrangements in meeting their basic require-ments. The comparative study of analogous systems has often been more rewarding than the study of homologous structures.

The traditional distinctions between endocrine and nervous systems appear to be largely artificial. The two systems function together to transform a loosely bound collection of cells, tissues, and organs into a cooperative enterprise, an organism that can adjust internal processes to changing conditions in the external world. Even the simplest organisms are complicated machines consisting

63

of a multitude of parts that must be integrated in order to make life possible. During the course of evolution there has been an increase in the number of cells comprising organisms and also differentiation of cells into tissues and organs, *i.e.,* into groups of cells specialized for rather specific functions. With evolutionary advancement the problem of knitting diverse tissues and organs into a smoothly operating unit assumed increasing importance. In a multi-cellular individual like man, the billions of cells are structural and functional units in a very real sense, but each cell has become an interacting part of the whole organism and hence has lost the capacity of being self-sustaining.

THE CONCEPT OF NEUROSECRETION

In addition to neurohumors, such as acetylcholine and nor-epinephrine, which function in the transmission of nervous impulses, it is known that certain neurons secrete long-range, long-acting neurohormones. These latter substances are more stable than the neurohumors and may act at many distant points within the organism over a period of hours rather than milliseconds.

Neurosecretory Cells

Some neurons have developed secretory functions to such an extent that they become morphologically distinguishable from other nerve cells. These are called "neurosecretory cells," since they are neurons that elaborate and discharge special products after the manner of glands. Glandular neurons of this type are almost ubiquitous among metazoan animals. Though some of the smaller invertebrate phyla have not been adequately studied, such cells appear to be present wherever a central nervous system exists and some degree of cephalization has occurred.[1, 6, 70, 81]

Since neurosecretory cells may have dendrites, axis cylinders, and Nissl bodies, they are modified neurons rather than glia cells that have migrated into the nervous system. Visible granules appear in the perikarya, undergo various transformations, and are eventually discharged from the axons. The neurosecretory substance is trans-mitted distally, probably by axoplasmic flow, and often accumulates in terminal bulbs. There are indications that in special cases the neurohormone may be released from other points along the axon or even from the perikaryon itself. The axons of neurosecretory cells often end in close association with blood vessels or hemocoels. This complex, formed of axonal bulbs and vascular structures, serves as a storage and release center for the neurohormones, and is called a *neurohemal organ*. The best known neurohemal organs are the neural lobe of the vertebrate pituitary, the caudal neurosecretory system (urophysis) of certain fishes, the sinus gland of crustaceans, and the corpus cardiacum of insects. Neurohemal organs do not always occur in connection with neurosecretory systems, but the absence of true synaptic terminations is quite characteristic of neurosecretory axons.

Very little is known concerning the form in which the active ingredients are contained within the neurosecretory granules. Electron microscopic studies indicate that the granules are surrounded by distinct membranes, and these are presumed to be semipermeable. The neurosecretory droplets present in the rat's neurohypophysis decrease in density after the animals are dehydrated in order to deplete the stores of antidiuretic hormone. When tested for effects on pigment cells, homogenates of the sinus gland of the crab (*Uca*) are almost inactive in isotonic sucrose, but are activated by dilution with water, heating, freezing, and other procedures that are known to damage or disrupt biologic membranes. Physicochemical studies suggest that the neurosecretory granules found in sinus gland extracts contain neurohormones that are polypeptide in nature and that they are probably bound to large protein carriers. The Gomori and other staining techniques probably do not actually stain the neurohormones within the granules, but rather carrier molecules with which the active principles are associated.

Though the neurosecretory axons do not synapse with other neurons, muscles, or exocrine glands, there are indications that the glandular neurons can conduct impulses.[77, 117] The intra-axonal transport of secretory droplets has been observed in fresh preparations of the hypophysial stalk of the goosefish, *Lophius*. The hypophysial stalk of this fish is exceptionally long and has been useful in the demonstration of action potentials. Direct electrical stimulation of these fibers near the proximal end of the stalk leads to activity that may be recorded at the distal end. Delayed responses result from stimulation of the hypothalamic region near the base of the stalk.

The *urophysis* is a neurosecretory structure located at the posterior end of the spinal cord in fishes.[86] Neurosecretory cells within the cord (Dahlgren cells) send axons ventrally and their enormous end-bulbs cause this region to bulge slightly. While it is agreed that the urophysis is analogous to the neurohypophysial division of the pituitary gland, its function remains obscure. There are suggestions that its products may be involved in osmoregulation and buoyancy,[7] but others do not confirm these findings.[97] It has been shown that the giant, neurosecretory cells contributing to the urophysis of the eel are capable of conducting impulses.

If neurosecretory cells can receive and conduct impulses, as is the case in certain instances, the significance of this action remains problematical. Two possibilities might be considered: (1) the impulse could conceivably trigger the release of secretion from the cell itself or (2) the impulse might activate pituicytes or other glia-like cells which are often closely applied to axonal endings within neurohemal organs. Some investigators have suggested that these glia-like elements may effect changes in the neurosecretions to form the active principles which reach the body fluids.

NONARTHROPOD INVERTEBRATES

Neurosecretory cells have been identified in all invertebrate phyla that possess well-defined nervous systems, with the possible exception of lower coelenterates and ctenophores. Evidence that the products of neurosecretory cells perform functional roles in certain invertebrate species has not been pursued far enough to be convincing. It is often difficult to correlate cytologic changes in the neurosecretory cells with prevailing physiologic states in the organism. Furthermore, classical deficiency experiments are often difficult or impossible, and as a substitute, extracts of the nervous system have been used in injection experiments. When extracts containing all elements of nervous tissue are employed, there is the danger of misconstruing what may be a pharmacologic effect of the tissue for a physiologic response to a neurohormone. Unfortunately, none of the invertebrate neurohormones are yet available in chemically pure form.

Some Lower Invertebrate Phyla

Neurosecretory cells are known to be present in the cerebral ganglia of flatworms such as *Dugesia* and *Polycelis*.[68] A water-soluble factor, prepared from planarian brain, induces the regeneration of excised eyespots. Since the number of neurosecretory cells in the brain of *Polycelis* increases while posterior regeneration is in progress, it is likely that neurohormones are involved in this process.

The circumoral ring and radial nerves of starfishes are said to contain neurosecretory cells, and a number of physiologic effects have been ascribed to their secretions.[103] Neurosecretory cells have been reported in the motor ganglia of the Ophiuroidea.[41] Materials obtained from nerve extracts are found to effect color change, locomotor activity, water content, and gamete shedding. Extracts of radial nerves from starfishes contain a principle (shedding substance) that induces the release of gametes from the ripe gonads, and another (shedhibin) that inhibits the shedding of eggs.[18, 19]

The exact cellular source of these agents acting upon the gonads is obscure, but they are thought to be neurosecretions.

NEUROENDOCRINE MECHANISMS IN ANNELIDA

Neurosecretory cells are present in the central nervous systems of all three major classes of annelids,[92] and neurohemal organs have been identified in some species. The neuroendocrine complexes of polychaetes and oligochaetes appear to be involved in the control of three processes: (a) maturation of the gonads, (b) somatic transformations related to reproduction, and (c) the regeneration of posterior segments. The presence of true, non-neural endocrine glands in this phylum has not been established.

Polychaeta

As many polychaetes become sexually mature, they undergo somatic modifications which equip them to swim at the surface of the sea and engage in spawning activity. This transformation of an immature individual (atoke) into a reproductive individual (epitoke) is called *epitoky,* and involves changes in the parapodia, chaetae, musculature, eyes, size of the segments, etc. (Fig. 3–1).

Much evidence indicates that neurosecretory cells within the brain of nereids are the source of a neurohormone that inhibits gonadal maturation and epitoky. By analogy with insects, this is sometimes called "juvenile hormone" since it acts to keep the animals sexually immature. Surgical removal of the cerebral ganglia, in nereids with or without natural epitoky, results in premature and accelerated development of the gametes. In species in which epitoky occurs, decerebration of the atokous worms causes the premature attainment of the same metamorphic transformations as normally occur when the worms become sexually mature. All these changes that follow decerebration can be prevented by implanting ganglia from atokous donors; ganglia contributed by epitokous donors do not prevent the precocious epitoky and sexual maturation. The onset of normal epitoky can be delayed in intact individuals by the implantation of ganglia from atokous donors. Production or liberation of the inhibitory brain neurohormone apparently ceases after the onset of sexual maturity. Certain species and races of nereids normally reproduce in the atokous condition (without epitoky) and, in these forms, decerebration does not induce epitoky; the operation, however, does result in the precocious maturation of male germ cells. It is not known what factors operate to shut off the production of brain neurohormone as the nereids approach sexual maturity.

Ablation and implantation experiments indicate that neuro-

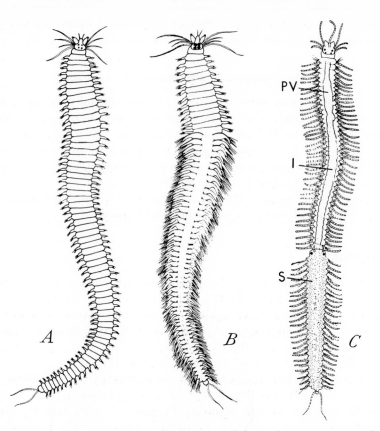

Figure 3-1. Metamorphosis in polychaete annelids. *A*, the immature or atokous stage of *Nereis; B*, the adult or epitokous stage of *Nereis; C*, stolonization in a syllid polychaete. I, intestine; PV, proventriculus; S, stolon. (From Charniaux-Cotton and Kleinholz: *In* Pincus, Thimann, and Astwood [eds.]: The Hormones, Vol. 4. New York, Academic Press, 1964; after Durchon, 1960.)

secretory cells in the posterior portions of the cerebral ganglia of nereids are the source of a neurohormone that controls the regeneration of posterior segments. Little or no posterior regeneration occurs if the cerebral ganglia are removed at the time of segment amputation. Intracoelomic implants of the ganglia into decerebrate hosts restore the ability to replace excised posterior segments. Studies on *Nereis* have shown that both normal growth and regenerative capacity decline as the worms age, and that neurosecretions from the cerebral ganglia are apparently involved in both processes. It is not known whether the growth-promoting and regeneration-promoting neurohormones are identical or distinct secretions.[22-24, 32, 33]

Oligochaeta

Neurosecretory cells within the supraesophageal ganglia of *Lumbricus* are the probable source of a secretion that governs the maintenance of external sex characters (*e.g.*, clitellum), and possibly the differentiation of gametes. This neurohormone has an inhibitory effect on gonad maturation and is probably involved in the process of egg laying. As in polychaetes, the brain is essential for the re-generation of posterior segments.

Hirudinea

The central nervous system of the leech is rich in cells that are obviously neurosecretory in nature,[49] but no physiologic role for their products has been established. The giant chromaffin cells in each ventral ganglion of *Hirudo* have been shown to contain an epinephrine-like substance. Other neurosecretory cells of the nerve cord and subesophageal ganglion are reported to give a positive chromaffin reaction.

NEUROENDOCRINE MECHANISMS IN MOLLUSCA

Neurosecretory cells are found within the brains of all mollusca that have been studied, and, in addition, appear in connection with many of the ganglia. The epithelial vesicles of cephalopods (squids and octopuses) show some structural evidence of neuro-secretory competence, though this has not been proved. The epi-stellar body of the octopus is such a structure, and the indications are that it is a rudimentary photoreceptor.[80]

The genital ducts and accessory glands of slugs (*e.g.*, *Limax*) undergo functional development at the time of gonadal maturation. Precocious development of these sex accessories may be induced by transplanting pieces of mature gonads into young recipients. The accessory sex organs involute following the castration of adults, and these changes are repaired by gonadal transplants. Accordingly, there is reason to believe that the gonads of pulmonate gastropods are the source of a hormone which is essential for the development and functioning of the accessory genital complex.[21] In addition to neurosecretory complexes, true endocrine glands are present in the Mollusca.

The optic glands of cephalopods are small *endocrine* organs lying on the optic stalks on either side of the brain (Fig. 3-2). Such glands have been found in all cephalopods examined, with the exception of *Nautilus*, and have been most carefully studied in *Octopus*.[105, 106] They contain no neurosecretory cells and are the source of a gonadotrophin which induces ovarian and testicular enlargement. The production of gonadotrophin by the gland is regulated by an inhibitory nerve supply extending to it from the subpedunculate lobe of the brain. The inhibitory centers in this portion of the brain seem to be governed by changes in photoperiod.

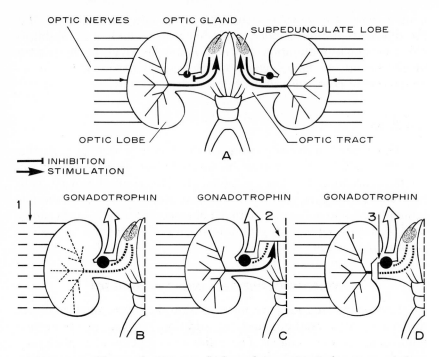

Figure 3-2. Neuroendocrine control of gonad maturation in the octopus. *A*, In an immature animal, unoperated upon, the production of gonadotrophin by the optic glands is held in check by an inhibitory nerve supply originating in the subpedunculate lobe of the brain. Activation of this brain center appears to depend upon changes in photoperiod. *B*, Section of the optic nerves (point 1) prevents activation (broken lines) of the inhibitory nerve center; the optic glands enlarge and secrete gonadotrophin, which induces hypertrophy of the gonads. The same result may be accomplished by ablation of the subpedunculate lobes (*C*, at point 2) or by section of the optic tract (*D*, point 3). (Modified from figures by Wells and Wells.)

Thus, light stimuli received by the eyes activate nerve centers in the brain and these hold the optic glands in check and the gonads are inhibited through a lack of gonadotrophin. After blinding or excision of the subpedunculate lobes, the optic glands enlarge and the ovaries develop precociously. These procedures have no effect on the gonads after removal of the optic glands (Fig. 3-2). Functioning of the brain-optic gland-gonadal system of *Octopus* is suggestive of the regulation of sexual maturity in vertebrates by the hypothalamic-pituitary-gonadal axis. It should be noted, however, that neurosecretory cells seem not to be involved in the case of *Octopus*.

After excision of the optic glands of *Octopus*, the oöcytes develop normally but follicle cells do not, and yolk deposition fails to occur. The gonadotrophin from the optic gland of the male appears to promote spermatogenesis. Ablation of the subpedunculate lobes of very young males results in enlargement of the optic gland, increased testicular weight, and the precocious appearance of spermatophores in the testis.

There is no information on the chemical nature of the optic gland hormone. Experiments on the transplanatation of optic glands and the effectiveness of fractionated organ extracts would probably yield interesting results.

NEUROENDOCRINE MECHANISMS IN THE CRUSTACEA

Location of Structures

The regulatory mechanisms of crustaceans are extremely complex and are very closely related to the central nervous system.[17, 65] The principal endocrine structures of a generalized crustacean are shown in Figure 3–3. Neurosecretory cells are abundant in the brain and in practically all of the other ganglia. The endocrine organs in crustaceans, as in insects, fall into three categories: (a) aggregations of neurosecretory cells that produce neurohormones and discharge them from their axonic terminals, (b) neurohemal organs for the storage, possible modification, and liberation of neurohormones, and (c) true endocrine glands (non-neural) that release hormones into the blood.

Important neurosecretory centers are found in connection with the optic ganglia which lie within the eyestalks. Best known of these are the "X organs" which are present in the eyestalks of most stalk-eyed species, or in the head when stalked eyes are absent (Fig. 3–3). Two kinds of X organs are now recognized: the *ganglionic X organ* and the *sensory pore X organ*. The two X organs fuse to form a single structure on the medulla terminalis of brachyurans but, in natantians, they are separated groups of neurosecretory cells. Clusters of secretory neurons are also found within the brain, the thoracic ganglia, the esophageal connective ganglia, and the tritocerebral commissure.

The sinus gland was early recognized as a potent source of hormones, and it was assumed initially that the secretions arose from glandular elements comprising the structure. Since the sinus glands do not show the histologic characteristics of a typical gland of internal secretion, it became apparent that their products probably arose elsewhere. As surgical procedures improved, it was possible to remove this small organ alone without resorting to ablation of the entire eyestalk. It became apparent that these two surgical procedures result in different physiologic effects, and this led Bliss and Welsh (1952) to conclude that the sinus glands are essentially reservoirs for the storage and discharge of neurohormones derived from the axons of neurosecretory neurons.[10] This concept has been amply confirmed and is now generally accepted. Like other neurohemal organs, the sinus glands consist chiefly of axonic terminals,

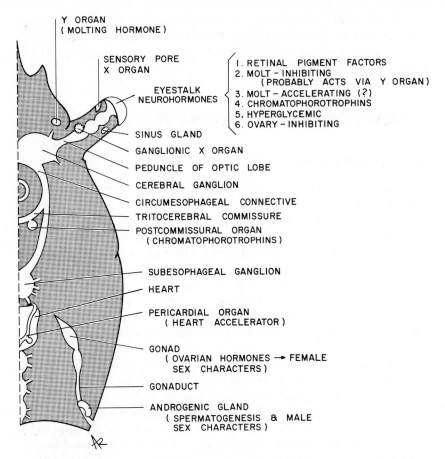

Figure 3–3. Summarizing diagram of the cephalothorax of a generalized crustacean, showing the locations of the best-known endocrine glands and neuroendocrine areas. The active principles from these structures are listed or shown in parentheses. Neurosecretory cells are present in all components of the central nervous system, and no attempt has been made to show them.

and are closely associated with rich vascular channels. In addition to discharged secretions, they contain nonglandular cells that seem comparable to the pituicytes present within the pars nervosa of the vertebrate neurohypophysis. These glia-like elements often appear to be wrapped around the bulbous terminals of the secretory axons. While it is possible that the sinus glands may possess some inherent secretory ability, like the corpora cardiaca of insects, they are chiefly storage-release centers for neurohormones.

The postcommissural and pericardial organs also appear to be essentially neurohemal in nature. The secretion-charged axons from cells within the brain and esophageal connective ganglia terminate in the postcommissural organs which store and discharge the neurohormones. Neurosecretory cells, having their perikarya within the ganglia of the ventral chain, deliver their products to the pericardial organs located near the openings of the large veins into the pericardial sac (Fig. 3–3).

Three endocrine glands, not composed of secretory neurons, are found in the Crustacea: the Y organs, the androgenic glands, and the ovaries. The Y organs are located in the antennary or maxillary segment and resemble, in some respects, the prothoracic, molt-regulating glands of insects. They appear to be devoid of direct innervation, and are probably regulated by neurosecretions derived from the eyestalk complex.[83] Androgenic glands have been found in a variety of crustaceans,[21] and in a few species of insects.[79] They are generally located outside the testes and are typically found along the vas deferens (Fig. 3–3). Although rudimentary androgenic glands are present in females, they develop only in males. These masculinizing glands are probably controlled by neurohormones from the X-organ sinus gland complex. The crustacean ovary, unlike the testis, serves in an endocrine capacity.

Retinal Pigment Migration

The compound eyes of higher crustaceans are composed of a large number of units called *ommatidia*. Three functionally distinct groups of pigments are possessed by each ommatidium: distal retinal pigment, proximal retinal pigment, and reflecting white pigment. The distal and proximal pigments screen the sensory component of the ommatidium, the rhabdome, in bright light, and migrate away from the rhabdome in darkness. The white pigment increases the effectiveness of dim light as a stimulus by reflecting the light that enters the eye over adjacent receptors. When the eye is adapted to darkness, the distal pigment migrates distally to enclose the dioptic apparatus, the proximal pigment moves to a position below the basement membrane, and the reflecting pigment surrounds the rhabdome. In the light-adapted eye, the distal pigment disperses proximally as far as the retinula cells, the proximal pigment moves distally to meet the distal retinal pigment, and the reflecting pigment moves away from the rhabdome and assumes a position below the basement membrane. Eyestalk extracts, prepared from light-adapted prawns, result in light adaptation of the distal and reflecting pigments when injected into dark-adapted recipients; the proximal pigment remains unchanged (Fig. 3–4).

It is probable that the responses of these retinal effectors are controlled by two neurosecretions, one light-adapting and the other dark-adapting.[14] There are many species variations but, in general, the two factors can be extracted from the eyestalk and various portions of the nervous system. The regulation of retinal pigments is a very complex process, and available extracts do not duplicate exactly the normal actions of variable illumination.[37, 63, 64]

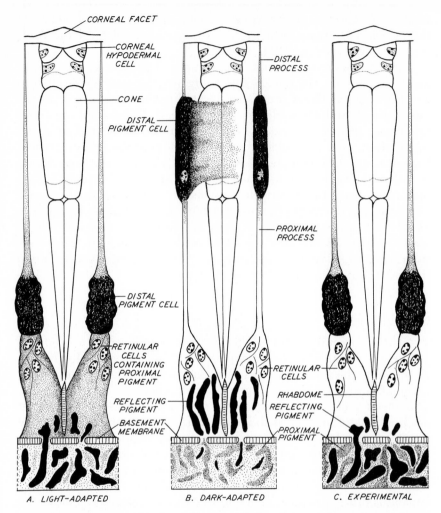

CORNEAL FACET

CORNEAL HYPODERMAL CELL

CONE

DISTAL PIGMENT CELL

DISTAL PIGMENT CELL

RETINULAR CELLS CONTAINING PROXIMAL PIGMENT

REFLECTING PIGMENT

BASEMENT MEMBRANE

DISTAL PROCESS

PROXIMAL PROCESS

RETINULAR CELLS

RHABDOME

REFLECTING PIGMENT

PROXIMAL PIGMENT

A. LIGHT–ADAPTED   *B. DARK-ADAPTED*   *C. EXPERIMENTAL*

Figure 3–4. Ommatidia from the eyes of the shrimp *Palaemonetes vulgaris*, showing general morphology and the positions of the pigments under different conditions. *A*, The light-adapted condition. The distal pigment has migrated inwardly and is concentrated near the retinular cells. Most of the proximal pigment, contained within the retinular cells, lies distad of the basement membrane. The reflecting pigment moves through the basement membrane, i.e., away from the rhabdome. *B*, The dark-adapted state. The distal pigment surrounds the distal end of the cone; the reflecting pigment surrounds the rhabdome, and the proximal pigment migrates into the portions of the retinular cells which lie below the basement membrane. *C*, An ommatidium from an animal which had been adapted to darkness and then had an injection of an extract of the eyestalks (sinus glands). The extract causes the distal and reflecting pigments to assume the positions characteristic of light adaptation; the proximal pigment apparently is not influenced in this species. (Modified after Kleinholz, 1936.)

Chromatophorotrophins and Color Change

The chromatophores, or pigment cells, of crustaceans may contain white, red, yellow, black, brown, and blue pigments. By appropriate condensation or dispersal of particular pigments within the chromatophores, crustaceans can approximate rather accurately the colored backgrounds upon which they rest. It is known that crustacean pigment cells are devoid of nerves and are adjusted by regulatory agents present in the blood (chromatophorotrophins). Studies involving eyestalk or X-organ ablation, coupled with the testing of extracts made from different regions of the nervous system, have demonstrated that the chromatophorotrophins are products of neurosecretory cells. Some of these factors are abundant in the tritocerebral commissure and the postcommissural organs. Multiple chromatophorotrophins have been extracted from the nervous systems of decapod crustaceans, but the exact number has not been agreed upon.[13, 36] It is possible that the effective agents obtained through the extraction of neurosecretory aggregations (*e.g.*, ganglionic X organ) are not of the same chemical form as the finished products liberated by neurohemal organs (*e.g.*, sinus gland).

Though barnacles have neither compound eyes nor chromatophores, extracts of their nervous systems have chromatophore-activating properties when tested on decapod crustaceans.[85] Blind cave crayfishes possess no retinal pigments and no chromatophores, yet their nervous systems contain both the distal pigment, light-adapting principle and another affecting integumentary chromatophores.[38]

Molting

Growth is a discontinuous process in arthropods, increase in size being restricted to the period between loss of the old exoskeleton and the production of a new one. Molting may be seasonal or continuous, and is influenced by a great variety of environmental conditions.[8, 9] Loss and replacement of the exoskeleton is an outward expression of a whole complex of major metabolic adjustments occurring within.[82] Four periods are recognized in the crustacean molt cycle: (1) During *premolt*, inorganic constituents of the old exoskeleton are resorbed and stored in gastroliths or hepatopancreas. Oxygen consumption increases, glycogen is deposited in the hypodermis, and lost limbs are regenerated rapidly. (2) *Molt* is the sloughing of the old cuticle, and this is accompanied by a marked increase in size. The immediate increase in size results from a rapid absorption of water, which thus reserves enough space to permit growth even after the new cuticle has hardened. (3) *Postmolt* is the period during which a new exoskeleton is formed through the redeposition of chitin and inorganic salts. (4) *Intermolt* is characterized by relative quiescence, but there is generally some storage of reserves in preparation for the next molt. Some crustaceans eventually cease molting and consequently undergo no further growth, a condition called *anecdysis*.

In most species of crustaceans, the ablation of both eyestalks results in accelerated molting and precocious growth. Extracts of the ganglionic X-organ sinus gland complex act to prevent molting. These and other observations led to the conclusion that neurosecretory cells in the ganglionic X organ secrete a molt-inhibiting neurohormone that is stored and released from the sinus gland. Studies on the formation of gastroliths in crayfish indicate that the molt-inhibiting factor is derived from components of the eyestalk. These concretions normally form in the stomach wall during premolt, but may be induced at any period of the molt cycle by ablating both eyestalks or by excision of the X-organ sinus gland complex.[74, 96] Gastrolith formation in eyestalkless animals can be prevented by the implantation of sinus glands. Profound quantitative shifts in the metabolism of carbohydrate, protein, lipid, and inorganic materials occur in relation to the molt cycle. As might be expected, these biochemical adjustments are facilitated by the endocrine factors that control molting.

Whether the components of the eyestalk produce a second factor, molt-accelerating principle, remains unresolved. Under certain conditions, and in certain species, molt inhibition may follow eyestalk abalation; certain workers feel that this can be explained on other grounds, and hence there is not sufficient evidence for a molt-accelerating neurohormone. On the other hand, it has been suggested, from studies on the crayfish (*Orconectes virilis*), that both molt-inhibiting and molt-accelerating factors from the eyestalk are involved in regulating the cyclical changes which characterize metabolism of the hepatopancreas.[75]

The Y organs were discovered by Gabe (1953), and it is certain that they produce a hormone which performs a positive role in the molting process.[45] Young crabs are prevented from molting by bilateral removal of the Y organs, but molting cycles may be restored in these animals by implanting several Y organs. These organs normally degenerate after puberty in the crab *Maia*, and no further molting occurs. It seems probable that the molt-inhibiting neurohormone from the ganglionic X-organ sinus gland complex may exert its effects by regulating the functional status of the Y organs. It would follow that the molt-inhibiting neurosecretion is continuously produced during postmolt and intermolt periods to stall the production of molting hormone by the Y organs; during premolt, the production of neurosecretion ceases, or diminishes, and the Y organs are allowed to secrete molting hormone.

The Y organs are analogous (possibly homologous) to the prothoracic glands of insects. It is interesting that both endocrine glands secrete hormones that control molting, and that both are regulated by neurosecretions from the central nervous system. The prothoracic glands degenerate in adult insects, following the last molt, and the Y organs are greatly reduced in crabs during anecdysis.

Reproduction

There is more evidence for the existence of sex hormones in the malacostracans, the higher crustaceans, than in the other invertebrates. Hormones regulating the differentiation of male and female sexual characters arise from the ovaries and the androgenic glands; the testis itself probably has no endocrine function.[21] Neurosecretions of the ganglionic X-organ sinus gland complex have inhibitory effects on ovarian maturation and secretory activity of the androgenic glands. There is evidence that the molting hormone from the Y organs is also essential for normal differentiation of both the ovary and the testis. After bilateral ablation of Y organs in very young crabs (*Carcinus*), mitotic processes are impaired in both the ovary and testis. In the ovary, oögonial mitoses cease and follicles are not formed around the oöcytes; vitellogenesis, or yolk deposition, does not occur in the oöcytes that lack follicles. Spermatogonial mitoses are arrested, and the testes become depleted of mature germ cells.

Bilateral removal of the ovaries in certain crustaceans (*e.g.*, *Orchestia*) results in the loss of specific secondary sex characters. Secondary characters of the female type may be induced in genetic males by removing the androgenic glands and implanting ovaries. Two ovarian hormones have been postulated on the basis of good evidence, but neither is known chemically.[21]

It has been shown in many species of crustaceans that ablation of the eyestalks, during periods of sexual quiescence, is followed by enlargement of the ovaries and by a precocious deposition of yolk in the oöcytes. Extracts prepared from eyestalks, ganglionic X organs, or sinus glands effectively prevent ovarian enlargement when administered to females that are entering the period of reproductive activity. Such extracts are without effect when given to very immature females or to females immediately after the end of the reproductive period. It appears that the primary action of this ovarian-inhibiting neurohormone is to prevent vitellogenesis. The production of this factor is apparently regulated by environmental stimuli that impinge on sensory receptors.

The important androgenic glands were discovered by Charniaux-Cotton (1954) in the amphipod *Orchestia gammarella*, and have since been found in quite a variety of crustacean species.[20, 21, 62] The following observations indicate that the androgenic gland hormone regulates spermatogenesis and the secondary sex characters of the male: (1) In *O. gammarella*, ablation of the androgenic glands causes spermatogenic activity in the testis to wane, and regenerated appendages develop neither the male nor the female sex characteristics; in *O. montagui*, oögenesis ensues in the testis. (2) If androgenic glands are grafted to intact female hosts, the ovaries eventually transform into testes and proliferate spermatocytes, spermatids, and functional spermatozoa. The appendages progressively assume male form, and masculine sexual behavior is acquired. The bipotentiality of the primordial germ cells is clearly indicated. (3) Castration of normal males, the androgenic glands remaining intact, has no effect other than to remove the source of germ cells. (4) If ovaries are grafted into males that have been deprived of androgenic glands, they persist as functional ovaries. When grafted into males possessing androgenic glands, with or without host testes, the ovaries quickly acquire testicular structure. (5) Aqueous extracts of androgenic glands, injected into males deprived of these organs, effectively prevent changes in the testes and secondary sex characters. In certain species, blood plasma from males, injected into female recipients, causes the ovary to assume testicular structure and function (Fig. 3–5).

It follows from these observations that the differentiation of germ cells of crustaceans is reversible, regardless of their genetic constitution: in the absence of androgenic gland hormone the gonads can become ovaries, but testicular differentiation requires the presence of this hormone. Several species of decapod crustaceans are protandric hermaphrodites, and it is known that androgenic glands are present during the male phase and are lost before the onset of the female phase. The androgenic glands of some species are closely applied to the testes, and it is probable that the sex reversals formerly attributed to destruction of the gonads by parasites actually result from destruction of or damage to the androgenic glands.

Heart Acceleration

The pericardial organs are neurohemal in nature and release a neurohormone which increases the frequency and amplitude of the heartbeat. Although extracts of pericardial organs contain 5-hydroxytryptamine, it is believed that the major activity of the extracts is due to another substance not yet identified.[71–73]

Metabolism

Striking variations in tissue metabolism occur during the molting cycle in Crustacea, and eyestalk factors, presumably neurosecretions, are known to be involved.[75] Identity of the active principles and the manner in which they interact are problems that require further elucidation. Molt-inhibiting and molt-accelerating factors from the eyestalk, and molting hormone from the Y organs are apparently implicated in these cyclical changes in metabolism. After removal of the eyestalks, the blood sugar concentration decreases, whereas the glycogen content of the hypodermis increases. The metabolic changes following eyestalk removal are comparable to those that

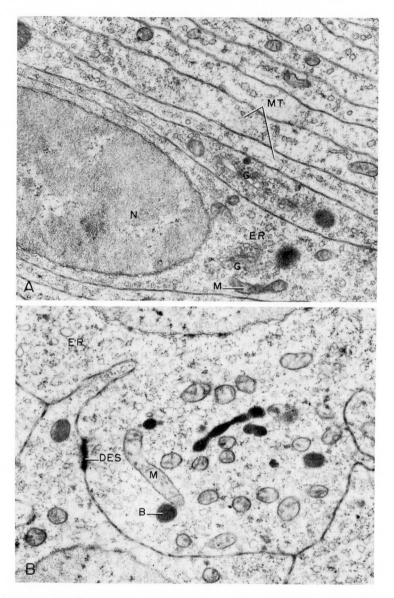

Figure 3–5. Electron micrographs of the androgenic glands of the amphipod *Orchestia gammarella*. The cells of these glands are characterized by a well-developed granular endoplasmic reticulum, long mitochondria with transverse cristae, and frequent Golgi bodies. These ultrastructural features make it very probable that the androgenic gland hormone is a polypeptide or protein, rather than a steroid. A, × 15,300; B, × 21,780. B, probably a lysosome; DES, desmosome; ER, endoplasmic reticulum; G, Golgi body; M, mitochondrion; MT, microtubules; N, nucleus. (Courtesy of Mr. Jean-Jacques Meusy, Centre National de la Recherche Scientifique, Paris.)

occur in the intact animal in preparation for a molt. Hyperglycemia may be induced by administering extracts of the eyestalk or X-organ sinus gland complex to normal animals. Since the same effect is induced by subjecting intact animals to stressful stimuli, it appears that the response is normally mediated by the neuroendocrine system of the eyestalk. The importance of carbohydrate metabolism in the molting process is indicated by the fact that chitin is one of the major constituents of the exoskeleton and is derived from glycogen.

Evidence for a hyperglycemic neurohormone has been adduced. It appears to be a protein and thus differs from the chromatophoro-trophins and the light-adapting retinal pigment principle.

NEUROENDOCRINE MECHANISMS IN THE INSECTA

The experiments of Kopec (1917 to 1922) provided the first clear evidence that hormones are of functional importance in the invertebrates. The original view that pupation in Lepidoptera is influenced by a factor coming from the brain has been confirmed and extended to other orders of insects. Among the Insecta, as in the Crustacea, the key position in the endocrine system is held by neurosecretory centers that elaborate neurohormones acting directly on target tissues or indirectly on endocrine glands. Since insects are a very diversified group, many kinds of microsurgical procedures have been employed for the study of hormonal mechanisms. Among these may be mentioned transplantation, ablation of organs, para-biosis, isolation of larval parts by constriction, tissue cultures, the fusion of individuals by capillary tubes, and the isolation of pupal parts by fusion to glass plates. Methods are being perfected for the bioassay of insect hormones, and one hormone has apparently been isolated in pure form. Certain unifying concepts of hormone action have emerged, making it clear that the same general principles operate in both hemimetabolous and holometabolous insects. It has become apparent that the various hormones interact with one another, just as in vertebrates, and this makes it difficult to assign definite actions to a specific hormone. What a particular hormone accomplishes often depends upon other hormones that are present with it, upon the hormone titer in the body fluids, and upon the com-petence of the target tissues to respond.

Insect Life Cycles

In hemimetabolous development, illustrated by the locust, the cockroach, and the blood-sucking bug *Rhodnius*, the newly hatched young resemble the adults in many respects; the most important differences are size, the absence of wings, and immature genitalia (Fig. 3–6). The young nymph, as it is called, undergoes a series of molts during which it gradually acquires adult characters, the most profound metamorphic changes occurring at the final molt. The number of nymphal instars varies with the species and may be altered by environmental conditions. All instars are capable of feeding, and there is generally no cessation of development during this type of cycle; however, growth occurs mostly between the nymphal molts.

Moths and butterflies are examples of holometabolous insects. Their eggs hatch into wormlike larvae that bear practically no resemblance to the adult (Fig. 3–6). These caterpillars feed and undergo a series of molts, and, since growth occurs at molting, each succeeding instar is somewhat larger than the preceding one. The larval instars, though differing in size, usually do not undergo profound structural changes. Eventually, the last instar molts and transforms into a chrysalis or pupa, a quiescent stage which is incapable of feeding. During pupation the individual undergoes a rather complete structural reorganization, so that it resembles the adult much more closely than did the preceding larval stages. Eventually, the pupal case is burst, and an imago emerges; it may feed, but it undergoes no further growth or profound modification in structure.

Though certain organs may be transmitted from the larva to the adult without much change, many must undergo a complete reorganization. These changes involve the destruction of larval tissues (histolysis) and the differentiation of adult tissues and organs (histogenesis and organogenesis) from larval anlagen called imaginal discs. All these postembryonic changes must be timed and coordinated properly in order to produce the normal adult.

Metamorphosis includes the changes in form normally undergone by an animal during its life cycle, and these events are genetically determined. Since the cells of the larva, pupa, and adult contain the same genetic information, it appears that different sets of genes are sequentially brought into action during the life cycle. There is increasing evidence that the genetic switch, or activation of an alternative set of genes, is triggered by neuroendocrine adjustments. The establishment of differential hormone environments, known to prevail during particular periods of the life cycle, may often be effected by external changes such as photoperiods, temperature, food, etc.[112]

Diapause

The life cycles of many insects include a period of dormancy, called *diapause*, during which growth and differentiation are almost

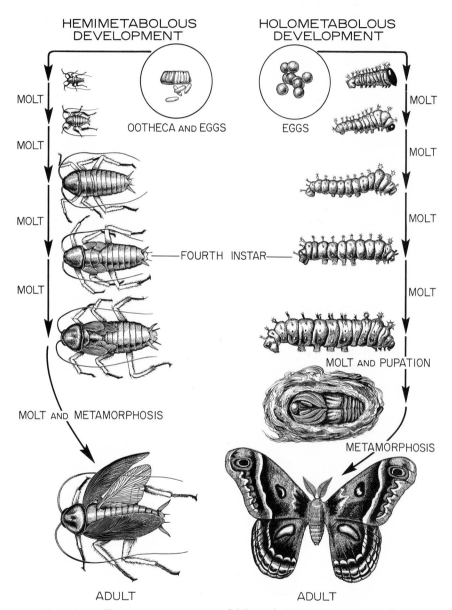

Figure 3–6. Two contrasting types of life cycles among insects. In those exhibiting direct or hemimetabolous development, the last nymphal instar molts and metamorphoses into the adult. In forms undergoing indirect or holometabolous development, the last larval instar passes through a pupal stage before metamorphosing into the adult. The cockroach (*Periplaneta americana*) is taken as an example of hemimetabolous development; the giant silkworm moth (*Hyalophora cecropia*) is used as an example of holometabolous development. The instars are drawn to scale.

in complete abeyance. The diapause may result from the direct effects of adverse environments, or it may appear regularly under the most favorable conditions as a phase of the life cycle. Depending upon the species, such periods of suspended development may occur at any time in the life cycle—egg, nymph, caterpillar, pupa, or adult. These periods of dormancy may have the net effect of producing young at a time when their chances for survival are maximal, of enabling the individual to survive hazardous environmental conditions.

Periods of developmental arrest in the egg are characteristic of certain insects. Some silkworm (*Bombyx mori*) races are single brooded or univoltine, each generation appearing in the spring following a period of arrested embryonic development during the winter. Other races are divoltine or multivoltine, the nondiapausing summer eggs producing one or more generations before the winter generation of diapausing eggs is produced. The diapausing eggs can be distinguished by the appearance of pigment in the serosa. Whether a female produces diapause or nondiapause eggs depends upon the photoperiod to which she was exposed while an egg or very young larva. In case of the divoltine race, the diapause eggs survive the winter and produce adults in spring. Females of the first generation produce nondiapause eggs because of their exposure to short days. Females of the second generation, derived from nondiapause eggs of spring, produce their eggs during midsummer, under the influence of long days and high temperatures. These eggs are of the diapause type and do not develop until spring. The necessary information for the production of diapause eggs by these moths is derived from the long hours of daylight, and this photoperiodic mechanism provides the basis for winter survival.

It has been shown that the immediate stimulus for the production of diapause eggs by *Bombyx* is a neurohormone derived from neurosecretory cells in the subesophageal ganglion of the mother, and this secretion is released only in mothers that were exposed to long periods of daylight when they themselves were eggs, or more precisely, developing embryos.[54] The neurohormone of the mother acts upon the eggs (embryos) before they are released from the genital tract. When the ovaries of a univoltine race (diapause eggs only) are transplanted into larvae of a divoltine race (diapause or nondiapause eggs), the eggs produced by the grafted ovary, after the host attains adulthood, always show the voltinism of the host. There are indications that the brain exerts an inhibitory effect, by way of the esophageal connectives, on the release of diapause neurohormone by the subesophageal ganglion.[44]

In certain butterflies (*e.g.*, *Araschnia levana*), the photoperiod to which the young larvae are exposed determines whether or not a pupal diapause occurs.[78] The adults emerging from diapausing and nondiapausing pupae may be quite different in appearance, and occasionally, spring and summer varieties have been mistaken for different species (Fig. 3–7).

The Cecropia moth (*Hyalophora cecropia*) undergoes a pupal diapause in nature, and the individual passes the winter in this condition. Mating occurs in the spring, and in about two weeks, the eggs hatch to give rise to the first larval instars. There are four larval molts, and the fifth instar spins a silken cocoon in which it pupates. With the rising temperatures of spring, the diapause ends and the adult emerges from the old pupal cuticle and escapes from the cocoon. Adult Cecropia do not feed, and between a quarter and a third of the pupal weight is utilized in the production of about 300 yolk-laden eggs.[99] Pupal dormancy in this species normally lasts for about eight months, but it has been found that the length of the diapause may be materially shortened by chilling the pupae and then returning them to room temperatures.

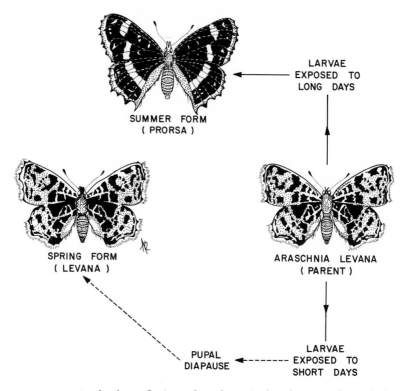

SUMMER FORM
(PRORSA)

LARVAE
EXPOSED TO
LONG DAYS

SPRING FORM
(LEVANA)

ARASCHNIA LEVANA
(PARENT)

PUPAL
DIAPAUSE

LARVAE
EXPOSED TO
SHORT DAYS

Figure 3–7. In the butterfly (*Araschnia levana*), the photoperiod to which the young larvae are exposed determines whether or not a diapause will occur at the pupal stage. Larvae exposed to short days undergo a pupal diapause; those exposed to long days do not. Diapausing pupae produce the spring form and nondiapausing pupae produce the summer form. The spring and summer varieties are so different in appearance that they have been mistaken as separate species. (Redrawn and modified from Wigglesworth, V. B.: Endeavour, 1965).

With the onset of pupal diapause, there is a sudden and complete cessation of growth, and few if any mitotic divisions occur during this long dormancy. The heart continues to beat and the animal utilizes oxygen and produces carbon dioxide, but all metabolic processes are reduced to a very low level. The rate of oxygen consumption in diapausing Cecropia is only 1.4 per cent that of the mature larva, and 5 per cent that of the adult moth just before the last molt. Just prior to the spinning of the cocoon, the larva ceases the intake of substances other than atmospheric oxygen; henceforth until its death as a mature moth 8 to 10 months later, the materials of its own body are reworked as a source of energy. The metabolism of an adult moth in flight is approximately 2000 times that of a diapausing pupa.[95]

The destructive larvae of the European corn-borer (*Ostrinia nubilalis*) enter pupal diapause in response to falling temperatures and short daily photoperiods.[4]

Some insects undergo diapause in the adult stage, and this generally takes the form of arrested reproduction in the female. In the Colorado potato beetle (*Leptinotarsa*), for example, the females begin to burrow into the soil during autumn and become quiescent; the metabolic rate falls, thoracic muscles degenerate, and egg maturation ceases. All these diapausal changes can be reversed in this beetle by implanting active corpora allata into their bodies. This suggests that the reproductive arrest is brought about by environmental factors which act via the corpora allata to inhibit the production of juvenile hormone.[112, 113]

Control of Postembryonic Development [47]

The endocrine mechanism regulating growth and differentiation in all insects centers in the neurosecretory system of the brain. The extrinsic stimulus varies from species to species: in the blood-sucking bug *Rhodnius*, stretching of the larval abdomen by a meal of blood provides a nervous stimulus to the brain; in locusts, the act of chewing and swallowing may accomplish the same effect; in Cecropia, temperature changes activate the brain. The activated neurosecretory cells of the brain produce a brain hormone (BH) which their axons discharge into the corpora cardiaca where it is stored and from whence it is liberated into the blood. The BH specifically stimulates the prothoracic glands to produce a hormone that has been variously named molting hormone (MH), growth and differentiation hormone, prothoracic gland hormone, and ecdysone. The MH acts directly upon the tissues of the body causing them to differentiate in the direction of adult structures. A second hormone, called juvenile hormone (JH), is secreted by the corpora allata, and its action is to encourage the laying down of larval or nymphal structures. In other words, JH suppresses pupal and imaginal differentiation (Fig. 3–8). The secretory activity of the corpora allata is also regulated by the nervous system, and the amount of JH present in the blood diminishes progressively with successive molts. Imaginal differentiation occurs under the influence of MH, when very little if any JH is present.

The body form attained by organisms depends upon the genetic control of developmental processes. It appears that multiple sets of genes are present in insect species, and that these sets can be called into expression successively during the life cycle.[112] As these genic complexes are activated (or suppressed), larval, pupal, and imaginal characters differentiate.

Studies on the salivary gland chromosomes of *Chironomus* show that molting hormone (ecdysone) acts promptly to cause puffing of only a few gene loci, but this is followed by sequential puffing of other loci. Since molting hormone seems to activate only several gene loci, it has been proposed that RNA messages produced by these genes, and the protein synthesis occurring as a consequence, set in motion certain cytoplasmic reactions which activate other genes.[5, 27, 28, 61]

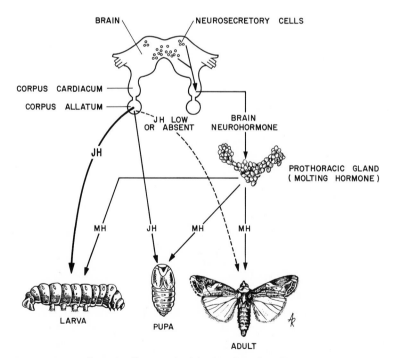

Figure 3–8. A diagram illustrating the neural and endocrine control of growth and molting in a moth. Neurosecretory cells of the brain release a principle which stimulates the prothoracic glands to secrete molting hormone (MH or ecdysone). Juvenile hormone (JH) arises from the corpora allata and promotes the retention of larval characters. Adult differentiation occurs when MH acts in the absence of JH.

Endocrine Structures and Their Secretions

Organs of Nervous Origin

Neurosecretory cells are numerous in insects and have important functions. Medial and lateral groups of such cells are present in the brain (protocerebrum); other aggregations are found in the subesophageal ganglion, and in all other ganglia of the ventral chain.

The corpora cardiaca arise from the nervous system and are situated behind the brain in close association with the dorsal aorta. They are paired in some species, but are fused in others. The corpora cardiaca are neurohemal organs and are composed of four cellular elements: (a) the bulbous endings of neurosecretory axons whose perikarya are located in the dorsum of the brain, (b) the perikarya of neurosecretory cells that send axons into nerves that supply various peripheral organs, (c) glia-like cells, and (d) intrinsic corpus cardiacum cells. Although the corpora cardiaca are storage-release centers, there is increasing evidence that their own cells are capable of producing secretions.[58, 89, 90]

Organs of Epithelial Origin

The best known endocrine glands of the insect originate from ectodermal cells proliferated from the surface epithelium in the vicinity of the mouth parts. Aggregations of such cells approach the posterior margin of the brain and become the corpora allata (Fig. 3–9). These glands are commonly paired and laterally placed (*Periplaneta*), or they may fuse to form a single structure (*Rhodnius*). Other clusters of cells, derived in the same manner, may come to rest in the head

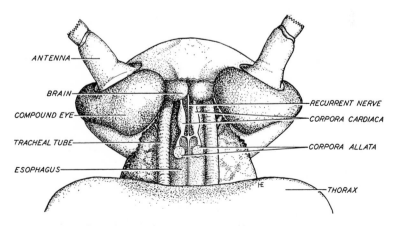

Figure 3–9. A dissection of the head of the roach (*Periplaneta americana*), showing the paired corpora allata and corpora cardiaca and the relations of these glands to other structures of the head.

or be carried farther back into the thorax. These anlagen form the *ventral glands* of the head in certain species, or the thoracic or *prothoracic glands* in others. The ventral and prothoracic glands are structurally and functionally comparable, differing only in location. The prothoracic glands are circumscribed and can be surgically removed in some species such as the roach, but in others, the tissue is so scattered that ablation is difficult or impossible. These glands

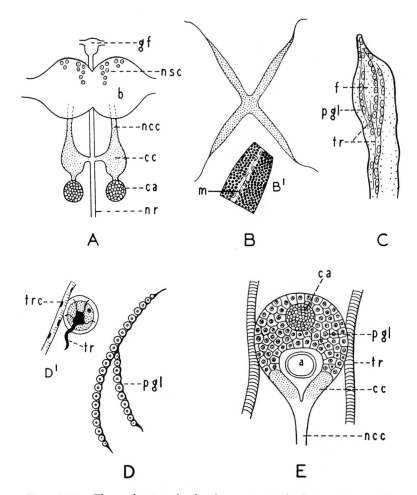

Figure 3–10. The endocrine glands of insects. *A*, The brain-corpus cardiacum-corpus allatum complex. *B*, Prothoracic gland of the roach *Periplaneta*. *B′*, Section showing small cells in relation to the muscle core. *C*, Prothoracic gland cells in the fat body of *Rhodnius*. *D*, Prothoracic gland of Lepidoptera. *D′*, A single gland cell showing its tracheal supply (*tr*). *E*, Ring gland of *Drosophila* showing its three components: prothoracic gland (*pgl*), corpus allatum (*ca*), and corpus cardiacum (*cc*). Abbreviations: *a*, aorta; *b*, brain; *ca*, corpus allatum; *cc*, corpus cardiacum; *f*, fat body; *gf*, ganglion frontale; *m*, muscles; *ncc*, nervus corporis cardiaci; *nr*, nervus recurrens; *nsc*, neurosecretory cells; *pgl*, prothoracic gland; *tr*, trachea; *trc*, tracheal cells. (From Bodenstein, D.: Rec. Prog. Horm. Res., *10*, 1954.)

undergo autolysis shortly after completion of metamorphosis, and hence are not present in adult insects.[91, 108]

The prothoracic glands were described in the goat moth by Lyonet as early as 1762, and Toyama followed their embryonic development in the silkworm in 1902. The functional significance of these ductless glands was not fully appreciated until the classic studies of Fukuda on the larvae of *Bombyx mori* in 1940.[43] Through ingenious ligation and transplantation experiments, he proved that the prothoracic glands are essential for the larvae of this moth to undergo pupation. The clear-cut experiments of Williams on the isolated pupal abdomens of the Cecropia moth demonstrated that the prothoracic glands are incapable of secreting molting hormone unless they are activated by a principle from the brain.[114]

In some of the Diptera, the corpus cardiacum, corpus allatum, and prothoracic gland fuse to form a structure surrounding the aorta (Fig. 3–10,E). This retrocerebral complex is called the *ring gland* of Weismann.

Epithelial cells of the hind gut are known to be the source of a hormone (proctodone) which is required to activate the neurosecretory system of the brain. The hormone has been found in two species of Lepidoptera in which it plays a role in photoperiodism and diapause.[3]

Neurohormones of the Brain

Kopeč (1917) used ligatures in order to divide the larva of the gypsy moth into blood tight compartments (Fig. 3–11). He correctly concluded that the brain is the source of a blood-borne factor which is required for pupation. Wigglesworth (1940), working on *Rhodnius*, traced the source of this brain principle to collections of neurosecretory cells present in the pars intercerebralis.[107] He accomplished this by excising the pars intercerebralis regions of brains from nymphs that had fed a few days previously (during the critical period), and implanting these into nymphal hosts that had been decapitated immediately after feeding (before the critical period). The decapitated hosts could live 6 to 10 months, but never molted; the activated neurosecretory cells contained in the brain implants induced them to molt. He found that no other part of the nervous system would stimulate molting when implanted into the same recipients. For the first time, it was possible to assign a functional role to particular neurosecretory cells.

Pupae of the Cecropia moth remain in diapause for 5 to 6 months when they are kept at a temperature of 25° C. After surgical removal of the brain, such pupae never metamorphose, though they may live for approximately a year. The intact pupae may be induced to metamorphose precociously by chilling (3–5° C.) them for about 6 weeks and then returning them to room temperatures. Implanted brains

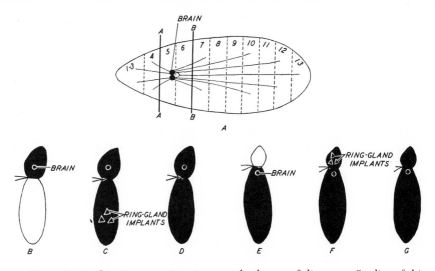

Figure 3-11. Ligation experiments upon the larvae of dipterans. Studies of this type indicate that the brain, or some closely associated structure, releases one or more blood-borne agents that are essential for pupation. *A,* Diagram of a muscid larva, showing the position of the brain. Ligatures may be placed in front of the brain (line *A−A*) or behind it (line *B−B*). In diagrams *B* to *G* the pupated regions of the body are indicated in black. *B,* Larva ligatured behind the brain before the critical period. Only the portion of the body containing the brain undergoes pupation. It is presumed that the posterior part of the body fails to pupate because the ligature prevents the dissemination of an essential substance (ecdysone) contained in the body fluid. *C,* Same as *B* with ring glands implanted into the body posterior to the ligature. The ring glands induce pupation in that portion of the body isolated from the brain. *D,* Same as *B,* but the ligature was placed after the critical period, i.e., after the essential endocrine substances had attained effective concentrations in the body fluid. The entire body pupates. *E,* Larva ligatured in front of the brain before the critical period. Pupation is accomplished only by the segment of the body containing the brain. *F,* Same as *E,* but with ring glands implanted into the fragment lacking the brain. This procedure produces pupation of the anterior region. *G,* Same as *E,* but the ligature was placed after the critical period. All the body pupates.

from chilled pupae induce metamorphosis when implanted into unchilled pupae. When chilled pupae are parabiotically united with unchilled pupae, both molt synchronously in a little less than 2 months. These experiments indicate that pupal diapause in Cecropia results from a failure of the brain to produce BH, brain activation depending upon a temperature stimulus.[116] Different mechanisms are undoubtedly involved in other species of Lepidoptera.

The chemical nature of brain hormone (BH) is still a subject of controversy (for review see Gilbert, L. I., 1964, p. 76). Kobayashi and Kirimura claimed that it is indistinguishable from cholesterol,[66] whereas Ichikawa and Ishizaki found it to be water soluble and lipid insoluble.[55] Brainless, diapausing pupae of the Cecropia moth provide a sensitive system for testing materials that are capable of activating prothoracic glands. Neither pure cholesterol nor any other lipid-soluble extract has been found effective in this system. It is well known, however, that many steroids, sterols, and steroid precursors can mimic the actions of BH in certain test systems.[94] Even epinephrine can activate the prothoracic glands in certain insect tests, though it is not found in insects.

While it is common practice to refer to the prothoracic gland-stimulating factor as "brain hormone" or "prothoracotrophin," it must be recognized that the neurosecretory cells of the brain produce additional secretions that have other actions. The medial neurosecretory cells in the brain of the blowfly (*Calliphora*) supply a neurohormone that stimulates egg maturation in this species. This is accomplished by evoking the formation of proteases in the gut, thereby facilitating the breakdown of proteins to supply amino acids for the synthesis of egg proteins.[102]

Another neurohormone arising from the neurosecretory system of the insect brain is the "darkening" or "tanning" factor.[29, 42] It is also present in two groups of neurosecretory cells in the thoracic ganglia. In newly emerged flies (*e.g.*, *Calliphora*), darkening and hardening of the cuticle (tanning) starts after about 15 to 20 minutes, but this effect can be abolished by ligaturing the head. It can also be prevented by section of the nerve cord posterior to the thoracic ganglia. Blood from a 15-minute-old fly induces tanning when injected into a head-ligatured fly. The tanning neurohormone is released in response to appropriate sensory impulses reaching the brain via the ventral cord a few minutes after the fly has emerged from the puparium. This factor seems to be a polypeptide, and is different from brain hormone and molting hormone (ecdysone). The tanning factor is found in a variety of insect species. A substance originating in the eyestalks of crayfishes plays some role in tanning of the newly formed exoskeleton.[39]

Hormones of the Corpora Cardiaca

Aqueous extracts of the corpora cardiaca of the roach *Periplaneta* elevate the blood concentration of trehalose, the main circulating carbohydrate of insects. The effective substance, reported to be a polypeptide, acts upon the enzyme system of the fat body (where glycogen is stored) to promote glycogenolysis.[98]

Efferent nerve activity in *Periplaneta* is inhibited by the subesophageal ganglion. Extracts of the corpora cardiaca mimic the surgical removal of this inhibitory system, but it is not known whether the effective substance arises *in situ* or is merely stored there.[76]

The corpora cardiaca of the cockroach appear to secrete a peptide hormone that acts indirectly to increase the heart rate. It apparently stimulates the pericardial cells, scattered along the heart, to produce a pharmacologically active factor which in turn acts upon the heart to increase its rate of beating.[30] The differential centrifugation of extracts from corpora cardiaca of the roach has yielded neurosecretory particles that accelerate the heart.[35] Studies on the roach indicate that many cardioregulatory substances, probably small peptides, can be isolated from various tissues such as the nervous system, gastrointestinal tract, heart, utricles, and hemolymph.[84]

Molting Hormone (Ecdysone)

In saturniid moths, activation of the brain and consequent termination of pupal diapause depends upon exposure to low temperatures. The classical experiments of Williams on Cecropia moths demonstrated conclusively that brain hormone (BH) does not act directly upon the tissues, but rather, that it exerts a trophic effect upon a specific target—the prothoracic glands. Brainless pupae survive for long periods, but never terminate diapause. When a brainless, diapausing pupa was grafted to a chilled pupa, the two animals metamorphosed simultaneously. The pupae of these moths could be transected anterior to the sixth abdominal segment, and the cut surfaces sealed over with coverslips; these parts were viable for 8 months or longer and made some instructive experiments possible. Chilled anterior parts, or brainless anterior parts that had received implants of chilled brains, metamorphosed into adults. The isolated abdomens (lacking prothoracic glands) did not metamorphose even after receiving multiple implants of chilled brains. The isolated abdomens could be induced to metamorphose by introducing both chilled brains and prothoracic glands; unactivated prothoracic glands alone were not adequate. It has been shown in a great variety of insects that metamorphosis depends upon two factors: brain hormone and molting hormone from the prothoracic glands. The prothoracic glands quickly regress after the final molt that gives rise to the adult stage.

What appears to be the molting hormone has been isolated and crystallized; it is a steroidal compound and its structural formula is partly known.[47, 60] The crystallized hormone has been called *ecdysone*. When tested on various insects, it is found to duplicate all the known effects of the natural hormone. Since it is quite certain that insects are unable to synthesize steroids from acetate, it is likely that they form ecdysone through the degradation of steroids consumed in their diets. By using labeled materials, it has been shown that *Calliphora* can form ecdysone from injected cholesterol. Five distinct fractions having ecdysone activity have been isolated from *Bombyx* material, and this indicates that present information is tentative.[16]

The life cycle of the flagellate *Trichonympha*, living symbiotically in the gut of the wood-eating roach *Cryptocercus*, undergoes modifications in response to endocrine fluctuations in the insect. The administration of ecdysone to adult roaches, themselves incapable of

molting in response to the hormone, induces encystment and gametogenesis in the flagellates. It is probable that this is a direct effect of
the host hormone upon the protozoa, and that it has adaptive value
in their survival.[25, 26]

Juvenile Hormone

The tissue reactions to molting hormone (MH) are modulated by
juvenile hormone (JH), which is a product of the corpora allata.[111]
The tropical bug *Rhodnius*, used so extensively by Wigglesworth and
his colleagues, was a convenient insect for the experimental elucidation of the factors involved in molt and metamorphosis.[110] There are
five nymphal instars in *Rhodnius*, and molting occurs a definite
number of days after a meal of blood; abdominal distention is the
stimulus that activates the neurosecretory complex of the brain. The
elongated head of *Rhodnius* made it possible to cut transversely at
different levels and obtain animals deprived of brain (corpus allatum
intact), or animals deprived of both brain and corpus allatum. The
decapitated animals survive six to 10 months. It was possible to join
decapitated animals by means of capillary tubes, or to graft instars
and adults in many telobiotic and parabiotic combinations.

Two grafting experiments in *Rhodnius* may be mentioned to
illustrate the action of JH. If a fourth stage nymph is decapitated after
the critical period and is telobiotically grafted to a fifth nymph also
decapitated after the critical period, both individuals molt, but the
fifth stage nymph becomes a giant, supernumerary nymph instead of
an adult. Though adult *Rhodnius* normally does not molt, it may be
induced to do so by grafting nymphal stages. When fourth stage
nymphs, possessing their corpora allata as a source of JH, are united
with an adult, the latter molts and shows a partial return to the
nymphal condition (Fig. 3–12).

In the roach *Leucophaea maderae*, the adult stage is preceded
by an average of eight nymphal instars. Removal of the corpora allata
(allatectomy) of the fifth, sixth, or seventh instars produces an abbre-
viation of development, the final molt being accomplished at an
earlier stage than in the unoperated controls. Fifth and sixth instars,
deprived of JH by allatectomy, develop characters that are intermediate between nymph and adult (preadultoids) and must molt
again before attaining adult characters to a conspicuous extent
(adultoids).[88]

Walking sticks (*Dixippus*) are neotenic insects, the females
beginning to reproduce parthenogenetically before they are fully
adult. If third stage larvae are allatectomized, two more molts ensue
before egg laying begins. By implanting corpora allata into the semi-
mature adults of *Dixippus*, they may be caused to molt two more
times and to become giant insects. After implanting corpora allata

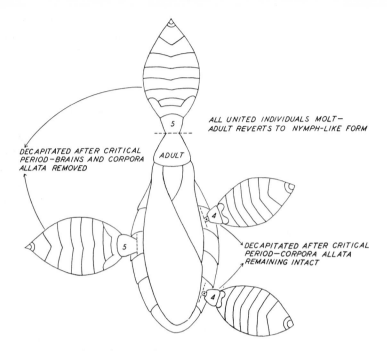

Figure 3-12. The induction of molt in adult *Rhodnius*. The broken lines indicate the level of decapitation; the blackened dot in the proximal end of the head represents the corpus allatum, and the number of the nymphal instar in indicated on the thorax. The decapitated adult is coupled with two fifth-stage nymphs, totally decapitated after the critical period, and with two fourth-stage nymphs partially decapitated after the critical period. The fifth nymphs provide the adult with ecdysone, whereas the fourth nymphs, having their corpora allata, provide juvenile hormone in addition to ecdysone. All the combined individuals molt; the fifth nymphs become supernumerary nymphs (sixth-stage), the fourth nymphs become fifth instars, and the adult reverts to a nymphlike form.

from young donors into sixth stage larvae, as many as four extra molts may be produced, and the insects become about twice the normal size.

Allatectomized caterpillars of the commercial silkworm undergo no further molts; they metamorphose prematurely into normally formed but miniature adults. The earlier the corpora allata are removed, the smaller the resulting adult. On the other hand, implantation of corpora allata produces supernumerary larval molts and giant caterpillars that metamorphose into giant adults (Fig. 3–13).

When pupae of the Cecropia moth are grafted to a decapitated adult male moth, the pupae undergo a second pupal molt rather than metamorphosing into adults. In other words, these pupae develop as though they had received a heavy dose of JH. Studies on these moths have shown that the corpora allata of adult males produce large quantities of JH and that it is stored in the abdomen. The tissues of the adult female abdomen contain only traces of this hormone.

It is apparent from experiments of this type that three endocrine factors are involved in the growth and metamorphosis of insects: BH from neurosecretory cells of the pars intercerebralis initiates the secretion of MH by the prothoracic glands; MH acts upon the cells to promote growth and differentiation to the adult stage; if the third hormone, JH, is present, MH and JH act in concert to retard metamorphosis. When high titers of JH are present with MH, the animal grows but remains immature; imaginal differentiation results when MH is unopposed by JH (Fig. 3–8).

Purified extracts of JH have been prepared and highly sensitive assays developed.[48, 109] The hormone is extremely stable and extracts with comparable activity have been prepared from museum insects following many years of drying. Substances having JH activity have been detected in human placenta, thymus, and adrenal glands; in higher plants, yeasts and some bacteria; and in a great variety of invertebrates.

It is known that certain parasites are capable of influencing the growth and development of their insect hosts by liberating a substance that has the same effects as JH from the corpora allata. The larvae of *Tribolium* (Coleoptera), when infected with the sporozoan parasite *Nosemba*, undergo supernumerary molts to produce giant

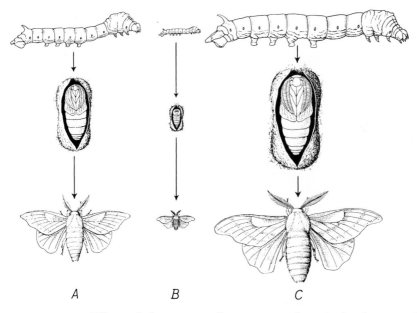

Figure 3–13. Effects of the corpora allata on postembryonic development of *Bombyx mori.* A, Normal fifth instar, pupa, and adult. B, Allatectomized third instar, diminutive pupa, and diminutive adult. C, Supernumerary larva produced from fifth instar by transplanting corpora allata of young larvae, giant pupa, and giant adult. (Drawn from figures of C. M. Williams, 1958.)

larvae which weigh twice as much as the uninfected controls. These infected larvae seldom pupate: the infection mimicks JH in prolonging larval life at the expense of pupal and imaginal differentiation. Studies indicate that the parasite itself produces a substance with JH activity, rather than acting upon the host's corpora allata to stimulate the production of intrinsic JH.[40]

The exact chemical nature of JH remains undetermined. Chemical studies indicate that effective extracts contain farnesol and farnesal. This is interesting because farnesol is an intermediate step in the biosynthesis of cholesterol and carotene. A number of steroids, terpenoids, and related compounds are known to copy the activities of JH when tested in appropriate ways.[11, 94] There are indications that all the insect hormones are chemically related: This is suggested by the fact that prothoracic glands can be activated by MH (ecdysone), BH, JH, cholesterol, and such compounds as farnesol. There are strong indications that ecdysone is a steroid. Schneiderman and Gilbert have pointed out that "Rather than being a recent innovation of the vertebrates, steroid hormones may prove to have a far more ancient lineage."[94]

Proctodone

Larval diapause in the European corn borer (*Ostrinia nubilalis*) is induced by short-day photoperiods and terminated by long-day photoperiods. When diapausing larvae are ligatured between the sixth and seventh abdominal segments, thus cutting off circulation in the two terminal segments of the abdomen, exposure to long-day photoperiods fails to terminate diapause. Cutting the ventral nerve cord at the level of the sixth abdominal segment does not prevent diapause termination in response to long days. These observations indicated that some endocrine mechanism, necessary for brain activation and consequent termination of diapause, might be located in the terminal abdominal segments. Glandular cells were found in the proctodeal epithelium, and because of its source, the name *proctodone* was applied to the hormone. It is blood-borne and participates in diapause termination by activating the neurosecretory complex of the brain.[3]

Endocrines in Insect Reproduction

Experiments on castration and gonad transplantation have failed to yield convincing evidence that insect gonads are the source of hormones. Gonadal functions, however, are conditioned by several internal secretions.[31, 34, 46] Juvenile hormone from the corpus allatum is essential for yolk deposition in the eggs and for formation of spermatophores, in many species of insects. In *Rhodnius*, for example, removal of the corpus allatum prevents the production of ripe eggs: the oöcytes grow as long as they are attached to the nurse cells, but degenerate at the period when yolk deposition should occur. Allatectomy and ligation experiments on the milkweed bug, *Oncopeltus fasciatus*, indicate a similar relationship, corpora allata being necessary for yolk deposition and secretion by the oviducts.[57] Full production of eggs in *Oncopeltus* also depends on the medial neurosecretory cells of the brain. Among certain flies (*e.g.*, *Calliphora*), the medial neurosecretory cells are of special importance inasmuch as their products promote the formation of amino acids to be used by the eggs for the synthesis of proteins.[100-102]

Reproduction in the cockroach *Byrsotria* depends upon the release of a volatile sex attractant by the female, this pheromone being essential for attracting males and releasing their courtship behavior.[2] Gonadectomy does not impair the mating behavior of either sex. Allatectomy of the female, shortly after the imaginal molt, prevents the production of sex pheromone; the production of pheromone is reinstated by the implantation of corpora allata. In this species of roach, secretions from the corpora allata are not only essential for oöcyte maturation and accessory gland secretion, but also for production of the sex attractant which makes mating behavior possible. Allatectomy of the male does not impair reproduction behavior.

In *Bombyx* as well as the Cecropia silkworm, the corpora may be removed from the pupae of either sex without disturbing the sexual functions of mature moths; the organs are not necessary for the maturation of gametes and the production of normal young. Molting hormone of the prothoracic gland appears to be the only one necessary for sexual maturation of both sexes in these moths (Fig. 3–14). Pupae deprived of their brains, corpora cardiaca, and corpora allata become sexually mature adults after the administration of crystalline ecdysone. Thus, in these Lepidoptera, the corpora allata are highly active in the adults, but no function has as yet been ascribed to them at this stage of the life cycle. It may be significant, however, that the silkworms that have been studied most carefully are short-lived moths which lack functional mouth-parts in the adult. The adult stage is greatly abbreviated and ripe eggs are ready for oviposition soon after the individual emerges from the pupa. It may be that the lack of functional mouth-parts in the adult correlates with a precocious maturation of the gonads which can occur in the absence of any gonadotrophic function of the corpora allata. The corpora allata of feeding, long-lived species of adult Lepidoptera may possibly exert gonadotrophic effects similar to those described for numerous other orders of insects.[115]

In *autogenous* mosquitoes of the genus *Culex*, ovarian development does not depend upon the consumption of food in the adult

Figure 3–14. *Above,* Isolated abdomen of a diapausing Cecropia pupa sealed to a plastic cover slip. Prothoracic glands from postdiapausing pupae are being introduced into the abdomen through a central hole in the slip. *Below,* The same abdomen after differentiating adult characters; eggs are being deposited. Corpora allata are not necessary for gamete maturation in these moths. (From Williams, C. M.: Biol. Bull., *103*, 1952.)

stage, but the ovaries of *anautogenous* species do not develop beyond a resting stage until a blood meal of adequate size has been consumed. The implantation of corpora allata from autogenous donors into anautogenous recipients enables the ovaries to mature without the consumption of a meal. When anautogenous ovaries are transplanted to autogenous hosts, egg maturation occurs in the grafts even though the host does not feed. Ovaries from autogenous donors do not mature after being transplanted to anautogenous hosts. In addition to a hormone from the corpus allatum, a factor from the brain is also involved in these phenomena.[67]

Studies on several species of insects show that the functional status of the corpora allata is regulated by the brain. In the milkweed bug and some of the roaches, the corpora allata are supplied by inhibitory nerves from the brain: section of these nerves releases the corpora allata from inhibition, and egg maturation and ovulation occur. Distention of the gut appears to be the effective signal for egg development and ovulation in anautogenous mosquitoes; in certain roaches, it is the act of mating.

Water Balance in Insects

Some insects that feed upon fluids have evolved mechanisms for the quick elimination of excessive water (diuresis). Rapid elimination of fluid occurs in *Rhodnius* following the consumption of a blood meal, and it has been reported that the fused thoracic ganglia are the source of a diuretic neurohormone which acts upon the malpighian tubules to promote the loss of fluid. The response can be evoked in isolated malpighian tubules by exposing them to blood taken from recently fed *Rhodnius*.[69]

Evidence for an antidiuretic principle in the roach *Periplaneta americana* has been obtained through studies on the rate of indigo carmine uptake by malpighian tubules, tested *in vitro*, following subjection of the animals to different osmotic conditions. Since the diet of these insects consists of solids or semisolids, there is little likelihood that excessive fluid intake would constitute a problem; however, periods of desiccation might require a diminished excretion of fluids and withdrawal of water from the gut. The malpighian tubules from dehydrated and salt-loaded animals showed lower than normal levels of dye uptake, indicating that they had been exposed to a factor inhibiting excretion. Extracts of corpora allata from normal animals, in contrast to those from dehydrated animals, reduced the rate of dye uptake by the tubules. Brain extracts, prepared from dehydrated subjects, also reduced dye uptake. The experiments were interpreted as indicating that an antidiuretic factor is produced by the brain and conveyed to the corpora allata where it is stored and released when the organism needs to conserve water.[104]

Color Changes in Insects

A few insects are capable of modifying the coloration of their bodies in response to various environmental changes. Both morphologic and physiologic color changes may occur, and the indications are that both are effected by hormonal agents in the body fluids (Fig. 3–15).

A morphologic color change occurs in the locust (*Locusta migratoria*) that is hormonally regulated by the corpora allata.[59] Animals

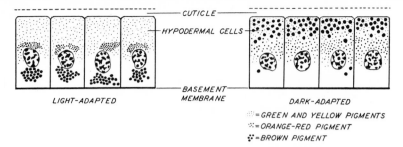

CUTICLE

HYPODERMAL CELLS

BASEMENT MEMBRANE

LIGHT-ADAPTED

DARK-ADAPTED

⬚ = GREEN AND YELLOW PIGMENTS
⬚ = ORANGE-RED PIGMENT
⬚ = BROWN PIGMENT

Figure 3–15. Physiologic color change in the walking-stick, *Dixippus morosus.* The pigments that condition the coloration of the body are contained within the hypodermal cells. In the light-adapted animal the brown and orange-red pigments are concentrated, but in the dark-adapted animal the same pigments are dispersed throughout the supranuclear regions of the cells. The green and yellow pigments have a permanent position in the cells and are not changed by light. (Modified from Hanström, after Giersberg.)

of the migratory type are orange-black and live together in swarms, but individuals of the solitary phase are green. When corpora allata are implanted into nymphs of the migratory type, the green pigment characteristic of the solitary type may appear after the next molt. These results are obtained even when the corpora allata are taken from nymphs or imagos of the migratory type.

Factors originating from neurosecretory cells in the brain and adjacent ganglia seem to be responsible for the physiologic color adaptations that occur in insects. Color changes in *Carausius* are predominantly under the control of a chromatophorotrophin present in the brain and in the corpora cardiaca. Extracts from these two structures lead to a darkening of the integument, whereas extracts of the corpora allata have little if any effect.

Examples of Rhythmic Activity in Insects

As fruitflies (*Drosophila*) reproduce in nature, the adults emerge from their pupal cases in the early morning. If the eggs, larvae, and pupae are maintained in complete darkness, the adults emerge at all hours of the day and night. Exposure of these metamorphosing flies to a single flash of light (as short as 1/2000 sec.) causes a resetting of the biological clocks, and the adults emerge synchronously at an hour corresponding to the hour of light exposure. These adjustments in response to illumination are probably mediated by the neuroendocrine system.

A diurnal rhythm of locomotion and feeding activity occurs in the cockroach *Periplaneta*: the animals are relatively quiescent during the day, but become active with the onset of darkness. By ingenious surgical methods, it was demonstrated that the circadian rhythm in this insect results from the action of blood-borne materials produced by neurosecretory cells.[52, 53] Cockroaches taken from continuous light, and showing no measurable activity rhythm, were parabiotically united with others which exhibited normal diurnal rhythms. The arrhythmic member of the pair assumed a circadian rhythm in which the phase times were the same as those shown by the rhythmic parabiont. The decapitation of animals, kept in alternating periods of light and darkness (12 hours each), abolished their rhythms.

The subesophageal ganglion in the head of the roach is the source of a neurosecretion which is associated with, and at least partly responsible for, the initiation of locomotor activity. Exposure of the subesophageal ganglion to low temperatures (3° C.) *in situ*, the remainder of the body not being chilled, stops the biological clock contained in the ganglion.[15] If the ganglion is chilled for 2 or 3 hours, and left within the individual, the clock is "reset" and timing of running activity is not altered. When the ganglion is chilled for as long as 8 hours, it does not "reset" even though left intact, and the onset of locomotor activity is delayed by a period of 8 hours. If the ganglion is transplanted to an arrhythmic host immediately after chilling, there is a time lag in the onset of host activity equaling the length of time the ganglion was chilled.

The timing of neurosecretory activity in the subesophageal ganglion can be adjusted to inverted light cycles, so that secretion occurs 12 hours out of phase. When ganglia from donors secreting 12 hours out of phase are transplanted to hosts whose ganglia are set to normal time of day, the tissues of the body are exposed to two cycles of neurohormone secretion per day. Under these conditions, the animals soon die from cancerous growths in the wall of the mid-gut. The tumors metastasize and are transplantable. Growths of this type seem comparable to those produced by B. Scharrer in the roach *Leucophaea* by cutting the recurrent nerve.[87]

The biological clock regulating and locomotor rhythm of the cockroach is set by the diurnal cycle of light and darkness, and this stimulus is perceived through the ocelli (simple eyes). The corpora cardiaca are indirectly activated and a neurosecretory stimulus from them is conveyed along nerves to the subesophageal ganglion. The neurosecretory cells in the latter ganglion normally release their products every 24 hours to initiate locomotor activity (Fig. 3–16).

Much remains to be learned about the operation of biological timepieces, and this simplified version of the clock system of the roach only serves as an illustration. The essential concept is that the central nervous system produces and rhythmically releases blood-borne agents, in response to external stimuli, which organize the behavioral patterns of the animal in adjusting to its particular habitat.[12, 51]

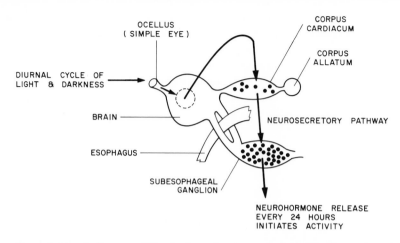

Figure 3–16. A diagram of the brain and retrocerebral glands of a cockroach to illustrate how diurnal cycles of activity may be regulated. Black circles represent neurosecretory cells. The change from light to darkness is perceived through the ocelli; impulses are integrated in the brain and these result in activation of the corpora cardiaca; a neurosecretory stimulus is conveyed from the latter organs to a biologic clock, consisting of neurosecretory cells, in the subesophageal ganglion; the clock is set to discharge neurosecretions into the blood at regular intervals to initiate locomotor activity.

ANALOGOUS NEUROSECRETORY SYSTEMS OF INVERTEBRATES AND VERTEBRATES

From the foregoing description of endocrine mechanisms in invertebrates, it is apparent that neurosecretory cells are a distinct cell type performing definite roles in the organism. They do not occur haphazardly in the nervous system, without rhyme or reason, but form definite groups that are always found in particular locations characteristic of the species. In invertebrates and vertebrates alike, external and internal stimuli are received and integrated by the central nervous system. This system has evolved its own endocrine mechanisms, aggregations of neurosecretory cells, which serve to translate nervous impulses into diffusible chemical messengers. The timing of biologic phenomena, such as hibernation, migration, estivation, molting, metamorphosis, reproduction, diapause, locomotor rhythms, etc., is possible because organisms possess both clocks and calendars. Many, if not all, of these devices in animals are controlled by chemical messengers of one kind or another.[93]

The simplest pituitary glands are found in the agnatha, and there is no certainty that structurally comparable organs exist in the invertebrates. Nevertheless, analogous neurosecretory systems are present in organisms as distantly related as crustaceans and primates.[50] The neurosecretory systems of crustaceans and insects consist of two chief components: clusters of neurosecretory cells in the brain and related ganglia, and neurohemal organs that serve principally as depots for the storage and release of neurohormones. The ganglionic X organ and other neurosecretory aggregations of the crustacean brain, as well as the medial and lateral neurosecretory cells of the insect brain, probably correspond to the supraoptic and paraventricular nuclei of the vertebrate hypothalamus. The sinus gland of crustaceans and the corpora cardiaca of insects are neurohemal organs and are analogous to the neural lobe of the vertebrate pituitary gland. Non-neural glands of internal secretion arise among the invertebrates: the optic glands of cephalopod molluscs, the Y organs, ovaries, and androgenic glands of crustaceans, and the prothoracic glands and corpora allata of insects have been mentioned. The Y organ is probably a crustacean analog of the insect prothoracic gland. The corpora allata of insects are comparable, in many ways, to the vertebrate adenohypophysis. The insect glands arise out of ectodermal proliferations from the ventral side of the head; the adenohypophysis develops from an ectodermal anlage (Rathke's pouch) which pushes upward from the stomodeum.

The endocrine systems of annelids, molluscs, crustaceans, insects, and vertebrates must have evolved independently. The caudal neurosecretory system of fishes (urophysis) illustrates how such comparable patterns can develop independently even within the same individual. The urophysis consists of large neurosecretory cells which send axons into a neurohemal structure that causes a bulging below the terminal end of the spinal cord. The function of the urophysis is uncertain, but, structurally it is strikingly comparable to the cephalic neurohypophysis.

The neurosecretory cells and endocrine glands of arthropods govern such processes as growth, reproduction, color change, metabolism, and water balance, thus covering about the same functional categories as the vertebrate pituitary gland. The exact manner in which the various hormones of the adenohypophysis are regulated remains a mystery, but they are clearly under hypothalamic control. The neurosecretory cells of vertebrates tend to be concentrated into one small area of the brain, the hypothalamus; whereas in invertebrates, such cells are much more widely distributed within and near the central nervous system.

REFERENCES

1. Bargmann, W., Hanström, B., and Scharrer, E. (eds.): Internationales Symposium über Neurosekretion, II. Berlin, Springer, 1958.
2. Barth, R. H., Jr.: The endocrine control of mating behavior in the cockroach *Byrsotria fumigata* (Guérin). Gen. & Comp. Endocrinol., 2:53, 1962.
3. Beck, S. D., and Alexander, N.: Hormonal activation of the insect brain. Science, *143*:478, 1964.

4. Beck, S. D., Cloutier, E. J., and McLeod, D. G. R.: Photoperiod and insect development. *In* V. J. Brookes (ed.): Insect Physiology: Proc. 23rd Biol. Colloquium. Corvallis, Oregon State University Press, 1963, p. 43.
5. Beerman, W., and Clever, U.: Chromosome puffs. Sci. Amer., April, 1964.
6. Bern, H. A.: The secretory neuron as a doubly specialized cell. *In* D. Mazia and A. Taylor (eds.): General Physiology of Cell Specialization. New York, 1963, p. 349.
7. Bern, H. A., and Takasugi, N.: The caudal neurosecretory system of fishes. Gen. & Comp. Endocrinol., 2:96, 1962.
8. Bliss, D. E.: Neuroendocrine control of locomotor activity in the land crab *Gecarcinus lateralis. In* H. Heller and R. B. Clark (eds.): Memoirs Soc. Endocrinol., No. 12. New York, Academic Press, 1962, p. 391.
9. Bliss, D. E., and Boyer, J. R.: Environmental regulation of growth in the decapod crustacean *Gecarcinus lateralis.* Gen. & Comp. Endocrinol., 4:15, 1964.
10. Bliss, D. E., and Welsh, J. H.: The neurosecretory system of brachyuran Crustacea. Biol. Bull., *103*:157, 1952.
11. Bowers, W. S., and Thompson, M. J.: Juvenile hormone activity: effects of isoprenoid and straight-chain alcohols on insects. Science, *142*:1469, 1963.
12. Brown, F. A., Jr.: Living clocks. Science, *130*:1535, 1959.
13. Brown, F. A., Jr.: Chromatophores and color change. *In* C. L. Prosser and F. A. Brown, Jr. (eds.): Comparative Animal Physiology, 2nd ed. Philadelphia, W. B. Saunders Co., 1961, p. 502.
14. Brown, F. A., Jr., Webb, H. M., and Sandeen, M.: Differential production of two retinal pigment hormones in *Palaemonetes* by light flashes. J. Cell. Comp. Physiol., *41*:123, 1953.
15. Brown, R. H. J., and Harker, J. E.: A method for controlling the temperature of insect neurosecretory cells *in situ.* Nature, *185*:392, 1960.
16. Burdette, W. J., and Bullock, M. W.: Ecdysone: five biologically active fractions from *Bombyx.* Science, *140*:1311, 1963.
17. Carlisle, D. B., and Knowles, F. G. W.: Endocrine Control in Crustaceans. New York, Cambridge University Press, 1959.
18. Chaet, A. B.: A mechanism for obtaining mature gametes from starfish. Biol. Bull., *126*:8, 1964.
19. Chaet, A. B.: Shedding substance and "shedhibin" from the nerves of the starfish, *Patiria miniata.* Amer. Zool., 4:407, 1964.
20. Charniaux-Cotton, H.: Contrôle endocrinien de la différenciation sexuelle chez les crustacés supérieurs. Arch. d'Anat. micro. et de Morphol. expér., *54*:405, 1965.
21. Charniaux-Cotton, H., and Kleinholz, L. H.: Hormones in invertebrates other than insects. *In* G. Pincus, K. V. Thimann, and E. B. Astwood (eds.): The Hormones. New York, Academic Press, 1964., p. 135.
22. Clark, R. B., and Ruston, R. J. G.: The influence of brain extirpation on oögenesis in the polychaete *Nereis diversicolor.* Gen. & Comp. Endocrinol., 3:529, 1963.
23. Clark, R. B., and Ruston, R. J. G.: Time of release and action of a hormone influencing regeneration in the polychaete *Nereis diversicolor.* Gen. & Comp. Endocrinol., 3:542, 1963.
24. Clark, R. B., and Scully, U.: Hormone control of growth in *Nereis diversicolor.* Gen. & Comp. Endocrinol., 4:82, 1964.
25. Cleveland, L. R., and Burke, A. W., Jr.: Modifications induced in the sexual cycles of the protozoan of *Cryptocercus* by change of host. J. Protozool., 7:240, 1960.
26. Cleveland, L. R., Burke, A. W., Jr., and Karlson, P.: Ecdysone induced modifications in the sexual cycles of the protozoa of *Cryptocercus.* J. Protozool., 7:229, 1960.
27. Clever, U.: Von der Ecdysonkonzentration Abhängige Genaktivitätsmuster in den Speicheldrüsenchromosomen von *Chironomus tentans.* Devel. Biol., 6:73, 1963.
28. Clever, U.: Actinomycin and puromycin: effects on sequential gene activation by ecdysone. Science, *146*:794, 1964.
29. Cottrell, C. B.: The imaginal ecdysis of blowflies. Detection of the blood-borne darkening factor and determination of its properties. J. Exp. Biol., *39*:413, 1962.

30. Davey, K. G.: The mode of action of heart accelerating factor from the corpus cardiacum of insects. Gen. & Comp. Endocrinol., 1:24, 1961.
31. Doane, W. W.: Endocrine control of reproduction. In V. J. Brookes (ed.): Insect Physiology: Proc. 23rd Biol. Colloquium. Corvallis, Oregon State University Press, 1963, p. 65.
32. Durchon, M.: L'endocrinologie chez les annélides polychètes. Bull. Soc. zool. Fr., 85:275, 1960.
33. Durchon, M., and Schaller, F.: Recherches endocrinologiques en culture organo-typique chez les annélides polychètes. Gen. & Comp. Endocrinol., 4:427, 1964.
34. Engelmann, F.: Mechanisms controlling reproduction in two viviparous cock-roaches (Blattaria). Ann. N. Y. Acad. Sci., 89:516, 1960.
35. Evans, J. J. T.: Insect neurosecretory material separated by differential centrifu-gation. Science, 136:314, 1962.
36. Fingerman, M.: The Control of Chromatophores. New York, Pergamon Press, 1963.
37. Fingerman, M., and Mobberly, W. C.: Physicochemical properties and differentia-tion of chromatophorotropins and retinal pigment light-adapting hormone in the dwarf crayfish, *Cambarellus shufeldti*. Amer. Midl. Nat., 64:474, 1960.
38. Fingerman, M., and Mobberly, W. C.: Trophic substances in a blind cave crayfish. Science, 132:44, 1960.
39. Fingerman, M., and Yamamoto, Y.: Endocrine control of tanning in the crayfish exoskeleton. Science, 144:1462, 1964.
40. Fisher, F. M., Jr., and Sanborn, R. C.: *Nosema* as a source of juvenile hormone in parasitized insects. Biol. Bull., 126:235, 1964.
41. Fontaine, A. R.: Neurosecretion in the Ophiuroid *Ophiopholis aculeata*. Science, 138:908, 1962.
42. Fraenkel, G., and Hsiao, C.: Tanning in the adult fly: a new function of neuro-secretion in the brain. Science, 141:1057, 1963.
43. Fukuda, S.: Induction of pupation in silkworm by transplanting the prothoracic gland. Proc. Im. Acad. Tokyo, 16:414, 1940.
44. Fukuda, S.: Hormonal control of diapause in the silkworm. Gen. & Comp. Endo-crinol., Suppl. 1, 337, 1962.
45. Gabe, M.: Sur l'existence, chez quelques crustacés malacostracés, d'un organe comparable à la glande de la mue des insectes. Comp. rend. Acad. Sci., Paris, 237:1111, 1953.
46. Gilbert, L. I.: Hormones controlling reproduction and molting in invertebrates. In U. S. von Euler and H. Heller (eds.): Comparative Endocrinology, Vol. 2. New York, Academic Press, 1963, p. 1.
47. Gilbert, L. I.: Hormones regulating insect growth. In G. Pincus, K. V. Thimann, E. B. Astwood (eds.): The Hormones, Vol. 4. New York, Academic Press, 1964, p. 67.
48. Gilbert, L. I., and Schneiderman, H. A.: The development of a bioassay for the juvenile hormone of insects. Trans. Amer. Micr. Soc., 79:38, 1960.
49. Hagadorn, I. R., Bern, H. A., and Nishioka, R. S.: Fine structure of the supra-esophageal ganglion of the leech *Theromyzon rude*, with special reference to neurosecretion. Zeit. Zellforsch., 58:714, 1963.
50. Hanström, B.: The comparative aspects of neurosecretion with special reference to the hypothalamo-hypophysial system. In H. Heller (ed.): The Neuro-hypophysis. London, Butterworth, 1957.
51. Harker, J. E.: Diurnal rhythms in the animal kingdom. Biol. Rev. 33:1, 1958.
52. Harker, J. E.: Endocrine and nervous factors in insect circadian rhythms. Cold Spring Harbor Symp. Quant. Biol., 25:279, 1960.
53. Harker, J. E.: The Physiology of Diurnal Rhythms. New York, Cambridge Uni-versity Press, 1964.
54. Hasegawa, K.: The diapause hormone of the silkworm, *Bombyx mori*. Nature, 179:1300, 1957.
55. Ichikawa, M., and Ishizaki, H.: Brain hormone of the silkworm, *Bombyx mori*. Nature, 191:933, 1961.
56. Ishibashi, T.: Electrical activity of the caudal neurosecretory cells in the eel, *Anguilla japonica* with special reference to synaptic transmission. Gen. & Comp. Endocrinol., 2:415, 1962.

57. Johansson, S. A.: Relation of nutrition to endocrine-reproductive functions in the milkweed bug *Oncopeltus fasciatus* (Dallas). Nytt Magasin for zool. (Oslo University Press), 7:1, 1958.

58. Johnson, B., and Bowers, B.: Transport of neurohormones from the corpora cardiaca of insects. Science, *141*:264, 1963.

59. Joly, P.: Analyse du fonctionnement des corpora allata chez la larve de *Locusta migratoria*. L. Compt. rend. Soc. biol., *149*:584, 1955.

60. Karlson, P., Hoffmeister, H., Hoppe, W., and Hüber, F.: Zur Chemie des Ecdysons. Ann. Chem., *662*:1, 1963.

61. Karlson, P., and Peters, G.: Zum Wirkungsmechanismus der Hormone. IV. Der Einfluss des Ecdysons auf den Nucleinsaeurestoffwechsel von *Calliphora*-Larven. Gen. & Comp. Endocrinol., 5:252, 1965.

62. King, D. S.: Fine structure of the androgenic gland of the crab, *Pachygrapsus crassipes*. Gen. & Comp. Endocrinol., 4:533, 1964.

63. Kleinholz, L. H.: Endocrinology of invertebrates, particularly of crustaceans. *In* B. T. Scheer (ed.): Recent Advances in Insect Physiology. Eugene, University of Oregon Press, p. 173.

64. Kleinholz, L. H., Burgess, P. R., Carlisle, D. B., and Pflueger, O.: Neurosecretion and crustacean retinal pigment hormone: distribution of the light-adapting hormone. Biol. Bull., *122*:73, 1962.

65. Knowles, F. G. W.: The structure of neurosecretory systems in invertebrates. *In* U. S. von Euler and H. Heller (eds.): Comparative Endocrinology, Vol. 2. New York, Academic Press, 1963, p. 47.

66. Kobayashi, M., and Kirimura, J.: The "brain" hormone in the silkworm *Bombyx mori*. L. Nature, *181*:1217, 1958.

67. Larsen, J. R.: Hormone-induced ovarian development in mosquitoes. Science, *127*:587, 1958.

68. Lender, T., and Klein, N.: Mise en évidence de cellules sécrétrices dans le cerveau de la Planaire *Polycelis nigra*. Compt. rend. acad. sci., *253*:331, 1961.

69. Maddrell, S. H. P.: Excretion in the blood-sucking bug *Rhodnius prolixus* Stal. J. Exp. Biol., *40*:247, 1963.

70. Matsumoto, K.: Morphological studies on neurosecretion in crabs. Biol. J. Okayama Univ., 4:103, 1958.

71. Maynard, D. M.: Thoracic neurosecretory structures in Brachyura. Gen. & Comp. Endocrinol., *1*:237, 1961.

72. Maynard, D. M., and Maynard, E. A.: Thoracic neurosecretory structures in Brachyura. III. Microanatomy of peripheral structures. Gen. & Comp. Endocrinol., 2:12, 1962.

73. Maynard, D. M., and Welsh, J. H.: Neurohormones of the pericardial organs of brachyuran Crustacea. J. Physiol., *149*:215, 1959.

74. McWhinnie, M. A.: Gastrolith growth and calcium shifts in the freshwater crayfish, *Orconectes virilis*. Comp. Biochem. Physiol., 7:1, 1962.

75. McWhinnie, M. A., and Chua, A. S.: Hormonal regulation of crustacean tissue metabolism. Gen. & Comp. Endocrinol., 4:624, 1964.

76. Milburn, N., Weiant, E. A., and Roeder, K. D.: The release of efferent nerve activity in the roach, *Periplaneta americana*, by extracts of the corpus cardiacum. Biol. Bull., *118*:111, 1960.

77. Morita, H., Ishibashi, T., and Yamashita, S.: Synaptic transmission in neurosecretory cells. Nature, *191*:183, 1961.

78. Müller, H. J.: Die Saisonformenbildung von *Arachnia levana*, ein Photoperiodisch Gesteuerter Diapause-Effekt. Naturwissenschaften, *42*:134, 1955.

79. Naisse, J.: Contrôle endocrinien de la différenciation sexuelle chez les insectes. Arch. d'Anat. micro. et de Morphol. expér., *54*:417, 1965.

80. Nishioka, R. S., Hagadorn, I. R., and Bern, H. A.: The ultrastructure of the epistellar body of the octopus. Zeit. Zellforsch., *27*:406, 1962.

81. Novak, V. J. A.: The phylogenetic origin of neurosecretion. Gen. & Comp. Endocrinol., 4:696, 1964.

82. Passano, L. M.: Molting and its control. *In* T. H. Waterman (ed.): The Physiology of Crustacea, Vol. 1. New York, Academic Press, 1960, p. 473.

83. Passano, L. M.: The regulation of crustacean metamorphosis. Am. Zoologist, *1*:89, 1961.

84. Ralph, C. L.: Heart accelerators and decelerators in the nervous system of *Periplaneta americana* (L). J. Insect Physiol., 8:431, 1962.
85. Sandeen, M. I., and Costlow, J. D., Jr.: The presence of decapod-pigment-activating substances in the central nervous system of representative Cirripedia. Biol. Bull., *120*:192, 1961.
86. Sano, Y.: Das Caudale Neurosekretorische System bei Fischen. Ergebn. Biol., *24*:191, 1961.
87. Scharrer, B.: Experimental tumors after nerve section in an insect. Proc. Soc. Exp. Biol. & Med., *60*:184, 1945.
88. Scharrer, B.: The role of the corpora allata in the development of *Leucophaea maderae* (Orthoptera). Endocrinol., *38*:35, 1946.
89. Scharrer, B.: The fine structure of the neurosecretory system of the insect *Leucophaea maderae*. *In* H. Heller and R. B. Clark (eds.): Neurosecretion. Memoirs Soc. Endocrinol., No. 12. New York, Academic Press, 1962, p. 89.
90. Scharrer, B.: Neurosecretion XIII. The ultrastructure of the corpus cardiacum of the insect *Leucophaea maderae*. Zeitschr. Zellforsch., *60*:761, 1963.
91. Scharrer, B.: Recent progress in the study of neuroendocrine mechanisms in insects. Arch. d'Anat. micro. et de Morphol. expér., *54*:331, 1965.
92. Scharrer, E., and Brown, S.: The formation of neurosecretory granules in the earthworm, *Lumbricus terrestris* L. Zeitschr. Zellforsch., *54*:530, 1961.
93. Scharrer, E., and Scharrer, B.: Neuroendocrinology. New York, Columbia University Press, 1963.
94. Schneiderman, H. A., and Gilbert, L. I.: Control of growth and development in insects. Science, *143*:325, 1964.
95. Schneiderman, H. A., and Williams, C. M.: Qualitative changes in the metabolism of the Cecropia silkworm during diapause and development. Biol. Bull., *106*:210, 1954.
96. Scudamore, H. H.: Sinus gland and O_2 consumption in crayfishes: hormonal control of gastrolith formation in crayfishes. Physiol. Zool., *20*:187, 1947.
97. Stanley, J. G., and Fleming, W. R.: The effect of urophysectomy on sodium metabolism of *Tilapia mossambica*. Amer. Zoologist, *4*:406, 1964.
98. Steele, J. E.: The site of action of insect hyperglycemic hormone. Gen. & Comp. Endocrinol., *3*:46, 1963.
99. Telfer, W. H.: The physiology of oöcyte differentiation in the Cecropia moth. *In* V. J. Brookes (ed.): Insect Physiology. Corvallis, Oregon State University Press, 1963, p. 13.
100. Thomsen, E.: Functional significance of the neurosecretory cells and the corpus cardiacum in the female blowfly, *Calliphora erythrocephala* Meig. J. Exp. Biol., *29*:137, 1952.
101. Thomsen, E.: Observations on the oenocytes of adult *Calliphora erythrocephala* Meig. *In* K. G. Wingstrand (ed.): Bertil Hanström, Zoological Papers in honour of his 65th birthday. 1956, p. 298.
102. Thomsen, E., and Moller, I. B.: Influence of neurosecretory cells and of corpus allatum on intestinal protease activity in the adult *Calliphora erythrocephala* Meig. J. Exp. Biol., *40*:301, 1963.
103. Unger, H.: Neurohormone bei Seesternen (*Marthasterias glacialis*). Symposia Biol. Hung., *1*:203, 1960.
104. Wall, B. J., and Ralph, C. L.: Evidence for hormonal regulation of malpighian tubule excretion in the insect *Periplaneta americana* L. Gen. & Comp. Endocrinol., *4*:452, 1964.
105. Wells, M. J.: Optic glands and the ovary of *Octopus*. Symp. Zool. Soc., London, *2*:87, 1960.
106. Wells, M. J., and Wells, J.: Hormonal control of sexual maturity in *Octopus*. J. Exp. Biol., *36*:1, 1959.
107. Wigglesworth, V. B.: The determination of characters at metamorphosis in *Rhodnius prolixus* (Hemiptera). J. Exp. Biol., *17*:201, 1940.
108. Wigglesworth, V. B.: The breakdown of the thoracic gland in the adult insect, *Rhodnius prolixus*. J. Exp. Biol., *32*:485, 1955.
109. Wigglesworth, V. B.: Some methods for assaying extracts of juvenile hormone in insects. J. Insect Physiol., *2*:73, 1958.

110. Wigglesworth, V. B.: The control of insect growth and form. Ithaca, N. Y., Cornell University Press, 1959.
111. Wigglesworth, V. B.: The action of moulting hormone and juvenile hormone at the cellular level in *Rhodnius prolixus*. J. Exp. Biol., *40*:231, 1963.
112. Wigglesworth, V. B.: Insect hormones. Endeavour, *24*:21, 1965.
113. Wilde, J. de: Photoperiodism in insects and mites. Ann. Rev. Entomol., 7:1, 1962.
114. Williams, C. M.: Physiology of insect diapause: the role of the brain in the production and termination of pupal dormancy in the giant silkworm, *Platysamia cecropia*. Biol. Bull., *90*:234, 1946.
115. Williams, C. M.: The juvenile hormone. Endocrine activity of the corpora allata of adult Cecropia silkworm. Biol. Bull., *116*:323, 1959.
116. Williams, C. M.: Insect metamorphosis: an approach to the study of growth. *In* M. X. Zarrow (ed.): Growth in Living Systems. New York, Basic Books, 1961, p. 313.
117. Yagi, K., Bern, H. A., and Hagadorn, I. R.: Action potentials of neurosecretory neurons in the leech *Theromyzon rude*. Gen. & Comp. Endocrinol., 3:490, 1963.

4_____

PITUITARY GLAND: ANATOMY; SECRETIONS OF THE ADENOHYPOPHYSIS

Although the human pituitary gland, or hypophysis, is a relatively small organ, weighing about 600 mg. in adult men and slightly more in women, no part of the body is exempt from its influences. It is concerned with a multiplicity of vital processes, and at least nine protein or polypeptide hormones have been isolated from it. The *trophic* hormones of the pars distalis stimulate specific endocrine glands, but probably do not limit their actions to these targets. A reciprocal relationship exists between the hypophysis and other endocrine glands as well as between the hypophysis and the central nervous system.

The pituitary is closely applied to the floor of the brain and remains attached to it by means of a delicate stalk. This relationship is not fortuitous since the functional capacity of the entire pituitary depends upon its neural and vascular connections with the hypothalamus. These anatomic connnections make it possible for the organ to adjust its output of hormones in response to stimuli arising from the exterior as well as from within the organism. The pituitary gland is an essential link in the neuroendocrine system, but it has little capacity to function independently. Since it is subservient to the nervous system and to some of the other endocrine glands, it is misleading to refer to it as the "master" gland of the body.

ANATOMY

Gross Anatomy

The pituitary is a compound gland of internal secretion located in the sella turcica, a concavity in the sphenoid bone (Fig. 4–1). Topographically, it is one of the best protected and most inaccessible organs of the body. The gland is encapsulated by the dura mater; a shelflike fold of this membrane forms the diaphragma sellae and extends around the infundibular stalk. The pituitary enlarges during pregnancy and certain other conditions, and, since it is situated immediately behind the optic chiasm, visual symptoms may result when the enlarged organ presses upon the optic tracts.

The pars tuberalis, a constituent of the anterior lobe, is a thin epithelial plate of cells that is formed by the fusion of two outgrowths from the embryonic pars distalis. The pars tuberalis of the adult may surround the infundibular stalk and extend some distance below the tuber cinereum. When the pituitary gland is surgically removed (hypophysectomy), it is practically impossible to ablate all of the pars tuberalis without some injury to the hypothalamus. Although the tuberalis is the most vascular region of the hypophysis and receives many sympathetic fibers, it is not known to have any definite endocrine function. During the hypophysectomy of laboratory mammals the delicate stalk usually breaks at the level of the diaphragma sellae.

In young human beings and in the majority of other vertebrates a narrow band of tissue, the pars intermedia, is demonstrable between the pars distalis and the neural lobe. The pars intermedia is conspicuous in most human infants, but in adults it merges with the neural lobe and tends to become obscure. This lobe is absent in

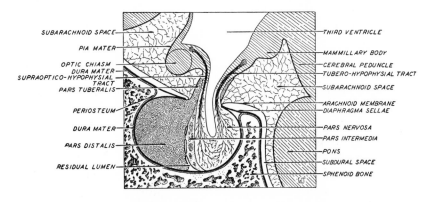

Figure 4–1. A diagrammatic sagittal section through the hypophysis cerebri of the human being, showing the relationships of this gland to adjacent structures.

birds and in certain mammals, such as the whale, Indian elephant, and armadillo.

The vascular supply of the pituitary varies with the species and from one individual to another, but the same general pattern is found in all of the mammalian species that have been studied. A pair of posterior hypophysial arteries, originating from the internal carotid arteries, supplies blood chiefly to the neural lobe. A series of anterior hypophysial arteries originates from the internal carotids and from the posterior communicating arteries of the circle of Willis. Some of these vessels supply the pars distalis directly, whereas others pass into the pars tuberalis and break up into a primary plexus in the median eminence. Venules, forming the hypophysial portal system, convey blood from the capillary meshwork of the median eminence to the sinusoids of the pars distalis. It thus appears that the arterial supply to the adenohypophysis, particularly to the pars distalis, is largely independent of that of the neurohypophysis. The whole organ is drained by means of short veins that empty into sinuses in the dura mater or in the basisphenoid bone (Fig. 2–2).

The nerve supply of the hypophysis consists of sympathetic fibers from the surrounding perivascular plexuses, parasympathetic fibers from the petrosal nerves, and the hypothalamo-hypophysial tract. A comprehensive study of pituitaries from 75 species of vertebrates from cyclostomes to man revealed the presence of sympathetic fibers in the pars tuberalis but none in the pars distalis. Very few workers still hold that the bulk of the anterior lobe cells receives any direct innervation. Since the pars tuberalis is not known to secrete hormones, the nerve fibers that end there are probably vasomotor rather than secretomotor. The weight of evidence indicates that if the main secreting mass of the pars distalis receives any nerve endings at all, they are very few; if any are present, it remains to be shown whether they are secretomotor or vasomotor. There is no convincing evidence that the sympathetic and parasympathetic innervations play any important role in regulating the secretory functions of the pars distalis.[42]

A conspicuous feature of the pars nervosa is the large number of secretory axons that terminate there. The perikarya of these axons are located in certain hypothalamic nuclei. The fibers sweep down the pituitary stalk and are grouped into supraoptico- and tuberohypophysial tracts. Some of these fibers are known to terminate in the median eminence and in the pars intermedia, but it is doubtful that any of them enter the pars distalis (Fig. 2–2).

Amphibians have been used extensively in experiments involving the pituitary gland. Figure 4–2 is a drawing of a ventral dissection of the frog's brain, showing the pituitary gland and adjacent structures.

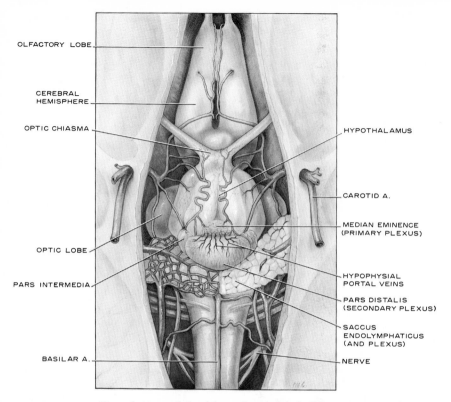

OLFACTORY LOBE

CEREBRAL
HEMISPHERE

OPTIC CHIASMA

HYPOTHALAMUS

CAROTID A.

MEDIAN EMINENCE
(PRIMARY PLEXUS)

OPTIC LOBE

PARS INTERMEDIA

HYPOPHYSIAL
PORTAL VEINS

PARS DISTALIS
(SECONDARY PLEXUS)

SACCUS
ENDOLYMPHATICUS
(AND PLEXUS)

BASILAR A.

NERVE

Figure 4–2. Ventral view of the brain of an adult bullfrog *Rana catesbeiana*, showing the pituitary gland and hypothalamus. The hypophysial portal veins, extending from the median eminence to the pars distalis, are clearly seen. (From a dissection by Mr. Hsien-Sung Lin.)

Developmental Anatomy

The entire pituitary is ectodermal, but this tissue arises from two different sources (Fig. 4–3). The neurohypophysis originates from the infundibulum of the brain, an outpocketing of the hypothalamus. The stalk permanently connects the neural lobe with the hypothalamus. The anterior and intermediate lobes differentiate from Rathke's pouch, an outgrowth from the roof of the mouth. This pouch promptly meets the infundibulum and loses its connection with the buccal epithelium. The cavity of Rathke's pouch becomes the residual lumen of the hypophysis. This lumen may persist between the anterior and intermediate lobes, or it may be obliterated entirely in certain species. The pars intermedia differentiates from the wall of Rathke's pouch, which comes in contact with the infundibulum. The remainder of the pouch thickens greatly and becomes the pars distalis. Paired lateral extensions differentiate from this anlage and eventually fuse to produce a thin plate of tissue, the pars tuberalis, which grows around the infundibular stalk and spreads out below the hypothalamus.

A body of typical anterior lobe tissue, the pharyngeal hypophysis, is commonly found in the vault of the human nasopharynx. This structure apparently differentiates from a fragment of Rathke's pouch which is left behind.[11]

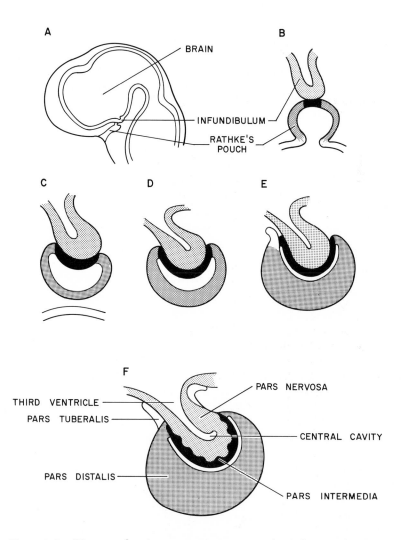

Figure 4–3. Diagrams showing progressive stages in the embryonic development of the pituitary gland. Rathke's pouch becomes detached from the oral epithelium at stage *C*. (Stage *A* is from Villee, Walker, and Smith: General Zoology, 2nd ed. Philadelphia, W. B. Saunders Co., 1963.)

Microscopic Anatomy

Pars Distalis

This part of the gland is composed of irregular masses and cords of epithelial cells separated by sinusoids and supported by a loose framework of connective tissue. Routine staining of the adenohypophysis with such stains as hemotoxylin and eosin, or with Mallory aniline blue or azan, reveals two major varieties of gland cells: the chromophils contain characteristic cytoplasmic granules and are generally considered to be secretory; whereas the *chromophobes* do not posses conspicuous secretory granules and are thought to be inactive in this respect. Most cytologists have interpreted the chromophobes as progenitors of the other cell types or as degranulated, resting stages of the chromophils. The chromophils are further divided into *acidophils* and *basophils* on the basis of their tinctorial responses. This terminology is very inadequate, since cytoplasmic granules often respond to both acid and basic stains, but it cannot be easily discarded until it becomes possible to redefine the cells confidently on the basis of the specific hormones they secrete. No morphological nomenclature, presently available, is acceptable to all workers, and applicable to all vertebrates.

Since six protein or polypeptide hormones can be extracted from the pars distalis, it is pertinent to know whether there is a cell type specialized for the secretion of each hormone or whether a single pituitary cell can secrete several hormones. If the latter is the case, we should like to know whether the multiple hormones are elaborated simultaneously or alternately by a given pituitary cell. Although considerable progress has been made in cytochemical techniques and there is some measure of agreement regarding the source of several anterior lobe hormones, it is still premature to conclude that any available stain unmistakably identifies a pituitary hormone with its cell of origin. The relative proportions of the cells may vary markedly during physiologic states; they may undergo changes, such as granulation, degranulation, hyalinization, and vacuolation, but the significance of such fluctuations is not certain. Since mitotic figures are extremely sparse in the pituitary gland, it has seemed apparent that cells are transformed from one variety to another, and the literature abounds with proposals for cell lineages based upon supposed transition stages.

MAMMALS. Pituitary cytology has been most intensively studied in the rat and other laboratory mammals. The periodic acid-Schiff technique and Gomori's adlehyde fuchsin have proved valuable in studying the cell types of the adenohypophysis. Electron microscopy has been of great help in identifying cell types on the basis of differences in cytoplasmic granules, endoplasmic reticulum, mitochondria, Golgi apparatus, nuclear structure, cell size and shape, etc. The cytochemical procedures, coupled with electron microscopy, have yielded important information when applied to animals known to be in different physiological states such as those produced by gonadectomy, adrenalectomy, thyroidectomy, pregnancy, lactation, and subjection to stress. Structural and functional changes in the pituitary may be detected following the administration of such agents as metopirone (adrenocortical inhibitor) and thiourea (thyroid inhibitor).

Three of the anterior lobe hormones, viz., follicle-stimulating hormone, luteinizing hormone, and thyroid-stimulating hormone, in contrast to the other hormones of this gland, are glycoproteins. The periodic acid-Schiff method (PAS stain) is used for the identification of mucopolysaccharides and mucoproteins, and its application to the adenohypophysis has been informative. A positive PAS reaction is interpreted as due to the presence within the cells of a carbohydrate-containing pituitary hormone. The Pearse PAS trichrome stain and other modifications have been useful in making differential cell counts.

On the basis of electron microscopy and various tinctorial methods, it is generally agreed that the rat's pars distalis contains two kinds of acidophils and four kinds of basophils. The somatotrophic acidophils secrete growth hormone (STH) and are distinct from lactotrophic acidophils, which are the source of prolactin. The basophils are gonadotrophic cells (FSH and LH), thyrotrophic cells (TSH), and corticotrophic cells (ACTH). Electron micrographs show that the chromophobes are not devoid of cytoplasmic granules, but merely have fewer than the chromophils.[35, 36, 55, 99, 111]

It has been suspected for many years that the acidophils were concerned with the secretion of somatotrophin. Pituitary dwarfism in man and other mammals correlates with a deficiency of acidophils, whereas in acromegaly and gigantism, characterized by excessive growth of the skeleton, there is typically a striking increase in the number of acidophils. In genetic dwarf mice, the acidophils are sparse and bioassays indicate that the pituitaries of such animals are deficient in STH.[66, 88]

Cytologic observations on the rat's pituitary from birth to maturity indicate that the gonadotrophic cells undergo degranulation at puberty, perhaps indicating an increased release of gonad-stimulating hormones at this time. Thyrotrophic cells, staining with aldehyde-fuchsin, are present in the rat's pituitary from birth onward.[94, 110]

Castration of various laboratory mammals results in a striking alteration of the gonadotrophic cells. Many of them become enlarged, degranulated, and eventually develop large cytoplasmic vacuoles that compress the nucleus against the cell membrane. The castration cells (signet-ring cells) appear after removal of either the testes or ovaries and persist indefinitely unless the animal is treated with gonadal steroids. Though not so extreme as in the rat, comparable cells appear in the human hypophysis after gonadectomy and are also seen in the glands of aged persons.[48]

In thyroidectomized rats and mice, as in certain other species, the thyrotrophic cells undergo degranulation and increase in size and number, forming the so-called thyroidectomy cells. The thyrotrophic cells of the rat's anterior lobe become rather completely degranulated within two days following thyroid ablation and, by the sixth day, have enlarged sufficiently to be recognized as thyroidectomy cells.

The term *amphophil* was originally used to refer to the thyroidectomy cells of the mouse. After the thyroid glands of the mouse are destroyed by appropriate treatment with I^{131}, the thyroidectomy cells in the pars distalis first increase in numbers, then form focal hyperplasias, and finally give rise to adenomatous nodules. The modified thyrotrophic cells, comprising the tumors, contain PAS postive granules, but by varying the fixatives and stains, the granules can be made to appear either basophilic or acidophilic. The amphoteric nature of cytoplasmic granules in these cells suggested the name "amphophils." Such cells are commonly found in the pituitaries of human subjects suffering from thyroid deficiency.[15, 38]

In the rat, at least, it appears that the six cell types, responsible for the six hormones secreted by the pars distalis, can be identified. A similar situation may prevail in many other mammals, but it would be premature to conclude that the same cell types are present in non-mammalian species. The pituitaries of different vertebrates show considerable variation in cytochemical patterns.[9]

BIRDS. The avian pituitary lacks a pars intermedia, and the anterior lobe is histologically divisible into caudal and cephalic regions. The cytology of the pars distalis is generally similar to that of mammals, but the functional roles performed by the different cell types have not been established with certainty. Two types of acidophils (Payne's A_1 and A_2 cells) can be delineated: these differ slightly in staining reactions and occur in different regions of the gland. The acidophils are conspicuous at the time of hatching and are more numerous in pullets than in cockerels. According to Yasuda, prolactin is secreted by one of the acidophil types.[122]

Assay of gonad-stimulating potencies of pituitaries from normal and caponized birds, as well as correlated changes in the basophils during development, indicates that the large basophils are the source of one or more gonadotrophins. Degranulation of basophils, suggesting a discharge of hormone, can be induced by exposure to light. A similar degranulation of basophils occurs in the mallard at the height of sexual activity.[53] Castration causes an increase in the number of basophils, but these do not transform into signet-ring cells as they do in mammals.

Acidophilic granules have been observed in the basophils of laying hens, but appear to be entirely absent from the basophils of cocks and nonlaying hens. Since ovulation-inducing hormone (OIH) is freed from the hen's pituitary between six and four hours before the release of an egg from the ovary, it may be that the acidophilic granules in these basophils are related in some manner to the formation of OIH.

As in mammals, thyroidectomy or treatment with antithyroid agents produces characteristic alterations in pituitary cytology. Thyroidectomy cells (Payne's T cells) appear during thyroid deficiency. While these cells may be markedly basophilic, Payne found that they differed from basophils in nuclear structure and site of origin within the gland, and hence regarded them as neither basophils nor acidophils.[91]

A striking alteration in the pars distalis of the domestic hen occurs at the onset of broodiness. The ordinary basophils and acidophils almost disappear and *broody cells* dominate the picture (Fig. 4–4). Although the latter cells may contain acidophilic granules, differences in size, nuclear configuration, and position in the gland suggest that they are distinguishable from both acidophils and basophils. Strangely, maximum development of the broody cells has been observed in the White Leghorn hen, which seldom exhibits broody behavior. While Payne was of the opinion that the broody cells might be the source of prolactin, Yasuda regarded them as chromophobes and hence not connected with such a role.[12, 92, 93, 122]

AMPHIBIANS AND FISHES. Seasonal alterations in the cytology of the pituitary have been observed in a variety of reptiles, amphibians, and fishes. The pars distalis generally enlarges and undergoes structural changes in connection with the annual breeding periods.[79] Several tinctorial cell types are present in the pars distalis of the frog, *Rana pipiens*, but it appears too early to assign functional roles to them. A closely related group of cells appears to be present

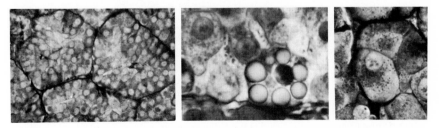

Figure 4–4. Pituitary cytology in the domestic fowl. *A*, Broody cells; *B*, aging change in a basophil of an old cock; *C*, a thyroidectomy cell (T cell). (Courtesy of Fernandus Payne.)

in the frog pituitary, and the identification of transitional stages suggests that one type may transform into another.[89] Relatively few studies have been made on the ultrastructure of amphibian pituitary glands, but cells types can be distinguished on the basis of specific granular size (Fig. 4–5 and 4–6).[17, 23, 27, 59]

The proximal pars distalis of teleost fishes contains basophilic cells which are probably the source of gonadotrophins. The periodic acid-Schiff method enables one to distinguish two types of basophils in the fish *Astyanax*. Some of these react to fluctuating levels of thyroid hormone (thyrotrophic cells), whereas others reflect changes in the gonads (gonadotrophic cells).[4]

Five tinctorial cell types have been identified in the bony fish *Poecilia* (Fig. 4–7). The rostral pars distalis contains cells (corticotrophs) which react specifically following treatment of the animals with metopirone, an adrenocortical inhibitor; and others (lactotrophs) which are rapidly activated by passing the animals from dilute seawater to freshwater. The latter cells probably secrete prolactin. The

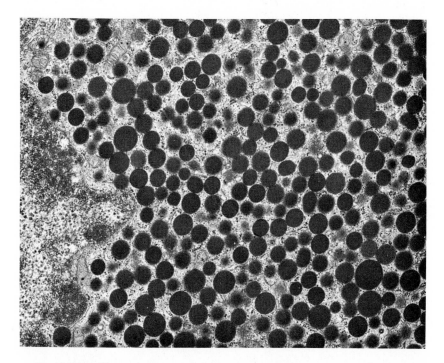

Figure 4–5.   Electron micrograph (× 18,000) of a portion of an orange G acidophil from the pituitary gland of the salamander *Diemyctylus viridescens*. These cells are believed to contain and secrete somatotrophin, which appears to be stored in the dark spherical granules. It is thought that the hormones are synthesized in the rough endoplasmic reticulum and transported to the Golgi complex, where they are condensed into protein granules. These lie in the cytoplasm until the cell is stimulated to release its hormone. The granules are then discharged into the pericapillary space and diffuse into the capillary lumen. The nucleus is to the left. (Courtesy of Robert R. Cardell, Jr.)

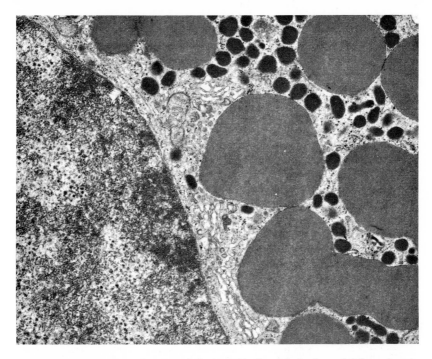

Figure 4–6. Electron micrograph (× 18,000) of a globular basophil from the pituitary gland of *Diemyctylus viridescens*. A significant feature of this cell type is that it contains two distinct types of cytoplasmic granules, the large globules and the smaller, irregularly shaped granules. This cell probably secretes two distinct hormones. The large globules are probably related to gonadotrophins; it is not known what the smaller granules contain. The nucleus is to the left. (Courtesy of Robert R. Cardell, Jr.)

proximal pars distalis contains cells (gonadotrophs) which show structural changes with the incidence of vitellogenesis in the ovary; and thyrotrophic cells which undergo changes after the animals are treated with thiourea to depress the thyroid glands. Somatotrophic cells are mingled with the thyrotrophs in this area of the proximal pars distalis.[87]

There seems to be more localization of the cell types in the pars distalis than was formerly supposed. Some observers find that the hypophysial portal veins drain particular areas of the median eminence and supply blood to special regions of the pars distalis.[63] The tendency for the cell types of the pars distalis to form regional aggregations seems to be more pronounced in the lower vertebrates than in mammals. The secretory cells within the adenohypophysis of fishes such as *Poecilia* are not extensively intermingled, but tend to form regional aggregations (Fig. 4–7). The morphologically distinguishable components of the elasmobranch pituitary may be excised and assayed for hormonal content. It has been found that ACTH activity in the elasmobranch pituitary is confined to the rostral pars distalis, none being present in the proximal pars distalis,

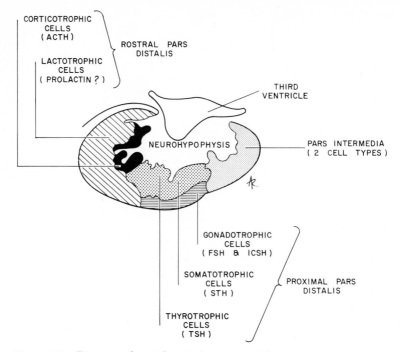

Figure 4-7. Diagram of a mid-sagittal section of the pituitary gland of a bony fish *(Poecilia)*, showing localization of cell types in the adenohypophysis. (Modified from Olivereau, M., and Ball, J. N.: Gen. & Comp. Endocrinol., 4:523, 1964.)

ventral lobe, or saccus vasculosus. On the basis of this physiologic information, one would expect to find corticotrophic cells (ACTH) present only in the rostral pars distalis of these species.[24]

Pars Intermedia

The intermediate lobe is composed of polygonal cells that take basic dyes and in which secretory granules have been described. Vesicles containing colloid are present in certain species. Although the colloid contains small amounts of iodine, it has not been shown to have any functional significance. Cytological alterations occur in the intermediate lobes of frogs as their integuments adapt to black and white backgrounds.

Neural Lobe

This portion of the neurohypophysis consists of branching cells, called pituicytes, and thick networks of fine unmyelinated nerve fibers that are the terminations of the hypothalamo-hypophysial tract. These fibers form plexuses in the vicinity of blood vessels and appear not to form synapses with the pituicytes. Most workers feel that the hormones of the neurohypophysis are not secreted by the pituicytes but that they are products formed by certain neurosecretory cells of the hypothalamic nuclei. The neurosecretory material is thought to move along the axons of the hypothalamo-hypophysial tract into the neural lobe where it is discharged, stored, possibly modified, and released into the general circulation as needed. It follows that the neural lobe per se is a depot for the storage of hormones and is not strictly an endocrine gland, since the secretions originate elsewhere.

Comparative Anatomy

The anatomic constituents of the vertebrate pituitary gland are remarkably constant. The most conspicuous phylogenetic changes have been the appearance of a consolidated neurohypophysis, the development of a system of portal vessels passing from the median eminence to the adenohypophysis, and the lack of a pars intermedia in birds and a few mammals.

The adenohypophysis of the cyclostome is an elongated structure, divided by connective tissue septa into three regions for which the noncommittal names pro-, meso-, and meta-adenohypophysis were proposed by Pickford and Atz.[95] The most posterior component is the pars intermedia, and the two anterior components are the rostral pars distalis and the proximal pars distalis (Fig. 4–8). The neurohypophysis is a slight thickening of the floor of the third ventricle, and is separated from the adenophypophysis by a thin layer of vascular tissue. Some of the hypothalamic neurosecretory axons, presumably conveying arginine vasotocin, terminate around blood vessels in the neurohypophysis, whereas others appear to liberate their secretions into the third ventricle.

The elasmobranchs and teleosts are specialized groups, and it is important to keep in mind that they are remote from the main line of vertebrate evolution (Fig. 4–8). The neurohypophysis of elasmobranchs is diffuse and intermingled with the pars intermedia, the two parts often being collectively referred to as the neurointermediate lobe. Neurosecretory axons from the preoptic nucleus and lateral hypothalamus terminate in the neurohypophysis, but these are absent from the anterior infundibular floor. A few such fibers terminate in the *saccus vasculosus*, a folded and highly vascularized structure lying posterior to the neurohypophysis. The function of the saccus has not been determined. The pars distalis lies below the infundibulum, and is divisible into proximal and rostral zones. The ventral lobe is a peculiar feature of the elasmobranch adenohypophysis; it varies greatly in size and shape among different species, and its function remains obscure. A primitive system of hypophysial portal veins, supplying both the distal and neurointermediate lobes,

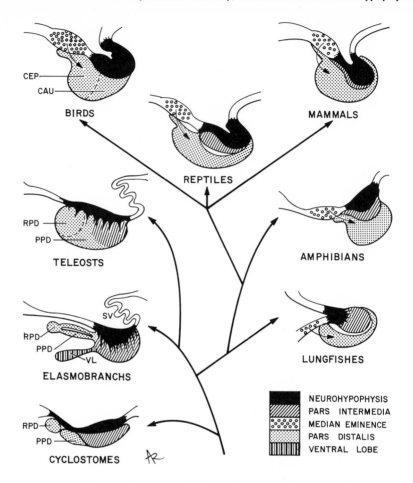

Figure 4–8. Schema showing probable evolutionary changes in the vertebrate pituitary gland. Arrows extending from the median eminence to the pars distalis represent the hypophysial portal system. CAU, caudal division of the avian anterior lobe; CEP, cephalic division of the avian anterior lobe; PPD, proximal pars distalis; RPD, rostral pars distalis; VL, ventral lobe of the elasmobranch pituitary; SV, saccus vasculosus.

has been described. The presence of an anatomically differentiated median eminence is questionable.

In teleosts, the adenohypophysis consists of a pars intermedia and an anterior lobe which is sometimes divisible topographically into rostral and proximal regions. These regions of the pars distalis appear to contain all of the cell types characteristic of the mammalian anterior lobe. Some workers have homologized the rostral pars distalis of teleosts with the tetrapod pars tuberalis, but it is not certain that this is true. The neurohypophysis of teleosts, as in elasmobranchs, is diffuse and interdigitates with the cells of the pars intermedia and, to a lesser extent, with the cells of the pars distalis. Neurosecretory fibers from the preoptic nucleus and the lateral tuberal nucleus terminate in all parts of the neurohypophysis, but their secretions have also been found in both regions of the pars distalis. The saccus vasculosus is well developed in many teleosts, but it does not appear to be supplied by neurosecretory tracts. Whether equivalents of a median eminence and a portal system are present in teleosts remains a controversial point.[8]

Among lungfishes (Dipnoi), the neurohypophysis is separable from the pars intermedia, and a pars tuberalis is absent. A cleft is typically present between the pars distalis and the pars intermedia, and the saccus vasculosus does not develop. A primitive system of portal veins conveys blood from the median eminence to the pars distalis. Except for the pars tuberalis, the dipnoan pituitary is anatomically comparable to the pituitaries of tetrapod vertebrates (Fig. 4–8).

The hypophysis of primitive urodeles is very similar to that of lungfishes; in anurans, the median eminence is more advanced and the portal system is conspicuous (Fig. 4–8). The pars tuberalis is often lacking in reptiles, and a cleft is typically present between the pars intermedia and pars distalis. A pars intermedia is absent in birds, the neural and anterior lobes being separated by a connective tissue septum. The avian neurohypophysis is highly specialized and, in certain species, the *zona externa* of the median eminence, as well as the pars nervosa, serves as a storage site (neurohemal organ) for neurosecretory material from hypothalamic neurons.[86, 117] The portal blood vessels of the avian pituitary run to the anterior lobe via the pars tuberalis; not in direct apposition to the infundibular stalk, as in mammals. Thus, the portal vessels can be divided without injury to other parts of the gland.[53]

THE ADENOHYPOPHYSIS

Effects of Hypophysectomy

As early as 1886, clinicians had associated pituitary enlargement with the syndromes of acromegaly and gigantism and suspected that the organ had a great influence upon skeletal growth. Little progress was made in elucidating hypophysial functions until surgical methods were devised for removing the gland from laboratory animals without attendant injury to the brain. Around 1910 a transsphenoidal approach was employed for hypophysectomizing dogs, and a similar method was worked out in 1926 for the rat. A simple method of hypophysectomy for the rat, approaching the gland through the external auditory canal, has been used by some workers. Studies have now been made on many species of hypophysectomized vertebrates ranging from fishes to man (Figs. 4–9 and 4–10).

Figure 4-9. Hypophysectomy of the immature rhesus monkey. At the time of the operation, the experimental animal (left) weighed 2.7 kg. and the control (right) weighed 2.9 kg. After 2 years, when this photograph was taken, the hypophysectomized animal weighed 2.7 kg., whereas the control matured normally and weighed 8.4 kg. (From Knobil, E.: *In* Zarrow, M. X., (ed.): Growth in Living Systems. New York, Basic Books, Inc., 1961.)

Total hypophysectomy could not be performed for the treatment of malignant diseases in the human subject until it became possible to prevent death from hypopituitarism by an adequate replacement therapy. The operation is now employed occasionally in case of advanced metastatic cancer of the breast in an attempt to reduce the somatotrophin and steroid hormones of the body by one surgical intervention. Because of the surgical risks and the difficulties of postoperative care, hypophysectomy is generally employed only after other measures have failed to control the cancer or other conditions. The physiologic disturbances in the hypophysectomized human being are quite the same as those that appear in other mammals.

The most striking alterations resulting from total hypophysectomy or from removal of the adenohypophysis alone may be summarized as follows:

1. Cessation of growth in young animals and the retention of juvenile hair coat and other immature features ensue (Fig. 4-10).[106]

Figure 4-10. Hypophysectomy of the prepuberal rat. The two animals are litter-mate brothers. The smaller one (experimental) was hypophysectomized at 28 days of age, and each weighed 72 grams at that time. At the time of this photograph, the two animals were 10 months of age; the hypophysectomized animal weighed 81 grams and the control 465 grams. The hypophysectomized animal never developed adult pelage, and testicular descent failed to occur. The juvenile hair was lost rapidly, and bald areas frequently appeared on the back, particularly near the base of the tail. When rats are hypophysectomized as adults, the coarse adult hair is gradually replaced by the soft, fluffy hair characteristic of juveniles.

Very young hypophysectomized rats do not stop growing immediately, but growth does cease after they reach an age of about 1 month. When the pituitary is removed from rats at 6 days of age, they do not live to be more than 75 days of age. These deaths result from brain damage; the brain continues to grow to normal size, but the growth of the cranium is prematurely arrested and does not enlarge enough to accommodate the brain (Fig. 4-11). Failure of the cranium to increase in length and width is due to the cessation of endochondral osteogenesis in the basal region. The administration of somatotrophin to these young animals causes normal skull development, and they survive without showing any neural symptoms. In the absence of the pituitary there is no regeneration of bones removed from the top of the skull, whereas extensive replacement occurs in normal or hypophysectomized animals receiving somatotrophin.[2]

Practically all primary and secondary centers of ossification are present in the skeleton of the 28-day female rat. The tibia of the rat and mouse is commonly used for the bioassay of STH, since it normally retains an open epiphysial disc at its proximal end until late in life (Fig. 4-12). After the pituitary gland is removed from the young animal, this disc promptly shows signs of inactivity. The disc diminishes in width and is far below normal by two weeks after the operation. Eventually, the epiphysial cartilage plate becomes separated from the marrow by a lamina of bone and persists into old age. Other epiphyses that, like the tibia, remain open until late in life become

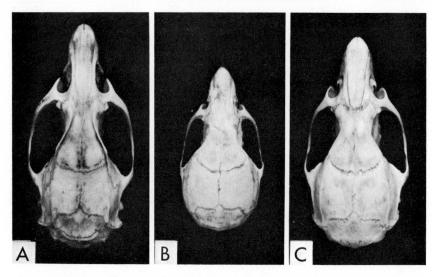

Figure 4–11. Effect of hypophysectomy and replacement therapy on the rat's skull. *A*, Normal rat 60 days of age; *B*, hypophysectomized at 6 days of age and killed at 60 days of age; *C*, hypophysectomized when 6 days of age and given growth hormone injections from 30 to 80 days of age. (From Asling, C. W., *et al.:* Anat. Rec., *114*, 1952.)

sealed and persist after hypophysectomy of the young animal. As a consequence of this premature arrest of growth, the epiphysial plates come to resemble those of intact rats during senescence (Fig. 4–13).

2. Atrophy of the adrenal cortex and metabolic derangements resulting from a deficiency of adrenal steroid hormones occur. While some residual secretion of cortical hormones apparently can occur in the absence of the hypophysis, augmented production cannot be accomplished in response to stressful conditions. The adrenal medulla seems to be independent of pituitary control and no changes in this tissue are known to follow hypophysectomy.

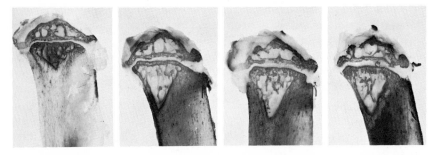

Figure 4–12. Effect of somatotrophin on the width of the epiphysial cartilage of the tibia of hypophysectomized mice over a 17-day period. *A*, Control; *B*, 1 microgram; *C*, 5 micrograms; *D*, 20 micrograms. (From Lostroh and Li: Endocrinology, *60*, 1957.)

Figure 4–13. Effect of hypophysectomy upon skeletal dimensions in the rat. *A*, Normal control; *B*, a littermate hypophysectomized at 36 days of age and killed at 144 days of age.

3. The thyroid gland atrophies and becomes practically non-functional. This accounts for the low basal metabolic rate and other symptoms of hypothyroidism. Hypophysectomy of the rat leads to a profound reduction in all phases of thyroid iodine metabolism. The thyroglobulin content of the thyroid is greatly reduced: the meager amounts present contain low percentages of I^{131}-thyroxine and other iodothyronines, but a normal percentage of I^{131}-diiodotyrosine, and a greater than normal amount of I^{131}-monoiodotyrosine. After the administration of I^{131} to the hypophysectomized rat, no detectable amounts of I^{131}-thyroxine appear in the blood. It is apparent that the synthesis of thyroid hormones is almost nihil in the absence of the pituitary gland.[116]

4. After hypophysectomy of the adult, the testes and ovaries become relatively nonfunctional and fail to produce mature germ cells or sufficient quantities of gonadal hormones to maintain the functional status of the accessory sex organs. After pituitary ablation in young animals, the gonads and sex accessories remain infantile and cyclic reproductive changes never occur. Although hypophysectomy may not terminate pregnancy, lactation fails to occur when the operation is performed during late pregnancy or post partum.

Hypophysectomy of the domestic cockerel is followed by a massive steatogenesis and formation of cholesterol in the seminiferous tubules of the testis. These degenerative changes appear to be identical with those that occur annually in wild birds at the end of the breeding season. As occurs normally in seasonal birds, the interstitial cells (Leydig cells) in the testes of hypophysectomized cockerels degenerate, and a new generation of Leydig cells begins to differentiate from connective tissue cells. In the absence of the pituitary, these presumptive Leydig cells become sudanophil and cholesterol positive. This suggests an intrinsic rehabilitative mechanism within the gonad; however, there is no indication that the renewed interstitial tissue can secrete testicular steroids after removal of the adenohypophysis.[22]

5. Many disturbances occur in the hypophysectomized animal in the metabolism of carbohydrates, lipids, and proteins. In some species, such as the pig, the blood sugar drops to fatal levels if the appetite fails or if food is withheld for a moderate period. Glycogen stores in liver and muscle also fall much more rapidly than in intact fasting animals. They are much more sensitive than normal to the hypoglycemic action of insulin. Fasting ketonemia is more severe in hypophysectomized rats than in intact animals and becomes more marked with the lapse of time after the operation. Nitrogen is lost from the body at an excessive rate immediately after hypophysectomy but is eventually reduced. There are indications that the incorporation of labeled amino acids into tissue proteins is diminished in the hypophysectomized rat. Hypophysectomy of the dog and certain other species causes a significant alteration in the pattern of proteins in the blood serum. The proliferation of red corpuscles is reduced in the hypophysectomized rat.

Since hypophysectomized animals are extremely sensitive to cold, infections, dietary deficiencies, and other stresses, they tend to live short lives unless given the very best attention. Chickens become very prone to hypoglycemia after removal of the pituitary. Nocturnal fasts and sudden temperature changes are often fatal.

6. In fishes, amphibians, and reptiles, ablation of the hypophysis causes a blanching of certain pigment cells in the skin and prevents the usual color adaptations in these vertebrates. The immersion of yellow goldfish (*Carassius auratus* L.) in a 0.7 per cent solution of sodium chloride causes the appearance of pigment cells and the formation of melanin granules within them. This treatment does not elicit these changes after the pituitary has been removed.[19]

The hypothalamus and pituitary constitute a structural and functional unit, the components being bound together by nerves, neurosecretions, and blood vessels (Fig. 2–2). Because of this intimate and diffuse relationship it is impossible to ablate the entire neural division surgically without injury to a vast number of contiguous structures. However, the physiology of the neurohypophysis has been clarified to some extent by using precision instruments that make it possible to place small lesions accurately in different regions of the hypothalamus. Removal of the neural lobe only, other components of the neurohypophysis remaining *in situ*, does not have such far-reaching physiologic consequences as total hypophysectomy or removal of the anterior lobe alone.

Hormones of the Adenohypophysis

Seven hormones have been obtained from the adenohypophysis. These are: somatotrophin (STH, or growth hormone), corticotrophin (ACTH), thyrotrophin (TSH), prolactin (lactogenic hormone or luteotrophin), follicle-stimulating hormone (FSH), luteinizing hormone (LH, or interstitial cell-stimulating hormone), and melanophore-stimulating hormone (MSH, intermedin). All these hormones are proteins or peptides, and three of them (FSH, LH, and TSH) contain carbohydrate in addition to amino acids.

At one time or another, investigators have postulated the existence of diabetogenic, pancreatrophic, glycostatic, glycotrophic, and ketogenic hormones in anterior lobe extracts. None of these factors has been convincingly established, and nearly all workers feel that all of these metabolic effects can be accounted for through the actions of the six hormones already known to be produced by the pars distalis.

Somatotrophin (STH)

Growth hormones, isolated from different species of vertebrates, exhibit different physicochemical properties. While they are all proteins, their molecular weights range from 21,500 to 48,000; bovine hormone being the largest and primate hormones (monkey and man) being about half that size (Table 4–1). The growth hormones with lower molecular weights are more acidic than those with higher weights. Pig, whale, and primate hormones have a single N terminal (end with a free NH_2-residue) and a single C terminal (end with a free COOH-residue) and hence are presumed to be straight chains of amino acids. In these species, phenylalanine is present at both termini. Bovine and ovine hormones have two N-terminal residues and one C-terminal residue; this suggests that the molecules have a branched configuration. Somatotrophins from all species have phenylalanine at the C terminal, and at least one N terminal has this amino acid. Human STH is composed of about 200 amino acid residues, whereas beef STH contains 400 or more residues, but not all of these residues are essential for biological activity of the molecules.[71, 77, 120]

Somatotrophins from various species have been fragmented by subjecting them to limited digestion with various proteolytic enzymes. With chymotrypsin up to 25% of bovine, ovine, whale, and pig hormones can be digested without impairment of biological activity; up to 20% of monkey hormone and up to 10% of human hormone can be digested with full activity of the hormone retained. As with other protein and peptide hormones, the natural molecules contain peptide sequences which may be deleted without affecting biological potency. For this reason, protein chemists feel that rela-

Table 4–1. Physicochemical Characteristics of STH from Different Species*

Properties	Beef	Sheep	Pig	Whale	Monkey	Man
Molecular weight	45,000	48,000	41,000	40,000	25,000	21,500
Isoelectric point, pH	6.8	6.8	6.3	6.2	5.55	4.9
Number of -S-S- bridges	4	5	3	3	4	2
N-terminal sequence	Phe.Thr.Ala.. Ala.Phe.Ala..	Phe... Ala...	Phe...	Phe...	Phe...	Phe.Pro.Thr..
C-terminal sequence	..Ala.Phe.Phe	..Ala.Leu.Phe	..Ala.Phe.Phe	..Leu.Ala.Phe	..Ala.Gly.Phe	..Gly.Leu.Phe

*From C. H. Li and W-K Liu, 1964.

tively small "activity sequences," possessing all of the biological potency, may be identified in the large molecules and synthesized with relative ease. There is the possibility that antigenicity of the molecule may not coincide with the biologically effective "core," thus making it feasible to obtain small, effective compounds from the pituitaries of slaughterhouse animals which can be used clinically.

Table 4–2 indicates that human beings and monkeys respond to primate growth hormones, but not to those from any other vertebrates. The guinea pig responds to no somatotrophin except its own. Fishes respond to bovine STH, but fish STH is ineffective in the rat and other mammalian species upon which it has been tested. It is noteworthy that the rat responds to somatotrophins from numerous mammalian species. It is well known, however, that young, hypophysectomized rats become resistant to repeated injections of primate STH and show no body-weight gains after ten or twelve days. Continuous body-weight increases are evoked in such rats by the administration of bovine, ovine, porcine, and whale preparations. Bovine STH is highly antigenic in the guinea pig: when this hormone is given to recipients, previously sensitized to the same preparation, 90 to 100 per cent of the animals die from anaphylactic shock.[60, 61]

Although growth is deficient in young birds deprived of their pituitary glands, a separate and distinct somatotrophin has not been demonstrated in avian species. Mammalian somatotrophins do not restore growth in hypophysectomized chickens, though sheep prolactin is effective in this respect.

The tibia test is most commonly employed for the bioassay of STH. After administration of the hormone, the increased width of the proximal epiphysial cartilage of the tibia of the hypophysectomized female rat or mouse is determined. STH produces continuous growth and widens the cartilages in proportion to the amount given (Fig. 4–12). The tibia test is sensitive enough to detect STH in the blood of calves and young pigs, and in cases of human gigantism and acromegaly, but not in normal human plasma. Other assays may be based on the increment of body weight and increased nitrogen retention. Low levels of blood sugar stimulate the adenohypophysis to release STH, and measurement of this hormone in plasma, after induced hypoglycemia, has been used as a specific test for pituitary somatotrophic function in man.[101]

BIOLOGIC ACTIONS. For many years it was erroneously assumed that STH had only an effect on general body growth, particularly the skeleton, and, when extracts rich in STH produced other actions, they were attributed to contaminating factors. It is known now that STH plays an important role in the metabolism of proteins, fats, and carbohydrates, and also serves as a synergist to enhance the effects of other hormones. Human STH exerts a number of actions compa-

Table 4–2.   Body-growth Responses to STH from Different Species*

Experimental animal	Beef STH	Sheep STH	Pig STH	Monkey STH	Human STH	Fish STH
Human	—	—	?	+	+	
Monkey	—		—	+	+	
Sheep	+					
Ox	+					
Rat	+	+	+	+	+	—
Guinea pig	—		—	—	—	
Dog	+		+	+	+	
Fish	+					+

— represents no response; +, a definite response; blanks, not tested.

*From C. H. Li and W-K Liu, 1964.

rable to those generally attributed to prolactin, and this suggests that the hormones may not be far apart chemically.[49]

Hypophysectomy of the young animal results in attenuation of linear growth, due in large measure to impaired development of the skeleton (Fig. 4–13). This results primarily from the loss of STH, which has a stimulatory effect on the formation of cartilage and bone. Changes resembling human acromegaly have been produced in various laboratory animals through the long-continued administration of STH. In the rat, for example, this increase in skeletal dimensions is accompanied by enlargement of visceral organs, hypertrophy of the musculature, the skin, connective tissues, and lymphoid organs. The nervous system seems to be exceptional inasmuch as it continues to grow in very young hypophysectomized animals, and its growth is not accelerated by the administration of exogenous STH. Some slight gain in weight may be observed in young animals following hypophysectomy, but this is due to the accumulation of fat rather than to the laying down of tissue protein. The carcasses of hypophysectomized animals, when compared with intact controls, are found deficient in protein and to contain proportionately too much fat. These parameters are reversed by the administration of STH.

Somatotrophin is a protein anabolic hormone which affects the growth of many tissues, not only the skeletal system. It appears to retard the catabolism of amino acids and to encourage their incorporation into body proteins. The hormone induces a positive nitrogen balance and, in fasting animals, the levels of amino acids in the blood are diminished. A retardation in the rate of urea production is indicated by reduced concentrations in the blood and urine. The protein anabolic effect of STH is facilitated by normal amounts of pancreatic, adrenocortical, and thyroidal hormones acting in conjunction with it to stimulate the metabolism of fats and carbohydrates.[109] While there is insufficient evidence to establish definitely the mechanism of action of STH, one important aspect of its action is to promote the transfer of extracellular amino acids across cell membranes, particularly into muscle cells.[60]

The bulk of amino acids not utilized by the organism is normally converted to urea, which is eliminated through the urine. STH, administered to the nephrectomized rat, retards the conversion of infused amino acids to urea. It thus appears that STH encourages the organism to retain amino acids, which are indispensable for the building of proteins. The increased body weight observed after hormone treatment is consequent upon an actual increase in tissue protein, water, and salts — not to an increased deposition of fat.

In view of its metabolic effects, STH has utility throughout the life span, and studies have shown that the quantity of STH in the pituitary does not vary appreciably in the adult. It has been suggested that STH acts in a conservative capacity and enables the organism to retain its tissue supply of nitrogen, particularly when the exogenous supplies of protein and carbohydrate drop to low levels. If this is the case, STH may assist in effecting those metabolic adjustments that must be made when the lack of food becomes a threat to the economy of the organism.[105]

Hypophysectomy retards the mobilization of depot fat and tends to ameliorate the ketosis in diabetic subjects. STH encourages the movement of unesterified fatty acids from fat reserves, consequently decreasing carcass fat and increasing the lipid content of the blood plasma and liver.[114] Certain adrenocortical steroids facilitate these effects of STH on lipid metabolism.

The discovery that the diabetic symptoms appearing in the dog after removal of the pancreas could be ameliorated by also removing the pituitary demonstrated convincingly that the hypophysis performs an important role in carbohydrate metabolism. The metabolism of carbohydrate is controlled by a well-regulated interplay of various hormones and other agents; in view of the many species differences and the complexity of the problem, no exhaustive treatment of the subject is attempted here. Several general statements may be made regarding the action of STH when administered to mammals: (1) the hormone tends to produce hyperglycemia, thus aggravating the diabetic state ("diabetogenic" effect); (2) it inhibits the action of insulin ("anti-insulin" effect); (3) it increases muscle glycogen when given to hypophysectomized subjects ("glycostatic" effect); and (4) the hormone produces permanent diabetes mellitus in certain species when given over prolonged periods. The latter effect probably results from the eventual destruction of the β-cells of the pancreatic islets, which secrete insulin. The excessive blood sugar levels, evoked by STH, apparently overwork the β-cells, causing hypersecretion, hyperplasia, and eventually, functional exhaustion and atrophy. It has been shown that rats receiving excessive carbohydrate by tube feeding develop temporary diabetes when given STH.

Some interesting studies have been made on the regulation of glycogen storage in the heart. Cardiac muscle, unlike skeletal muscles, must work continuously, and it is known to maintain rather high levels of glycogen as an emergency substrate. When the heart works under anaerobic conditions, its glycogen is mobilized rapidly. Studies have shown that heart muscle incorporates C^{14}-glucose into cardiac glycogen to a greater extent than ordinary skeletal muscles. It is also interesting that the glycogen content of the heart is increased during fasting, whereas the glycogen stores in other muscles tend to be depleted under these conditions. Hypophysectomy of the rat prevents the rapid increase in cardiac glycogen during fasting, but the administration of STH restores this capacity. When STH is given to normal subjects at the beginning of the fasting period, extremely high concentrations of glycogen accumulate in heart muscle. It has been suggested that the main role of STH in carbohydrate metabolism may be to promote the conservation of carbohydrate stores.[104]

STH AS A BIOLOGIC SYNERGIST. Four of the anterior lobe hormones (ACTH, TSH, FSH, and LH) are often referred to as "trophic" hormones because their principal actions are exerted upon specific target glands. Whereas STH alone has little effect on such target glands as the adrenal cortex, thyroid, and gonads, it markedly enhances the effectiveness of the trophic hormone specific for that organ when administered together with it. In the hypophysectomized mammal, the adrenal cortices become atrophic and incapable of secreting effective amounts of most of their steroid hormones. The cortices may be repaired by administering ACTH for a limited period after hypophysectomy, but the action of the latter hormone is enhanced by giving STH together with it.[67, 75]

In all vertebrates that have been studied a full growth response requires both thyroid hormone and STH. The two hormones are complementary, although they differ in their specific manner of operation: thyroid hormone encourages maturation but has little effect on growth; STH promotes growth without any effect on maturation.

The administration of STH to the hypophysectomized animal results in a modest improvement in the histologic appearance of several endocrine glands and of other tissues as well. The sex accessory organs of the hypophysectomized-castrated male rat are no exception. Furthermore, when the male sex hormone is given concurrently with STH, the two hormones function synergistically, and the male accessories are repaired rapidly and completely. Thus, STH enables the hypophysectomized animal to respond more effectively to other exogenous hormones.

There are reasons for believing that STH plays a supporting role in many biologic phenomena by producing in the tissues the type of environment that is necessary for certain hormones and other agents to express their functional potencies fully. Normal rats treated for long periods with STH often develop neoplastic growths, particularly in the lungs, adrenal medulla, and reproductive organs. Such neoplasms are seldom found in hypophysectomized animals similarly treated. Furthermore, removal of the hypophysis has been reported to suppress the response of the rat to carcinogenic agents such as 9,10-dimethyl-1,2-dibenzanthracene. Injecting purified STH in the hypophysectomized animals reinstates their usual capacity to respond to carcinogenic agents. While STH itself is not the cause of the tumors, it may create the type of biologic environment in which the carcinogen can manifest its actions speedily and completely.[80]

Prolactin (Lactogenic Hormone)[100]

The pituitary hormone that stimulates the crop glands of pigeons and doves is the same as that which elicits lactation in mammals. This hormone has gone by many names including lactogenic hormone, mammotrophin, galactin, lactogen, and luteotrophin. The term "luteotrophin" was applied to this hormone after discovering that it is essential for activation of the corpora lutea in the rat. Since this ovarian effect has been demonstrated only in a few mammalian species, some workers feel that "luteotrophin" is not an appropriate name for the hormone. The endocrine and nervous factors responsible for the regression of mammalian corpora lutea (luteolysis) are complex and remain largely unknown.[102]

Both sheep and ox prolactins have molecular weights of about 25,000, and their isoelectric points are 5.73. The two hormones have the same N- and C-terminal sequences, but there are differences in solubility and in amino acid composition. The crop sac test in pigeons is the most common method of assay. This specific and convenient method of assay facilitated progress in chemical purification of the hormone, and it was the first pituitary hormone to be isolated as a pure or nearly pure protein. Sheep prolactin retains its crop-sac stimulating activity after chymotryptic digestion to an extent of 50 per cent.

The human placenta contains a hormonal substance having high lactogenic activity; it contains no growth hormone activity, but is immunochemically related to human STH. It was suggested that this substance might function in combination with human chorionic gonadotrophin to maintain corpus luteum secretion in the human ovary.[57]

BIOLOGIC ACTIONS. There is some doubt regarding the presence of prolactin in the pituitary glands of fishes:[6, 96] extracts of teleost pituitaries, tested by the pigeon crop assay method, have yielded conflicting results.[82] The hormone is presumably present in amphibians since extracts of their pituitaries produce the typical responses in the pigeon crop.

It is well known that in certain geographic areas the spotted newt (*Diemyctylus viridescens*) metamorphoses and lives a terrestrial life for three or four years, then returns to water where it becomes sexually mature. Prolactin has been identified as the pituitary principle responsible for this migration to water. Hypophysectomized newts migrated to water from 4 to 10 days after being treated with mammalian prolactin, but they failed to acquire adult pigmentation and associated characteristics presumably dependent upon other pituitary hormones. Extracts and implants of fish pituitaries elicit the water drive response in hypophysectomized newts, and this suggests that the fish pituitary contains prolactin or a related substance.[40]

In birds, prolactin seems to be involved in stimulation of the feather papillae to produce a new plumage. It acts synergistically with estrogen to produce brood patches in birds. These defeathered areas appear on the ventral surface of the body during incubation in one or both sexes in species of many orders. After hypophysectomy, estrogen alone produces vascularization of these presumptive areas, but prolactin is required to produce edema and the loss of feathers. Prolactin has no effect unless the area has first been vascularized by estrogen.[5]

In pigeons and doves both parents participate in incubating the eggs and in feeding the young. "Crop milk" is a mass of desquamated cells from the epithelium of the crop sacs; this is regurgitated and given to the young. Under the influence of prolactin these crop changes begin to occur during the second half of incubation and continue during the subsequent period of brooding and feeding the squabs. There is some evidence that the pituitary increases its output of prolactin as a result of the stimulation provided by the experience of incubation. It is thought that prolactin elicits the regurgitation-feeding behavior by causing engorgement of the crop and suppression of sexual activities.[64]

There is substantial evidence that prolactin has antigonadal effects in both male and female birds. Whether these are direct effects on the gonads or are produced by suppressing the pituitary release of gonadotrophins is not known. Cooing in doves is suppressed by castration, and the administration of prolactin has the same effect. In avian species in which the male assists in feeding the young, the seminiferous tubules of the testes undergo fatty degeneration after the eggs are laid. This testicular collapse seems to correlate with the augmented secretion of prolactin by the pituitary. Similar testicular changes may be produced by hypophysectomy or by the administration of prolactin to intact animals.[73]

Prolactin functions in the rat and mouse to promote the secretion of progesterone by the corpora lutea—the so-called "luteotrophic" effect. When mammals are hypophysectomized during lactation, the production of milk ceases rapidly and completely, indicating that the pituitary hormones are essential for this process. After the mammary glands have been prepared anatomically, through the actions of ovarian hormones (estrogen and progesterone), the pituitary releases a hormone at the end of parturition to evoke milk secretion. This galactopoietic hormone of pituitary origin was formerly thought to be prolactin, but there are increasing indications that it may be growth hormone (STH). There is a high degree of functional overlap between these two protein hormones, and until there is more clarification of their chemical structures in different species, the problems are not likely to be resolved.

RELATIONSHIP BETWEEN STH AND PROLACTIN. Highly purified preparations of human STH have been prepared, and it has been found that these possess intrinsic prolactin-like activities. Human STH promotes growth and secretion of the pigeon crop, induces local milk production when injected into the milk ducts, and stimulates the corpora lutea of the rat's ovary to secrete progesterone. Immunological studies have shown that antisera, prepared to human STH, eliminate both growth and prolactin-like activities. The somatotrophins of nonhuman species appear to possess little, if any, prolactin-like activity, though there are structural differences among them. In sheep and ox, prolactin and STH are believed to be distinctly different molecules; in man, it is not possible at present to decide whether the two activities reside in the same or different molecules. Partial separation of growth and prolactin-like activities has been reported in studies on fractionated preparations of the human pituitary.[120]

It appears that these two hormones have undergone some very subtle evolutionary changes. Protein chemistry is a very difficult area, but there is hope that further physicochemical studies on prolactin and growth preparations from human pituitaries will indicate whether the molecules of man are identical or merely similar. It is unfortunate that practically nothing is known about the chemistry of these hormones in non-mammalian species. It would be interesting and instructive, from a biological point of view, to know the nature of these substances in the pituitaries of birds, reptiles, amphibians, and fishes.

Follicle-stimulating Hormone (FSH)[21]

FSH has not been isolated in pure form and knowledge of its structure is rudimentary. It is a water-soluble glycoprotein, and molecular weights ranging from 30,000 to 67,000 have been reported. Incubation with amylase or takadiastase, enzymes attacking carbohydrates, inactivates the molecule. Activity is lost following treatment with neuraminidase, an enzyme which splits off sialic acid residues. This indicates that the sialic acid moiety is required for activity. Progress has been made, since 1958, in purifying human and equine FSH preparations.[72]

Since FSH activity is influenced by LH, it is essential to employ hypophysectomized animals in the bioassay of FSH. Two criteria may be utilized in bioassay procedures: (1) increased ovarian weight and stimulation of young ovarian follicles in hypophysectomized rats and (2) increased testicular weight, without stimulation of accessory sex organs, in hypophysectomized rats.

The main action of FSH in the female is to stimulate young ovarian follicles to develop multiple layers of granulosa and to form antra. When FSH acts alone in hypophysectomized females, LH being absent, these follicles do not reach full size nor do they secrete estrogen. Under these conditions, the vagina, uteri, and oviducts remain infantile. FSH, acting alone in hypophysectomized male rats, stimulates the seminiferous tubules but does not activate the Leydig cells. The male accessories, therefore, remain atrophic. It is probable that FSH preparations have only gametogenic effects, if they are uncontaminated with LH.

The same gonadotrophins are present in the pituitary glands of both sexes, but the hypothalamus is sexually dimorphic and this results in different patterns of pituitary release. The amount of prolactin in the pituitary glands of female rats not only varies with reproductive states, but has been shown to follow a circadian rhythm.[20]

That the gonadotrophins can act independently of other endocrine tissues is shown by the fact that the ovary of the mouse, maintained in an *in vitro* system, responds to such hormones as it ordinarily does under *in vivo* conditions.[74]

Gonad-stimulating hormones are known to be present in the pituitaries of fishes and other lower vertebrates, but they appear to be quite different from those of mammals. A purified factor from carp pituitaries was found to facilitate spermiation in the frog, to promote the uptake of P^{32} by the testes of the eel, and to enlarge the testes of amphibian larvae. This factor was inactive in all mammalian tests.[16]

Luteinizing Hormone (LH or ICSH) [21]

LH has been isolated in pure form, and like FSH, it is a carbo-hydrate-containing protein.[113] The molecular weight of sheep LH (Squire and Li) is 28,000 to 30,000, and the isoelectric point is 7.3. The human hormone has a molecular weight of about 26,000 and an isoelectric point of 5.4. Ovine hormone contains high contents of cystine and proline, but no tryptophan. Immunological tests indicate that marked species differences occur. Some chemical similarity has been noted between LH and another pituitary glyco-protein, the thyroid-stimulating hormone. Unlike the FSH molecule, LH is *not* inactivated by the removal of sialic acid through treatment with neuraminidase: this provides a method for selectively elim-inating one gonadotrophin in the presence of the other.

BIOASSAY.   Ascorbic acid depletion from the luteinized ovary of the rat provides a highly sensitive and specific bioassay for LH. The method consists of administering the test solution intravenously to rats which had been made pseudopregnant by treatment with pregnant mare serum followed by human chorionic gonadotrophin. The decrease in ovarian content of ascorbic acid is proportional to the amount of LH contained in the material being tested. Follicle-stimulating hormone has no effect on the content of ascorbic acid in the luteinized ovary.[37, 90, 107] A second assay method is based on the capacity of LH to increase hyperemia in the immature rat ovary. A method has been introduced for estimating the degree of hyperemia through the use of I^{131}-labeled serum albumin.[30] This method is simple and rapid, but appears not to be valid if the material being tested contains an excess of FSH. Since LH acts upon the interstitial cells of the testis to induce androgen secretion, increased weights of male accessory sex organs (ventral prostate, etc.) of im-mature or hypophysectomized animals may be employed for assay purposes.

The weaver finch feather test is an interesting biologic reaction occasionally used for detecting the presence of LH activity. The weaver finch is a small bird, native to South Africa, but it has been imported into many countries and sold by bird dealers. With the onset of the breeding season the male acquires a bright yellow and black plumage; at the close of the breeding season two or three months later the animal molts and dons the hen-type plumage, like that worn by the female throughout the year. The hen plumage contains white feathers on the breast and lacks the black ones completely. Castrated males continue to don the nuptial plumage rhythmically, showing that the plumage change is not controlled by testicular hormones. The administration of anterior pituitary extracts to females or non-breeding males, castrate or intact, is followed by the appearance of dark feathers. The melanization of the feathers seems not to be a *direct* effect of LH.[97]

In testing an unknown preparation for LH, one plucks the breast feathers and waits until the white tips of the regenerating feathers become visible. The test material is then injected. If the material is positive for LH a black band appears across the newly formed feathers; otherwise the pigmented band is absent.

BIOLOGIC ACTIONS. The administration of purified LH to hypophysectomized rats repairs the involuted interstitial cells of the ovary; the uterus and vagina are not stimulated, and this indicates that the ovaries are failing to secrete estrogen. LH acts synergistically with FSH to promote the secretion of estrogen by follicles undergoing maturation and to cause ovulation. It is also concerned with the formation of corpora lutea and, in the rat and mouse, works together with prolactin to stimulate the production of progesterone and estrogen by the corpora lutea.

Luteinizing hormone functions in the male to activate the interstitial cells of the testis (Leydig cells), with the consequent production of testicular androgen. Therefore, the extratesticular effects of LH are the same as those that result from the administration of male sex hormone.

The testes of adult hypophysectomized animals cease producing spermatozoa and the cells of Leydig do not secrete enough androgen to maintain the accessory sex organs. In certain mammals, the administration of androgen immediately after hypophysectomy prevents the loss of the spermatogenic function of the seminiferous tubules and may even reinstate spermatogenesis in atrophic tubules. From studies on the effects of impure FSH and LH preparations on the testes of hypophysectomized rats, the concept has developed that LH stimulates the cells of Leydig to produce testosterone, which in turn acts upon the accessory reproductive organs, whereas FSH promotes spermatogenesis by acting directly upon the seminiferous tubules. The action of LH on the Leydig cells has been confirmed, using an essentially pure preparation of the hormone, but there is doubt whether or not FSH is required to stimulate the seminiferous tubules. Sheep LH (β-ICSH) administered to hypophysectomized mice can reinvoke spermatogenic activity in the testes in the absence of FSH, even though the degeneration of the germ cells has progressed to the point where spermatozoa, spermatids, and secondary spermatocytes are no longer in evidence. When injections of LH were begun two weeks after hypophysectomy, degeneration and desquamation of the primary spermatocytes ceased, and, in about half of the injected animals, spermatozoa appeared in the epididymides. It thus appears that LH directly stimulates the Leydig cells to secrete androgen, and the latter hormone affects the seminiferous tubules. Whether FSH exerts an effect upon spermatogenesis at a stage earlier than the primary spermatocyte is unknown.[29, 98]

Gonadotrophins of Pituitary Origin in the Blood and Urine of Human Subjects

Gonadotrophins having FSH and LH effects can be detected in the urine of normal and castrate men and women and in menopausal women. It is supposed that these are excretion products of the gonadotrophins arising in the pituitary gland. Augmented amounts of these agents appear in the blood and urine of both sexes following castration and after menopause. These urinary gonadotrophins, like those present in pituitary extracts, are proteins and have a high content of carbohydrate. An old problem is whether or not FSH and LH activities reside in single or separate molecules, and it remains unsettled to this day.[1]

Human chorionic gonadotrophin (HCG) and pregnant mare serum gonadotrophin (PMSG) are not of pituitary origin and are discussed in Chapter 15.

Thyrotrophin (Thyroid-stimulating Hormone, TSH)

Though highly purified extracts containing TSH have been prepared, the hormone has not been isolated in pure form. It is a glycoprotein and contains sulfur. Estimates of molecular weight have ranged from 10,000 to 30,000. Bovine TSH is effective in all vertebrates from fishes to primates, but species differences probably exist.

After ablation of the pituitary, the thyroid becomes atrophic and its secretory capacity is reduced to a minimum. The gland diminishes in size and appears less vascular than normal. Histologically, the secretory epithelium is flattened, and colloid is retained in the acini. The uptake of I^{131} is reduced to very low levels. The thyroid of the hypophysectomized animal may be returned to normal by giving fresh pituitary implants, or through the injection of purified preparations of TSH. Since TSH acts mainly on the thyroid, its administration is followed by the various metabolic changes that the thyroid hormones produce.

The most common methods of assay may be listed as follows: (a) procedures based on increased height of the secretory epithelium of the thyroid, (b) determination of the number of colloid droplets in the cells of the guinea pig thyroid after treatment with the test material, (c) iodine depletion in the thyroids of 1-day-old chicks, and (d) the uptake of radioactive iodine by the thyroids of hypophysectomized rats.

Corticotrophin (ACTH)

Highly purified ACTH has been isolated from beef, sheep, pig, and human pituitaries. In all four species, the hormone is a straight-chain polypeptide composed of 39 amino acid residues, with serine at the N terminus and phenylalanine at the C terminus. These natural hormones have molecular weights of about 4,500. Though there are species differences in the structure of these hormones, it appears that they are equivalent in their abilities to stimulate the adrenal cortex. Furthermore, the species variations are confined to the amino acids that occupy positions 25 through 33, and these are not essential for biological activity (Fig. 4–14). That portion of the molecule extending from position 25 to the C terminus can be removed without impairing adrenal-stimulating activity. The active portion of the molecule (positions 1 through 24) is identical in all corticotrophins investigated.

Complete synthesis of the natural hormone has been accomplished, and much information has been obtained through the synthesis of fragments of the natural molecule.[25] Peptides containing the first 24, 23, and 20 units of the peptide chain have been synthesized, and they appear to possess full activity. Synthetic peptide, consisting of the first 19 units, has an activity of about 80 per cent of the natural product. The synthetic fragment, consisting of the first 16 units, has very little ACTH potency. These studies indicate that the active core of the 39-amino acid chain consists of the first 20 or so NH_2-terminal residues.[50–52, 68–70]

BIOASSAY. The most common bioassay methods for ACTH are: (1) Measuring the loss of ascorbic acid from the adrenal cortex of the hypophysectomized rat after intravenous injection of the test substance. This appears to be a highly specific and sensitive test. The release of ascorbic acid from the cortex is not known to be accomplished by any agent other than this hormone. (2) Determining the reappearance of lipid in the atrophic cortices of the hypophysectomized rat after administering preparations that contain ACTH. (3) Determining the amount of ACTH-containing material that is necessary to maintain normal adrenal weights in rats when injected immediately after hypophysectomy. There are other techniques based upon the capacity of the adrenal cortical tissue, either *in vivo* or *in vitro*, to synthesize steroid hormones.

BIOLOGIC ACTIONS. The adrenal cortex is the main target upon which ACTH acts, although a number of extra-adrenal functions have been described (Fig. 4–15). The hormone enlarges the adrenal cortices of normal animals and repairs the atrophic cortices of hypophysectomized subjects. It promotes the output of adrenocortical steroids, as is shown by the elevated titers of these hormones in adrenal venous blood after ACTH treatment. The metabolic changes

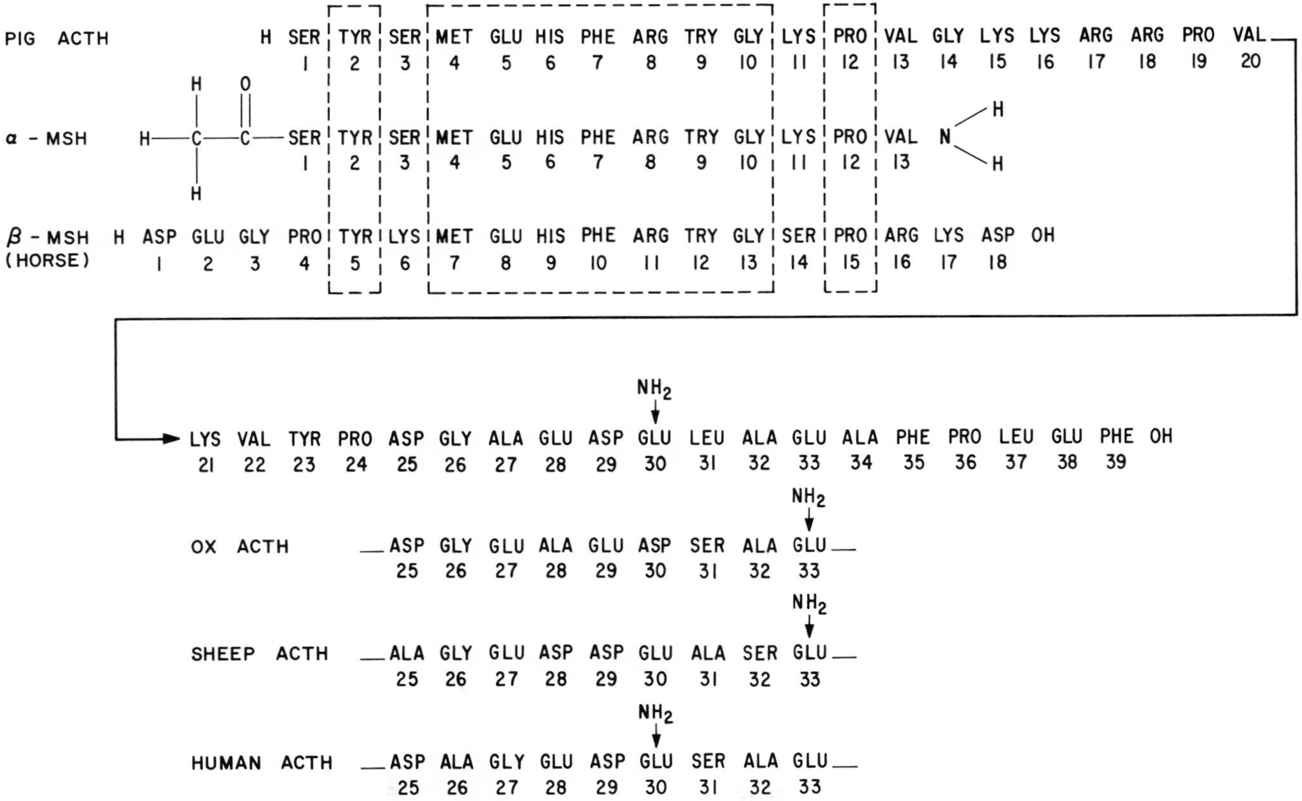

Figure 4–14. *Above,* Comparison of amino-acid sequences in alpha and beta MSH's with those of pig ACTH. *Below,* Species differences in corticotrophins occurring in positions 25 through 33.

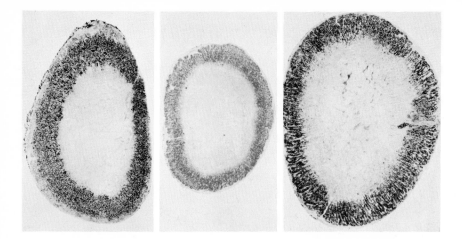

Figure 4–15. Effect of hypophysectomy and administration of ACTH on the adrenal cortex of the mouse. Frozen sections stained with Sudan black B stain. *A,* Adrenal of normal mouse showing moderate amounts of lipid in the zona glomerulosa and abundant lipid in the zona fasciculata. *B,* Section showing marked shrinkage of the cortex 20 days after hypophysectomy. *C,* Adrenal of hypophysectomized mouse injected with α-corticotrophin for 7 days; the glomerulosa and fasciculata contain considerable lipid and the cortical cells are large. (From Lostroh and Woodward: Endocrinology, 62, 1958.)

resulting from ACTH are largely equivalent to those produced by specific steroids of the adrenal cortex.

It is now known that ACTH effects certain adjustments which are not mediated by its main target, the adrenal cortex. For example, when ACTH peptides are incubated with small pieces of epididymal fat tissue from rats, there is an increase in the concentration of non-esterified fatty acids in the adipose tissue and in the medium. It is probable that ACTH produces this effect by activating a lipolytic enzyme in the tissue. Under these conditions, any possible mediation of the adrenal cortex is ruled out.[119] ACTH stimulates melanin synthesis in the xanthic goldfish through an extra-adrenal action. When pieces of caudal fin are grown in tissue culture by the roller tube method, the addition of ACTH stimulates melanogenesis in the dermal melanophores. Cortical steroids and, more surprisingly, intermedin from various sources do not elicit this effect.[54]

Another extra-adrenal action of ACTH is to induce dispersion of pigment granules within the melanophores, thus darkening the skin. This action simulates that of the intermediate-lobe peptides which are especially potent in this respect. Before the corticotrophins had been chemically elucidated, this effect on melanophores was thought to indicate that the preparations were contaminated with MSH peptides: it is known now that melanin dispersion is an inherent property of ACTH peptides. Melanophore activity seems to reside in the heptapeptide sequence – Met.Glu.His.Phe.Arg.Try.Gly. –, and it should be noted that this sequence occurs in both ACTH and MSH peptides (Figs. 4–14 and 4–16). Natural ACTH peptides have comparatively weak actions on melanophores, but this activity can be increased by deleting residues from the C terminal of the ACTH molecule. The natural MSH peptides have very little ability to stimulate the adrenal cortex, though activity of this kind may be induced by effecting small changes in molecular structure.

Melanophore-stimulating Hormones (MSH, Intermedin)

It has been known for many years that the intermediate lobe of the pituitary gland is the source of hormones which act upon several kinds of chromatophores. The term "intermedin" was coined to designate the principle which affects the erythrophores of teleost fishes. While the term "melanophore-stimulating hormone" is misleading inasmuch as it implies that these agents employ only melanophores as their targets, it is currently used in referring to this family of chemically characterized peptides.

Two general types of MSH molecules are found in pituitary extracts, α-MSH and β-MSH. Figure 4–16 shows the structure of several MSH's, together with part of the structure of ACTH for comparison. Alpha-MSH has been obtained from the pituitaries of cattle, sheep, hogs, monkeys, and human beings; no species variations are known to occur. The amino acid sequence of α-MSH is identical with the 13 amino acids from the N terminus of ACTH; the only difference is that in α-MSH the α-amino group of the NH_2 terminal serine is acetylated, and the C-terminal residue is an amide. Beta-MSH peptides from beef, pig, sheep, horse, and monkey are straight chains composed of 18 amino-acid residues. Unlike α-MSH, species variations occur. Human β-MSH contains 22 residues; the addition of the tetrapeptide sequence Ala.Glu.Lys.Lys at the N terminus makes it the largest MSH (Fig. 4–16). Electrophoretic studies on *single* (not pooled) pituitaries from ungulates indicate that they contain two forms of β-MSH, in addition to α-MSH.[13, 14]

The synthesis of α-MSH, β-MSH, and related compounds has been accomplished by several groups of workers. The "core" sequence that is necessary for melanin dispersion in pigment cells seems to be the heptapeptide, Met.Glu.His.Phe.Arg.Try.Gly. This fragment of MSH and ACTH molecules has been synthesized and both *in vitro* and *in vivo* tests indicate that it possesses MSH potency. The smallest synthetic fragment having significant potency was found to be the pentapeptide, His.Phe.Arg.Try.Gly. While the same heptapeptide sequences are present in both ACTH and MSH peptides, and ACTH contains the whole amino-acid sequence of α-MSH, ACTH is only about 1/200 as active in melanin dispersal as α-MSH.

ACTH H | SER TYR SER | MET GLU HIS PHE ARG TRY GLY LYS | PRO VAL | GLY LYS — PHE OH
            1   2   3   4   5   6   7   8   9 10 11   12 13   14 15   39

α–MSH CH₃ CO | SER TYR SER | MET GLU HIS PHE ARG TRY GLY LYS | PRO VAL | NH₂
                  1   2   3   4   5   6   7   8   9 10 11   12 13

OX β–MSH H ASP SER GLY PRO | TYR LYS | MET GLU HIS PHE ARG TRY GLY | SER PRO | PRO LYS ASP OH
             1   2   3   4   5   6   7   8   9 10 11 12 13   14 15   16 17 18

PIG β–MSH H ASP GLU GLY PRO | TYR LYS | MET GLU HIS PHE ARG TRY GLY | SER PRO | PRO LYS ASP OH
              1   2   3   4   5   6   7   8   9 10 11 12 13   14 15   16 17 18

HORSE β–MSH H ASP GLU GLY PRO | TYR LYS | MET GLU HIS PHE ARG TRY GLY | SER PRO | ARG LYS ASP OH
                1   2   3   4   5   6   7   8   9 10 11 12 13   14 15   16 17 18

MONKEY β–MSH H ASP GLU GLY PRO | TYR ARG | MET GLU HIS PHE ARG TRY GLY | SER PRO | PRO LYS ASP OH
                 1   2   3   4   5   6   7   8   9 10 11 12 13   14 15   16 17 18

HUMAN β–MSH H ALA GLU LYS LYS ASP GLU GLY PRO | TYR ARG | MET GLU HIS PHE ARG TRY GLY | SER PRO | PRO LYS ASP OH
                1   2   3   4   5   6   7   8   9 10   11 12 13 14 15 16 17   18 19   20 21 22

Figure 4–16. The structure of several MSH peptides for comparison with the first 15 N-terminal residues of ACTH.

Indications are that the presence of a long peptide chain, beyond the heptapeptide core, reduces the MSH-activity of ACTH.[26, 39, 65]

The MSH peptides are generally assayed on the basis of pigment changes induced in the integumentary chromatophores of amphibians (e.g., *Rana*) or reptiles (e.g., *Anolis*).

Fat-mobilizing Peptides in Pituitary Extracts

Several of the anterior lobe hormones act to mobilize depot fat, and a number of lipolytic peptides can be isolated from pituitary extracts. Since these agents do not correspond in chemical composition or biological activity to any of the conventional pituitary hormones, their significance in glandular extracts remains to be determined.[3, 10, 103]

HYPOTHALAMIC CONTROL OF ADENOHYPOPHYSIAL FUNCTIONS

Scientists and laymen alike have speculated for many years about the effects of the mind on the body and vice versa. There is no longer any doubt that "mind" or central nervous system, in response to exteroceptive and interoceptive stimuli, can bring about physiologic adjustments of many types. Emotional upsets, for example, prevailing for long periods without resolution, actually lead to physical sickness. At the human level, at least, much depends upon how the individual evaluates the stressful or threatening situation. There are at least two conceivable mechanisms whereby the brain and spinal cord could modulate bodily functions: the effects might be purely nervous, impulses being relayed over chains of neurons directly to somatic and visceral targets; or the adjustments might be neuroendocrine in nature, the nervous system activating glands of internal secretion which, in turn, affect various somatic and visceral targets. From many kinds of observations and experiments, it can now be stated with confidence that the nervous system does regulate and control certain endocrine glands, and that hormones in the blood act back upon the nervous system to condition the psychologic and behavioral characteristics of the organism.[46, 58, 62, 81]

Environmental changes, often perceived through the organs of special sense, induce functional changes which are obviously mediated by the trophic hormones of the adenohypophysis. The sexual rhythms of many vertebrates are conditioned by environmental changes such as photoperiods, temperature, food supply, nesting materials, and social contacts. It is common knowledge that ovulation in certain mammals (*e.g.*, rabbit, cat) is normally triggered by coitus, or a comparable form of sexual excitement. Since reproductive functions are directly dependent upon gonadal hormones, and the functional capacity of the gonads is determined by gonadotrophic hormones of the pituitary, it is obvious that environmental effects on reproduction are mediated via the pituitary.

In man and other vertebrates, an outpouring of adrenocortical steroids occurs in response to such emotional and sensory stimuli as intense light, sudden temperature changes, sound, restraint, handling, strange environments, and, in general, any situation resulting in anxiety, frustration, anger, or pain. The functional status of the adrenal cortex is regulated by adrenocorticotrophin (ACTH), and it is apparent that these environmental stimuli have affected the adenohypophysis. In agreement with these findings are clinical observations indicating that Graves' disease is often preceded by emotional shock, and that the menstrual cycles can be altered by environmental changes and mental upsets. Since changes in the menstrual cycle involve both ovarian and pituitary hormones, the sequence of events may be: emotional upset→central nervous system→adenohypophysis→ovary→uterus→clinical symptoms.

Observations such as these made it clear that environmental effects on the endocrine glands had to be mediated by the central nervous system, yet histologic studies of such endocrine glands as the adenohypophysis and adrenal cortices failed to reveal nerve terminals in close association with the secretory cells. The hypothalamus, in view of its close anatomic relationship with the pituitary gland, and its numerous afferent connections with other parts of the brain, seemed to be a likely center for the integration of impulses which promote or suppress the release of adenohypophysial hormones. Since direct neural connections between the hypothalamus and adenohypophysis were found to be practically nonexistent, alternative pathways which might link the two structures were sought. Attention turned to the hypophysial portal veins, after it was established that the direction of blood flow is from the median eminence to the adenohypophysis, and the concept developed that the link is vascular rather than neural (Fig. 2–2). If adenohypophysial contact were accomplished via vascular connections, the next problem would be the source and identity of the blood-borne agents that transmit the information.

The Neurovascular Hypothesis

This working hypothesis was put forward in the 1940's to explain how a gland could be subject to nervous control without itself being supplied with secretomotor nerve terminals.[41] It is known that nerve fibers from the hypothalamus end in close association with capillaries of the primary plexus in the median eminence. These are presumably neurosecretory cells whose products (release factors) enter the capillaries and are delivered to the adenohypophysis via the hypophysial portal veins. The release factors (RF) are thought to stimulate or retard the production of adenohypophysial hormones in accordance with the type of nervous stimulation that is channeled into the hypothalamus. A family of peptides, having molecular weights of about 1000, is found in extracts of the median eminence; since these differentially affect adenohypophysial secretion, they are thought to function as RF's. Though these median eminence factors are thought to be separate and distinct from the octapeptide hormones of the neurohypophysis (*viz.*, vasopressin and oxytocin), the question has not been conclusively settled. The hypothalamic influence in mammals is stimulatory with respect to FSH, LH, ACTH, TSH, and STH, but appears to be inhibitory with respect to prolactin.[33, 44, 108]

The belief that the release factors are neurosecretions is strengthened by electron microscopic observations on the median eminence. Many axons in this region terminate along perivascular spaces that surround the capillaries. The terminals contain synaptic vesicles and opaque globules of neurosecretory material. The capillary endothelium is fenestrated, as is typically the case in areas where secretion and absorption are occurring.[47] If chemical methods were available for identifying the release factors in blood from the portal veins, it would be instructive to determine whether their quantitative variations correlate with fluctuations in the output of particular adenohypophysial hormones.

Experimental Observations

Various procedures have been employed to ascertain the extent and nature of the hypothalamic control of pituitary functions. Among these may be mentioned the placement of lesions in different areas of the hypothalamus, electrical stimulation of such areas, implantation of hormone pellets into the hypothalamus, section of the pituitary stalk, transplantation of the adenohypophysis to ectopic sites, testing extracts of the median eminence, *in vitro* techniques involving both pituitary and hypothalamic tissues, and surgical ablation of the hypothalamus in early amphibian embryos.

Ovulation in the rabbit depends upon copulation and normally occurs 10 hours thereafter. It is the consequence of a neuroendocrine reflex arc which results in the release of pituitary luteinizing hormone (LH). Electrical stimulation of certain areas of the hypothalamus was found to induce ovulation, in the absence of coitus, whereas direct stimulation of the adenohypophysis did not do so.

Section of the pituitary stalk, including the portal vessels, generally produces only transient effects on pituitary functions because the blood vessels quickly revascularize the gland. If regeneration of the portal vessels is prevented by placing a sheet of metal foil between the pituitary and the hypothalamus, the release of pituitary hormones is seriously impaired.

When the pituitary gland of a cyclic female rat is removed from its normal position in the sella turcica, and is autotransplanted below the kidney capsule, physiologic changes in the host reveal that the ectopic graft performs abnormally. Estrous cycles cease, functional corpora lutea persist in the ovaries for abnormally long periods, and the adrenal cortices and thyroid involute much as they do following hypophysectomy. The bulk of the pituitary graft consists of chromophobes and degranulated acidophils; all of the secretory cells are reduced in volume, and the gonadotrophs and thyrotrophs are less prevalent than in the normal gland. If the same graft is removed from the kidney and retransplanted to its normal position below the median eminence, it becomes vascularized by median eminence capillaries, undergoes cellular repair, and again produces its hormones normally. These experiments suggest that pituitaries, transplanted to ectopic sites, liberate reduced amounts of ACTH, TSH, FSH, and LH, but produce prolactin for abnormally long periods. It follows that the hypothalamic factor controlling prolactin secretion is inhibitory, whereas the others exert positive influences. Ectopic pituitary grafts in the male rat function more completely than similar grafts in females.[34, 85, 112]

The pituitary glands of rats may be maintained *in vitro,* and these are found to secrete much like the pituitary grafts that are removed from hypothalamic influences. The production of prolactin by the excised pituitary is inhibited by pieces of hypothalamic tissue cultured with it; the addition of small amounts of estrogen or thyroxine to the medium causes an accentuated release of pro-lactin.[78, 83, 84, 115]

There are numerous species differences in the extent to which adenohypophysial functions are dependent upon anatomic connections with the hypothalamus. In chickens, autotransplanted anterior lobes, persisting in the kidneys, fail to support testicular functions; however, they do have some capacity to maintain the adrenals, thus enabling the host to survive environmental stresses that would otherwise be fatal. While the kidney grafts do not produce gonadotrophins, they apparently can secrete some TSH and ACTH. The avian adrenal is somewhat more independent of pituitary support than that in mammals, and some workers believe that there may be an extrahypophysial source of ACTH. There is no evidence in birds that ectopic pituitary grafts liberate excessive prolactin.[76]

In amphibians such as *Hyla regilla,* a pars intermedia fails to differentiate unless the adenohypophysial anlage comes in contact with the infundibulum; the pars distalis, on the other hand, does develop. These animals lack MSH hormones and remain albino.

Even though the pars distalis is spatially separated from the floor of the brain, it produces enough thyroid-stimulating hormone to enable metamorphosis to occur.[28]

It is possible to surgically remove the posterior hypothalamic primordium (hypothalectomy) in the open neurula stages of *Rana pipiens*. Such animals fail to develop a neurohypophysis and pars intermedia, but the pars distalis develops without any anatomical connections with the brain. The hypothalectomized animals remain light, due to the absence of melanophore-stimulating hormones; they grow at about the same rate as unoperated controls and undergo delayed metamorphosis (Fig. 5–8). It is apparent that the isolated pars distalis secretes "growth" hormone rather normally and enough TSH to maintain thyroid secretion at levels sufficient for metamorphosis to be accomplished eventually. TSH production is probably subnormal since the thyroid glands show histologic indications of inactivity (Fig. 7–13).[18, 43, 45]

The experiments of Etkin and Lehrer on tadpoles of *Rana pipiens* gave different results. Tailbud embryos were hypophysectomized, and the adenohypophyses were autotransplanted to the tails. The animals carrying the ectopic grafts remained dark (hypermelanotic), and grew faster than the normal controls. The pars intermedia of the grafts was greatly hypertrophied, and the darkening of the skin indicated that this region was hyperactive in its output of MSH peptides. These workers suggested that, by analogy with the results obtained on rats, the ectopic grafts of the tadpoles might be releasing excessive prolactin and that this hormone might serve as a "growth" hormone in these anurans. Since these ectopic grafts seem to liberate excessive MSH's and "growth" hormone, it would be assumed that the hypothalamus normally exerts an inhibitory influence on the release of these particular secretions.[31, 32, 56, 118]

Pituitary glands of the fish *Poecilia* function abnormally after being separated from the hypothalamus. The ectopic pituitary grafts secrete TSH and prolactin in considerable amounts, moderate ACTH, very reduced amounts of STH, and no gonadotrophin.[7]

The studies on different species of vertebrates lead to the conclusion that the hypothalamus is an important terminus which receives information channeled in from the external environment and other parts of the brain, and which translates this neural information into chemical messengers (neurohormones). These messengers, or release factors, are conveyed over the hypophysial portal system to the adenohypophysis where they accelerate or suppress the output of particular hormones. This is the essence of the neurovascular hypothesis, and it could turn out to be one of the most important conceptual formulations ever advanced in the field of endocrinology. Final proof of this working hypothesis rests upon the ability of future investigators to determine the chemical identity of the hypothalamic releasing factors.

REFERENCES

1. Albert, A. (ed.): Human Pituitary Gonadotropins. Springfield, Ill., Charles C Thomas, 1961.
2. Asling, C. W., Walker, D. G., Simpson, M. E., Li, C. H., and Evans, H. M.: Death in rats submitted to hypophysectomy at an extremely early age and the survival effected by growth hormone. Anat. Rec., *114*:49, 1952.
3. Astwood, E. B., Barrett, R. J., and Friesen, H.: Two metabolically active peptides from pituitary extract. Science, *133*:1364, 1961.
4. Atz, E. H.: Experimental differentiation of basophil cell types in the transitional lobe of the pituitary of a teleost fish, *Astyanax mexicanus*. Bull. Bingham Oceanogr. Coll., *14*:94, 1953.
5. Bailey, R. E.: The incubation patch of passerine birds. Condor *54*:121, 1952.
6. Ball, J. N.: A regenerated pituitary remnant in a hypophysectomized killifish (*Fundulus heteroclitus*): Further evidence for the cellular source of the teleostean prolactin-like hormone. Gen. & Comp. Endocrinol., 5:181, 1965.
7. Ball, J. N., Olivereau, M., Slicher, A. M., and Kallman, K. D.: Functional capacity of ectopic pituitary transplants in the teleost *Poecilia formosa,* with a comparative discussion of the transplanted pituitary. Phil. Trans. Roy. Soc. London, B., *249*:69, 1965.
8. Belsare, D. K.: Vascular supply of the pituitary gland in *Channa punctatus* Bloch. Nature, *206*(4980):211, 1965.
9. Benoit, J., and DaLage, C. (eds.): Cytologie de l'adénohypophyse. Colloq. Intern. Centre Natl. Rech. Sci. (Paris), No. 128, 1963.
10. Birk, Y., and Li, C. H.: Isolation and properties of a new, biologically active peptide from sheep pituitary glands. J. Biol. Chem., *239*:1048, 1964.
11. Boyd, J. D.: Observations on the human pharyngeal hypophysis. J. Endocrinol., *14*:66, 1956.
12. Breneman, W. R.: Reproduction in birds: the female. Memoirs Soc. Endocrinol., No. 4, 94, 1955.
13. Burgers, A. C. J.: Occurrence of three electrophoretic components with melanocyte-stimulating activity in extracts of single pituitary glands from ungulates. Endocrinol., *68*:698, 1961.
14. Burgers, A. C. J.: Melanophore-stimulating hormones in vertebrates. Ann. N. Y. Acad. Sci., *100*:669, 1963.
15. Burt, A. S., Landing, B. H., and Sommers, S. C.: Amphophil tumors of the hypophysis induced in mice by I[131]. Cancer Res., *14*:497, 1954.
16. Burzawa-Gerard, E., and Fontaine, Y. A.: Activités biologiques d'un facteur hypophysaire gonadotrope purifié de poisson téléostéen. Gen. & Comp. Endocrinol., 5:87, 1965.
17. Cardell, R. R., Jr.: Observations on the cell types of the salamander pituitary gland: an electron microscopic study. J. Ultrastructure Res., *10*:317,(515), 1964.
18. Chang, C. Y.: Hypothalectomy in *Rana pipiens* neurulae. Anat. Rec., *128*:531, 1957.
19. Chavin, W.: Pituitary-adrenal control of melanization in xanthic goldfish, *Carassius auratus* L. J. Exp. Zool., *133*:1, 1956.
20. Clark, R. H., and Baker, B. L.: Circadian periodicity in the concentration of prolactin in the rat hypophysis. Science, *143*:375, 1964.
21. Cole, H. H. (ed.): Gonadotropins: Their Chemical and Biological Properties and Secretory Control. San Francisco, W. H. Freeman & Co., 1964.
22. Coombs, C. J. F., and Marshall, A. J.: The effects of hypophysectomy on the internal testis rhythm in birds and mammals. J. Endocrinol., *13*:107, 1956.
23. Dent, J. N.: Cytological response of the newt pituitary gland to thyroidal depression. Gen. & Comp. Endocrinol., *1*:218, 1961.
24. deRoos, R., and deRoos, C. C.: Demonstration of corticotropin activity in the pituitary gland of chondrichthyean fishes. Amer. Zool., *4*:393, 1964.
25. Dixon, H. B. F.: Chemistry of pituitary hormone. *In* G. Pincus, K. V. Thimann, and E. B. Astwood (eds.): The Hormones, Vol. 5. New York, Academic Press, 1964, p. 1.

26. Dixon, J. S., and Li, C. H.: The isolation and structure of β-melanocyte-stimulating hormone from horse pituitary glands. Gen. & Comp. Endocrinol., *1*:161, 1961.
27. Doerr-Schott, J.: Evolution des cellules gonadotropes β au cours du cycle annuel chez la grenouille rousse *Rana temporaria* L. Étude au microscope électronique; observations histochimiques et cytophysiologiques. Gen. & Comp. Endocrinol., 2:541, 1962.
28. Eakin, R. M., and Bush, F. E.: Development of the amphibian pituitary with special reference to the neural lobe. Anat. Rec., *129*:279, 1957.
29. Eik-Nes, K. B.: Effects of gonadotrophins on secretion of steroids by the testis and ovary. Physiol. Rev., *44*:609, 1964.
30. Ellis, S.: Bioassay of luteinizing hormone. Endocrinol., 68:334, 1961.
31. Etkin, W., and Lehrer, R.: Excess growth in tadpoles after transplantation of the adenohypophysis. Endocrinol., 67:457, 1960.
32. Etkin, W., and Sussman, W.: Hypothalamo-pituitary relations in metamorphosis of *Ambystoma*. Gen. & Comp. Endocrinol., *1*:70, 1961.
33. Everett, J. W.: Central neural control of reproductive functions of the adenohypophysis. Physiol. Rev., *44*:373, 1964.
34. Everett, J. W., and Nikitovitch-Winer, M.: Physiology of the pituitary gland as affected by transplantation or stalk section. *In* A. V. Nalbandov (ed.): Advances in Neuroendocrinology. Urbana, University of Illinois Press, 1963, p. 289.
35. Farquhar, M. G., and Rinehart, J. F.: Cytologic alterations in the anterior pituitary gland following thyroidectomy: an electron microscope study. Endocrinol., 55:857, 1954.
36. Farquhar, M. G., and Rinehart, J. F.: Electron microscopic studies on the anterior pituitary gland of castrate rats. Endocrinol., 54:516, 1954.
37. Foreman, D.: Effects of gonadotrophic hormones on the concentration of ascorbic acid of the rat ovary. Endocrinol., 72:693, 1963.
38. Furth, J., and Burnett, W. T., Jr.: Pituitary adenomas in I[131] thyroidectomized mice. Proc. Soc. Exp. Biol. & Med., 78:222, 1951.
39. Geschwind, I. I.: Species variation in protein and polypeptide hormones. *In* A. Gorbman (ed.): Comparative Endocrinology. New York, John Wiley & Sons, 1959, p. 421.
40. Grant, W. C., Jr., and Grant, J. A.: Water drive studies on hypophysectomized efts of *Diemyctylus viridescens:* the role of the lactogenic hormone. Biol. Bull., *114*:1, 1958.
41. Green, J. D., and Harris, G. W.: The neurovascular link between the neurohypophysis and adenohypophysis. J. Endocrinol., 5:136, 1947.
42. Green, J. D., and Maxwell, D. S.: Comparative anatomy of the hypophysis and observations on the mechanism of neurosecretion. *In* A. Gorbman (ed.): New York, John Wiley & Sons, 1959, p. 368.
43. Guardabassi, A.: The hypophysis of *Xenopus laevis* Daudin larvae after removal of the anterior hypothalamus. Gen. & Comp. Endocrinol., *1*:348, 1961.
44. Guillemin, R., and Schally, A. V.: Recent advances in the chemistry of neuroendocrine mediators originating in the central nervous system. *In* A. V. Nalbandov (ed.): Advances in Neuroendocrinology. Urbana, University of Illinois Press, 1963, p. 314.
45. Hanaoka, Y.: The effect of hypothalectomy at open neurula embryos in *Rana pipiens*. Amer. Zool., 3:509, 1963.
46. Hansel, W.: The hypothalamus and pituitary function in mammals. Internat. J. Fertil., 6:241, 1961.
47. Harris, G. W.: The central nervous system and the endocrine glands. Triangle, 6:242, 1964.
48. Hartley, M. W., McShan, W. H., and Ris, H.: Isolation of cytoplasmic pituitary granules with gonadotropic activity. J. Biophys. & Biochem. Cytology, 7:209, 1960.
49. Hayashida, T.: Further observations on the question of specificity of antihuman growth hormone rabbit serum. Endocrinol., 70:846, 1962.
50. Hofmann, K.: Chemistry and function of polypeptide hormones. Ann. Rev. Biochem., *31*:213, 1962.

51. Hofmann, K., and Yajima, H.: Synthetic pituitary hormones. Rec. Prog. Hormone Research, *18*:41, 1962.
52. Hofmann, K., Yajima, H., Yanaihara, N., Liu, T., and Lande, S.: The synthesis of a tricosapeptide possessing essentially the full biological activity of natural ACTH. J. Amer. Chem. Soc., *83*:487, 1961.
53. Höhn, E. O.: Endocrine glands, thymus and pineal body. *In* A. J. Marshall (ed.): Biology and Comparative Physiology of Birds, Vol. 2. New York, Academic Press, 1961, p. 87.
54. Hu, F., and Chavin, W.: Induction of melanogenesis *in vitro*. Anat. Rec. (Abst.), *125*:600, 1956.
55. Hymer, W. C., McShan, W. H., and Christiansen, R. G.: Electron microscopic studies of anterior pituitary glands from lactating and estrogen-treated rats. Endocrinol., *69*:81, 1961.
56. Jørgensen, C. B., and Larsen, L. O.: Nature of the nervous control of pars intermedia function in amphibians: rate of functional recovery after denervation. Gen. & Comp. Endocrinol., *3*:468, 1963.
57. Josimovich, J. B., and MacLaren, J. A.: Presence in the human placenta and term serum of a highly lactogenic substance immunologically related to pituitary growth hormone. Endocrinol., *71*:209, 1962.
58. Kanematsu, S., and Sawyer, C. H.: Blockade of ovulation in rabbits by hypothalamic implants of norethindrone. Endocrinol., *76*:691, 1965.
59. Kerr, T.: Histology of the distal lobe of *Xenopus laevis* Daudin. Gen. & Comp. Endocrinol., *5*:232, 1965.
60. Knobil, E.: The pituitary growth hormone: some physiological considerations. *In* M. X. Zarrow (ed.): Growth in Living Systems. New York, Basic Books, Inc., 1961, p. 353.
61. Knobil, E., and Sandler, R.: The physiology of the adenohypophyseal hormones. *In* U. S. von Euler and H. Heller (eds.): Comparative Endocrinology, Vol. 1. New York, Academic Press, 1963, p. 447.
62. Kuroshima, A., Ishida, Y., Bowers, C. Y., and Schally, A. V.: Stimulation of release of follicle-stimulating hormone by hypothalamic extracts *in vitro* and *in vivo*. Endocrinol., *76*:614, 1965.
63. Landsmeer, J. M. F.: A survey of the analysis of hypophyseal vascularity. *In* A. V. Nalbandov (ed.): Advances in Neuroendocrinology. Urbana, University of Illinois Press, 1963, p. 29.
64. Lehrman, D. S.: The physiological basis of parental feeding behavior in the ring dove (*Streptopelia risoria*). Behavior, *7*:16, 1955.
65. Lerner, A. B., and McGuire, J. S.: Effect of alpha- and beta-melanocyte stimulating hormones on skin colour of man. Nature, *189*:176, 1961.
66. Lewis, U. J., Cheever, E. V., and VanderLaan, W. P.: Studies on the growth hormone of normal and dwarf mice. Endocrinol., *76*:210, 1965.
67. Li, C. H.: Pituitary growth hormone as a metabolic hormone. Science, *123*:617, 1956.
68. Li, C. H.: Synthesis and biological properties of ACTH peptides. Rec. Prog. Hormone Research, *18*:1, 1962.
69. Li, C. H.: Perspectives in the biochemical endocrinology of adenohypophyseal hormones. Bull. N.Y. Acad. Med., *39*:141, 1963.
70. Li, C. H.: The ACTH molecule. Sci. American, July, 1963.
71. Li, C. H.: Human growth hormone. Experientia, *20*:169, 1964.
72. Li, C. H., Squire, P. G., and Gröschel, U.: Purification and properties of human follicle-stimulating and interstitial cell-stimulating hormones. Arch. Biochem. Biophys., *86*:110, 1960.
73. Lofts, B., and Marshall, A. J.: The effects of prolactin administration on the internal rhythm of reproduction in male birds. J. Endocrinol., *13*:101, 1956.
74. Lostroh, A. J.: The response of ovarian explants from post-natal mice to gonadotrophins. Endocrinol., *65*:124, 1959.
75. Lostroh, A. J., and Woodward, P.: Changes in the adrenal of the hypophysectomized C3H mouse with α-corticotropin and growth hormone. Endocrinol., *62*: 498, 1958.
76. Ma, R. C. S., and Nalbandov, A. V.: *In* A. V. Nalbandov (ed.): Advances in neuroendocrinology, Urbana, University of Illinois Press, 1963, p. 306.

77. Matsuzaki, F., and Raben, M. S.: Growth hormone. Ann. Rev. Pharmacol., 5:137, 1965.
78. Meites, J., Nicoll, C. S.: and Talwalker, P. K.: The central nervous system and the secretion and release of prolactin. *In* A. V. Nalbandov (ed.): Advances in Neuroendocrinology. Urbana, University of Illinois Press, 1963, p. 238.
79. Miller, M. R., and Robbins, M. E.: Cyclic changes in the pituitary gland of the urodele amphibian *Taricha torosa (Triturus torosus)*. Anat. Rec., 122:105, 1955.
80. Moon, H. D., Li, C. H., and Simpson, M. E.: Effect of pituitary hormones on carcinogenesis with 9,10-dimethyl-1,2-dibenzanthracene in hypophysectomized rats. Cancer Res., 16:111, 1956.
81. Nalbandov, A. V. (ed.): Advances in Neuroendocrinology. Urbana, University of Illinois Press, 1963.
82. Nicoll, C. S., and Bern, H. A.: "Prolactin" and the pituitary gland of fishes. Gen. & Comp. Endocrinol., 4:457, 1964:
83. Nicoll, C. S., and Meites, J.: Estrogen stimulation of prolactin production by rat adenohypophysis *in vitro*. Endocrinol., 70:272, 1962.
84. Nicoll, C. S., and Meites, J.: Prolactin secretion *in vitro*: effects of thyroid hormones and insulin. Endocrinol., 72:544, 1963.
85. Nikitovitch-Winer, M., and Everett, J. W.: Functional restitution of pituitary grafts re-transplanted from kidney to median eminence. Endocrinol., 63:916, 1958.
86. Oksche, A., Wilson, W. O. and Farner, D. S.: The hypothalamic neurosecretory system of *Coturnix Cotournix Japonica*. Zeitschr. Zellforsch., 61:688, 1964.
87. Olivereau, M., and Ball, J. N.: Contribution à l'histophysiologie de l'hypophyse des téléostéens, en particulier de celle de *Poecilia* species. Gen. & Comp. Endocrinol., 4:523, 1964.
88. Ortman, R.: A study of some cytochemical reactions and of the hormone content of the adenohypophysis in normal and genetic dwarf mice. J. Morphol., 99: 417, 1956.
89. Ortman, R.: Anterior lobe of pituitary of *Rana pipiens*. A cytological and cytochemical study. Gen. & Comp. Endocrinol., 1:306, 1961.
90. Parlow, A. F.: *In* A. Albert (ed.): Human Pituitary Gonadotropins. Springfield, Ill., Charles C Thomas, 1961, p. 300.
91. Payne, F.: Anterior pituitary-thyroid relationships in the fowl. Anat. Rec., 88: 337, 1944.
92. Payne, F.: Effects of gonad removal on the anterior pituitary of the fowl from 10 days to 6 years. Anat. Rec., 97:507, 1947.
93. Payne, F.: Some observations on the anterior pituitary of the domestic fowl with the aid of the electron microscope. J. Morphol., 117:185, 1965.
94. Phillips, J. B., and Piip, L. K.: A cytochemical study of pituitary glands of 1-to 15-day-old rats utilizing the aldehyde-fuchsin staining technique. Anat. Rec., 129:415, 1957.
95. Pickford, G. E., and Atz, J. W.: The Physiology of the Pituitary Gland of Fishes. New York, New York Zool. Soc., 1957.
96. Pickford, G. E., Robertson, E. E., and Sawyer, W. H.: Hypophysectomy, replacement therapy, and the tolerance of the euryhaline killifish *Fundulus heteroclitus*, to hypotonic media. Gen. & Comp. Endocrinol., 5:160, 1965.
97. Ralph, C. L., Hall, P. F., and Grinwich, D. L.: Failure to demonstrate a direct action of luteinizing hormone (LH or ICSH) on regenerating feathers in African weaver birds. Amer. Zoologist, 5:212, 1965.
98. Randolph, P. W., Lostroh, A. J., Grattarola, R., Squire, P. G., and Li, C. H.: Effect of ovine interstitial cell-stimulating hormone in the hypophysectomized mouse. Endocrinol., 65:433, 1959.
99. Rennels, E. G.: An electron microscope study of pituitary autograft cells in the rat. Endocrinol., 71:713, 1962.
100. Riddle, O.: Prolactin in vertebrate function and organization. J. Nat. Cancer Inst., 31:1039, 1963.
101. Roth, J., Glick, S. M., Yalow, R. S., and Berson, S. A.: Hypoglycemia: a potent stimulus to secretion of growth hormone. Science, 140:987, 1963.
102. Rothchild, I.: The luteolytic effect of luteinizing hormone (LH) in the rat. Acta Endocrinol., 49:107, 1965.

103. Rudman, D., Reid, M. B., Seidman, F., DiGirolamo, M., Wertheim, A. R., and Bern, S.: Purification and properties of a component of the pituitary gland which produces lipemia in the rabbit. Endocrinol., 68:273, 1961.
104. Russell, J. A.: Hormonal control of glycogen in the heart and other tissues in rats. Endocrinol., 58:83, 1956.
105. Russell, J. A.: Effects of growth hormone on protein and carbohydrate metabolism. Amer. J. Clin. Nutr., 5:404, 1957.
106. Rust, C. C.: Hormonal control of pelage cycles in the short tailed weasel (*Mustela erminea bangsi*). Gen. & Comp. Endocrinol., 5:222, 1965.
107. Sakiz, E., and Guillemin, R.: On the method of ovarian ascorbic acid depletion as a test for luteinizing hormone (LH). Endocrinol., 72:804, 1963.
108. Sawyer, W. H.: Neurohypophysial hormones. Pharmacol. Revs., 13:225, 1961.
109. Scow, R. O., Wagner, E. M., and Ronov, E.: Effect of growth hormone and insulin on body weight and nitrogen retention in pancreatectomized rats. Endocrinol., 62:593, 1958.
110. Siperstein, E., Nichols, C. W., Griesbach, W. E., and Chaikoff, I. L.: Cytological changes in the rat anterior pituitary from birth to maturity. Anat. Rec., 118:593, 1954.
111. Siperstein, E. R., and Allison, V. F.: Fine structure of the cells responsible for secretion of adrenocorticotrophin in the adrenalectomized rat. Endocrinol., 76:70, 1965.
112. Smith, P. E.: Postponed pituitary homotransplants into the region of the hypophysial portal circulation in hypophysectomized female rats. Endocrinol., 73:793, 1963.
113. Squire, P. G., and Li, C. H.: Purification and properties of interstitial cell-stimulating hormone from sheep pituitary glands. J. Biol. Chem., 234:520, 1959.
114. Swislocki, N. I., and Szego, C. M.: Acute reduction of plasma nonesterified fatty acid by growth hormone in hypophysectomized and Houssay rats. Endocrinol., 76:665, 1965.
115. Talwalker, P. K., Ratner, A., and Meites, J.: The *in vitro* inhibition of pituitary prolactin synthesis and release by hypothalamic extract. Amer. J. Physiol., 205:213, 1963.
116. Taurog, A., Tong, W., and Chaikoff, I. L.: Thyroid I^{131} metabolism in the absence of the pituitary: the untreated hypophysectomized rat. Endocrinol., 62:646, 1958.
117. Vitums, A., Mikami, S., Oksche, A., and Farner, D. S.: Vascularization of the hypothalamo-hypophysial complex in the white-crowned sparrow. *Zonotrichia leucophrys gambelii*. Zeitschr. Zellforch., 64:541, 1964.
118. Voitkevich, A. A.: On the relation of neurosecretion to growth and cell differentiation in the amphibian adenohypophysis. Gen. & Comp. Endocrinol., 3:554, 1963.
119. White, J. E., and Engel, F. L.: Fat mobilization by purified corticotropin in the mouse. Proc. Soc. Exper. Biol. & Med., 102:272, 1959.
120. Wilhelmi, A. E.: Comparative biochemistry of growth hormone from ox, sheep, pig, horse and fish pituitaries. In R. W. Smith, Jr., O. H. Gaebler, and C. N. H. Long (eds.): The Hypophyseal Growth Hormone. New York, McGraw-Hill, 1955, p. 59.
121. Wilhelmi, A. E.: Fractionation of human pituitary glands. Can. J. Biochem. & Physiol., 39:1659, 1961.
122. Yasuda, M.: Cytological studies of the anterior pituitary in the broody fowl. Proc. Japan Acad., 29:586, 1953.

5

PARS INTERMEDIA: CHROMATOPHORE REGULATION AMONG VERTEBRATES

Many vertebrates, especially the poikilotherms, possess integumentary pigment cells which function as chromatic effectors. These special cells, called chromatophores, enable the organism to change color in response to many environmental stimuli. Color adjustments may serve several functions: (1) to render the animal inconspicuous by imitating the color pattern of the environment; (2) to display colors which "signal" to other individuals a state of sexual readiness; and (3) to protect the body tissues against excessive illumination. Since dark surfaces absorb heat and light surfaces reflect it, integumentary pigments may be important in thermoregulation in certain species of reptiles.

The chromatophores of vertebrates are of ectodermal origin since they differentiate from cells that migrate out of the neural crest and neural plate (melanoblasts)[36] Among amphibians, it has been shown that cells other than melanoblasts can be induced to become pigment cells. The melanoblasts, or precursors of pigment cells, begin synthesizing pigment after they reach their definitive sites in the body and become *melanocytes*. The melanocyte represents the terminal stage in birds and mammals; whereas in fishes and perhaps in amphibians and reptiles, the melanocytes transform into pigment-effector cells called melanophores. The melanomas of platyfish-swordtail hybrids have been interpreted as resulting from populations of pigment cells that have been arrested at the melanocyte stage by a genetic defect.[23]

The chromatophores of vertebrates are usually single cells which contain one type of pigment (monochromatic). These cells possess elaborate dendritic processes and not only synthesize pigments, but effect redistributions of the pigment granules to influence the coloration of the body. Little effect is exerted if the pigment is withdrawn from the cell processes and concentrated into a small mass near the nucleus (punctate); maximal effect is brought about by dispersion of the pigment into the cytoplasmic extensions of the cell (reticulate). It is generally held that the cytoplasmic processes retain a more or less constant form, undergoing little, if any, change in shape as the pigment granules are dispersed or concentrated. It is known, however, that chromatophores may discharge their pigments. Amphibian melanophores, maintained in tissue cultures, appear more prone to undergo changes in form than those functioning *in vivo*.

Melanin is the predominant pigment in vertebrates, and melanophores are responsible for many of the conspicuous color changes. The melanin appears black, but it may be partially oxidized to impart yellow, orange, or light brown colorations. Lipophores, carrying fat-soluble red pigment (erythrophores) or yellow pigment (xanthophores), are often encountered. Guanophores (leukophores, iridosomes) are chromatophores which contain highly reflective granules or plate-like crystals of white guanine.

The chromatophores lie mainly in the epidermis or dermis, but may be present in deeper tissues such as the peritoneal and meningeal membranes and the walls of blood vessels. In certain vertebrates such as the lizard (*Anolis*), the cell bodies of the melanophores are located below a superficial layer of light-colored pigment. This passive layer is responsible for the tint of the body when the melanophores are not actively contributing. When the melanophores are activated by appropriate stimuli, melanin disperses within the cytoplasmic processes of the melanophores and comes to occupy a position external to the light-colored layer, thus obscuring the latter and rendering the animal dark.[28]

It is convenient to distinguish between physiologic and morphologic color changes, though the line between them is not very sharp. Physiologic color change involves the rapid dispersion or concentration of pigments within the chromatophores, without any obvious change in the quantity of pigment. Morphologic color change is accomplished more slowly through the actual synthesis or destruction of pigment within the chromatophores, or by increasing or decreasing the number of chromotophores per unit area of skin. It has been observed by many workers that a prolonged concentration of pigment within a chromatophore correlates with a loss of pigment, and, conversely, prolonged dispersion tends to increase the quantity of pigment. There are many reasons for believing that both types of color change are effected by the same controlling mechanisms.

Functional chromatophores, capable of producing reversible changes in skin color, occur only among cold-blooded vertebrates, namely cyclostomes, elasmobranchs, teleosts, amphibians, and reptiles. A pigmentary effector system is absent in birds and mammals. Chromatophores may be regulated entirely by nerves (neuronic), entirely by hormones (aneuronic), or by both nerves and hormones, Some chromatophores are singly innervated (mononeuronic), whereas others are doubly innervated (dineuronic). Certain chromatophores seem to function as independent effectors, responding directly to external stimuli without the mediation of either nerves or hormones. In some vertebrates it appears that separate hormones function to produce pigment dispersion and pigment concentration; in other instances, only one hormone causing pigment dispersion appears to be involved. Chromatophore regulation is a large area, and many of the early studies need to be repeated, using hormones of known purity. While there are many cursory reports in the literature, intensive studies have been limited to only a few species.[8, 10, 22, 47]

Morphologic color changes, involving relatively slow alterations in the quantity of pigment, are presumably the only ones that occur in birds and mammals. It was formerly supposed that special pigment cells were absent from the human skin, and that the basal cells of the epidermis were capable of both keratinization and pigment synthesis. Melanocytes of neural crest origin are now known to be present in human skin in the plane of the dermoepidermal interface. The melanocytes send branches between the basal epidermal cells and transfer their pigments into them. The melanocytes contain a specific tyrosinase which oxidizes tyrosine to melanin, and are the only cells in the skin capable of synthesizing the pigment. Each square millimeter of the human integument contains about 1500 melanocytes, though there is some regional variation in the number. No significant variation in the number of melanocytes has been found with reference to race or sex. Since the number of melanocytes does not depend upon such external factors as solar irradiation, it follows that variations in the color of the skin depend upon the degree of activity of the pigment cells rather than upon their number.[9, 30, 31]

CHEMICAL REGULATION OF VERTEBRATE CHROMATOPHORES

Rapid color changes among vertebrates are restricted to fishes, amphibians, and reptiles. The chromatophores are effector cells in which the various kinds of pigment granules can be dispersed or

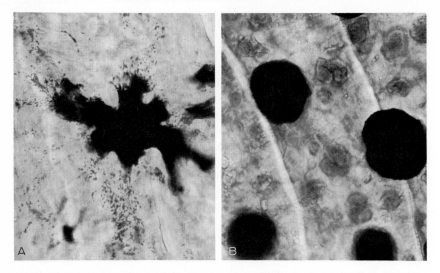

Figure 5–1. The effect of hypophysectomy on the integumentary melanophores of black goldfish. *A,* The beginning of perinuclear migration of melanin granules in a macromelanophore 3 hours after hypophysectomy. Many granules are still present in the cell dendrites. *B,* Complete perinuclear aggregation of melanin granules in macromelanophores, 24 hours after hypophysectomy. The pigment cells eventually degenerate after loss of the pituitary gland. (Courtesy of Walter Chavin, Wayne State University.)

concentrated. Long-term, morphologic color adjustments may involve changes in the number of chromatophores and the amounts of pigments. Flounders, for example, may be induced to form new melanophores on the normally unpigmented ventral surface by being kept in black aquaria illuminated from below, or by being blinded and illuminated from above. Hypophysectomy of black goldfishes results in degeneration of the melanophores and a consequent loss of melanin (Fig. 5–1). Light, temperature, humidity, psychic stimuli, and inherent rhythms may all be important factors in the induction of color responses. There are many species variations, but, among fishes and reptiles, the chromatophores are regulated to a large extent by the nervous system, or by both endocrine glands and the nervous system. Amphibian chromatophores are aneuronic and respond to blood-borne hormones, but neurogenic factors are clearly involved in eliciting the production of endocrine gland products.

Some chromatophores of amphibians may also act as independent effectors. The melanophores of the African clawed frog, *Xenopus,* are aneuronic, and local effects of a narrow beam of light may be demonstrated in isolated tailfins of the tadpoles. The pigment granules in the tailfin melanophores disperse completely if kept in darkness; single melanophores may be induced to concentrate their pigment by being exposed to narrow beams of light. When only a third of the melanophore is exposed to light, pigment concentration occurs in all of its branches; exposure of a smaller fraction of the cell to illumination produces only a local effect. Primary responses of this character have been observed in fishes following complete denervation of the pigment cells, or by locally stimulating the pigment cells of immature animals whose normal, secondary controls are not yet in operation.[12]

Neurohumoral Agents

Chromatic responses in fishes have been more intensively studied than in any other vertebrate group, and it is certain that great diversity prevails. Much of the early information is conflicting, and many of the experiments ought to be repeated, using modern techniques and instrumentation.[39, 41]

In some of the teleosts, it appears that the melanophores are dineuronic, one type of fiber producing melanin concentration and a second type producing melanin dispersion. It is generally agreed that the fish melanophores receive at least one type of axon, the stimulation of which produces melanin concentration. The color responses in fishes typically depend upon the eyes. Impulses from the receptors are passed to the central nervous system, and the efferent limb of the arc may be either neural or neuroendocrine. Efferent fibers may make direct contact with the chromatophores and influence their behavior through the release of chemical mediators, or the fibers may supply endocrine glands and initiate the release of blood-borne hormones which affect the chromatophores.

The melanophores of the killifish *Fundulus* appear to be doubly innervated, neurohumors playing a major role in their regulation. Since hypophysectomized *Fundulus* continue to respond rather normally to background changes, it appears that their chromatic physiology is relatively independent of pituitary hormones. However, the denervated melanophores of this fish disperse their pigment granules in response to treatment with melanophore-stimulating hormones (MSH's). *Fundulus* pituitaries contain MSH, and it is probable that this family of peptides plays some role in color changes, especially under conditions where dark adaptation prevails for long periods.

According to the *neurohumoral* concept of Parker, melanin concentration may result from the release of epinephrine-like agents from the adrenergic terminals, and melanin dispersion may be effected through the release of acetylcholine (or a similar mediator) from cholinergic terminals. Such transmitter agents produce only local effects, since they are destroyed before they can attain effective concentrations in the blood. Acetylcholine is known to cause fish melanophores to disperse their pigments, especially when the subjects are eserinized to prevent rapid destruction of the mediator.

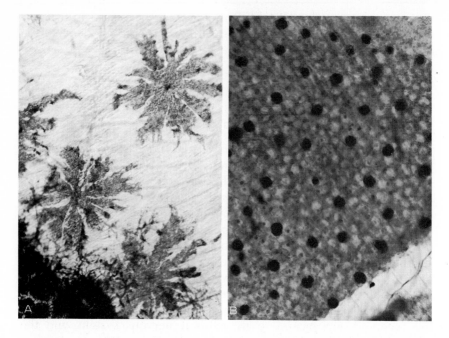

Figure 5–2. The effect of epinephrine on the melanophores of the black goldfish. *A*, Normal melanophores. The large stellate cells are the macromelanocytes. Smaller pigment cells, the micromelanocytes, are visible in the lower part of the figure. Large melanocytes are clustered along the edge of the integumental fold. *B*, Aggregation of pigment in melanophores (both micro- and macro-) and lipophores (small dark gray cells) 10 minutes after immersion of the scale in a dilute solution of epinephrine (1 to 10,000). Both figures are at the same magnification. (Courtesy of Walter Chavin, Wayne State University.)

Epinephrine and other sympathomimetic agents generally cause blanching in fishes by concentrating the melanin granules (Fig. 5–2), but some species are irresponsive or respond in a reverse manner. The guanophores of *Fundulus* respond to epinephrine by dispersing their reflecting-white pigment, showing that the same substance does not affect all chromatophores in the same way. Drug actions, in the absence of other evidence, do not justify the conclusion that each melanophore is supplied by a set of antagonistic nerve terminals. There is no doubt that teleost melanophores are under direct nervous control, but this does not rule out the possibility that blood-borne hormones may exert supplemental actions.

Endocrine Gland Secretions

Pigmentation in poikilothermic vertebrates involves two distinct types of reaction: the rapid dispersion or concentration of pigment granules, and the slower increase or decrease in the number of pigment cells. The coloration of the body reflects the interaction of multiple hormones, the controlling mechanisms varying with the species. Genetic factors are clearly important, as well as hormones from the pituitary gland, adrenals, thyroids, gonads, and pineal organ. The gonadal steroids play an important role in species where sexual differences in pigmentation exist, as well as in the seasonal assumption of nuptial coloration.

Melanophore-stimulating Hormones (MSH's)

These peptide hormones are products of the pars intermedia, and their chemistry was discussed in Chapter 4. Since the isolation and chemical characterization of these hormones, acting to disperse melanin granules within the melanophores of poikilotherms, the designation "MSH" has gained wide acceptance. Photoelectric measurement of the darkening in isolated pieces of frog skin has provided a sensitive method of bioassay. From a comparative standpoint, it should be noted that the only MSH's to be chemically elucidated are from mammalian species; it would be interesting to know what chemical variations exist among the poikilotherms where physiologic color changes commonly occur.[8]

Since physiologic color changes do not occur in birds and mammals, but MSH still persists in their pituitaries, it seems important to determine more accurately how MSH might be involved in morphologic color changes in all classes of vertebrates. Though melanocytes remain in warm-blooded vertebrates, they lose most of their ability to disperse or concentrate melanin granules in response to environmental changes. They retain, however, their capacity to synthesize pigments and to transfer them to epidermal cells; this transfer obviously involves granule movement. When either alpha- or beta-MSH is administered to the human subject, some darkening of the skin occurs rather promptly. This darkening persists for several weeks after cessation of the treatment. It may well be that this action is in part, at least, a physiologic color change involving transfer of melanin as well as a morphologic one involving the synthesis of new pigment (melanogenesis).

Studies have been made to determine the amount of MSH in single pituitaries of *Xenopus* following chromatic adaptation to different backgrounds. Normal *Xenopus* are yellowish (melanophore contraction) after adjustment to white backgrounds, and very dark (melanophore expansion) when kept on black backgrounds. The content of MSH in the pituitaries increases during white background adaptation, indicating that the hormones are stored instead of being released into the blood. MSH is continuously released when animals are maintained on dark backgrounds, but the supply is not exhausted.[11]

The MSH peptides were named on the basis of their effects on melanophores, but it must be recognized that they also affect other kinds of chromatophores. They cause amphibian guanophores to contract, and inhibit the synthesis of guanine and hypoxanthine within these cells. MSH also promotes the deposition of pteridines in the skin of larval amphibians. There are suggestions in the literature that MSH may have effects other than upon integumental pigments, and it is probable that it will be found to have a broader spectrum of activities than is presently supposed.[3, 5]

Corticotrophic Hormones (ACTH)

It is interesting that ACTH, primarily functioning to stimulate adrenocortical tissue, possesses an intrinsic melanophore-stimulating action which cannot be ascribed to impurities. Here again, it must be stressed that mammalian ACTH's have a pigment-dispersing action when tested on amphibian melanophores; consequently, it is not known whether amphibian ACTH normally plays any role in the chromatic adjustments of these poikilotherms. It would be instructive to comparative endocrinologists to know the chemical properties and structures of both MSH and ACTH from the pituitaries of nonmammalian vertebrates.

Since entirely xanthic goldfish do not possess melanocytes or melanophores, and such cells have to differentiate in order for melanin synthesis to occur, induced melanogenesis can be readily detected in these fish. Chavin found that stress elicits melanogenesis in intact goldfish, but fails to do so in hypophysectomized animals, indicating that the hormones involved are derived from the pituitary gland. This response to stress is not impaired by removing only the pars intermedia, but is blocked after removal of the anterior lobe constituents, the pars intermedia remaining *in situ*. The surgical experiments suggest that the hormone promoting melanogenesis in this species arises from the anterior lobe, and not from the pars intermedia. Melanogenesis occurs in hypophysectomized goldfish after ACTH administration, but is not induced by thyrotrophin, gonadotrophin, thyroxine, gonadal steroids, adrenocorticoids, epinephrine, or neurohypophysial peptides. Pieces of skin from xanthic goldfish have been tested *in vitro*, and the indications are that ACTH stimulates melanogenesis in the goldfish, whereas MSH does not.[13, 14, 36, 34, 35]

A different situation was found in *Fundulus heteroclitus* by Kosto and Pickford. Their studies indicate that MSH, rather than ACTH, promotes the differentiation of melanocytes, and that prolactin is required for the synthesis of melanin. In hypophysectomized *Fundulus,* the macromelanophores lose their melanin; prolactin treatment restores their pigment granules, but it does not induce the proliferation of new cells.[29, 41]

Epinephrine and Norepinephrine

In the majority of amphibians, the administration of epinephrine produces a blanching of the skin, due to the rapid concentration of pigment in the melanophores. Certain fishes and reptiles show characteristic color changes as a consequence of rough handling, or excitement. The skin of the horned lizard *Phrynosoma* blanches on strong excitement, a condition known as "excitement pallor." The African frog *Xenopus* is exceptional among amphibians inasmuch as it darkens during excitement; epinephrine administration has the same effect. Hypophysectomized *Xenopus* react to epinephrine by darkening the skin, and this shows that the melanin dispersion does not result from an outpouring of MSH by the pituitary under the influence of epinephrine. The melanophores of *Xenopus* skin, maintained *in vitro*, disperse their pigments when epinephrine is added to the medium. Cultured melanophores of *Ambystoma* and *Tarida*, on the contrary, concentrate their melanin granules when epinephrine is added. This differential response among amphibian species indicates that there are inherent differences at the cellular level.

The Whitening Substance of Hogben[25]

Experiments on fishes and amphibians led some workers to believe that a second hormone ("W substance"), opposing the action of MSH, might be present in the pituitary gland. This hypothetical hormone was thought to arise in the pars distalis or pars tuberalis and to promote melanophore concentration, thus leading to lightening of skin color. This factor is not demonstrable in the pituitaries of many species, and has never been isolated as a pure substance. Steggerda *et al.* attempted to remove the pars tuberalis of *Rana pipiens* by cautery and found that their operated animals were unable to concentrate melanin granules.[45] They concluded that the destruction of this part of the pituitary eliminated the "W substance," thus preventing melanin concentration in response to light backgrounds. Since there may have been injury to other parts of the pituitary and to the hypothalamus, these experiments are not convincing. Knowing that epinephrine, norepinephrine, melatonin, as well as stimulation of adrenergic nerves, have potent melanophore-concentrating effects in certain species, the presence of a body-lightening hormone from the anterior pituitary must be regarded with skepticism until more proof is forthcoming.

The Pineal Gland and Color Change

In their search for the principle that causes melanin concentration in the melanophores of frog skin, Lerner and his colleagues isolated a very potent substance from bovine pineal glands and called it *melatonin*.[32] Norepinephrine was previously thought to be the most active lightening agent, but melatonin was found to be about 100,000 times more potent. The minimal effective dose of melatonin required to produce melanophore contraction in *Xenopus* is 0.0001 μg per ml of water in which the larvae are kept. Relatively high concentrations of serotonin (5-hydroxytryptamine), catechol-amines, and histamine are also present in pineal extracts. Serotonin has a relatively weak action on frog and fish chromatophores and may induce, according to circumstances, a dispersion or a concentration of pigment. Isolated skin of *Rana pipiens*, previously darkened by caffeine or MSH, is a very sensitive preparation for testing body lightening agents. In this test, melatonin is effective in concentrations as low as 10^{-7} μg per ml of liquid; serotonin is 10 million times less active in this test.[17]

Melatonin is highly localized in the pineal glands of mammals, and lesser concentrations are found in peripheral nerves. It has been isolated from the pineal glands of man, monkey, cow, and rat; it has not yet been obtained from the glands of poikilothermic vertebrates. This should not be interpreted as meaning that melatonin is absent from the pineal complex of reptiles, amphibians, and fishes, but rather that not much effort has been made to find it in these forms. Melatonin apparently is formed by the chicken pineal, since the enzyme hydroxyindole-O-methyl transferase, essential for its syn-thesis, is present in this tissue.[2, 50]

The pineal contains all of the substrates and enzymes essential for the synthesis of melatonin, and, so far as known, is the only tissue possessing these. Chemically, melatonin consists of an indole nucleus, an N-acetylated side chain, and a methoxy group (Fig. 5–3). The pineal gland synthesizes melatonin from serotonin in the fol-lowing manner: (1) an N-acetylating enzyme converts serotonin to N-acetylserotonin, (2) the latter compound is O-methylated through the action of hydroxyindole-O-methyl transferase, an enzyme found only in the pineal organ. Melatonin is metabolized largely in the liver, and is excreted through the urine as a conjugate with sulfate or glucuronide.

Over the years there has been no lack of speculation as to what the functions of the pineal might be, but there has been a dearth of documented research. Long before melatonin was discovered, it was known that bovine pineal extracts, injected or fed to frogs, or applied to the skin *in vitro*, would lighten the skin through melanin concentration. With the chemical isolation and pharmacologic eluci-dation of the substance, and the recognition that it is an exclusive product of the pineal, one would think that ablation of the organ would produce measurable disturbances if it has any physiologic

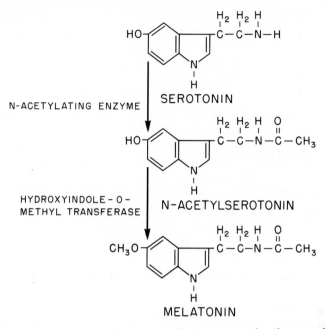

Figure 5-3. The synthesis of melatonin from serotonin by the pineal gland.

utility. Pinealectomy has been reported to produce defects in two instances: (1) Bagnara found that pinealectomized tadpoles of the frog *Xenopus* do not blanch (melanophore contraction) in darkness as intact animals normally do, and (2) Wurtman *et al.* found that pinealectomy of 28-day-old rats causes their ovaries to become abnormally enlarged. Subcutaneous injections of melatonin, like bovine pineal extracts, inhibit ovarian growth in rats. Exposure of rats to prolonged periods of light or darkness alters the estrous cycles, presumably via the pineal gland.[4, 49]

Emphasis is currently being placed upon the pineal as a light receptor, and a widely held concept is that light affects the synthesis of specific compounds in the pineal. These pineal substances are thought to be hormones which enter the blood stream and alter the functional economy of the body. There is perhaps sufficient evidence now to justify considering both the thymus and the pineal as organs of internal secretion.

Serotonin and Excitement Reactions in the Amphibian Skin

Stressful stimuli produce "pallor" of the skin in the great majority of amphibians, but *Xenopus* responds to such stimuli by darkening the skin; these skin reactions are the same as those produced by exogenous catecholamines. The large exocrine glands of the amphibian integument release their secretions in response to irritating stimuli, whereas the smaller mucous glands liberate their contents continuously. Secretion from the large integumental glands of *Xenopus* is known to contain appreciable quantities of serotonin. The injection of secretion from the large glands into a recipient having concentrated melanophores results in darkening of the body (melanophore expansion), and this effect has been shown to result from the serotonin content of the secretion.

While the excitement "darkening" effect in *Xenopus* could be due to the reflexive release of such pigment-dispersing hormones as MSH or the catecholamines, the above facts suggest that the serotonin in the secretion of the large glands might act locally upon the integumental melanophores and thus facilitate the excitement "darkening."[12]

EXPERIMENTAL ANALYSIS OF CHROMATIC SYSTEMS

Space forbids mentioning the numerous species differences encountered among poikilotherms, and the varying interpretations recorded in the voluminous literature; even if space were ample, to do so would be more confusing than helpful. Only a few examples are mentioned in this section, and these have been selected with the idea that they provide clues to a common theme prevailing in the vertebrate groups.

Teleosts

Color changes in fishes appear to involve pituitary hormones as well as nerves and typically depend upon the eyes. The direct innervation of chromatic effectors, coupled with speedy physico-chemical changes within the pigment cells, makes it possible for the organism to respond more promptly to background changes than would be possible if it depended exclusively upon blood-borne hormones.

The mechanisms controlling the melanophores have been more carefully worked out in the killifish *Fundulus,* the catfish *Ameiurus,* the eel *Anguilla,* and the minnow *Phoxinus* than in other teleosts. This discussion will be limited to the melanophores of the eel (*Anguilla*). When these fish rest on a black background, with an overhead light source, the melanophores disperse their pigment and the integument becomes dark; on white backgrounds, illuminated from above, the melanin is concentrated and the integument is pale. An intermediate shade is attained after maintenance in complete darkness. The melanophores are innervated, and electrical stimulation of the fishes evokes melanophore concentration. Background responses are exhibited by completely hypophysectomized *Anguilla*, though these may fluctuate after long periods. Such animals are unable to attain the fully dark condition. In the absence of the pituitary gland, the color changes are undoubtedly effected by the nervous system. Hypophysectomized fish are more sensitive than intact ones to exogenous MSH.

If *Anguilla* rested on a white background and received direct light from above, direct light would fall on the ventral retina and scattered light from the white background on the dorsal retina, resulting in blanching of the skin. In contrast, if the animal were on a black background, most of the stimulation would come from the light source since the black background absorbs so much light and reflects so little. Under these circumstances, the skin would become dark (Fig. 5–4). Four hypothetical pathways, leading from the retina to the chromatophores, are shown diagrammatically in Figure 5–4.

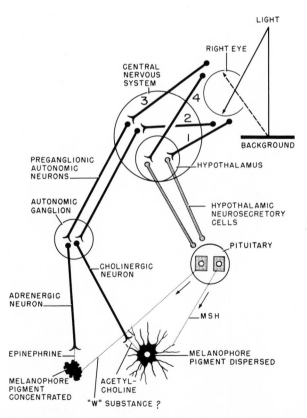

Figure 5–4. Possible mechanisms involved in regulating the melanophores of the eel *Anguilla*, according to the published observations of Waring and Parker. (Redrawn and slightly modified from Scharrer, E., and Scharrer, B.: Neuroendocrinology, New York, Columbia University Press, 1963.)

Arcs 1 and 4 reach the pigment cells via the hypothalamus and pituitary gland and are neuroendocrine in nature; arcs 2 and 3 are purely nervous. Arc 1 extends from the ventral retina to the hypothalamus, and it is probable that neurosecretory cells activate the pars intermedia and cause an outpouring of MSH which induces melanin dispersion. Arc 2 from the ventral retina passes via the central nervous system to autonomic ganglia and cholinergic fibers; the latter terminate on melanophores and release acetylcholine which causes dispersion of the melanin pigment. Arc 3 from the dorsal retina terminates in adrenergic neurons which liberate epinephrine; this neurotransmitter concentrates the melanin and thus blanches the skin. Arc 4 is highly questionable in *Anguilla*: fibers from the dorsal retina extend to the hypothalamus, and neurosecretory cells (?) possibly activate the anterior pituitary (pars tuberalis) and cause the release of a hormone ("W substance") which opposes the action of MSH. Unlike the latter hormone, it causes pigment concentration and results in lightening of the skin.[40, 46]

In the dogfish *Mustelus*, there is evidence for an adrenergic arc and a neuroendocrine arc involving the pars intermedia. Photoreceptors in the skin of the catfish *Ameiurus* send fibers via the central nervous system to the pars intermedia. Activation of this pathway causes a release of MSH and a consequent darkening of the skin. The simplest arrangement is probably found in *Fundulus*, where the melanophores are controlled largely by adrenergic and cholinergic innervations.

Amphibians

P. E. Smith and B. M. Allen, working independently in 1916, showed that removal of the epithelial placode of the adenohypophysis from early tailbud embryos of *Rana pipiens* results in a silvery or "albino" larva.[1, 44] Since then, many species of urodeles and anurans have been subjected to hypophysectomy, and the same results consistently obtained. The light color of the integument is due to the permanent concentration of pigment in the melanophores and a tendency for such cells to diminish in number; the guanophores are expanded and, in some species at least, tend to multiply. Pituitary transplants, persisting in hypophysectomized hosts, reverse these chromatophore defects. The hormones from the pituitary grafts not only disperse the melanophores, but cause their number to increase (melanogenesis). Bagnara found that the administration of purified MSH to hypophysectomized tadpoles of *Rana pipiens* not only stimulated melanogenesis, but reduced the number of guanophores.[7]

Striking defects have been produced in *Hyla regilla* by immersing the young embryos in a 10 per cent solution of sucrose (Figs. 5–5 and 5–6). The neurohypophysis and pars intermedia do not develop

Figure 5–5. A larva of *Hyla regilla* developing from a gastrula which was treated with a 10 per cent solution of sucrose. The albinism is due to a deficiency of the melanophore-stimulating hormone of the pars intermedia; the melanophores are punctate whereas the guanophores are expanded. The left eye is poorly developed and the external nares are fused. (From Eakin, R. M.: Science, *111*, 1950.)

in many of these animals, but the pars distalis differentiates and appears to function. Such animals are devoid of MSH and hence are albinos.[16]

Etkin observed that transplantation of the adenohypophysial anlage in *Rana* leads to an excessive production of MSH, indicated by darkening of the skin, and to excessive growth of the tadpoles.

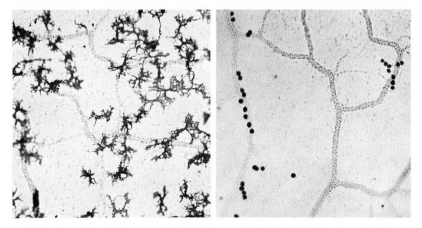

Figure 5–6. Integumentary melanophores of the frog *Hyla regilla. Left,* Normal animal showing expanded melanophores; *right,* a similar mount from a sugar-albino showing hypoplasia and contracted state of the melanophores resulting from developmental failure of the pars intermedia. (From Driscoll and Eakin: J. Exp. Zool., *129*, 1955.)

When early tailbud stages are hypophysectomized, and the adeno-hypophysis autotransplanted to the side of the tail, the tadpoles grow excessively and the skin is maximally black due to the dispersion of melanin and the proliferation of melanophores. The cells of the pars intermedia proliferated more extensively than other components of the grafts, and apparently release abnormally large amounts of MSH. The autografts, released from hypothalamic control, also seem to secrete excessive growth substances. Since the "growth" hormone of amphibians has not been characterized, Etkin and Lehrer speculated that the autografted pituitaries might be secreting excessive prolactin, as such ectopic grafts are known to do in mammals, and that this hormone might have "growth" actions in amphibians. It follows from these experiments that the hypothalamus normally exerts inhibitory influences upon the production of "growth" hormone and of MSH by the adenohypophysis.[18, 19, 20]

Electrical stimulation of the hypothalamus of adult *Rana* evokes melanin dispersion and darkening of the skin. One interpretation is that the electrical stimulation blocks neural elements in the hypothalamus which normally act to inhibit MSH release.[15] It is not known whether the hypothalamic elements that respond to stimulation are ordinary neurons, neurosecretory cells, or both.

A plexus of adrenergic nerve terminals has been demonstrated in the pars intermedia of the frog through the use of a sensitive and specific fluorescence method. A similar adrenergic innervation of the pars intermedia has been reported for the rat and mouse.[16a]

The output of MSH from the intermediate lobe of the frog's pituitary is inhibited by incubating this tissue with saline extracts of frog or rat median eminence, anterior hypothalamus, and cerebrum. Extracts of the median eminence produced more inhibition than the other parts of the brain that were tested. The quantity of MSH in the rat's pars intermedia, however, was found not to be affected by such extracts under similar conditions. The chemical identity of the neural factor which inhibits the release of MSH in amphibians remains obscure.[42a]

Some interesting studies have been made on *Rana pipiens* after surgically removing the primordium of the posterior hypothalamus at the open neurula stage (stage 13–14). Tadpoles resulting from the operated neurulae lack a pars intermedia, infundibulum, median eminence, and pars nervosa (Fig. 5–7). The pars distalis, on the other hand, differentiates independently and lies below the brain without connecting to any part of it. The operated animals grew at about the normal rate, suggesting that the adenohypophysis produced "growth" substance at a normal rate, notwithstanding the lack of normal connections with the hypothalamus. As might be

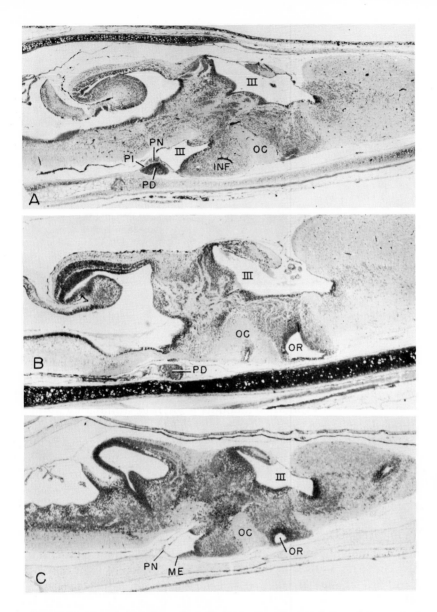

Figure 5-7. Saggital sections through the brains of normal, hypothalectomized, and hypophysectomized tadpoles of *Rana pipiens*. *A*, Brain of a normal tadpole (stage 30; age 19 weeks), showing the pituitary gland in its normal position. *B*, Brain of a hypothalectomized tadpole (stage 30; 1 year old); the pars intermedia is absent and the pars distalis is not connected to any part of the brain. *C*, Brain of a hypophysectomized tadpole (stage 27a; 1 year old). Note that the adenohypophysial constituents are completely absent, but the posterior hypothalamus (infundibulum, median eminence, pars nervosa) develops normally. INF, infundibulum; ME, median eminence; OC, optic chiasma; OR, optic recess; PN, pars nervosa; PI, pars intermedia; PD, pars distalis; III, third ventricle. (Courtesy of Dr. Y. Hanaoka, Gunma University, Maebashi, Japan.)

Figure 5-8. The posterior hypothalamus may be surgically removed at the open neurula stage in *Rana pipiens*. Since the hypothalectomized tadpoles do not develop a pars intermedia, they lack MSH peptides and their integuments remain blanched. Such animals grow, but they remain at stage 30 for more than six months. *Left,* normal tadpole; *right,* hypothalectomized tadpole. (Courtesy of Dr. Y. Hanaoka, Gunma University, Maebashi, Japan.)

expected, the hypothalectomized tadpoles were light in color, since they lacked a pars intermedia as a source of MSH (Fig. 5-8). Observations on the thyroid indicated that the hypothalectomized animals secreted subnormal amounts of thyroid-stimulating hormone (Fig. 7-13).[24]

On the basis of his studies on *Xenopus laevis,* Bagnara believes that the pineal gland is involved in the body lightening reaction which occurs in nearly all amphibian larvae during exposure to darkness. He found that pinealectomy prevents blanching, and that melatonin (a product of the pineal) induces the same kind of pallor as exposure to darkness. His hypothesis is that the absence of light stimulates the pineal to release melatonin, or a related substance, which quickly induces melanophore contraction and a consequent blanching of the skin (Fig. 5-9). It is thought that the absence of light may bring about this change through the action of photoreceptors located in either the stirnorgan or the pineal gland, or possibly located in both these organs. It is believed that the pineal hormone acts directly upon the melanophores of the skin, and not indirectly upon the pars intermedia to inhibit the release of MSH. Melatonin has not been demonstrated in the pineal complex of amphibians, though attempts to identify it or similar substances have not been sufficiently exhaustive to justify the conclusion that such materials are absent.[4, 6]

The melanophores in the tailfin of young *Xenopus* larvae respond differently than those in other parts of the body: the melanin granules concentrate in light and disperse in darkness. Pigment in the body

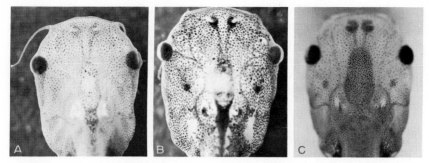

Figure 5-9. The effects of pinealectomy and melatonin administration upon the melanophores of *Xenopus* larvae (stage 54). *A,* Normal larva in darkness for one hour; note melanophore contraction. *B,* A pinealectomized larva in darkness for one hour; the melanophores are not contracted. *C,* A normal larva which received 0.1 μg melatonin; note melanophore contraction. (From Bagnara, J. T.: Gen. & Comp. Endocrinol., 3:86, 1963.)

melanophores disperses under the influence of light. The tail-darkening reaction, occurring in the larvae when they are placed in darkness, appears to be due to a photochemical substance which is rapidly destroyed by light. It can be concluded that light has a direct effect upon the melanophores of the tail. In summary, the state of the melanophores at any particular time depends upon MSH from the pars intermedia, melatonin, or a similar agent from the pineal gland, and the direct effects of light.

Reptiles

Recent investigators have devoted little attention to the chromatophores of reptiles, and most of the information centers around the lizards. The iguanid *Anolis carolinensis* ranges in color from dark brown to light green, a mottled condition appearing when the animals are excited. This mottling results from irregular patches of black pigment which contrast with the green color of the skin. Hypophysectomized *Anolis* are permanently light green, but such animals darken in response to MSH. Electrical stimulation of the whole body, one electrode being placed in the mouth and the other in the cloaca, causes a generalized darkening of the skin in intact *Anolis*. In hypophysectomized subjects, this treatment darkens only the postorbital region and causes mottling of the remainder of the skin. Electrical stimulation of the whole body does not produce mottling when the animals are both hypophysectomized and adrenalectomized. This suggests that generalized darkening depends upon an intact pituitary gland and not upon direct innervation of the melanophores. The denervation of skin areas does not interfere with normal color changes in *Anolis*. Grafted pieces of skin promptly undergo color changes which are synchronous with those of the host.[10, 21, 22, 28]

Mottling of the skin in *Anolis* appears to be due to the action of epinephrine. It occurs as a consequence of excitement and may be duplicated by administering exogenous epinephrine. Elevation of the body temperature or decrease in the partial pressure of oxygen intensifies the chromatic changes in response to epinephrine. Paling of the skin probably results from the gradual loss of MSH from the blood, rather than from the action of catecholamines.[42]

SOME ASPECTS OF THE MECHANISM OF MSH ACTION

Physiologic color changes result from the movement of pigment granules within the arborizations of the pigment cells: dark colors result from the dispersion of granules into the delicate cytoplasmic processes; light colors are a consequence of the aggregation or concentration of the same granules in the vicinity of the nucleus. These movements are reversible and, in some respects, resemble muscular contraction and the movement of chromosomes in dividing cells. Electron microscopic observations on the chromatophores of the guppy (*Lebistes*) indicate that the pigment granules in this fish are enclosed in sacs which are associated with cytoplasmic fibrils; contraction of these fibrils may be an important factor facilitating the concentration of the pigment. Endocrinologists would like to know the physicochemical mechanisms employed by hormones and neurohumoral agents in bringing about pigment dispersal or concentration within the chromatophore.

It has been reported that *dispersed* melanin granules may be easily displaced by a centrifugal force of 70,000 times that of gravity, but, in the *concentrated* state, the granules are not displaced by forces up to 125,000 times that of gravity. One effect of MSH on the frog melanophore may be to change the colloidal state of the cytoplasm from a gel to a sol. This colloidal change of state might be correlated with alterations in permeability of the cell membrane to specific ions. The melanophores of frog skin, maintained *in vitro*, disperse their melanin granules when exposed to hypotonic media or when the hydrogen ion concentration is increased. Hypertonic media tend to prevent pigment movements; MSH is relatively ineffective in dispersing melanin granules under these conditions.[33, 43]

Kinosita inserted microelectrodes into melanophores and found that electrical potentials varied between the center and the periphery of the cells. His interpretation was that intracellular pigment granules might move along electrical gradients, in a manner analogous to the movement of charged chemical substances during electrophoresis.[27]

Novales found that the darkening of *Anolis* skin by MSH is markedly reduced if sodium ions are deficient. Extensive studies have indicated that the same is true of amphibian melanophores. From his *in vitro* observations on *Rana* and *Ambystoma* melanophores, he has proposed that MSH may act upon the pigment cells by rendering their cell membranes permeable to sodium. Melanin dispersion is thought to be triggered by the entry of sodium ions, the degree of dispersion being proportional to the amount of sodium entering the cell. Melanophores of the goldfish are also unresponsive to MSH when maintained in a sodium-free medium. The cultured melanophores of *Ambystoma* do not respond to MSH when maintained in calcium-free media.[37–38a]

Wright has published interesting observations on the source of energy required for the migration of melanin granules within amphibian melanophores. He found that the rate of oxygen consumption by pieces of frog skin is not appreciably increased during either MSH-induced dispersion or epinephrine-induced concentration. This suggested than an anaerobic process might provide the energy for the granule movements. By using chemicals to block glycolysis, the anaerobic source of energy, it was found that the melanin granules remained dispersed. Wright's point of view is that the dispersed state, rather than the concentrated state, represents the *relaxed* phase of the granules. If this is true, MSH could produce melanin dispersion by blocking glycolytic pathways, thus depriving the cells of the energy necessary to move the granules into a punctate condition.[48]

REFERENCES

1. Allen, B. M.: Extirpation of the hypophysis and thyroid glands of *Rana pipiens*. Science, *44*:755, 1916.
2. Axelrod, J., Wurtman, R. J., and Winget, C. M.: Melatonin synthesis in the hen pineal gland and its control by light. Nature, *201*:1134, 1964.
3. Bagnara, J. T.: Hypophyseal control of guanophores in anuran larvae. J. Exp. Zool., *137*:265, 1958.
4. Bagnara, J. T.: Pineal regulation of the body lightening reaction in amphibian larvae. Science, *132*:1481, 1960.
5. Bagnara, J. T.: Chromatotrophic hormone, pteridines, and amphibian pigmentation. Gen. & Comp. Endocrinol., *1*:124, 1961.
6. Bagnara, J. T.: The pineal and the body lightening reaction of larval amphibians. Gen. & Comp. Endocrinol., *3*:86, 1963.
7. Bagnara, J. T.: Stimulation of melanophores and guanophores by melanophore-stimulating hormone peptides. Gen. & Comp. Endocrinol., *4*:290, 1964.
8. Barrington, E. J. W.: Hormones and the control of color. *In* G. Pincus, K. V. Thimann, and E. B. Astwood (eds.): The Hormones, Vol. 4. New York, Academic Press, 1964, p. 299.
9. Billingham, R. E., and Silvers, W. K.: The melanocytes of mammals. Quart. Rev. Biol., *35*:1, 1960.
10. Brown, F. A., Jr.: Chromatophores and color change. *In* C. L. Prosser and F. A. Brown, Jr. (authors): Comparative Animal Physiology. Philadelphia, W. B. Saunders Company, 1961, p. 502.
11. Burgers, A. C. J., Imai, K., and van Oordt, G. J.: The amount of melanophore-stimulating hormone in single pituitary glands of *Xenopus laevis* kept under various conditions. Gen. & Comp. Endocrinol., *3*:53, 1963.
12. Burgers, A. C. J., and van Oordt, G. J.: Regulation of pigment migration in the amphibian melanophore. Gen. & Comp. Endocrinol., Suppl. 1,99, 1962.
13. Chavin, W.: Pituitary-adrenal control of melanization in xanthic goldfish, *Carassius auratus*. L. J. Exp. Zool., *133*:1, 1956.

14. Chavin, W.: Pituitary hormones in melanogenesis. *In* M. Gordon (ed.): Pigment Cell Biology. New York, Academic Press, 1959, p. 63.
15. Dierst, K. E., and Ralph, C. L.: Effect of hypothalamic stimulation on melanophores in the frog. Gen. & Comp. Endocrinol., 2:347, 1962.
16. Eakin, R. M.: Developmental failure of the pituitary in amphibian embryos treated with sugar. Science, 111:281, 1950.
16a. Enemar, A., and Falck, B.: On the presence of adrenergic nerves in the pars intermedia of the frog, *Rana temporaria.* Gen. & Comp. Endocrinol., 5:577, 1965.
17. Erspamer, V.: 5-Hydroxytryptamine. *In* U. S. von Euler and H. Heller (eds.): Comparative Endocrinology, Vol. 2. New York, Academic Press, 1963, p. 159.
18. Etkin, W.: On the control of growth and activity of the pars intermedia of the pituitary by the hypothalamus of the tadpole. J. Exp. Zool., 86:113, 1941.
19. Etkin, W.: Hypothalamic inhibition of pars intermedia activity in the frog. Gen. & Comp. Endocrinol., Suppl. 1, 148, 1962.
20. Etkin, W., and Lehrer, R.: Excess growth in tadpoles after transplantation of the adenohypophysis. Endocrinol., 67:457, 1960.
21. Fingerman, M.: The physiology of chromatophores. Internat. Rev. Cytol., 8:175, 1959.
22. Fingerman, M.: The Control of Chromatophores. New York, The Macmillan Company, 1963.
23. Gordon, M.: The melanoma cell as an incompletely differentiated pigment cell. *In* M. Gordon (ed.): Pigment Cell Biology. New York, Academic Press, 1959, p. 215.
24. Hanaoka, Y.: The effect of hypothalectomy at open neurula embryos in *Rana pipiens.* Amer. Zoologist, 3:509, 1963.
25. Hogben, L. T., and Slome, D.: The dual character of endocrine coordination in amphibian colour change. Proc. Roy. Soc., B, 108:10, 1931.
26. Hu, F., and Chavin, W.: Hormonal stimulation of melanogenesis in tissue culture. J. Invest. Dermatol., 34:377, 1960.
27. Kinosita, H.: Study on the mechanism of pigment migration within fish melanophores with special reference to their electric potentials. Annot. Zool. Japon., 26:115, 1953.
28. Kleinholz, L. H.: The pituitary and adrenal glands in the regulation of the melanophores of *Anolis carolinensis.* J. Exp. Biol., 15:474, 1938.
29. Kosto, B., Pickford, G. E., and Foster, M.: Further studies on the hormonal induction of melanogenesis in the killifish *Fundulus heteroclitus.* Endocrinol., 65:869, 1959.
30. Lerner, A. B.: Hormones and skin color. Sci. American, 205:99, 1961.
31. Lerner, A. B., and Case, J. D.: Pigment cell regulatory factors. J. Invest. Dermatol., 32:211, 1959.
32. Lerner, A. B., Case, J. D., and Heinzelman, R. V.: Structure of melatonin. J. Amer. Chem. Soc., 81:6084, 1959.
33. Lerner, A. B., and Takahashi, Y.: Hormonal control of melanin pigmentation. Recent Prog. Hormone Research, 12:303, 1956.
34. Loud, A. V., and Mishima, Y.: The induction of melanization in goldfish scales with ACTH *in vitro.* J. Cell Biol., 18:181, 1963.
35. Mishima, Y., and Loud, A. V.: The ultrastructure of unmelanized pigment cells in induced melanogenesis. Ann. N. Y. Acad. Sci., 100:607, 1963.
36. Niu, M. C.: Some aspects of the life history of amphibian pigment cells. *In* M. Gordon (ed.): New York, Academic Press, 1959, p. 37.
37. Novales, R. R.: The effects of osmotic pressure and sodium concentration on the response of melanophores to intermedin. Physiol. Zool., 32:15, 1959.
38. Novales, R. R., and Novales, B. J.: Sodium dependence of intermedin action on melanophores in tissue culture. Gen. & Comp. Endocrinol., 1:134, 1961.
38a. Novales, R. R., and Novales, B. J.: The effects of osmotic pressure and calcium deficiency on the response of tissue-cultured melanophores to melanocyte-stimulating hormone. Gen. & Comp. Endocrinol., 5:568, 1965.
39. Parker, G. H.: Animal color changes and their neurohumors. Quart. Rev. Biol., 18:205, 1943.
40. Parker, G. H.: Melanophore activators in the common American eel *Anguilla rostrata* Le Sueur. J. Exp. Zool., 98:211, 1945.

41. Pickford, G. E., and Atz, J. W.: The physiology of the pituitary gland of fishes. New York Zool. Soc., 1957.
42. Rahn, H.: The relationship between hypoxia, temperature, adrenalin release and melanophore expansion in the lizard, *Anolis carolinensis*. Copeia, 1956:214, 1956.
42a. Ralph, C. L., and Sampath, S.: Inhibition of melanin dispersing hormone release from frog pituitaries by brain extracts of frog and rat. Amer. Zoologist, 5, Dec., 1965.
43. Shizume, K., Mori, W., and Lerner, A. B.: On the action of melanocyte stimulating hormone. Gen. & Comp. Endocrinol., Suppl. 1, 110, 1962.
44. Smith, P. E.: Experimental ablation of the hypophysis in the frog embryo. Science, 44:280, 1916.
45. Steggerda, F. R., and Soderwall, A. L.: Relationship of the pars tuberalis to melanophore response in Amphibia (*Rana pipiens*). J. Cell & Comp. Physiol., 13:31, 1939.
46. Waring, H.: The chromatic behaviour of the eel (*Anguilla vulgaris* L.). Proc. Roy. Soc. London, B, 128:343, 1940.
47. Waring, H.: Color Change Mechanisms of Cold-Blooded Vertebrates. New York, Academic Press, 1963.
48. Wright, P. A.: Physiological responses of frog melanophores *in vitro*. Physiol. Zool., 28:204, 1955.
49. Wurtman, R. J., Altschule, M. D., and Holmgren, U.: Effects of pinealectomy and bovine pineal extract in rats. Amer. J. Physiol., 197:108, 1959.
50. Wurtman, R. J., and Axelrod, J.: The formation, metabolism, and physiologic effects of melatonin in mammals. *In* J. A. Kappers and J. P. Schadé (eds.): Progress in Brain Research, Vol. 10. Amsterdam, Elsevier Publishing Co., 1965.

6

NEUROHYPOPHYSIS: NEUROHORMONAL PEPTIDES

The oxytocins and vasopressins are neurosecretory products of the neurohypophysis, and a large body of information is available on their chemical structures, physiologic and pharmacologic actions, and their phyletic distribution among the vertebrates. The extremely rapid progress made in the elucidation of these peptides since 1953 stems largely from the fact that their molecular structures are known and the natural secretions, as well as many analogues not found in nature, may be prepared synthetically. Information is accumulating on relations between chemical structure and biologic effectiveness, and on possible mechanisms whereby they may act at the cellular level.

Five functions have been ascribed to these neurohormones: (1) contraction of the smooth muscle of the uterus (oxytocic effect), (2) contraction of the myoepithelial cells which surround the mammary alveoli (milk ejection), (3) actions upon the kidney to prevent excessive loss of water (antidiuretic effect), (4) contraction of the smooth muscle in the walls of blood vessels (vasopressor effect), and (5) regulation of the release of adenohypophysial hormones, especially in fishes in which the neurohypophysis and adenohypophysis are intimately associated. An examination of these actions reveals that the effectors employed are contractile elements and semipermeable membranes such as the kidney tubules and, in anuran amphibians, the skin and urinary bladder. The action on the kidney promotes the reabsorption of water from the glomerular filtrate, thus resulting in the excretion of a concentrated urine. The effect in amphibians is not only upon the kidney, but also upon the skin to increase its permeability and allow water from the environment to pass into the body. The mammalian vasopressins are often referred to as antidiuretic hormones (ADH) since their main action is to conserve water. Although vasopressin elevates the blood pressure of mammals, and has the reverse effect in birds, there is no satisfactory evidence that it normally plays any role in the regulation of vascular tone or blood pressure. The effect may be pharmacologic, rather than physiologic, since the dose required is seemingly in excess of the amounts normally released by the intact neurohypophysis.

CHEMISTRY AND PHYLETIC DISTRIBUTION

Chemistry

The secretions that are stored in the mammalian pars neuralis are oxytocin and vasopressin. Oxytocin is very potent in causing uterine contractions, in lowering the blood pressure of birds, and in promoting milk ejection. One milligram of pure oxytocin contains about 500 USP units of each activity. Vasopressin produces all of these effects to a much slighter degree. Vasopressin is unquestionably the main pressor and antidiuretic principle. Oxytocin produces the same effects, but only to about 1 per cent and 0.5 per cent, respectively, of the activity possessed by vasopressin.

All of the neural lobe secretions are octapeptides; that is, they consist of eight different amino acids, the two sulfur-linked cysteine molecules generally being counted as one cystine molecule (Fig. 6–1). Three of the amino acids are present in the form of amides. The sulfur linkage forms a pentapeptide ring (five amino acids) to which is attached a side chain composed of three amino acids. All of the neurohypophysial principles whose structures are known show this pattern. Substitutions occur in the natural secretions at positions

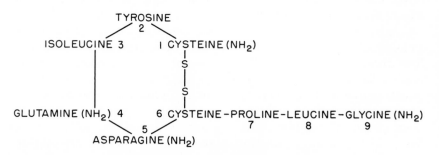

Figure 6–1. The arrangement of amino acids in a molecule of oxytocin.

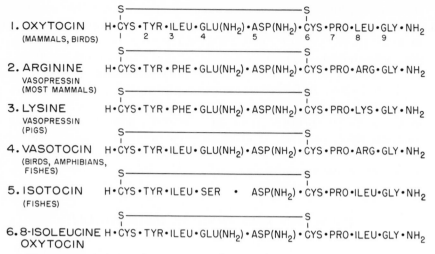

Figure 6–2. Amino acid sequences in the natural neurohormones of the posterior lobe (neurohypophysis).

3, 4, and 8, producing peptides with different biologic potencies. The six naturally occurring principles known at present are arginine vasopressin, lysine vasopressin, arginine vasotocin, oxytocin, isotocin, and 8-isoleucine oxytocin (Fig. 6–2). Two oxytocin-like peptides have been found in pituitaries from different species of elasmobranchs, but their structures have not been determined.[13, 19]

Oxytocin was first identified in extracts prepared from the pituitary glands of cattle and swine, and was synthesized in 1953 by du Vigneaud and his colleagues. Shortly thereafter, the molecular structures of the vasopressins were determined and synthetically duplicated. These were brilliant chemical achievements, since these were the first peptides to be synthesized. The mammalian neurohypophysis is the source of three principles; oxytocin, arginine vasopressin, and lysine vasopressin. By reference to Figure 6–2, it may be seen that oxytocin has isoleucine at position 3 and leucine at position 8; the vasopressins have phenylalanine at position 3, and either arginine or lysine at position 8. While these differences in molecular structure might seem to be slight, they have profound effects upon biologic potencies.

Arginine vasotocin was first identified in the chicken. It has isoleucine at position 3 (like oxytocin) and arginine at position 8 (like arginine vasopressin). This analogue had been synthesized and named "arginine vasotocin" before it was found to be present in the pituitaries of a large variety of nonmammalian vertebrates.[8] An analogue of oxytocin, called *ichthyotocin* or *isotocin*, has recently been obtained from the pituitary glands of holostean and teleostean fishes. This peptide is the same as oxytocin, except for serine at position 4 and isoleucine at position 8. Chemically, the compound is 4-serine, 8-isoleucine oxytocin. Another oxytocin-like principle,

8-isoleucine oxytocin, has been identified in the pituitaries of the primitive ray-finned fish *Polypterus,* lungfishes, and several species of Amphibia.[6, 19]

Phyletic Distribution

Neurohypophysial octapeptides are found in all classes of vertebrates, but they have undergone changes in amino-acid composition which make them pharmacologically different. The natural peptides vary in potency, when tested in the same or in different species, and this suggests that the receptor sites have also changed during the course of evolution.

Arginine vasotocin is the most widely distributed neurohormone. It is the only principle present in cyclostomes, the most primitive of all living vertebrates. Very small amounts of an octapeptide, closely resembling arginine vasotocin, have been found in elasmobranch pituitaries.[20] Even though it is not known to occur among mammals, it must be regarded as a very ancient molecule. It is present in the four major lines of evolution that lead respectively to cyclostomes, the chondrichthyes (shark-like fishes), the actinopterygians (ray-finned fishes), and the tetrapods (Fig. 6–3). Arginine vasotocin, together

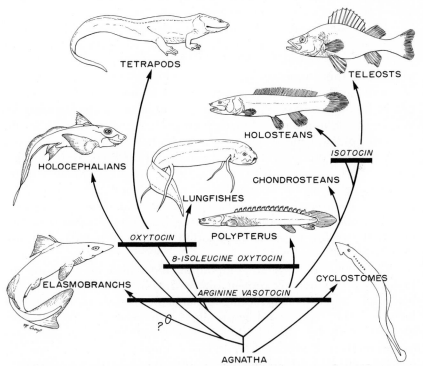

Figure 6–3. Schematic representation of the evolution of vertebrates. The distribution of the chief neurohypophysial principles is indicated by the heavy bars which cut across the arrows. Observe the wide distribution of arginine vasotocin. (Based on Sawyer, W. H.: Endocrinol., 75:981, 1964, and other publications of the same author.)

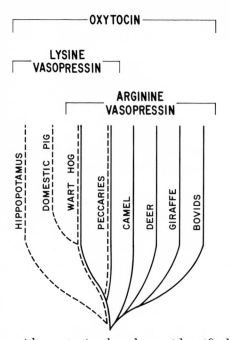

Figure 6–4. Distribution of the neurohypophysial hormones among the artiodactyls superimposed on a scheme showing their probable evolution. Arginine vasopressin is indicated by solid lines; lysine vasopressin by broken lines. (From Sawyer, W. H.: Endocrinol., 75:981, 1964.)

with oxytocin, has been identified in the pituitaries of teleostean fishes, amphibians, reptiles, and birds.[11, 17, 22, 23]

Two vasopressins are found among mammals, the arginine variety being most widely distributed. Arginine vasopressin has been identified in marsupials and also in *Echidna*, an egg-laying monotreme, and this suggests that it appeared very early in the evolution of mammals.[21] Lysine vasopressin has only been identified in the neural lobes of surviving Suiformes, a suborder of the Artiodactyla or even-toed ungulates. Lysine vasopressin alone occurs in the domestic pig and hippopotamus, whereas both kinds of vasopressin are found in certain wart hogs and peccaries (Fig. 6–4). Arginine vasopressin could have evolved from arginine vasotocin, present in the reptilian ancestors of mammals, by a single mutation causing isoleucine at position 3 to be replaced by phenylalanine. Lysine vasopressin could have arisen from arginine vasopressin through another mutation causing arginine in position 8 to be replaced by lysine (Fig. 6–5).[18, 19]

Oxytocin and similar compounds must also be very ancient molecules. Oxytocin is present in two evolutionary lines; the one leading to lungfishes and tetrapods, and the one giving rise to cartilaginous fishes. Oxytocin-like principles are present in the pituitaries of elasmobranchs, though their specific structures have not been determined, and oxytocin itself is presumably present in the chimaeras or ratfish (holocephalians). 8-Isoleucine oxytocin appears to be present in lungfishes and in *Polypterus*, a primitive ray-finned fish. Isotocin (4-serine, 8-isoleucine oxytocin) has been identified

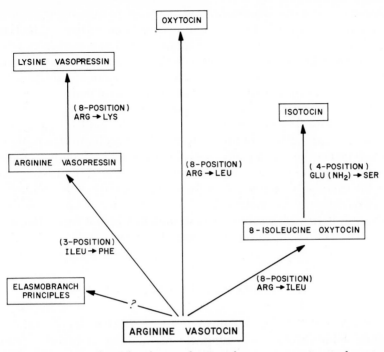

Figure 6–5. Hypothetical scheme showing how vasopressins and oxytocins may have arisen from arginine vasotocin during the course of vertebrate evolution. Each step involves a single amino-acid substitution, and it is presumed that each change was the consequence of a gene mutation. The molecular positions where changes occurred are indicated in parentheses. (Based on the publications of W. H. Sawyer.)

only in the pituitaries of holostean and teleostean fishes. Since arginine vasotocin seems to be the most primitive octapeptide, one could postulate that oxytocin arose from it by a mutation which caused leucine to be substituted for arginine at the 8 position. 8-Isoleucine oxytocin could have arisen from vasotocin by substituting isoleucine for arginine at position 8. Isotocin could have been derived from 8-isoleucine oxytocin by substituting serine at position 4 for glutamine (Fig. 6–5).[19]

It is apparent from the above discussion that the octapeptide neurohormones are very similar in chemical structure. Accordingly, there is considerable overlapping of pharmacologic properties, though relative potencies may be strikingly different in the various bioassays. Arginine and lysine vasopressins are antidiuretic principles in mammals, but arginine vasotocin performs this function in amphibians, reptiles, and birds. Antidiuresis is an adaptation to terrestrial life, and it is not surprising to find that the neurohypophysial principles have no effect on water conservation in fishes, though they may promote the loss of sodium through the kidneys. Oxytocin is known to regulate milk ejection, and probably facilitates parturition and sperm transport in the female reproductive tract of mammals;

its function in male mammals, if it has any, is unknown. Arginine vasotocin acts in birds to stimulate contractions of the oviduct and to promote oviposition, effects that are essentially oxytocic. When administered to mammals, vasotocin has potent oxytocic and milk-ejecting actions, whereas the vasopressins do not. It appears that during evolution vasotocin was discarded in mammals, and a clear separation appeared between octapeptides promoting water conservation (vasopressins) and the octapeptide controlling uterine contractility and milk ejection (oxytocin). The functions of neurohypophysial principles in aquatic vertebrates remain largely undetermined. It has been suggested, however, that these neurosecretions may be especially important in fishes in regulating the release of adenohypophysial hormones. The mere presence of these peptides in the pituitaries of the lowest vertebrates does not mean that they have to function as systemic hormones in these groups.

FORMATION, STORAGE, RELEASE, AND TRANSPORT

Oliver and Schäfer demonstrated in 1895 that whole pituitary extracts, administered intravenously to the dog, induced vasoconstriction and elevated the blood pressure. Other workers promptly showed that this effect was attributable to the pars nervosa, and not to any other component of the pituitary. Since this part of the pituitary does not show cytologic characteristics of a gland, the source of the active principle became a problem. Some investigators postulated that the active material might be secreted by the adenohypophysis and passed to the pars nervosa for storage; others thought that it might be produced *in situ* by the pituicytes, even though these cells did not appear to be glandular. Kamm and his co-workers (1928) succeeded in separating two active fractions from neural lobe extracts, one being especially potent in elevating the blood pressure of mammals and the other acting principally to induce uterine contractions. Evidence contributed by many other workers made it clear that blood-borne hormones were present in neural lobe tissue, but it remained hard to believe that they could originate in such a nonglandular structure. The problem was finally clarified by the Scharrers and Bargman and their co-workers in the early 1950's. They established the concept that oxytocin and vasopressin are neurosecretory products which arise in the neurons of certain hypothalamic nuclei. The neurohormones are actually synthesized by these glandular neurons, moved along the axons of the hypothalamo-hypophysial tract, and discharged around blood vessels in the pars nervosa (a neurohemal organ). The pituicytes are neuroglia and are no longer regarded as the source of these secretions; there is still the possibility, however, that the pituicytes may be involved in either the release mechanism or the separation of the active peptides from the carrier substance.[2, 3, 24]

The paired supraoptic and paraventricular nuclei are the most important ones for the production of these neurohormones. These two pairs of nuclei in the dog contain about 100,000 neurons. Oxytocin and vasopressin are identifiable in these areas of the hypothalamus, and it must be assumed that under certain conditions the secretions can be freed directly into the hypothalamic circulation. The dog stores exceptionally large amounts of vasopressin in the hypothalamus. The administration of vasopressin and oxytocin to the snake (*Diadophis punctatus*) leads to a marked accumulation of neurosecretory material in the hypothalamic nuclei and pars nervosa.[14]

In birds, in which a septum separates the two lobes of the pituitary, it is possible to remove the pars nervosa without disturbing the adenohypophysis. Ablation of the posterior lobe of the laying hen results in a prompt and permanent diuresis, but impairs neither ovulation nor oviposition. The consumption of water increases rapidly, and birds weighing 1000 to 2000 grams may drink as much as 1000 grams of water daily. The diabetes insipidus in the operated birds may be controlled by the administration of neurohypophysial principles. The posterior lobe principles are known to facilitate oviposition in birds but, in the absence of the posterior lobe, enough oxytocin is apparently released from the hypothalamic neurons to take care of this need.[12]

Totally hypophysectomized mammals seldom show any serious disturbances in water metabolism. In the hypophysectomized rat, neurosecretory material accumulates at the broken end of the pituitary stalk, the latter undergoing reorganization to form a normal but miniature neural lobe. On the other hand, if the hypothalamo-hypophysial tracts are severed near the supraoptic nuclei, the cell bodies of the latter deteriorate, and the organism is practically deprived of oxytocin and vasopressin. Under these conditions, a permanent diabetes insipidus results, the animals consuming large quantities of water and eliminating it through the kidneys.

The factors involved in the release of neurohypophysial secretions have not been completely elucidated. The release of antidiuretic hormone (ADH; synonymous with vasopressin) may be altered by changes in osmotic pressure and volume of the blood, certain sensory reflexes, and actions occurring within the central nervous system itself. In snakes as in other amniotes, intraperitoneal injections of sodium chloride, or the withholding of water, cause neurosecretory material in the hypothalamic nuclei and pars nervosa to be rapidly depleted.[14] The osmoreceptors in dogs are thought to be located in some area of the prosencephalon which is supplied by the internal carotid artery. If hypertonic solutions of sugar or salt are injected into the carotid artery of normal animals during water diuresis, a prompt fall in urine output occurs. Changes in blood volume and in electrolyte concentration of the plasma can bring about striking increases in ADH. Various emotions, as well as coitus and pain, reflex stimulation as in suckling and milking, changes in environmental temperatures, etc., are known to promote the release of such neurohormones.[15]

Certain drugs, probably acting on hypothalamic nuclei, are known to reduce the flow of urine by increasing the release of ADH. Among these may be mentioned morphine, nicotine, ether, and various barbituates. Since the main nervous connection between the hypothalamus and pars nervosa is the hypothalamo-hypophysial tract, one wonders whether the neurons that elaborate neurosecretions can also conduct nervous impulses. There is some evidence that they can do both.

Various staining techniques have been employed in order to identify neurosecretory cells in different components of the neurohypophysial complex. It is probable that these techniques stain a protein "carrier substance" to which the peptide principles are adsorbed or attached, rather than the peptides themselves. Van Dyke *et al.* isolated a protein (30,000 mol. wt.) from neurohypophysial extracts which has vasopressor and oxytocic activities in the ratio of 1:1. These activities could be separated from the protein by treatment with acid. The van Dyke protein has more recently been named "neurophysin," and has been obtained from a number of mammalian species. The natural neurohormonal peptides may be combined with neurophysin *in vitro*, and subsequently dissociated from the protein. Neurophysin is so specific in its binding of neurohypophysial principles that it can be utilized in separating these principles from other peptides which are present in pituitary extracts. These studies suggest that the neurohormonal peptides are bound to neurophysin within the neurosecretory cells, and probably after they are released into the pars nervosa. It is not known whether these neurohormones exist as free peptides in the blood plasma or as peptide-protein complexes.[4, 25]

BIOLOGIC ACTIONS OF NEUROHYPOPHYSIAL PRINCIPLES

It appears that the principles of the neurohypophysis may not be indispensable for life. Although vasopressin has strong pharmacologic actions on the circulation, there is no proof that it performs a physiologic role. Oxytocin has been assigned a role in promoting uterine contractility in mammals during coitus and at the time of delivery, but individuals of some species seem to deliver young quite well after the supply has been eliminated, or reduced, by hypothalamic lesions. Most mammals could not rear their young without ejecting milk, but the individual could live without doing so. Even in the absence of the antidiuretic principle, mammalian organisms may rely upon other homeostatic mechanisms for the regulation of body water. To what extent desert animals conserve water through the release of ADH is not known. When the laboratory rat is deprived of water, it not only increases the output of ADH but also diminishes the consumption of food, thus reducing the loss of water through the feces.

Antidiuretic Effects

Even before the chemical identification of neurohypophysial principles, physiologists had demonstrated that they act upon the kidney to reduce the volume of urine. If a dog's kidney is isolated and perfused with blood from the trunk of another dog, it produces a large volume of dilute urine. The addition of small amounts of pituitary extract to the perfusate causes the kidney to excrete a smaller volume of more concentrated urine. Inclusion of the dog's head in the perfusion circuit causes the excised kidney to diminish its output of urine, but this effect of the head is abolished by removing the pituitary gland.

There can be no doubt that ADH (vasopressin) is of physiologic utility in the regulation of water balance in mammals. By acting upon the epithelial cells of the distal portion of the renal tubule, it encourages the reabsorption of water. Diabetes insipidus (excretion of a large volume of dilute urine) can be produced in mammals, such as the cat, dog, and monkey, by hypothalamic lesions that destroy the supraoptico-hypophysial tracts. Approximately 90 per cent of the fibers in these tracts must be severed before any profound disturbances occur in water metabolism. Such diabetic animals consume large quantities of water (polydipsia) and eliminate a large volume of urine (diuresis); the excessive water loss may be corrected by the administration of vasopressin. The essential effect of the peptide on the distal segment of the nephron is to increase the permeability of the epithelial surface to water.

Members of most mammalian species die when 20 per cent of the body water is lost, but the camel can survive after losing more than 40 per cent of its body water. Hibernating mammals, such as the hedgehog and certain desert rodents, have remarkable abilities to economize water. The Mongolian gerbil and similar desert species can survive for years without drinking water, living on a diet of dry grain without weight loss. The kangaroo rat (*Dipodomys*) obtains water through the oxidation of its food, but it does not store an excess of water in the tissues and has no especial resistance to dehydration. When excess water is administered by stomach tube, it is excreted with great difficulty, and the animals are likely to show symptoms of "water intoxication." The urine volume is about half that of the laboratory rat and is much more concentrated. The neural lobe of the kangaroo rat is relatively larger than that of the laboratory rat and contains more vasopressin per microgram of tissue. This suggests that vasopressin may have some special importance in desert rodents with respect to water metabolism.

Striking antidiuretic actions have been demonstrated in birds, reptiles, and certain amphibians. Most anurans, maintained in water and injected with neurohypophysial peptides, increase in weight. This is known as the "Brunn" or "water balance" effect. This weight increase results from a composite effect of the neurohormones; water loss through the kidneys is diminished, water uptake through the skin is increased, and water is absorbed from the urinary bladder and returned to the blood. Pieces of frog skin *in vitro* respond to ADH by accelerating the movement of water from the outside to inside, but only if the inside is hypertonic to the outside as it normally is *in vivo*. The urinary bladder of toads and frogs may also be used in *in vitro* experiments; it responds to ADH by increasing water absorption from the luminal surface. In many urodele amphibians that never leave the water (*e.g.*, *Necturus*), antidiuresis either cannot be produced by these peptides, or the required dose is so high that it is obviously unphysiologic. Posterior lobe principles have not been demonstrated to exert antidiuretic effects in fish, though they may be important in these vertebrates in promoting the renal loss of sodium. The administration of vasotocin to the teleost *Carassius auratus* causes sodium to be lost through the kidneys and promotes the intake of sodium, perhaps by an effect on the gills.[7, 10]

Amphibian skin and bladder are useful tissues since they may be observed *in vitro* after the application of neurohypophysial principles. Evidence has been adduced that ADH acts upon amphibian membranes by dilating the pores. Isotopically labeled thiourea penetrates the toad's skin at a slower rate than water, presumably because of the larger molecules. ADH increases the rate of flux of the thiourea molecules. On the basis of the *pore theory* this is explained by assuming that the pores of the skin are normally just large enough to admit water molecules, but ADH dilates them sufficiently for thiourea molecules to pass through. It has been suggested that the pore theory may be applied to account for the actions of ADH on the kidney.[1, 5, 9, 16]

Oxytocic Effects

Two main functions have been ascribed to oxytocin in the promotion of uterine contractility: (a) to facilitate the ascent of spermatozoa in the female tract after intromission and (b) to expel the fetus from the female tract at parturition. Owing to the intermittent nature of these events it has been difficult to obtain quantitative information. Many workers have felt that in many species the spermatozoa reach the fallopian tubes too rapidly to be accounted for by the flagellate motility of the spermatozoa themselves. Moreover, nonmotile spermatozoa are known to ascend the female tract as quickly as motile ones. Oxytocin has been observed to increase the ascent of spermatozoa and various fluids introduced into the bovine uterus maintained *in vitro.*

Increased contractility of the uterus has been demonstrated in domestic animals after natural mating, tactile stimulation of the external genitalia, and mechanical stimulation of the uterus. In cows the content of oxytocin in external jugular blood was found to be increased after rectal palpation of the uterus and cervix. Milk ejection may accompany natural mating in several species, suggesting that there is an augmented release of oxytocin at this time.

Extracts containing oxytocin have been used clinically for many years to induce uterine contractions and facilitate delivery of the fetus. The neural lobes of rats and dogs contain very little oxytocin for several hours after labor, suggesting that the stored peptides have been used to support the process. The fact that parturition may occur normally in the absence of the pituitary gland does not prove that oxytocin is unimportant in parturition; sufficient quantities of neurohormone may continue to be produced by the hypothalamus. It is generally agreed that the sensitivity of the uterine muscle to oxytocin varies in accordance with the sex hormones that act upon it. Furthermore, there are differences in the reactivity of different regions of the same uterus. While the evidence is suggestive, no final conclusions can be made concerning the physiologic role of oxytocin in parturition.

There are indications that posterior lobe peptides may be important in the reproductive physiology of birds and reptiles. They effect oviposition in the hen by inducing contraction of the shell gland and of the vagina. Vasopressin stimulates contractions of the oviducts of the painted turtle, *Chrysemis picta.* Assay studies have shown that the oxytocic activity of the hen's neural lobe is practically depleted prior to oviposition.

Neural lobe secretions appear to influence reproductive behavior in certain fishes. It has been reported that synthetic oxytocin induces the spawning reflex in *Fundulus.*

Galactogogic Effects

One of the best-established functions of oxytocin is its role in stimulating milk ejection. The milk ejection reflex manifests itself by a sudden rise in milk pressure within the glands and, like other reflexes, can be conditioned. The lactating female becomes conditioned to a variety of tactile, visual, and auditory stimuli associated with suckling or milking. In this manner the lactating mother unconsciously participates and makes it possible for the nursing young to obtain a full supply of milk. This reflex arc is a neurohormonal one, the efferent component being a neurohormone that is, in all probability, oxytocin. This principle is released from the neurohypophysis and causes contraction of the branching myoepithelial cells around the mammary alveoli.

The development of the mammary glands and milk secretion require a large number of hormones. There are indications that all of the anterior pituitary hormones may be involved in normal mammary functions. It has been proposed that an important effect of oxytocin is to prevent involution of the lactating mammary gland. Oxytocin, reflexively discharged, is thought to reach the anterior pituitary and cause it to release prolactin. The latter hormone then maintains the functional integrity of the mammary alveolar tissue. Factors involved in lactation are discussed more fully in Chapter 15.

REFERENCES

1. Andersen, B., and Ussing, H. H.: Solvent drag on non-electrolytes during osmotic flow through isolated toad skin. Acta Physiol. Scand., 39:228, 1957.
2. Bargmann, W.: The neurosecretory system of the diencephalon. Endeavour, 19:125, 1960.
3. Bargmann, W., and Scharrer, E.: The site of origin of the hormones of the posterior pituitary. Amer. Scientist, 39:255, 1961.
4. Chauvet, J., Lenci, M-T, and Archer, R.: L'ocytocine et la vasopressine du mouton. Reconstitution d'un complexe hormonal actif. Biochim. et Biophys. Acta, 38:266, 1960.
5. Frazier, H. S., Dempsey, E. F., and Leaf, A.: Movement of sodium across the mucosal surface of the isolated toad bladder and its modification by vasopressin. J. Gen. Physiol., 45:529, 1962.
6. Heller, H.: Neurohypophyseal hormones. *In* U. S. von Euler and H. Heller (eds.): Comparative Endocrinology, Vol. 1. New York, Academic Press, 1963, p. 25.
7. Heller, H., and Bentley, P. J.: Phylogenetic distribution of the effects of neurohypophysial hormones on water and sodium metabolism. Gen. & Comp. Endocrinol., 5:96, 1965.
8. Katsoyannis, P. G., and du Vigneaud, V.: Arginine-vasotocin, a synthetic analogue of the posterior pituitary hormones containing the ring of oxytocin and the side chain of vasopressin. J. Biol. Chem., 233:1352, 1958.
9. Leaf, A., and Hays, R. M.: The effects of neurohypophyseal hormone on permeability and transport in a living membrane. Recent Prog. Hormone Res., 17:467, 1961.
10. Maetz, J., Bourguet, J., Lahlough, B., and Hourdry, J.: Peptides neurohypophysaires et osmoregulation chez *Carassius auratus*. Gen. & Comp. Endocrinol., 4:508, 1964.
11. Munsick, R. A., Sawyer, W. H., and van Dyke, H. B.: Avian neurohypophysial hormones: pharmacological properties and tentative identification. Endocrinol., 66:860, 1960.
12. Nalbandov, A. V.: Reproductive Physiology, 2nd ed. San Francisco, W. H. Freeman and Company, 1964, p. 107.
13. Perks, A. M., and Dodd, M. H. I.: The properties of the oxytocic, milk ejection and antidiuretic principle of the neurointermediate lobe of the elasmobranch pituitary. Gen. & Comp. Endocrinol., 3:184, 1963.

14. Philibert, R. L., and Kamemoto, F. I.: The hypothalamo-hypophyseal neuro-secretory system of the ring-necked snake, *Diadophis punctatus*. Gen. & Comp. Endocrinol., 5:326, 1965.
15. Pickford, M.: Factors affecting milk release in the dog and the quantity of oxytocin liberated by suckling. J. Physiol., *152*:515, 1960.
16. Ridley, A.: Effects of osmotic stress and hypophysectomy on ion distribution in bullfrogs. Gen. & Comp. Endocrinol., *4*:481, 1964.
17. Sawyer, W. H.: Comparative physiology and pharmacology of the neurohypophysis. Recent Prog. Hormone Res., *17*:437, 1961.
18. Sawyer, W. H.: Neurohypophyseal secretions and their origin. *In* A. V. Nalbandov (ed.): Advances in Neuroendocrinology. Urbana, University of Illinois Press, 1963, p. 68.
19. Sawyer, W. H.: Vertebrate neurohypophysial principles. Endocrinol., *75*:981, 1964.
20. Sawyer, W. H.: Active neurohypophysial principles from a cyclostome (*Petromyzon marinus*) and two cartilaginous fishes (*Squalus acanthias* and *Hydrolagus colleri*). Gen. & Comp. Endocrinol., 5:427, 1965.
21. Sawyer, W. H., Munsick, R. A., and van Dyke, H. B.: Pharmacological character-istics of neurohypophysial hormones from a marsupial (*Didelphis virginiana*) and a monotreme (*Tachyglossus (Echidna) aculeatus*). Endocrinol., 67:137, 1960.
22. Sawyer, W. H., Munsick, R. A., and van Dyke, H. B.: Evidence for the presence of arginine vasotocin (8-arginine oxytocin) and oxytocin in neurohypophyseal extracts from amphibians and reptiles. Gen. & Comp. Endocrinol., *1*:30, 1961.
23. Sawyer, W. H., and van Dyke, H. B.: Isolation of the oxytocin-like pituitary prin-ciple of a teleost fish (*Pollachius virens*) and comparison of its properties with those of synthetic 4-serine, 8-isoleucine oxytocin. Endocrinol., 73: 394, 1964.
24. Scharrer, E., and Scharrer, B.: Hormones produced by neurosecretory cells. Recent Prog. Hormone Res., *10*:183, 1954.
25. van Dyke, H. B., Chow, B. F., Greep, R. O., and Rothen, A.: The isolation of a protein from the pars neuralis of the ox pituitary with constant oxytocic, pressor and diuresis-inhibiting effects. J. Pharmacol., *74*:190, 1942.

7_____

THE THYROID
GLAND

The human thyroid consists of two lobes that lie on either side of the trachea and are usually connected by a thin isthmus extending over the anterior surface of the trachea. Thyroids are present in all vertebrates but they are quite variable in shape and anatomic position. In some of the lower vertebrates, thyroid follicles are present, but they are not encapsulated and organized into a compact gland. The thyroid follicles of lampreys and bony fishes tend to be dispersed along the ventral aorta and are frequently found along the branchial arteries of the gills. The thyroid tissue of certain teleosts is extremely mobile and may disperse from the pharyngeal region to distant areas, such as the eye, brain, spleen, and kidney. The function of the thyroid is to elaborate, store, and discharge secretions that are concerned principally with the regulation of metabolic rate. If the thyroid secretions of adult, cold-blooded vertebrates perform important functions, they remain to be demonstrated convincingly.

The hormonal variants that derive from the thyroid gland will be referred to by the term *thyroid hormone*, which unless otherwise stated, will designate thyroxine, 3,5,3'-triiodothyronine, and any other active compounds that may be produced from these in the body.

ANATOMIC FEATURES

Gross Anatomy

The human thyroid is encapsulated by two layers of connective tissue; the outer layer is continuous with the cervical fascia and is loosely connected with the inner capsule that adheres intimately to the surface of the gland. The normal thyroid of the adult weighs 25 to 40 gm., but it is one of the most labile organs of the body, and its size fluctuates with age, reproductive states, habitation, and diet. The vascular supply to the thyroid is exceptionally rich (Fig. 7–1). It is probable that more blood flows through this gland, in proportion to its size, than through any other organ of the body with the possible exception of the adrenal. The most outstanding feature of the thyroid is its ability to concentrate large amounts of iodine. The amount of iodine within the gland may be fifty to several hundred times that of the blood plasma.

Postganglionic sympathetic fibers from the superior and inferior cervical ganglia and vagal fibers from the superior and inferior laryngeal nerves enter the gland along with the blood vessels. The fact that the thyroid secretes when its normal nerve supply is interrupted and when the gland is transplanted to unnatural sites indicates that the most important function of the nerve supply is to regulate the flow of blood through the organ. The thyrotrophic hormone (TSH) of the

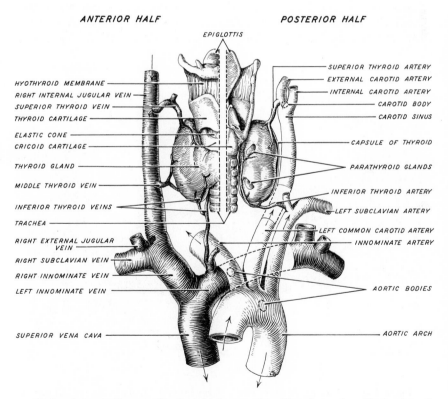

Figure 7–1. A diagram showing the human thyroid and parathyroid glands and their relations to adjacent structures. The anterior surfaces of the thyroid, larynx, and trachea are shown in the left half of the figure; the posterior surfaces are shown in the right half.

anterior hypophysis is the principal factor that controls the rate of release of thyroid hormone.

Thyroid tissue regenerates rapidly after subtotal thyroidectomy if the dietary intake of iodine is low, but regeneration does not occur if exogenous thyroid hormone is administered.

Microscopic Anatomy

The thyroid has a greater capacity than any other endocrine gland to store its secretions, and this is reflected in its histologic structure. The gland is composed of an aggregation of spherical or ovate cystlike *follicles* of variable size (Figs. 7–2 and 7–3). The interfollicular areas are occupied by a highly vascularized network of connective tissue in which a few lymphocytes and histiocytes may be found. Each follicle is a microscopic unit and is lined by a secretory epithelium composed of a single layer of cuboidal or low columnar cells. The closed cavities of the follicles normally contain a homogeneous, gelatinous, amber-colored globulin. This secretion is the so-called *colloid*, which gives to the gland its most distinguishing histologic peculiarity. The colloid is a storage product of the secretory epithelium. Its density varies in different glands and in different follicles

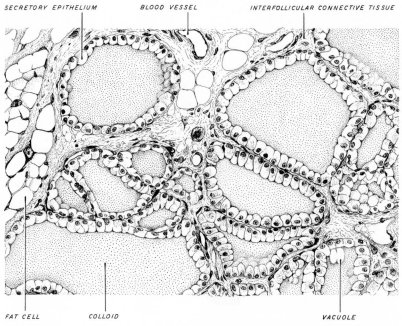

SECRETORY EPITHELIUM   BLOOD VESSEL   INTERFOLLICULAR CONNECTIVE TISSUE

FAT CELL   COLLOID   VACUOLE

Figure 7–2. Histologic features of the normal thyroid gland of the rat. All normal thyroid glands are structurally similar, though slight variations occur with age, diet, habitation, and sexual status. The normal animals of this colony were maintained on a high protein ration, which probably accounts for the slight hypertrophic condition of the secretory epithelium.

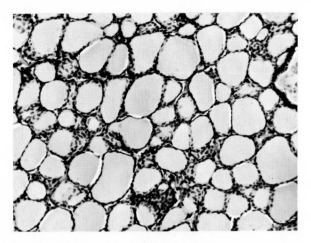

Figure 7–3. Thyroid gland of a normal cock, showing general histology. The secretory epithelium is low, and the follicles contain colloid.

of the same gland. The amount of colloid fluctuates in pathologic glands and may be reduced or increased by controlled experimental conditions. The thyroid of the normal rat contains in the neighborhood of 100,000 follicles, and these vary widely in size. The larger follicles are generally located near the periphery and the smaller ones in the center.

When the thyroid is inactive, there is a tendency for colloid to accumulate and for the epithelium to become low cuboidal or squamous; when it is overactive, the colloid stores are depleted, and the epithelium becomes columnar and plicated. There are, however, many exceptions, and histologic examination alone does not suffice to establish the functional state of the gland.

Electron microscopy of thyroid cells reveals cytoplasmic granules of different sizes and densities, and these vary with secretory states. The cell membrane at the base of the cell is extremely plicated, the folds extending deeply into the cell. Microvilli are prominent along the apical surfaces of the cells, and their number is increased following the administration of TSH (Fig. 7–4). In addition to uniodinated globulin, the thyroid cells probably secrete several enzymes into the follicular cavities. While merocrine secretion is probably employed most commonly, the release of entire secretion-laden cells (holocrine secretion) may occur to some extent in all vertebrates, but evidence of it is most often observed in the thyroids of cyclostomes and teleosts.

Developmental Anatomy

The thyroid is an embryonic derivative of the alimentary tract. It first appears as a median, unpaired evagination from the floor of the embryonic pharynx at the level of the first pair of pharyngeal pouches

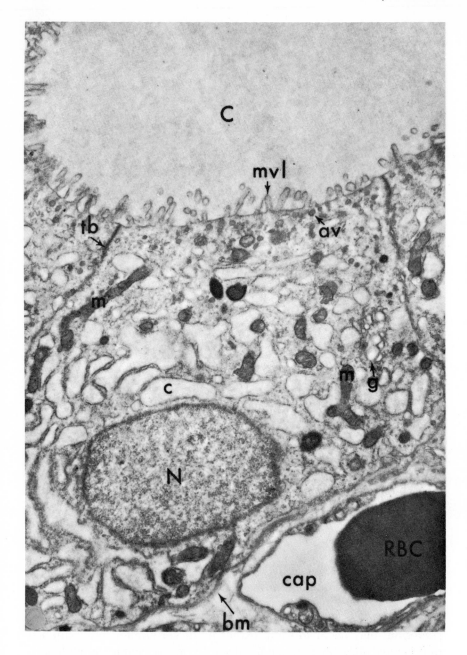

Figure 7–4. Electron micrograph of a follicular cell from the thyroid gland of the rat. The lumen of the follicle is uniformly filled with colloid (C); microvilli (mvl) arise from the apical end of the cell; apical vesicles (av) are numerous below the microvilli; terminal bars (tb) are present at the junctions of the lateral membranes; the cytoplasm contains mitochondria (m), Golgi bodies (g), and large cisternae of the ergastoplasm (c). At the bottom of the figure is the basement membrane (bm), and a blood capillary (cap) containing a red blood cell (RBC). (From Nadler, N. J., Young, B. A., Leblond, C. P., and Mitmaker, B.: Endocrinol., *74:*333, 1964.)

(Fig. 8–3). The distal end of this outgrowth gradually expands and becomes bilobed, while the stalked attachment narrows to form the *thyroglossal duct*. The branched terminal end of the thyroid primordium assumes a position on the anterior surface of the trachea, and the thyroglossal duct is normally obliterated. The *foramen caecum*, a slight depression at the root of the tongue near the apex of the sulcus terminalis, persists in adult human beings and marks the point where the thyroglossal duct opened into the embryonic pharynx.

Studies on the embryos of several vertebrates indicate that a kind of biochemical maturation occurs in thyroid tissue. In the chick embryo, for example, the immature thyroid can accumulate iodide after incubation for 7 to 8 days, but cannot form iodinated organic compounds. A brief monoiodotyrosine stage occurs on the 9th day, and this is followed by the successive appearance of diiodotyrosine and thyroxine. Similar work on mice embryos has shown that colloid formation begins before the thyroid cells are organized into follicles, and that the synthesis of thyroxine begins later than the collection and organic binding of iodine.[81]

EVOLUTION OF THYROIDAL FUNCTION

Vertebrates

Thyroid glands are present in all vertebrate groups. In adult cyclostomes, the most primitive vertebrates, thyroid follicles are embedded in the fibrous tissue along the floor of the pharynx. The follicles of cyclostomes are histologically comparable to those of any other vertebrate, although they are scattered individually along the pharynx. The elasmobranch thyroid is an encapsulated organ usually located near the point where the afferent branchial arteries leave the ventral aorta. In most teleosts the thyroid follicles are scattered along the ventral aorta, and the lack of an organ capsule probably correlates with their tendency to disperse to remote sites. Thyroid follicles are often found in the head kidneys of the platyfish (*Platypoecilus*), the number increasing with age.[4, 5] In a few teleosts such as the Bermuda parrot fish, the follicles are aggregated to form a compact, unpaired gland. The elasmobranch thyroid is typically an unpaired organ lying below the pharynx. The thyroids of amphibians (Fig. 7–5) and birds are paired and widely separated; in turtles and snakes, a single thyroid is found anterior to the heart (Figs. 8–4 and 8–5). Thyroid follicles are not present in the protochordates and other invertebrates.

Since the vertebrate thyroid originates as an outpocketing of the pharyngeal floor, it is not surprising to find that the endostyle of *Amphioxus* shares some functional properties with the thyroid.

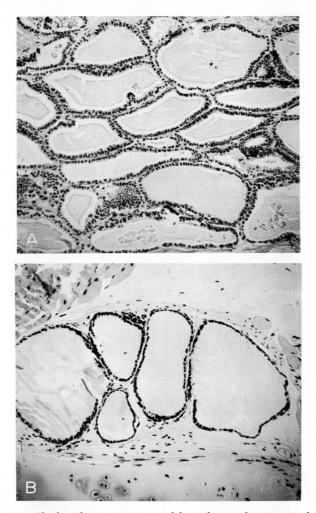

Figure 7–5. The histologic appearance of thyroid tissue from two urodele amphibians. A, *Amphiuma tridactylum*; B, *Necturus maculosus*. (From Kerkof, P. R., Tong, W., and Chaikoff, I. L.: Endocrinol., 73:185, 1963.)

Radioautographs prepared from *Amphioxus* after immersion in sea water containing I^{131} demonstrate that the endostyle region does contain organically bound iodine. Some capacity for iodine binding has also been demonstrated in hemichordates and urochordates.[6, 8, 80]

The life history of the cyclostomes seems to provide a connecting link between the endostyle organ of *Amphioxus* and the ductless glands of all higher chordates. The embryo of the lamprey develops into a larval stage known as the *Ammocoetes*, which has a *subpharyngeal gland* (endostyle) and many other characteristics of *Amphioxus* (Fig. 7–6). Although the endostyle of *Amphioxus* communicates with the pharynx throughout its extent, the endostyle of *Ammocoetes* becomes roofed over both anteriorly and posteriorly so that only a

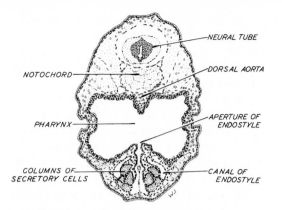

NEURAL TUBE

NOTOCHORD

DORSAL AORTA

PHARYNX

APERTURE OF
ENDOSTYLE

COLUMNS OF
SECRETORY CELLS

CANAL OF
ENDOSTYLE

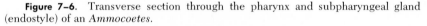

Figure 7–6. Transverse section through the pharynx and subpharyngeal gland (endostyle) of an *Ammocoetes*.

slitlike opening into the pharyngeal cavity remains at the level of the third gill pouch.

The endostyle of *Amphioxus* contains longitudinal glandular tracts, and it is generally held that its mucus-like secretions entrap particles of food material. It has been shown that the *Ammocoetes* endostyle functions in part at least as a holocrine gland; clumps of cells and amorphous materials may be traced through the endostylar duct and into the pharynx. These products from the endostyle are presumably passed into the intestine. After a period of three or more years the *Ammocoetes* larva transforms into an adult lamprey. During this metamorphosis some of the epithelial cells of the endostyle persist and transform into the follicles of the thyroid gland. While the endostyle of *Ammocoetes* contains nothing during its long larval life that resembles thyroid follicles, studies using radioiodine have shown that the endostylar epithelium functions like thyroidal cells, inasmuch as it accumulates and produces iodinated protein substances. Thyroid hormones have not been demonstrated to have any effect on the metamorphosis of the *Ammocoetes*.[7, 17, 18]

Invertebrates

Diiodotyrosine, one of the precursors of thyroxine, **was** first identified in the organic skeleton of gorgonid corals. It is now known that the skeletons of sponges and corals contain monoiodotyrosine in addition to diiodotyrosine, mono- and dibromotyrosine, and even traces of thyroxine. Thyroxine and its precursors have been detected in a great variety of invertebrate forms. Studies on various protochordates, insects, molluscs, and polychaete worms have shown that a high percentage of protein-bound iodine is localized in the scleroprotein forming the hard, horny structures of the body. In the freshwater mollusc *Musculium* and in a number of insects much of the total tracer iodine is in the form of thyroxine. Two other iodinated thyronines, triiodothyronine and diiodothyronine, have been found in the snail, *Planorbis corneus*, but, in this species, thyroxine was not found. 3,5,3'-Triiodothyronine has been identified chromatographically in the gorgonian, *Eunicella*.[10, 36, 37]

While it is surprising to find thyroxine so prevalent in the tissues of thyroidless invertebrates, it is known that mammalian tissues may produce thyroxine in the absence of the thyroid gland. Furthermore, the iodination of various proteins (*e.g.*, casein, blood proteins), followed by hydrolysis, yields crystals of thyroxine without enzymatic intervention. When iodine and proteins are incubated together under the proper conditions, the tyrosine in the protein molecule takes up this element and forms mono- and diiodotyrosine. The iodinated tyrosines are then coupled to yield thyroxine. Thus, the thyroid gland is not the only tissue capable of synthesizing thyroxine. Since tissue proteins are certain to contain tyrosine, it is reasonable to assume that this amino acid can be converted to thyroxine if iodine is available and if suitable oxidizing systems are present. This view would regard the synthesis of thyroxine as a general biologic reaction, the thyroid gland merely being an organ highly specialized in this direction and capable of storing the hormone. There are indications that tyrosine iodination may occur in rainbow trout following the complete destruction of thyroid follicles by radiothyroidectomy.[29, 54, 71, 73]

Studies on the invertebrates indicate that thyroid hormones and their precursors became available to organisms long before a discrete thyroid gland developed. However, the mere presence of iodinated thyronines in the invertebrates does not mean that these substances are being used for any particular purpose. There is no clear evidence that the administration of thyroxine and similar substances to invertebrates produces any kind of a response. It is probable that the phylogenetic appearance of a thyroid gland coincides with the development of a metabolic use for thyroxine and similar compounds.

Summary of Evolution

The diagrams in Figure 7–7 summarize the important events that appear to have occurred during evolution of the thyroid gland. Iodoproteins have been identified in most invertebrate phyla, but these have a tendency to be localized in hard exoskeletal structures, such as setae, byssus threads, periostracum, and in pharyngeal teeth. It is supposed that the source of iodoproteins shifted into the pharyngeal region after such materials became of metabolic utility to the organism. It is possible that structures like pharyngeal teeth (second "invertebrate type") provided a large and dependable source of iodoprotein, and that this material was digested in the intestine to

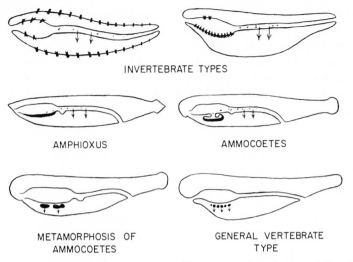

INVERTEBRATE TYPES

AMPHIOXUS

AMMOCOETES

METAMORPHOSIS OF
AMMOCOETES

GENERAL VERTEBRATE
TYPE

Figure 7-7. Diagrams showing a possible pattern of evolution of the thyroid gland. Iodoproteins are indicated as solid black. See text for explanation. (From Gorbman, A.: *In* Columbia University Symposium on Comparative Endocrinology. New York, John Wiley & Sons, 1959.)

form thyroxine and similar compounds. In *Amphioxus* and *Ammocoetes* the iodoprotein is no longer a scleroprotein associated with pharyngeal teeth but emanates from a pharyngeal gland of exocrine type, the endostyle. While the endostyle of the lamprey contains a protease, it is more likely that hydrolysis of the iodoprotein occurs in the digestive tract. In contrast to *Amphioxus*, the iodoprotein-forming gland of the *Ammocoetes* drains its products into the pharynx by means of a duct. When the endostylar duct closes at metamorphosis, the substance of the organ differentiates into a thyroid that already contains a thyroprotein-splitting enzyme (protease) like that of mammals. At this point in the life cycle of the lamprey, the vertebrate type of thyroid gland is differentiated; the local protease makes possible the closure of the duct to the pharynx, the storage of iodoproteins, and the release of hormones directly into the circulation. It is reasonable to assume that these changes occurring in the lamprey's endostyle at metamorphosis represent, at least in part, the general pattern of changes that ensued during the evolution of the vertebrate thyroid.[34, 36]

BIOCHEMISTRY OF THYROID HORMONE

Thyroglobulin is the most important protein present in the colloid of the thyroid follicle.[67] It is an iodized glycoprotein having a molecular weight of about 680,000 and is considered to be the storage form of the thyroid hormone. Thyroglobulin does not normally appear in the circulation. Under physiologic conditions this large protein is hydrolyzed by a mixture of catheptases and yields a number of iodinated amino acids, *viz.*, mono- and diiodotyrosine, 3,3'-diiodothyronine, 3,5,3'-triiodothyronine, 3,3',5'-triiodothyronine, and 3,5,3',5'-tetraiodothyronine (thyroxine) (Fig. 7–8). Mono- and diiodotyrosine do not leave the follicle; they are rapidly deiodinated within the thyroid cells, the iodine being reutilized for a recycling synthesis

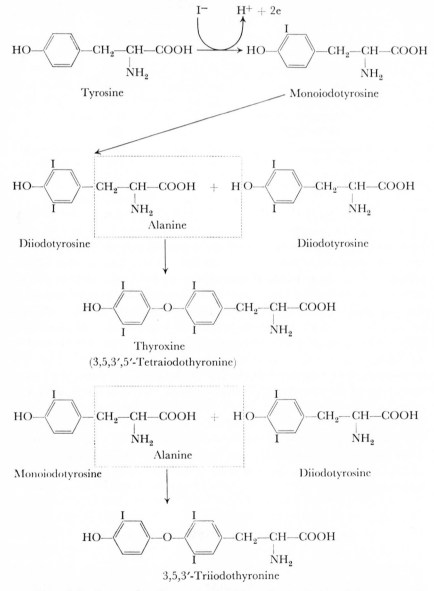

Figure 7–8. Proposed pathways in the biosynthesis of thyroid hormones. No mechanism has yet been discovered that explains the coupling of two molecules of diiodotyrosine.

of thyroglobulin. This change is effected by the enzyme deiodinase, which has only mono- and diiodotyrosine for its substrate. About 60 per cent of the iodine present in thyroglobulin is due to the iodotyrosines, and 30 per cent to the iodothyronines. Of the thyronines that are secreted into the circulation, only 3,5,3′-triiodothyronine and thyroxine are known to have any biologic activity. In certain tests 3,5,3′-triiodothyronine (TRIT) is found to be over seven times as active as thyroxine, and the latent period required for it to produce its effect is less than with thyroxine.

The deaminated analogues, such as tetraiodothyroacetic acid (TETRAC) and triiodothyroacetic acid (TRIAC), have so far been demonstrated only in peripheral tissues. They have not been found in the blood and appear in the tissues only after the administration of radioactive thyroxine. They have not been found to appear in the tissues after the administration of radioiodide. The biologic effects of TETRAC and TRIAC are qualitatively different from those of the thyronines found in the blood. For example, TRIAC is much more potent than thyroxine and triiodothyronine in inducing the metamorphosis of amphibian larvae, but it is relatively weak in preventing goiter and in elevating the consumption of oxygen in the rat. TETRAC, on the other hand, stimulates tissue metabolism but is weak in promoting amphibian metamorphosis.

It is not known in what form the thyroid hormone acts upon the peripheral tissues, and this lack of information has hampered studies aimed at determining the mechanism of action of the hormone. It is known that both thyroxine and triiodothyronine are natural products of the gland and that the latter has even greater potency than the former. Though thyroxine is present in the blood in greater concentration than any other product of the thyroid, many investigators have felt that it may not be the active form of the hormone and have suggested that it may be converted to triiodothyronine or some other form before affecting peripheral tissues. There are indications that the kidney may play an important role in converting thyroxine to a more active form of the hormone. Surviving kidney slices can deiodinate thyroxine to triiodothyronine, whereas homogenates of this organ do not. The mitochondrial fraction of rat kidney homogenates converts thyroxine and triiodothyronine to their respective acetic acid analogues, TETRAC and TRIAC. Both analogues uncouple oxidative phosphorylation in mitochondrial preparations, but they are less active by mammalian tests than their respective precursors. It may be that a complex of thyroid compounds operates at the tissue level, or it may be that the cellularly active form of the hormone has not been discovered yet.[55, 56]

The thyroid hormones are transported in the blood in close association with the albumin and α-globulin fractions of serum protein. The latter is referred to as thyroxine-binding protein (TBP).

Thyroxine is bound very tightly to this protein and only a small fraction is bound to albumin. Triiodothyronine is less discriminating than thyroxine in its choice of carrier. The plasma contains more TBP than is necessary to bind normal concentrations of thyroxine, only about one-third of the protein-binding capacity of the serum proteins being used normally. During pregnancy and after the administration of estrogens there is a profound increase in the thyroxine-binding capacity of the blood proteins. As the hormones circulate through the tissues they are freed from their protein carriers, pass through the capillary walls, and impinge upon the tissue cells.[30, 40, 79]

Very little is known about the binding of thyroid hormones by tissue proteins. However, it has been reported that rat skeletal muscle contains a protein fraction that can bind physiologic concentrations of levorotatory thyroxine and 3,5,3'-triiodothyronine. This appears to be a specific protein and is not the same as TBP of the serum.

The naturally occurring thyroid hormones are levorotatory. Synthetic thyroxine is a mixture of the D- and L-isomers (racemic) and is much less active biologically than L-thyroxine. It has been reported that enzyme systems from rat kidney do not deiodinate D-thyroxine to triiodothyronine. It might be that the failure of D-thyroxine to undergo these transformations correlates with its biologic inactivity.[26]

Biosynthesis of Thyroid Hormone

Knowledge of thyroid metabolism has been advanced by applying the techniques of chromatography and radioautography of compounds labeled with I^{131}. The first procedure makes it possible to separate minute amounts of material, and the second to locate iodinated products in tissues and measure their rate of accumulation. The various antithyroid agents have also proved useful in investigating thyroid chemistry and physiology. The process of thyroid hormone formation may be divided into three stages: (1) the accumulation or trapping of iodide from the circulation, (2) the iodination of tyrosine, and (3) the proteolysis of thyroglobulin.[70, 75]

Iodide Accumulation

The diet may contain iodine in several forms. Most of it is reduced to iodide before it is absorbed from the gastrointestinal tract and appears in the blood as inorganic iodide. The concentration of inorganic iodide in the blood plasma is very low, but the cells of the thyroid epithelium have a greater avidity for it than any other tissue. The concentration gradient for iodide achieved by the normal thyroid is 20:1, or more, over the blood plasma. Inorganic iodide comprises only about 1 per cent of the total iodine content of the thyroid under

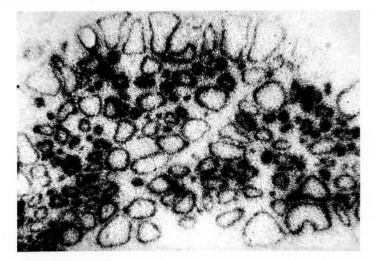

Figure 7–9. A radioautograph of rat's thyroid one hour after the intraperitoneal injection of radioiodide. Note that at this early stage the radioiodide collects in the periphery of the follicles, rather than being distributed throughout the colloid. (From Nadler and Leblond: Brookhaven Symposia in Biology, No. 7, 1955.)

physiologic conditions. Within 15 minutes after the administration of radioiodide to the rat, 90 per cent of the radioactivity in the thyroid is present in organic compounds (Fig. 7–9). However, after the administration of certain antithyroid drugs that inhibit the iodination of tyrosine, high concentrations of inorganic iodide may accumulate in the gland.

Iodination of Tyrosine

The inorganic iodide that accumulates in the follicular epithelium is oxidized to I_2 (elemental iodine) or to IO^-. This process is controlled by one or more enzyme systems. Tyrosine is first iodinated to monoiodotyrosine and then to diiodotyrosine (Fig. 7–8). Whether this process takes place at the level of protein molecules rather than at the level of the free amino acid remains unknown. However, it is easier to form thyroxine *in vitro* by the iodination of protein than by the iodination of free tyrosine. Though the mechanism remains obscure, it has been postulated that thyroxine is formed by the coupling of two molecules of diiodotyrosine, with the loss of one alanine side chain. Triiodothyronine may be produced by the coupling of one molecule each of monoiodotyrosine and diiodotyrosine, or possibly by the loss of one iodine atom from the thyroxine molecule. Apparently the thyroid cell continuously produces thyroglobulin and passes it into the lumen of the follicle where it is stored. The synthesis of thyroid hormones is accelerated by pituitary thyrotrophin and blocked by certain antithyroid agents. Certain forms of cretinism have been traced to an inability of the thyroid to couple iodotyrosines.[76]

Proteolysis of Thyroglobulin

The enzymatic elaboration and breakdown of thyroglobulin in the follicle occurs continuously, and this insures a regular turnover of thyroglobulin. The epithelial cells secrete a protease into the colloid, and this enzyme splits thyroglobulin into smaller molecules, including the series of iodinated derivatives of tyrosine that exist as amino acid residues in thyroglobulin. Among these are thyroxine and triiodothyronine, which pass into the circulation possibly as a consequence of a concentration gradient between the colloid and the tissue fluids. Mono- and diiodotyrosine are deiodinated by the enzyme deiodinase, the resultant iodide being returned to the thyroid iodide pool. The synthesis of thyroid hormones in amphibia is similar to that of mammals.

It is clear that thyroglobulin is the storage form of the thyroid hormone. Thyroxine is the principal circulating hormone. Triiodothyronine is also present in the blood but only in relatively small amounts. It is not known what form of the hormone is active at the level of the peripheral tissues. It may well be that a complex of hormones including thyroxine, triiodothyronine, and their metabolites is active in the peripheral tissues. The fact that thyroid functions are conditioned by the pituitary, adrenals, pancreas, and other endocrine glands suggests that secretions from multiple glands may be required at the tissue level in order for thyroid hormones to produce their characteristic effects.

The liver and kidneys are the chief organs concerned in the *catabolism* of thyroid hormones. Since the liver is an important organ in the destruction of excessive hormone and in the regulation of biliary excretion mechanisms, it appears to play an important role in regulating the thyroid hormone content of the body. Thyroxine and triiodothyronine are conjugated as glucuronides in the liver and then passed through the bile into the intestine. An alternative pathway in the liver is the oxidative deamination of these hormones to form the corresponding pyruvic acid derivatives. Small amounts of thyroxine and triiodothyronine and their deaminated metabolites are excreted through the bile in an unconjugated form. Both free and conjugated thyroxine are excreted in small amounts through the kidneys. Thyroidal compounds may be extensively deiodinated in the liver and in certain other organs, such as the salivary glands. There is also some evidence that certain metabolites of the thyroid hormones may be resorbed from the intestine and circulate repeatedly through the liver. The iodide produced from hormone degradation is reutilized by the thyroid gland or excreted by the kidney. Only minute amounts of organically bound iodine are lost through the kidneys. The body shows great economy in handling its iodine stores and normally retains most of that freed through the metabolism of thyroid hormones.

Figure 7–10. System of numbering the aromatic carbon atoms in the thyroxine nucleus.

A large number of *thyroxine analogues* have been prepared, and many of these exhibit biologic potencies quite different from those of the hormones secreted by the thyroid. For example, triiodothyropropionic acid is some three hundred times more potent than thyroxine in stimulating the metamorphosis of *Rana pipiens* tadpoles, and one hundred thirty times more effective in this respect when tested on *Rana catesbeiana.* Small variations in the thyroxine molecule may greatly alter its potency. Thyroxine declines in potency if more than one atom of iodine is replaced by another halogen. The iodine atoms must be attached to positions 3 and 5; the 2, 6 analogues actually inhibit certain thyroxine effects (Fig. 7–10). Furthermore, the hydroxyl group (OH) must occupy the 4′ position; physiologic activity is lost if it is moved to another position on the aromatic nucleus. The side chain at position 1 may be modified in various ways without impairing biologic potency.

Mode of Action of Thyroid Hormone

Though much biochemical information has accumulated on the mechanism of action of thyroxine, the literature is tenuous, often contradictory, and subject to objections. Since we are dealing with hormones which produce many and varied effects in different species, some of the actions apparently being indirect, it is difficult to decide what cellular response could be most profitably investigated. Most biochemical studies have centered around the capacity of thyroxine to elevate the consumption of oxygen, even though this response is largely limited to warm-blooded vertebrates; it is not readily demonstrable in tissues cultured *in vitro*, and the "tissue" form of the hormone remains unknown. The fact that a latent period intervenes between the administration of thyroxine and the onset of its actions has led many workers to believe that the hormone may stimulate the synthesis or activation of oxidative enzymes, processes that require time. By use of many kinds of tissues from thyroidectomized mammals or animals that had received thyroxine, it has been shown that the quantity of many enzymes is proportional to the amount of hormone acting within the organism.

A number of studies have suggested that thyroid hormone may affect the rate of metabolism by acting at one or more points in the citric acid cycle. Since the enzymes involved in this cycle are localized in the mitochondria, there have been suggestions that thyroid hormone may act by altering the permeability of the cell membrane or the membrane system of the mitochondrion. One concept that has received much attention is that the hormones act to "uncouple oxidative phosphorylation." The mitochondria are known to be the sites where the energy released by oxidative processes is incorporated into adenosine triphosphate (ATP). The increased oxygen consumption occurring in hyperthyroid states is accounted for, according to this view, as resulting from an impairment of the phosphorylation of ATP. Everyone agrees that no adequate explanation of the mode of action of thyroid hormones is yet available, though a start has been made.

Antithyroid Agents (Goitrogens)

A number of chemical agents can interfere, in one way or another, with the thyroid mechanisms involved in the synthesis of hormones. These antithyroid substances have the common property of causing a fall in the blood level of thyroxine, and this leads to an augmented output of thyrotrophin (TSH) by the anterior pituitary. The latter hormone causes hypertrophy of thyroid tissue and, if there is conspicuous enlargement of the thyroid, it may be termed *goiter*. Hence these agents are sometimes called goitrogens.

Iodine

Since iodine is an essential atom of the thyroid hormone molecule, the gland cannot synthesize its hormones without adequate quantitites of iodide in the blood. Inadequate dietary intake of this element leads to thyroid hormone deficiency and to compensatory hypertrophy and hyperplasia of the thyroid epithelium, a condition known as simple hyperplastic goiter. Conversely, large doses of iodide, administered to those whose thyroids are hyperactive and secreting excessive hormone, reduce the hypertrophy and hyperplasia of the gland and promote the storage of colloid. High levels of blood iodide inhibit the thyroid of the normal subject in a comparable manner, although the effect is transitory and less pronounced. The mechanism whereby iodide produces this effect remains largely unknown. It is certain that its action is different from that of the goitrogens and that it does not interfere with the peripheral action of thyroid hormone.[38, 74, 83]

There are some suggestions that high levels of iodide may diminish thyroid function by antagonizing the action of TSH. It is known that the ability of the thyroid of the hypophysectomized rat to concentrate iodide in response to exogenous TSH is influenced by the iodine content of the diet. The thyroid concentrates radio-iodide more effectively when iodine intake is low than when it is high. This effect is not due to the level of circulating iodide *per se* but rather to products arising through the organification of iodide within the thyroid itself. Probably organic iodine-containing compounds within the thyroid, possibly thyroid hormone itself, in some manner antagonize the stimulating action of TSH on the iodine-accumulating mechanism.

Prolonged iodine deficiency produces goiter in many species of laboratory animals. When rats are fed a diet low in iodine, the animals first develop hyperplastic goiters owing to excessive stimulation by TSH; if the iodine deficiency persists, the thyroids become progressively larger and go on to develop nodules and different types of tumors. The histologic aspects of diffuse colloid goiter have been produced in the hamster by maintaining them on iodine-deficient diets and then administering iodine. The glands become very hyperplastic and lose colloid while the diet lacks iodine; when iodine is administered, large amounts of colloid distend the follicles.[3, 27]

Antithyroid Compounds

Goiters have been produced experimentally by feeding different kinds of natural foods and by administering chemical compounds that block the synthesis of thyroid hormone.[58] Two principal categories of compounds have been found to possess antithyroid activity. The first and most active group includes the thiocarbamide derivatives such as thiourea, thiouracil, and propylthiouracil. The second category contains compounds that have an amino-benzene ring in their structure, including the sulfa drugs. paraaminobenzoic acid, paraaminosalicylic acid, etc. Other compounds such as 5-vinyl-2-thioöxazolidine, from the seeds of rape, cabbage, kale, and turnips, are also active goitrogens. The sulfonylureas, a group of compounds used clinically in the treatment of diabetes mellitus, also have antithyroid properties.[65, 69]

SULFONAMIDES AND THIOUREAS. It was first shown in 1941 that goiter could be produced in rats by the administration of sulfaguanidine. Shortly thereafter, it was found that other sulfonamides and thiourea also acted in a similar manner and produced large hyperplastic goiters in rats, mice, and dogs. Furthermore, the important observation was made that goiters of this type could not be prevented by giving even massive doses of iodide, leading to the conclusion that the drugs acted by suppressing the synthesis of thyroid hormone. The hyperplasia of the thyroid in response to these agents did not occur after hypophysectomy, indicating that the goiter was mediated by some pituitary factor, most probably TSH. These studies also provided convincing evidence that hormone synthesis by the thyroid could be divorced completely from the histologic picture of overactivity. Such enlarged, hyperplastic goiters produced little, if any, thyroid hormone, and the basal metabolic rates of the animals were at or near the thyroidectomy level. The administration of thyroxine to intact animals receiving antithyroid drugs restored the metabolic rate and completely prevented the thyroid hyperplasia.[62, 63]

The thioureas, sulfonamides, and related compounds apparently produce goiter in the following manner. The thyroids of treated animals can accumulate iodide in a normal manner, but the iodination of tyrosine in the gland is blocked. Thyroxine cannot be synthesized and oxygen consumption falls. The low levels of circulating thyroxine elicit an augmented output of TSH by the anterior pituitary, and the latter hormone causes hypertrophy, hyperplasia, and loss of colloid from the thyroid. Although the thyrotrophin causes enormous enlargement of the thyroid and an increased secretory surface, it still cannot synthesize thyroxine (Fig. 7–11). The goiter can be relieved only by administering thyroxine or withdrawing the anti-thyroid drug. The enlarged thyroid (goiter) could be made to shrink below normal size by removing the pituitary, the source of TSH, but such glands would not produce any thyroxine so long as the goitrogen was administered.

While the thioureas and sulfonamides both prevent the iodina-tion of tyrosine, the goiters produced by these two classes of com-pounds respond differently to dietary iodine. The goiters resulting from relatively low levels of thiourea and thiouracil can be reduced in weight by feeding small amounts of iodide, but no such effect

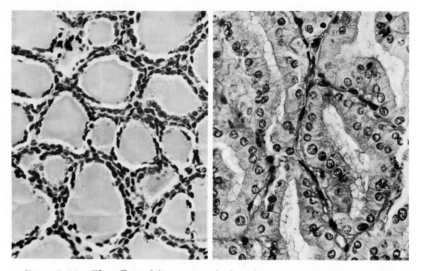

Figure 7–11. The effect of thiourea on the histology of the rat's thyroid. *A*, Normal thyroid; *B*, thyroid of rat fed 0.6 per cent thiourea for 21 days. Notice the loss of colloid and the hyperplastic epithelium in the gland of the treated animal. (From Mackenzie, C. G.: Federation Proceedings, *17*, 1958.)

is observed in the goiters resulting from the sulfonamides. The dietary iodide reduces the hyperplasia and loss of colloid in the thiourea- and thiouracil-induced goiters, but in the sulfonamide-induced goiters, these changes are intensified by the same amounts of dietary iodide.

The mechanisms involved in the production of goiter by the anti-thyroid agents seem to be essentially the same in warm-blooded and cold-blooded vertebrates. Thyroid tumors appear frequently on the gills and in the leg cartilages of *Ambystoma punctatum* reared in solutions of propylthiouracil.[19] Cells from the hyperplastic thyroids apparently are carried through the heart to the gill capillaries where they are filtered out and differentiate into thyroid follicles. Similar thyroid growths have been found in the lungs of mice after thiouracil feeding.[12, 15, 21, 22]

THIOCYANATE.   Goiters may be produced by the administration of thiocyanate, if the blood iodide concentration is low. Its goitrogenic activity can be abolished by adding iodide to the diet. Thiocyanate, perchlorate, periodate, and other oxyacids of the two latter substances produce goiter by interfering with the "trapping" of iodide ions by the thyroid gland and by causing a discharge of concentrated iodide already in the gland at the time of their administration. These substances do not block any of the synthetic mechanisms in the thyroid, *i.e.*, oxidation, iodination of tyrosine, and coupling, but act in some way to inhibit the accumulation of iodide within the gland. If the dietary intake of iodide is high, enough may enter the gland to permit the synthesis of adequate amounts of thyroxine, and goiter does not occur. The mechanism involved in the reduced iodide accumulation is unknown.

THYROCALCITONIN AND CALCITONIN

Much experimental evidence has accumulated since 1961 indicating that the thyroid-parathyroid complex of mammals is the source of a fast-acting hormone which lowers the level of serum calcium. The hormone is released in response to hypercalcemia, and opposes the action of parathormone, the hormone of the parathyroid gland. The main point of controversy at present is whether the calcium-lowering principle originates in the parathyroid gland or in the thyroid gland, or in both glands. Investigators have arrived at contradictory conclusions, and it is too early to foresee the outcome of this dilemma.[20, 43]

Copp and his co-workers first identified a calcium-lowering factor which existed as an impurity in commercial parathyroid extracts and called it "calcitonin." Munson reported that removal of the parathyroids of the rat by cautery produced a greater fall in serum calcium than removal of the same glands by surgical excision. Hirsch *et al.* found that cautery of the thyroid produces hypocalcemia in the rat, and this was offered as an explanation of the earlier findings of Munson. They adduced evidence that the calcium-lowering principle originated in the thyroid, rather than in the parathyroid, and called the substance "thyrocalcitonin." By using rats carrying functional parathyroid grafts, Talmage *et al.* have substantiated the presence of a hypocalcemic factor from the thyroid and demonstrated that it is normally conveyed by the blood. Thyrocalcitonin is distinct from thyroxine and triiodothyronine and appears to be a polypeptide.[44, 66, 78]

In an attempt to reconcile conflicting data, it has been suggested that the parathyroid itself is not the source of the hypocalcemic principle, but that the parathyroid produces a humoral substance (releasing factor) which stimulates the thyroid to release thyrocalcitonin. This view implies that both parathyroid and thyroid tissues are needed in the rat for normal responses to hypercalcemia. If this interpretation is correct, the close spatial relationship of the two glands, as occurs in mammals, may not be fortuitous.[33]

PHYSIOLOGY OF THE THYROID GLAND

Control of Thyroid Secretion

Pituitary Thyrotrophin (TSH)

This is the main factor controlling thyroid function under normal conditions (Figs. 7–12 and 7–13). After hypophysectomy the capacity of the thyroid to trap I^{131} is greatly decreased, and only traces of thyroxine appear in the circulation. The synthesis and discharge of thyroid hormone are automatically adjusted to the demand in accordance with the levels of hormone present in the blood. High circulating levels of thyroid hormone depress the output of pituitary TSH, whereas low levels increase it. As mentioned previously, goiter develops when the thyroid cannot meet the demands of the organism for thyroxine and TSH stimulates it at an excessive rate for prolonged periods. Furthermore, derangement of the physiologic feedback mechanism can produce neoplastic growths in the anterior hypophysis. A marked and sustained deficiency of thyroid hormone in the circulation may induce tumors involving the pituitary thyrotrophs, the cells that appear to be responsible for the secretion of TSH. Pituitary tumors of this type have been produced in laboratory rodents by surgical thyroidectomy, radiothyroidectomy, and by giving propylthiouracil for long periods.[31, 35]

It has not been finally decided whether the pituitary gland

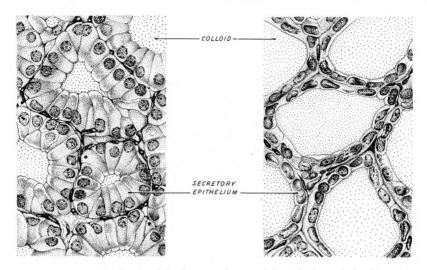

Figure 7–12. Regulation of the functional state of the rat's thyroid gland by means of thyrotrophic hormone from the anterior lobe of the hypophysis. *Left,* Thyroid from a normal rat which had received ten daily injections of thyrotrophic hormone. Notice the high columnar cells of the secretory epithelium and the loss of colloid. *Right,* Thyroid from a rat six months after complete removal of the pituitary gland. When an animal is deprived of thyrotrophic hormone, the thyroid gland becomes inactive; the cells of the secretory epithelium become low cuboidal or nearly squamous in type, and colloid distends the follicles. The two glands are drawn to scale.

produces one or several thyrotrophins. Clinical studies have suggested that abnormal kinds of thyrotrophins may appear in the serum of some thyrotoxic patients.[1] A substance closely related to TSH has been found in pituitary extracts; it is especially potent in producing exophthalmos, an abnormal protrusion of the eyeball. Most workers feel that the "exophthalmos-producing substance" is not a distinct anterior pituitary hormone, but that it may be an abnormal kind of TSH involved in the etiology of this eye defect.[23, 42]

Compensatory Adjustments

Unless adequate amounts of iodide are provided, the thyroid cannot meet the requirements of the body for thyroid hormone. During iodine deficiency, the pituitary secretes augmented amounts of TSH and, under its influence, a compensatory adjustment occurs that results in the production of a more extensive secretory epithelium. The thyroid cells enlarge (hypertrophy) and increase mitotically (hyperplasia); thus the gland enlarges in an attempt to make up for the deficient activity of the individual cells. While the hyperplastic gland loses colloid, the epithelial cells increase in height, the follicular walls are plicated, vascularity is increased, and the gland generally increases in weight. *Goiter* is a term generally applied to the various types of thyroid enlargement. These morpho-

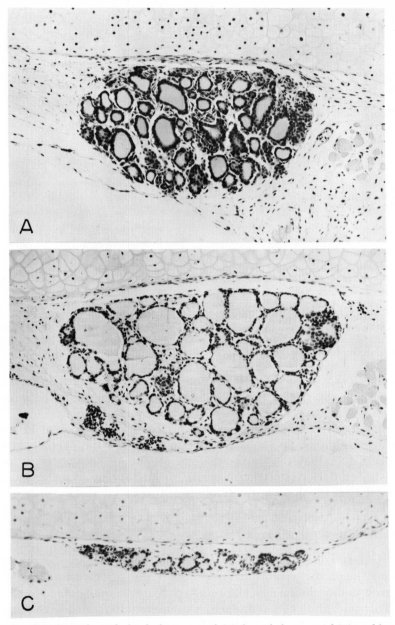

Figure 7-13. Thyroid glands from normal (*A*), hypothalectomized (*B*), and hypophysectomized (*C*) tadpoles of *Rana pipiens*. The hypothalectomized animals possess a pars distalis which is not connected with the brain. Since the thyroid glands from such animals contain follicles with very flat epithelia and contain abundant colloid, it may be concluded that the output of TSH by the disconnected pars distalis is subnormal. In the hypophysectomized animal, TSH is lacking and the thyroids are very small and atrophic (*C*). (Courtesy of Dr. Y. Hanaoka, Gunma University, Maebashi, Japan.)

logic changes indicate excitation, and so far as is known, TSH is the sole instrument that induces them. Since transplanted thyroids react to changing physiologic states exactly as do the intact glands, it seems that hormones are more essential than regulatory nerves to the organ.

If, over a period of time, the pituitary stimulation does not succeed in restoring the thyroid secretion to normal, the gland enters into a phase of exhaustion from which it may never recover. The secretory cells of the exhausted gland decrease in size, and some of the cells degenerate and are removed from the epithelium (atrophy). On the other hand, if a more adequate iodine supply becomes available, pituitary stimulation is reduced and the hyperplastic gland subsides. The thyroid gland may repeat this cycle many times during the life of the individual:

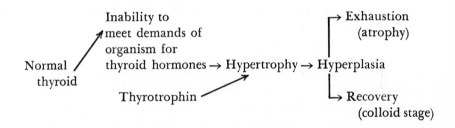

Marine advanced the concept that large colloid goiters might result from subjecting the thyroid repeatedly to hyperplasia and regression. This theory has been tested by administering sulfaguanidine to rats and withholding the treatment at intervals. When the goitrogen was withdrawn at the end of the third feeding period, the hyperplastic thyroids promptly accumulated colloid and the follicular epithelium regressed to the low cuboidal type. After a month, no sulfaguanidine being given, the thyroids continued to be two and a half times the normal size. Similar results have been obtained in the hamster, the animals being placed repeatedly on iodine-deficient diets.

Environment and Thyroid Function

It is known that many kinds of environmental stimuli can affect the release of hormones from the thyroid gland. The exposure of warm-blooded animals to cold environments increases thyroid activity. On the other hand, emotional and systemic stressors exert inhibitory effects on thyroid function. While noxious stimuli promote an augmented release of ACTH and a consequent activation of the adrenal cortex, the same stimuli apparently reduce the pituitary release of TSH and diminish thyroid functions.

TEMPERATURE. When rats are exposed to cold, an increase in metabolic rate occurs rapidly and thyroid hyperplasia becomes apparent after prolonged exposure. Thyroidectomized animals survive only for relatively short periods at low environmental temperatures. Survival apparently depends on the presence of thyroid hormone and an increase in metabolic rate. Histologic changes in the thyroid gland of the guinea pig, indicating TSH stimulation, occur within 30 minutes after exposure to cold. When TSH is administered to rabbits pretreated with I^{131}, labeled thyroxine appears in the thyroid vein blood after a very short latent period. These results indicate that the response of the pituitary-thyroid axis to cold is too rapid to be explained on the basis of increased utilization of thyroxine by the peripheral tissues and the operation of a feedback mechanism. It is more probable that the cold stimulus activates a nervous reflex, which operates through the hypothalamus to augment and maintain the release of pituitary thyrotrophin.[13, 25, 46, 77]

EMOTIONAL AND SYSTEMIC STRESSORS. Physical stressors, such as hemorrhage, trauma, and the injection of irritating substances, induce a prompt and prolonged inhibition of thyroid secretion, presumably a consequence of diminished release of TSH. Pain, restraint, changing illumination, and other emotional situations likewise cause a prompt reduction of thyroid hormone secretion. This inhibitory influence on the thyroid also occurs rapidly and most probably involves the nervous system. During the period of thyroid inhibition, the concentration of thyroxine in the circulation is diminished; if the response were due to the operation of a feedback mechanism, the blood levels of thyroxine would be expected to rise in order to reduce the output of TSH. It is difficult to account for the observation that surgical trauma in the rabbit continues to cause thyroid inhibition after the pituitary stalk has been sectioned.[14]

Hypothalamus and TSH Secretion

It is well known that reducing the secretory surface of the thyroid gland by subtotal thyroidectomy diminishes the blood thyroxine levels and the pituitary gland accordingly augments its release of TSH. When about three-fourths of the rat's thyroid is removed, the remaining fragment undergoes hypertrophy and the thyroid:serum iodide ratio (T:S ratio) increases. After destroying proper areas of the hypothalamus by electrolytic lesions, the compensatory hypertrophy of the thyroid fragment does not occur. This indicates that the hypothalamic lesions may prevent the elevated output of TSH by the pituitary gland. Much evidence from different mammalian species indicates that the pituitary gonadotrophins, corticotrophin, and thyrotrophin may be independently affected, depending upon the specific area of the hypothalamus that is destroyed. The implication of these studies is that nervous impulses discharged in hypothalamic centers result in the formation of release factors that are carried to the anterior hypophysis *via* the hypophysial portal veins.

Using the remote control method, it is possible to apply localized electrical stimuli to the hypothalamus for prolonged periods of time. A coil of wire is implanted subcutaneously in the lumbar region, and leads are passed under the skin to connect this coil with electrodes implanted into the brain with the aid of a stereotaxic instrument. The hypothalamic area of the unanesthetized animal may be stimulated by remote control by placing it in an electromagnetic field and inducing a certain voltage in the coil implanted under the skin. Particular areas of the hypothalamus may be stimulated continuously for several days in this manner. Since hypothalamic stimulation may cause ACTH release and since the adrenal cortical hormones are known to depress thyroid activity in the rabbit, adrenalectomized animals give the most reliable results in studies with TSH. Stimulation of the anterior median eminence results in an accelerated release of thyrotrophin from the anterior pituitary, as determined by the release of radioactive materials from the thyroid. There is general agreement that a neural mechanism concerned with TSH secretion is located in the median eminence region of the hypothalamus.[41]

The problem of how the circulating thyroid hormones regulate the pituitary release of TSH is a very complicated one and has not been settled. The fact that radioactive thyroxine and triiodothyronine tend to collect in the paraventricular region of the hypothalamus, as well as in the neuro- and adenohypophysis, is an interesting observation but of unknown significance. It is quite possible that the blood level of thyroid hormone affects the release of TSH by way of a hypothalamic mechanism, as well as by action directly on the pituitary gland. The hypothalamic mechanism appears to influence TSH secretion in both an excitatory and inhibitory manner, and there are strong indications that the integrity of the hypophysial portal system is essential for this control. On the other hand, injected thyroxine effectively decreases the output of TSH by pituitary transplants persisting in the anterior eye chambers of hypophysectomized rabbits. Thyroxine exerts the same effect in rabbits after section of the pituitary stalk. Thus, it seems reasonably well established that high levels of blood thyroxine can act directly on the pituitary to inhibit the release of TSH, but such studies do not rule out the possibility of hypothalamic mechanisms also being involved in the regulation of TSH secretion.

Metabolic Effects of Thyroid Hormone

Calorigenesis

HOMOIOTHERMS. In warm-blooded animals the most characteristic effect of thyroid hormone is to increase the energy production and oxygen consumption of most normal tissues. The basal metabolic rate (BMR) falls rapidly after thyroidectomy or hypophysectomy and may be elevated above the normal level by administering thyroid hormone. The increased metabolism of hyperthyroid animals is reflected in the accelerated respiration of its excised tissues; tissues taken from thyroidectomized animals respire at a comparatively low rate. After administration of thyroid hormone to the animal, the respiration of surviving liver, kidney, skeletal muscle, cardiac muscle, gastric mucosa, and diaphragm is strikingly increased. Several workers have found that the respiration of surviving brain, spleen, and testis is not enhanced by hormone administered to the animal and that the respiration of thyroid tissue is decreased by the same procedure. A number of enzyme systems, notably cytochrome oxidase, cytochrome c, and succinoxidase, increase in the tissues after thyroxine administration to the animal and are diminished by thyroidectomy or thiouracil feeding.

Calorigenesis in the normal organism is regulated by a balance of hormonal factors, thyroid hormone not being the only hormone involved. Heat production in the rat declines more abruptly after hypophysectomy than after thyroidectomy. Thyroxine and triiodothyronine elevate the BMR more effectively in thyroidectomized animals than in hypophysectomized animals. Doses of TSH sufficient to cause thyroid hypertrophy in hypophysectomized rats increase the BMR but do not restore it to normal. It is apparent that the anterior pituitary affects calorigenesis in some manner in addition to its production of TSH. Corticotrophin (ACTH), acting to promote the secretion of adrenal steroids, appears to be an important factor. Certain adrenal cortical hormones (and ACTH) are calorigenic in the absence of the pituitary, of the thyroid, or of both glands. There is a gradual decline in ACTH production after thyroidectomy, and the adrenal cortices undergo considerable involution. When thyroxine is administered to the thyroidectomized animal, it not only restores the functional capacity of the adrenal cortex but also promotes the release of somatotrophin (STH) by the anterior pituitary and intensifies the action of this hormone on the peripheral tissues. The decline in growth rate that follows thyroidectomy of the young rat parallels the decline in BMR. Hypophysectomized rats stop growing almost immediately, whereas thyroidectomized animals are capable of growing at a reduced rate. It is probable that the immediate loss of STH after hypophysectomy accounts, in part at least, for the more rapid decline in BMR and growth than occurs after thyroidectomy.

Experiments on the rat provide evidence that STH augments the action of exogenous TSH on the thyroid gland of the hypophysectomized rat, both hormones increasing calorigenesis more effectively than when TSH is given alone. STH also potentiates the calorigenic action of thyroxine in hypophysectomized rats, indicating that the calorigenic effect of STH is exerted in part at the level of the peripheral tissues.

Epinephrine, a hormone of the adrenal medulla, also has a calorigenic effect. It has been proposed that an important role of thyroxine in cold acclimatization of the rat is to potentiate the calorigenic action of endogenous epinephrine. Observations of this type provide an excellent example of the interaction of multiple hormones in conditioning metabolic processes.

POIKILOTHERMS. While thyroid hormones are identifiable in the thyroids of all vertebrate classes, it has been difficult to demonstrate calorigenic effects in the poikilotherms, or cold-blooded vertebrates. Both positive and negative results have been reported with fishes and amphibians. Numerous observations on fishes seem to imply that the piscine thyroid is more involved in the metabolism of salts and water than in oxidative metabolism. The thyroid gland of the goldfish (*Carassius auratus*) appears to be very inactive throughout the year, and at no season does it undergo hypertrophy after the administration of thiourea and other goitrogens. It does, however, respond strongly to the administration of TSH. It has been suggested that the inactive thyroid in this species may enable it to tolerate an exceptionally wide range of temperatures (0 to 41°C.). The thyroid of *Triturus viridescens*, an aquatic urodele, is more inactive than that of *Desmognathus fuscus*, a terrestrial urodele, and the thyroids of the two species respond differently to goitrogenic agents. The thyroidal differences may correlate with the temperature ranges of the two amphibians. Thyroidectomy of the teleost parrot fish does not diminish oxygen consumption, nor does the administration of L-thyroxine elevate it.[9, 28, 64]

While birds and mammals can maintain their body temperatures in the cold, the reptile can only demonstrate a temperature sensitivity. There is evidence that the turtle, a poikilotherm, is sensitive to temperature changes, although it cannot regulate its body temperature. Exposing turtles to cold stress produces eosinopenia, whereas epinephrine injections cause eosinophilia. Cold stress appears to activate nervous and hormonal mechanisms, but the animal fails to maintain a fixed body temperature; this may indicate that the stress hormones cannot stimulate heat production or that the animal cannot reduce heat loss at low temperatures.

There are strong indications that environmental temperature

may be a very important factor in conditioning thyroidal responses in the poikilotherms. If the lizard, *Anolis carolinensis*, is maintained at room temperature (20 to 24°C.), thyroidectomy, or the administration of thyroxine or TSH, has no effect on oxygen consumption. When these lizards are maintained at a constant temperature of 30°C., thyroidectomy reduces oxygen consumption, and thyroxine or TSH elevates it.

HIBERNATION. In warm-blooded animals that are active throughout the year, the thyroids are generally more active during the cold winter months than during the summer. However, in hibernating mammals, the thyroid tends to be inactive during the winter and reaches a high peak of activity in the spring as the animals emerge from hibernation. Most observations indicate that the reverse is true among hibernating poikilotherms. In hibernating frogs and toads, for example, the thyroid is moderately active during the winter and is most inactive during the summer.

Electrolytes and Water

In hypothyroidism there is an extracellular retention of sodium and chloride and water, the blood volume being considerably reduced. When thyroid hormone is administered under these conditions, it causes diuresis and urinary loss of sodium. The plasma volume is elevated. Administration of the hormone to normal subjects also produces excessive water loss through the kidney, but under these conditions the urine is especially rich in potassium. This suggests that there has been a mobilization of intracellular fluid. When small amounts of thyroxine are given to young growing animals, they enhance calcium retention. This is probably a secondary effect resulting from the protein anabolic action of the hormone, which facilitates the deposition of new bone matrix. In hyperthyroid states there is increased mobilization of calcium from the skeleton and increased loss through the urine and feces. The calcium concentration of the blood is not appreciably changed.

Protein Metabolism

One of the most characteristic effects of cretinism and myxedema in human subjects is the deposition of a mucoprotein substance in the skin and other tissues. This protein is thought to be the same as that which constitutes the intercellular cement normally found between tissue cells. It is similar in composition to the mucin in which the fetal tissues are embedded. Thyroid hormones relieve the excessive accumulation of mucoprotein in the tissues of hypothyroid subjects.

Thyroid hormone may produce either a protein anabolic or a protein catabolic effect. Human cretinism may be simulated experimentally by removing the thyroid gland of the young animal or by feeding antithyroid drugs. Cretinic rats may be produced by feeding thiouracil to the pregnant mother and continuing it during the course of lactation. At the time of weaning (22 days) the cretinic rats weigh about 19 gm. as compared with 42 gm. for normal controls. The subnormal growth of these animals is due partly to the voluntary reduction of food intake consequent upon a low BMR, but it also suggests a deficiency in protein synthesis. The carcass of young thyroidectomized rats contains less protein and more fat than normal controls. When such animals are force-fed to cause a weight gain, there is a further reduction in carcass protein and a further increase in carcass fat. Although thyroid deficiency favors increased nitrogen excretion, thyroidectomized rats are able to maintain a positive nitrogen balance. Profound shifts in protein stores occur in the thyroidectomized animal. The total plasma protein of the rat increases as much as 30 per cent after thyroidectomy, whereas the liver and kidneys are small and deficient in protein. The deficiencies of hypothyroidism can be corrected by adequate doses of thyroid hormone. Nitrogen retention is obtained and growth occurs at a normal rate; liver enlargement and the elevated plasma globulin are corrected.[57]

A protein anabolic effect of thyroxine has been demonstrated in the young hypophysectomized rat. The growth of nearly all tissues may be stimulated by thyroxine in the absence of pituitary hormones. The protein content of the pelt, including hair, is greatly increased. Physiologic doses of thyroxine must be employed in order to demonstrate protein anabolic effects; toxic amounts of the hormone do not stimulate growth.[72]

Fat Metabolism

Hypothyroidism is generally associated with a rise in serum cholesterol and phospholipid, which may be restored to normal levels by administering thyroxine. Since thyroid hormone increases the oxidative processes of the body, the carbohydrate stores may be depleted. If this occurs, fat is mobilized from the tissue deposits to the liver, and the rate of ketone body formation is augmented. Depot fat is usually not increased appreciably during thyroid deficiency because of reduced caloric intake.

Carbohydrate Metabolism

Thyroid hormone accelerates the rate of absorption of monosaccharides from the alimentary tract. Liver glycogen stores are diminished as a consequence of hepatic glycogenolysis, and the blood sugar levels tend to rise. The hyperglycemic effect of thyroid hormone is partially offset by the simultaneous increase in the oxidation of sugar by the tissues. Hypothyroidism increases hepatic glycogen without altering the fat content. The administration of thyroid hormone can produce diabetes mellitus in animals after the removal of a portion of the pancreas, but it does not produce diabetes in animals having an intact and healthy pancreas. Insulin requirements generally increase in hyperthyroidism and decrease in hypothyroidism. The administration of thyroxine or triiodo-thyronine to the rat increases the rate of degradation of insulin-I^{131}, and removal of the thyroid decreases it. Pancreatic diabetes in the cat and dog is not ameliorated by thyroidectomy, as it is by hypophysectomy or adrenalectomy.

Effects of Thyroid on Reproduction

There is ample evidence that normal reproductive functions depend upon thyroid activity, though there appear to be many species and age differences. Testicular functions are more easily impaired in young animals than in adults. Histologic defects have been observed in the testes of cretinic rats, produced by feeding thiouracil to the mother during pregnancy and lactation. At 40 days of age the testes from the cretinic animals weigh about 112 mg. as against 893 mg. for the controls. The cretinic testes contain spermatozoa, but the infantile nature of the sex accessory organs indicates that androgens are not being secreted at this age. Hypothyroidism appears to delay sexual development in the young male and toxic levels of thyroxine to impair reproductive functions. However, moderate amounts of thyroid hormone have been reported to stimulate spermatogenesis in the rabbit, mouse, ram, and human subject, even when there is no demonstrable thyroid deficiency.

Thyroid deficiencies or excesses in the female may impair the ovaries and cause the cycles to cease or to become irregular. Reproduction in most species may occur after removal of the thyroid, but fecundity is usually subnormal. The litter size of hypothyroid rats is reduced and many of the young die because of insufficient lactation by the mother. There is evidence that thyroid deficiency may render the ovary particularly susceptible to cyst formation, a disorder frequently associated with infertility in man and domestic animals. At 40 days of age the ovaries of cretinic rats do not contain vesicular follicles and lack lipid and cholesterol. When equine gonadotrophin is administered to the cretinic animals, the ovaries respond by forming large follicles without luteinization; normal ovaries respond to this gonadotrophin by forming both follicles and corpora lutea. Thus hypothyroidism in the rat brings about some change in the ovary that favors the development of cystic follicles.[45, 59, 68]

Little is known about the exact manner in which thyroid hormones influence reproductive processes. Some of the impairments may be consequent upon disturbances in protein metabolism; others may be attributable to pituitary malfunctions. The anterior pituitary secretes large amounts of TSH after thyroidectomy, and under these conditions the gland enlarges and vacuoles appear in the basophils (thyrotrophs). The vacuolated basophils are generally regarded as active rather than degenerating elements. Thyroxine not only reinstates growth in the thyroidless rat but also repairs the pituitary defects. In the hypophysectomized animal, thyroxine increases the rate of oxygen consumption, accelerates the heart rate, etc., but it does not restore normal body growth, adrenocortical growth, or reproductive development. These facts suggest that thyroid hormones exert some control over the release from the hypophysis of somatotrophin, corticotrophin, and gonadotrophins. There is no direct evidence indicating whether these defects of the thyroidectomized animal are due to reduced ability of the pituitary to secrete gonadotrophins, ACTH, and STH or to an inability of the target organs to respond normally in the absence of thyroid hormone.

Growth and Differentiation of Tissues

Most vertebrates cannot attain normal adult form and dimensions in the absence of thyroid secretions. There is evidence that thyroid hormone and somatotrophin act synergistically in promoting normal skeletal growth. The arrest of endochondral ossification that occurs in the young hypophysectomized rat may be prevented by the administration of thyroxine. In the absence of pituitary hormones, thyroxine permits the erosion of cartilage and its replacement by bone to continue, but chondrogenesis itself is not maintained. (Fig. 7–14).[2]

Thyroxine has been shown to have a direct effect on skeletal tissue of the chick grown *in vitro*. In these experiments it was found that the same concentration of hormone may be stimulatory or toxic depending upon the stage of differentiation of the tissue and the particular bone rudiment treated.

Thyroid hormone is essential for the metamorphosis of amphibian larvae, and this response has provided a useful method for bioassaying the hormone. The capacity of thyroid hormone to promote tissue differentiation is not directly related to its calorigenic action. Dinitrophenol increases the metabolic rate, but it does not produce

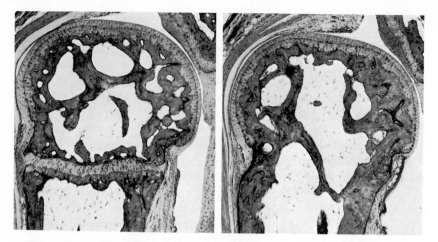

Figure 7-14. The effect of thyroid hormone on the epiphyseal plates of the hypophysectomized rat. *A*, Distal end of third metacarpal of a rat one year after removal of the pituitary gland. Hypophysectomy retards skeletal maturation; the epiphyseal cartilage plates persist in the hypophysectomized subject, but in the normal animal, they close at about 100 days of age. *B*, Comparable bone from a hypophysectomized animal that received thyroxine injections for one year. Note that the epiphyseal cartilages have been resorbed. (From Asling, Simpson, Li, and Evans: Anat. Rec., *119*, 1954.)

this morphogenetic effect. Furthermore, certain stages of amphibian metamorphosis are promoted by thyroid hormone without being accompanied by an elevated metabolic rate.

Effects on Cardiovascular and Nervous Systems

In hypothyroidism the heart enlarges, and its rate and amplitude are diminished. Under these conditions the mass movement of blood is less than normal. The isolated perfused heart increases in rate and stroke volume when thyroxine is added to the perfusion medium. In hyperthyroidism there is typically a tachycardia, increased stroke volume, peripheral vasodilatation, and an increase in pulse pressure.

Numerous controlled experiments have demonstrated that thyroid hormone sensitizes the nervous system. There is good correlation between the basal metabolic rate and the rate of emanation of alpha waves from the brain. That a functional impairment of the nervous system results from hypothyroidism is indicated by the lowered resistance to narcotics, the increased thresholds to light and sound stimulations, the diminished alpha rhythms, and the decreased speed of reaction to electric shocks.

In hyperthyroid patients, as well as in rats receiving thyroxine injections, the BMR is elevated but the oxygen consumption of the brain remains normal. Dinitrophenol elevates the BMR but has no effect on brain excitability. These facts indicate that the increased excitability of the central nervous system after thyroid hormone administration is separable from the metabolic effects of the hormone. Changes in electrolyte distribution brought about by the hormone appear to be associated with brain excitability. Triiodothyronine is about five times more effective than thyroxine in increasing brain excitability in the rat. However, the effects of triiodothyronine are more transient than those of thyroxine.

Hormones and Molting

In mammals without seasonal molts (*e.g.*, mouse and man), the replacement of hair is an autonomous property of the hair follicle, but endocrine factors influence the cycle to some extent. Thyroidectomy of the mouse retards hair replacement, whereas adrenalectomy or gonadectomy accelerate it. Seasonal molting is characteristic of many mammals (*e.g.*, ferret), and in these species, neuroendocrine mechanisms play a very important role in the mediation of environmental stimuli.[47]

Molting has been extensively studied in birds, and it is a very complex process involving the interaction of genetic and neuroendocrine factors. There are many species differences, and not all areas of the body respond in the same way. Thyroxine acts to promote molting, though in some species it is not absolutely essential; thyroidectomy has the reverse effect. Estrogens and androgens counteract the molt-inducing effects of thyroxine; progesterone encourages molting, especially in those species that breed throughout the year.[52] Prolactin also causes molting in some birds.[49] Seasonal molting is apparently controlled by external factors, acting *via* the hypothalamus, to induce variations in the endocrine system.

Molting in amphibians is a dual process involving (a) an inherent tendency of the skin to stratify and to keratinize and (b) the periodic removal of the slough which is regulated by neuroendocrine mechanisms. The specific hormonal controls differ in the anurans and urodeles.

Toads (Bufonidae) molt at intervals varying from one to two weeks, each animal maintaining its own individual rhythm rather precisely under uniform environmental conditions. Normal molting is abolished by hypophysectomy and is not restored by the administration of thyroxine. Adrenocortical steroids, on the other hand, induce molting in hypophysectomized toads. Molting can be produced in toads carrying ectopic autotransplants of the anterior pituitary by administering vasopressin. The neurohypophysial principle apparently stimulates the graft to release ACTH, which causes the adrenocortical tissue to discharge its steroids. Autonomous cyclic processes seem to be inherent in the skin, but these are sensitive to varying levels of hormones in the circulation. The hormones of the steroidogenic component of the adrenal, rather than those

Figure 7–15. Thyroidectomized newts *(Diemictylus viridescens)* undergoing molts following the subcutaneous implantation of thyroxine-cholesterol pellets. *A,* General molt produced by 0.96 μg thyroxine; *B,* local molt (arrow) over an implant containing 0.03 μg thyroxine; *C,* local molt (arrow) over an implant containing 0.07 μg thyroxine. (From Clark, N. B., and Kaltenbach, J. C.: Gen. & Comp. Endocrinol., *1*:513, 1961.)

of the thyroid, seem to be the major ones affecting the anuran integument.[48]

Among urodeles, the thyroid hormones seem to perform a more important role in the molting process. Thyroidectomy or hypophysectomy prevents molting in urodeles; after these operations, the keratinized layers accumulate but are not sloughed. TSH induces shedding when administered to hypophysectomized urodeles; exogenous thyroxine is effective both in hypophysectomized and thyroidectomized animals. Prolactin has been reported to produce shedding in hypophysectomized urodeles. The implantation of thyroxine pellets into the skin of thyroidectomized newts produces localized molting (Fig. 7–15). This indicates that thyroxine acts directly upon the skin in these amphibians.[16, 50, 51]

Amphibian Metamorphosis

The best-known function of the thyroid gland in poikilotherms is the control of amphibian metamorphosis (Fig. 7–16 and frontispiece). This effect was discovered by Gudernatsch (1912), who fed many kinds of mammalian tissues to amphibian larvae and found that thyroid tissue, unlike all others, caused suppression of growth and precocious metamorphosis (see frontispiece).[39] Thyroid feeding produced this effect in both anurans and urodeles. Other workers devised methods for removing the anlage of the thyroid in early larval stages and showed that thyroidless larvae continued to grow normally but failed to metamorphose. Such larvae may become gigantic in size, since they continue to grow long after the unoperated controls have metamorphosed into adults. Adler (1914) found that hypophysectomy of the larvae prevented accumulation of colloid in the thyroid and that such animals fail to metamorphose. These

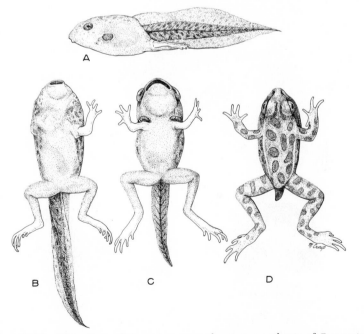

Figure 7–16. The effect of thyroxine upon the metamorphosis of *Rana pipiens* tadpoles. *A*, Untreated control removed at the end of the experiment (about life size). *D*, A metamorphosed tadpole killed two weeks after the first thyroxine was added to the aquarium water. Animals *B* and *C* were removed at intervals during this period. *B*, *C*, and *D* are a little larger than life size. Note the changes in the mouth, paired appendages, and tail.

findings have been confirmed and extended by many investigators, and it is now definitely established that thyroid activity is controlled by TSH from the anterior pituitary. Iodine and various iodine compounds can replace the thyroid secretions in promoting amphibian metamorphosis, but this is probably due to the formation of thyroid hormone through the combination of iodine with tyrosine present in body tissues other than the thyroid itself.

Before the onset of metamorphosis the frog tadpole is an aquatic animal having well-developed gills, a long flattened tail, and lidless eyes and, being herbivorous, has horny rasping teeth and a relatively long intestine. The adult frog is adapted to terrestrial life, breathes by means of lungs, has well-developed limbs and no tail, and is carnivorous. During metamorphosis, therefore, larval structures such as gills, tail, and horny teeth are lost, whereas eyelids, lungs, and limbs develop (Fig. 7–17). Many of the larval structures that are carried over to the adult undergo extensive changes. The skin thickens and becomes more glandular, the brain becomes more highly differentiated, the gill arches become modified into the hyoid apparatus, and the intestine becomes proportionately shorter. It is obvious that certain tissues do not respond to thyroid hormone at metamorphosis; some exhibit marked growth, whereas others de-

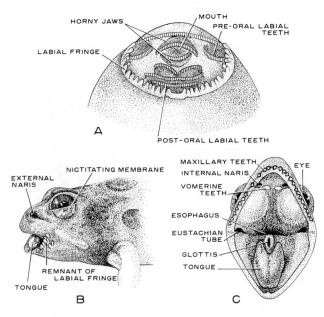

Figure 7–17. Changes in the mouth parts during the metamorphosis of *Rana pipiens*. *A*, The mouth of a young tadpole at an early stage of metamorphosis. The mouth is bounded above and below by horny beaks; two rows of pre-oral labial teeth and three rows of post-oral labial teeth are present, and the labial fringe is prominent. *B*, A tadpole at about stage 21 showing a remnant of the labial fringe at each corner of the mouth. *C*, The mouth parts of a completely metamorphosed frog.

generate.[61] Certain tissues show a sharp rise in mitotic activity during the period of metamorphic climax. Localized regression of the dorsal fin of the tadpole may be produced by inserting pellets of thyroxine or its analogues into this region of the tail. Adrenal cortical steroids, mixed with the thyroid hormone in the pellet, have been found to render the thyroid hormone more effective in producing localized regressions of the fin.

The hind-brain of amphibian larvae contains a pair of giant neurons, called Mauthner's cells, and they regress at metamorphosis instead of undergoing further differentiation as the neighboring neurons do. The implantation of thyroid tissue or thyroid pellets to the hind-brain causes Mauthner's cells to regress promptly, whereas the adjacent nervous tissue responds by enlargement and increased mitotic activity.

The functional activity of the amphibian thyroid, as in mammals, is regulated by hypophysial thyrotrophin. The concentration of thyroid hormone in the blood of the anuran tadpole is extremely low during the early phases of metamorphosis, but it rises slowly, reaches a peak at the height of the metamorphic changes, and then drops rapidly after the transformations are completed. The metamorphosing tadpole must be regarded as a mosaic of parts, some of which develop a sensitivity to thyroid hormone and respond in characteristic ways to it. Exogenous hormones produce no changes until the tissues have developed a *readiness to respond*. There is apparently a progressive increase in sensitivity to the hormone, and not all of the tissues become reactive at the same time. A very important action of thyroid hormones during prometamorphosis is to stimulate the differentiation of the median eminence and its neurosecretory mechanism.[24, 82] The *increasing* concentrations of thyroid hormone in the blood, after metamorphosis starts, are probably an important factor, since different thresholds are required by different tissues. This may be demonstrated by keeping the larvae at constant temperature and administering a constant dosage of hormone. If these thresholds are not exceeded, metamorphosis progresses to a particular stage and cannot be carried to completion.[53]

Temperature is a factor of great importance in amphibian metamorphosis. Metamorphic changes do not occur in either anurans or urodeles at temperatures below 5°C. Tadpoles of *Rana pipiens* attain larger body sizes when maintained in cold water than in warm water. When thyroxine is administered to hypophysectomized tadpoles and some maintained at high temperatures and others at low temperatures, the latter animals take longer to transform and never progress as far as the ones at high temperatures. This suggests that the temperature effect on metamorphosis is largely independent of thyroid function. It is thoroughly established that the effectiveness of thyroxine analogues in promoting amphibian metamorphosis is not necessarily correlated with their capacity to elevate the metabolic rate in mammals.

Anuran and urodele larvae differ with respect to the quantity of thyroxine required for development of the corneal reflex. This is a reflexive retraction of the eye into the orbit and elevation of the nictitating membrane in response to touching the cornea. The neural center regulating this action is located in the medullary portion of the brain. A relatively high concentration of thyroid hormone is required for the full development of the corneal reflex in frog larvae, but, in urodele larvae, it appears after the quantity of thyroid hormone is radically reduced by hypophysectomy. The local application of thyroxine to the medulla, through the implantation of pellets, accelerates the development of this reflex in relation to other metamorphic changes occurring in the remainder of the body.

While most amphibians have an aquatic larval stage and a terrestrial adult stage, there are several groups in which the aquatic stage is abbreviated or omitted entirely. Members of the genus *Eleutherodactylus* lay their eggs on land, and the young are hatched as tiny, fully formed frogs.[60] External gills and other features of an aquatic tadpole are greatly suppressed or lacking entirely. In such forms exhibiting direct development, the changes can occur after thyroid hormone synthesis has been blocked by antithyroid agents, and they are not stimulated by the administration of thyroxine. Although thyroxine has some effect in hastening tail resorption, pronephros degeneration, and loss of the egg tooth, these are all retrogressive processes that are characteristic of late embryonic stages.

Nectophrynoides occidentalis is a small viviparous toad inhabiting the summits of Mount Nimba in Africa. The ovaries develop corpora lutea, and the young are retained in the maternal uterus during the nine months of pregnancy. An aquatic stage is omitted entirely, and some larval structures fail to appear or are vestigial. External and internal gills, spiracle, branchial cavity, tail fin, and horny teeth do not develop in this species. The thyroid glands of the uterine young grow and progressively accumulate colloid during the early months of gestation. At about the eighth month of gestation limbs are quickly developed and the tail regresses; these events correlate with the disappearance of colloid from the thyroid follicles. The thyroid begins to store colloid again after birth.[32]

Neoteny and the Thyroid

It is well known that certain urodeles fail to metamorphose and retain the larval body form throughout life. The animals become sexually mature and are able to reproduce without adults ever appearing. Neoteny was first described in the American axolotl, *Ambystoma tigrinun*, in which it was noted that members of this species

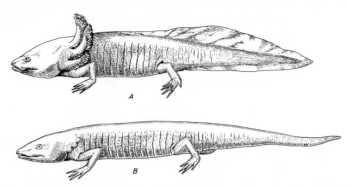

Figure 7–18. The effect of iodine implantation upon the metamorphosis of the American axolotl *(Ambystoma tigrinum)*. A, Untreated gilled or axolotl stage; B, a similar specimen 30 days after the implantation of iodine crystals below the skin. Observe the atrophy of the gills and the loss of the tail fin.

inhabiting high mountain lakes failed to metamorphose, whereas specimens of the same species living at lower altitudes metamorphosed as do most other amphibians. Axolotls can be induced to metamorphose by treating them with thyroxine or various iodine compounds. Inorganic iodine is also effective if it is implanted under the skin or into the peritoneal cavity so that it is rapidly absorbed (Fig. 7–18). These observations suggest that the failure of metamorphosis in the axolotl is due to the inability of the thyroid to secrete hormone or to a decreased sensitivity of the tissues to the hormone.

It is reasonably certain that the Mexican axolotl, *Ambystoma mexicanum*, never undergoes metamorphosis in its natural habitat. When pituitary glands of *A. tigrinum*, a readily metamorphosing form, are transplanted into *A. mexicanum* larvae, metamorphosis is induced. On the other hand, pituitaries of *A. mexicanum* do not promote metamorphosis when transplanted to the larvae of *A. tigrinum*. This indicates that the pituitary gland of the Mexican axolotl is defective and apparently does not release the proper thyrotrophin.[11]

The perennibranchiate salamanders (*e.g., Necturus, Amphiuma*) are not known to undergo metamorphosis. They retain gills, tail fins, and other larval traits throughout their lives. Even large doses of thyroid hormone or other iodine compounds fail to produce any appreciable morphologic change in these species. The indications are that the perennibranchiate amphibians retain larval characters chiefly because their tissues have not developed a responsiveness to thyroid hormone. Studies have shown that the thyroids of *Necturus* and *Amphiuma* are very slow in accumulating radioiodine and in synthesizing thyroid hormone. In salamanders, as well as in certain fishes and reptiles, great variations are observed in the capacity of the thyroid to bind iodine and synthesize hormone, complex factors such as seasonal changes and the accompanying fluctuations in endocrine balance undoubtedly being involved.

Metamorphosis in Fishes

It is well known that cyclostomes and certain teleost fish undergo metamorphic changes during their life histories, but the hormonal mechanisms involved are not so clear as in amphibians. Metamorphosis of the lamprey is striking, but it has not been possible to influence this process through the administration of exogenous thyroxine to the larvae. There are some reasons for believing that adrenocortical hormones, rather than thyroid hormones, may be involved in the metamorphic process of cyclostomes.

While metamorphosis in teleost fishes is not so impressive as in amphibians, it does occur in certain species. In the salmon, for example, the freshwater parr transforms into the migratory, marine smolt. This involves a silvering of the integument, due to the deposition of guanine, and certain physiologic adjustments which equip the smolt for life in the sea. These transformations are accompanied by increased metabolic rate and hyperactivity of the thyroid. These facts imply that thyroid hormones are important in bringing about these changes in salmonids, though it is probable that other hormones play some part.

REFERENCES

1. Adams, D. D.: The presence of an abnormal thyroid-stimulating hormone in the serum of some thyrotoxic patients. J. Clin. Endocrinol., *18*:699, 1958.
2. Asling, C. W., Simpson, M. E., Li, C. H., and Evans, H. M.: The effects of chronic administration of thyroxin to hypophysectomized rats on their skeletal growth, maturation and response to growth hormone. Anat. Record, *119*: 101, 1954.
3. Axelrad, A. A., and Leblond, C. P.: Induction of thyroid tumors in rats by a low iodine diet. Cancer 8:339, 1955.
4. Baker, K. F.: Heterotopic thyroid tissue in fishes. J. Exp. Zool., *138*:329, 1958.
5. Baker-Cohen, K. F.: Renal and other heterotopic thyroid tissue in fishes. *In* A. Gorbman (ed.): Comparative Endocrinology. New York, John Wiley & Sons, 1959, p. 283.
6. Barrington, E. J. W.: Hormones and vertebrate evolution. Experientia, *18*:201, 1962.
7. Barrington, E. J. W.: On the responses of the glandular tracts and associated regions of the endostyle of the larval lamprey to goitrogens and thyroxine. Gen. & Comp. Endocrinol., 3:153, 1963.
8. Barrington, E. J. W.: The Biology of Hemichordata and Protochordata. London, Oliver and Boyd, 1965, p. 133.
9. Berg, O. A., and Gorbman, A.: Normal and altered thyroidal function in domesticated goldfish *Carassius auratus*. Proc. Soc. Exp. Biol. & Med., 86:156, 1954.
10. Berg, O., Gorbman, A., and Kobayashi, H.: The thyroid hormones in invertebrates and lower vertebrates. *In* A. Gorbman (ed.): Comparative Endocrinology. New York, John Wiley & Sons, 1959, p. 302.

11. Blount, R. F.: The effects of heteroplastic hypophyseal grafts upon the axolotl, *Ambystoma mexicanum.* J. Exp. Zool., *113*:717, 1950.
12. Bradley, W. O.: The effects of certain antithyroid drugs on the uptake of radioactive iodine by the frog thyroid. Biol. Bull., *101*:62, 1951.
13. Brown-Grant, K.: Changes in the thyroid activity of rats exposed to cold. J. Physiol., *131*:52, 1956.
14. Brown-Grant, K., Harris, G. W., and Reichlin, S.: The effect of emotional and physical stress on thyroid activity in the rabbit. J. Physiol., *126*:29, 1954.
15. Claire, Sister M. The uptake of I¹³¹ by the thyroid gland of turtles after treatment with thiourea. Biol. Bull., *111*:190, 1956.
16. Clark, N. B., and Kaltenbach, J. C.: Direct action of thyroxine on skin of the adult newt. Gen. & Comp. Endocrinol., *1*:513, 1961.
17. Clements, M., and Gorbman, A.: Protease in ammocoetes endostyle. Biol. Bull., *108*:258, 1955.
18. Clements-Merlini, M.: The secretory cycle of iodoproteins in ammocoetes. II. A radioautographic study of the transforming larval thyroid gland. J. Morphol., *106*:357, 1960.
19. Copenhaver, W. M.: Growth of thyroid tissue in the gills of *Amblystoma punctatum* reared in propylthiouracil. J. Exp. Zool., *129*:291, 1955.
20. Copp, D. H., and Henze, K. G.: Parathyroid origin of calcitonin — Evidence from perfusion of sheep glands. Endocrinol., *75*:49, 1964.
21. Dent, J. N., and Lynn, W. G.: A comparison of the effects of goitrogens on thyroid activity in *Triturus viridescens* and *Desmognathus fuscus.* Biol. Bull., *115*:411, 1958.
22. Dimond, Sister M. T.: The reactions of developing snapping turtles, *Chelydra serpentina serpentina* (Linné), to thiourea. J. Exp. Zool., *127*:93, 1954.
23. Dobyns, B. M., and Steelman, S. L.: The thyroid stimulating hormone of the anterior pituitary as distinct from the exophthalmos producing substance. Endocrinol., *52*:705, 1953.
24. Etkin, W.: Metamorphosis-activating system of the frog. Science, *139*:810, 1963.
25. Evans, E. S., Contopoulos, A. N., and Simpson, M. E.: Hormonal factors influencing calorigenesis. Endocrinol., *60*:403, 1957.
26. Flock, E. V., David, C., Hallenbeck, G. A., and Owen, C. A., Jr.: Metabolism of D-thyroxine. Endocrinol., *73*:764, 1963.
27. Follis, R. H., Jr.: Experimental colloid goiter in the hamster. Proc. Soc. Exp. Biol. & Med., *100*:203, 1959.
28. Fortune, P. Y.: Comparative studies of the thyroid function in teleosts of tropical and temperate habitats. J. Exp. Biol., *32*:504, 1955.
29. Fraser, R. C.: Acceleration of frog metamorphosis with iodinated proteins. J. Exp. Zool., *133*:519, 1956.
30. Freinkel, N., Dowling, J. T., and Ingbar, S. H.: The interaction of thyroxine with plasma proteins: localization of thyroxine-binding protein in Cohn fractions of plasma. J. Clin. Invest., *34*:1698, 1955.
31. Furth, J.: Experimental pituitary tumors. Recent Prog. Hormone Research, *11*:221, 1955.
32. Gallien, L.: Endocrine basis for reproductive adaptations in Amphibia. *In* A. Gorbman (ed.): Comparative Endocrinology. New York, John Wiley & Sons, 1959, p. 479.
33. Gittes, R. F., and Irvin, G. L.: Thyroid and parathyroid roles in hypercalcemia: evidence for a thyrocalcitonin-releasing factor. Science, *148*:1737, 1965.
34. Gorbman, A.: Some aspects of the comparative biochemistry of iodine utilization and evolution of thyroidal function. Physiol. Rev., *35*:336, 1955.
35. Gorbman, A.: Pituitary tumors in rodents following changes in thyroid function: a review. Cancer Res., *16*:99, 1956.
36. Gorbman, A.: Problems in the comparative morphology and physiology of the vertebrate thyroid gland. *In* A. Gorbman, (ed.): Comparative Endocrinology. New York, John Wiley & Sons, 1959, p. 266.
37. Gorbman, A., Clements, M., and O'Brien, R.: Utilization of radioiodine by invertebrates with special study of several Annelida and Mollusca. J. Exp. Zool., *127*:75, 1954.
38. Greer, M. A., and De Groot, L. J.: The effect of stable iodide on thyroid secretion in man. Metabolism, *5*:682, 1956.

39. Gudernatsch, J. F.: Feeding experiments on tadpoles. Arch. Entwicklungsmech. Organ., 35:457, 1912.
40. Hamolsky, M. W., Stein, M., Fischer, D. B., and Freedberg, A. S.: Further studies of factors affecting the plasma protein-thyroid hormone complex. Endocrinol., 68:662, 1961.
41. Harris, G. W.: Neuroendocrine control of TSH regulation. *In* A. Gorbman (ed.): Comparative Endocrinology. New York, John Wiley & Sons, 1959, p. 202.
42. Haynie, T. P., Winzler, R. J., Matovinovich, J., Carr, E. A., Jr., and Beierwaltes, W. H.: Thyroid-stimulating and exophthalmos-producing activity of biochemically altered thyrotropin. Endocrinol., 71:782, 1962.
43. Hirsch, P. F., Gauthier, G. F., and Munson, P. L.: Thyroid hypocalcemic principle and recurrent laryngeal nerve injury as factors affecting the response to parathyroidectomy in rats. Endocrinol., 73:244, 1963.
44. Hirsch, P. F., Voelkel, E. F., and Munson, P. L.: Thyrocalcitonin: hypocalcemic hypophosphatemic principle of the thyroid gland. Science, 146:412, 1964.
45. Hopper, A. F.: Uptake of P^{32} by cystic ovary of the rat. Endocrinol., 71:740, 1962.
46. Hsieh, A. C. L., and Carlson, L. D.: Role of the thyroid in metabolic response to low temperature. Amer. J. Physiol., 188:40, 1957.
47. Jørgensen, C. B., and Larsen, L. O.: Molting and its hormonal control in toads. Gen. & Comp. Endocrinol., 1:145, 1961.
48. Jørgensen, C. B., Larsen, L. O., and Rosenkilde, P.: Hormonal dependency of molting in amphibians: effect of radiothyroidectomy in the toad *Bufo bufo* (L). Gen. & Comp. Endocrinol., 5:248, 1965.
49. Juhn, M., and Harris, P. C.: Molt of capon feathering with prolactin. Proc. Soc. Exp. Biol. & Med., 98:669, 1958.
50. Kaltenbach, J. C.: Direct action of thyroxine analogues on peripheral tissues of anuran larvae. Anat. Rec., 128:572, 1957.
51. Kaltenbach, J. C., and Clark, N. B.: Direct action of thyroxine analogues on molting in the adult newt. Gen. & Comp. Endocrinol., 5:74, 1965.
52. Kobayashi, H.: On the induction of molt in birds by 17α-oxyprogesterone-17-capronate. Endocrinol., 63:420, 1958.
53. Kollros, J. J.: Thyroid gland function in developing cold-blooded vertebrates. *In* A. Gorbman (ed.): Comparative Endocrinology. New York, John Wiley & Sons, 1959, p. 340.
54. La Roche, G., Johnson, C. L., and Woodall, A. N.: Thyroid function in rainbow trout (*Salmo gairdneri*, Rich.). I. Biochemical and histological evidence of radiothyroidectomy. Gen. & Comp. Endocrinol., 5:145, 1965.
55. Lardy, H., Tomita, K., Larson, F. C., and Albright, E. C.: The metabolism of thyroid hormones by kidney and the biological activity of the products. Colloq. Found. Endocrinol., 10:156, 1957.
56. Larson, F. C., and Albright, E. C.: Distribution of 3:5:3'-triiodothyroacetic acid in the rat. Endocrinol., 63:183, 1958.
57. Leathem, J. H.: Relationships between the thyroid and protein metabolism. *In* W. H. Cole (ed.): Protein Metabolism, Hormones and Growth. New Brunswick, N.J., Rutgers University Press, 1953, p. 17.
58. Leathem, J. H.: Goitrogen-induced thyroid tumors. Ciba Found. Colloq. Endocrinol., 12:50, 1958.
59. Leathem, J. H.: Nutritional effects on endocrine secretions. *In* W. C. Young, (ed.): Sex and Internal Secretions, Vol. 1. Baltimore, The Williams & Wilkins Co., 1961, p. 666.
60. Lynn, W. G., and Peadon, A. M.: The role of the thyroid gland in the anuran *Eleutherodactylus martinicensis*. Growth, 19:263, 1955.
61. Lynn, W. G., and Wachowski, H. E.: The thyroid gland and its functions in cold-blooded vertebrates. Quart. Rev. Biol., 26:123, 1951.
62. Mackenzie, C. G.: Experimental goiter. Fed. Proc., 17:72, 1958.
63. Mackenzie, J. B., Mackenzie, C. G., and McCollum, E. V.: The effect of sulfanilylguanidine on the thyroid of the rat. Science, 94:518, 1941.
64. Matty, A. J.: Thyroidectomy and its effect upon oxygen consumption of a teleost fish, *Pseudoscarus guacamaia*. J. Endocrinol., 15:1, 1957.

65. Mulvey, P. F., Jr., and Slingerland, D. W.: The *in vitro* stimulation of thyroidal activity by propylthiouracil. Endocrinol., 70:7, 1962.

66. Munson, P. L.: Biological assay of parathyroid hormone. *In* R. O. Greep and R. V. Talmage (eds.): The Parathyroids. Springfield, Ill., Charles C Thomas, 1961, p. 94.

67. Nadler, N. J., Young, B. A., Leblond, C. P., and Mitmaker, B.: Elaboration of thyroglobulin in the thyroid follicle. Endocrinol., 74:333, 1964.

68. Parrott, M. W., Johnston, M. E., and Durbin, P. W.: The effects of thyroid and parathyroid deficiency on reproduction in the rat. Endocrinol., 67:467, 1960.

69. Pitt-Rivers, R.: Mode of action of antithyroid compounds. Physiol. Rev., 30:194, 1950.

70. Pitt-Rivers, R.: Iodine metabolism in the thyroid gland. Memoirs Soc. Endocrinol., No. 11, 71, 1961.

71. Reineke, E. P.: The formation of thyroxine in iodinated proteins. Ann. New York Acad. Sci., 50:450, 1949.

72. Scow, R. O.: Effect of thyroxine on the weight and composition of muscle, pelt and other tissues in young hypophysectomized rats. Endocrinol., 55:344, 1955.

73. Selenkow, H. A., and Asper, S. P., Jr.: Biological activity of compounds structurally related to thyroxine. Physiol. Rev., 35:426, 1955.

74. Serif, G. S., and Kirkwood, S.: The metabolism of the antithyroid action of iodide ion. Endocrinol., 58:23, 1956.

75. Shellabarger, C. J., and Brown, J. R.: The biosynthesis of thyroxine and 3:5:3'-triiodothyronine in larval and adult toads. J. Endocrinol., 18:98, 1959.

76. Stanbury, J. B., Ohela, K., and Pitt-Rivers, R.: The metabolism of iodine in 2 goitrous cretins compared with that in 2 patients receiving methiomazole. J. Clin. Endocrinol., 15:54, 1955.

77. Swanson, H. E.: The effect of temperature on the potentiation of adrenalin by thyroxine in the albino rat. Endocrinol., 60:205, 1957.

78. Talmage, R. V., Neuenschwander, J., and Kraintz, L.: Evidence for the existence of thyrocalcitonin in the rat. Endocrinol., 76:103, 1965.

79. Tata, J. R.: A cellular thyroxine-binding protein fraction. Biochim. Biophys. Acta, 28:91, 1958.

80. Tong, W., Kerkof, P., and Chaikoff, I. L.: Identification of labeled thyroxine and triiodothyronine in *Amphioxus* treated with [131]I. Biochim. Biophys. Acta, 56:326, 1962.

81. van Heynigen, H. E.: The initiation of thyroid function in the mouse. Endocrinol., 69:720, 1961.

82. Voitkevich, A. A.: Neurosecretory control of the amphibian metamorphosis. Gen. & Comp. Endocrinol., Suppl. 1:133, 1962.

83. Yamada, T., Iino, S., and Shichijo, K.: Inhibitory effect of excess iodide on thyroidal radioiodine release in the rat. Endocrinol., 72:83, 1963.

8

THE PARATHYROID GLANDS

The first anatomic description of the parathyroids was provided by Sandström. He dissected such domesticated mammals as the dog, cat, rabbit, and ox; it is apparent now that the parathyroids lying some distance from the thyroid lobes escaped his attention. Gley (1891) discovered that the rabbit possesses an external pair of parathyroids, in addition to the pair that is closely applied to the thyroid lobes, and demonstrated that total thyroidectomy (external parathyroids remaining intact) did not result in tetany. This was the first clear demonstration that the thyroid and parathyroids have separate and different functions.

Almost all the information available on parathyroid functions is confined to a limited number of eutherian mammals. There has been a conspicuous lack of comparative research on nonmammalian species. This may be due in part to the impression that parathyroids are not very important in poikilothermic vertebrates since they seem to be absent in fishes, the awareness that only mammalian extracts are available, or to surgical difficulties attendant upon the removal of small organs whose positions may be variable.

ANATOMY OF THE PARATHYROID GLANDS

The human parathyroids are flattened, ovate, or pyriform bodies situated on the posterior surfaces of the lateral lobes of the thyroid, near their mesial edges. There are usually four glands in man, a superior and an inferior pair (Fig. 7–1). The number and location of the glands are quite variable in all vertebrates that have them. Occasionally, some of them may be buried deeply in the substance of

238

the thyroid or thymus, and this association stems from the close origin of these structures in the embryo. Though one or both of the inferior parathyroids may be located some distance caudad of the thyroid, they usually follow the branches of the inferior thyroid arteries. Parathyroid rests may be scattered widely in the fat and connective tissue of the neck or in the mediastinum. In an adult they average from 6 to 8 mm. in length and from 3 to 4 mm. in breadth.

The blood supply is chiefly from the inferior thyroid arteries, but a certain amount of blood may be received through anastomosing branches of the superior thyroid arteries. Veins from the parathyroids enter those that drain the thyroid gland. Although the vascular supply is rich, the nervous connections are very meager and are probably vasomotor. Secretory nerve fibers have not been demonstrated, and transplanted glands appear to function quite normally in the absence of the usual nervous connections. The parathyroids undergo no conspicuous change after hypophysectomy and do not appear to be controlled by any of the pituitary trophic hormones.

Each parathyroid is surrounded by a connective tissue capsule from which septa extend into the substance of the gland and imperfectly divide it into lobules. The substance of the gland consists of densely packed masses and cords of epithelial cells between which are interspersed numerous small blood vessels (Figs. 8–1 and 8–2).

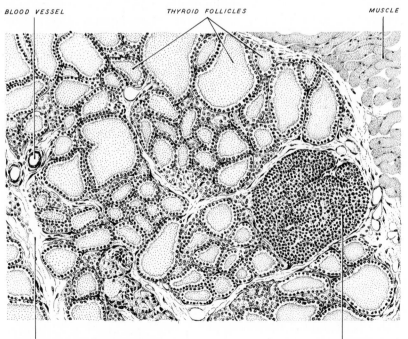

Figure 8–1. A section of the thyroid and parathyroid glands of the rat as seen under low power of the microscope. Notice that the parathyroid gland lies near the surface and is surrounded on three sides by the thyroid follicles.

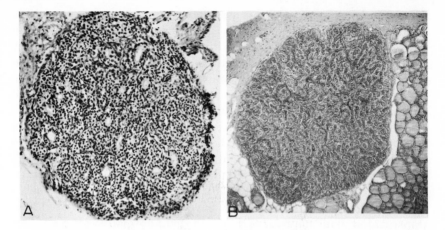

Figure 8–2. A, Posterior parathyroid gland of the turtle, *Pseudemys scripta*, × 120. B, Parathyroid gland of the dog, × 56. (A, Courtesy of Nancy B. Clark, University of Washington, Seattle.)

In glands from adult human beings, principal cells and oxyphile cells are distinguishable. The principal cells are the more numerous and probably are the source of the parathyroid hormone. The oxyphile cells of the human gland appear between the fourth and seventh years and are said to increase in number after puberty. The parathyroids of the horse are cytologically more comparable to human glands than those of other mammals that have been studied. Follicle-like groups of cells enclosing colloid are found infrequently in the parathyroids; these resemble thyroid follicles but the colloid does not contain iodine.

Seasonal changes have been described in the parathyroids of amphibians. The summer glands of *Rana pipiens* are composed of spindle-shaped cells arranged in whorls; during the winter, the cells seem to lose their functional integrity and undergo a type of reticular degeneration.[12] The glands of the bullfrog (*R. catesbeiana*) undergo extreme cytolysis during the winter, and replacement occurs in the spring from the few viable cells that remain below the fibrous capsule. While dense capillary networks are present about the periphery of the glands, internal blood vessels are not conspicuous. The parathyroid cells of all vertebrates contain relatively few secretory granules, indicating that hormone storage is meager.

Developmental Anatomy

The parathyroids of mammals originate from the dorsal halves of the third and fourth pairs of pharyngeal pouches (Fig. 8–3); thymic tissue differentiates from the ventral halves of the same pouches. In amphibians, reptiles, and birds, unlike mammals, the parathyroids arise from the *ventral* portions of pouches 2, 3, and 4, and thymic tissue from the *dorsal* portions of the same pouches. Some of the parathyroid anlagen may disappear or fuse during the course of development. In amphibians, for example, the anlagen from pouch 2 generally disappear, so that the adults typically have only two pairs arising from pouches 3 and 4. This also happens in turtles, but in other reptiles all 3 pairs of anlagen may persist and give rise to adult parathyroids. In crocodiles, only the anlagen from pouch 3 survive. In the chicken embryo, the parathyroid anlagen from pouches 3 and 4 remain together, and usually tend to fuse, so that the adult glands are easily identifiable on the common carotid arteries a short distance caudad of the thyroids (Fig. 8–4).

The parathyroids of amphibians arise from the pharyngeal pouches during metamorphosis. Parathyroid glands have not been found in permanently neotenous amphibians, such as the Mexican axolotl and *Necturus*, and are presumably absent.

It should be noted that the embryonic pharynx gives rise to the thyroids, parathyroids, thymus, and ultimobranchial bodies, all of these structures being intimately associated during development. In turtles, for example, the anterior parathyroids are embedded in the thymus, whereas the posterior pair is closely associated with

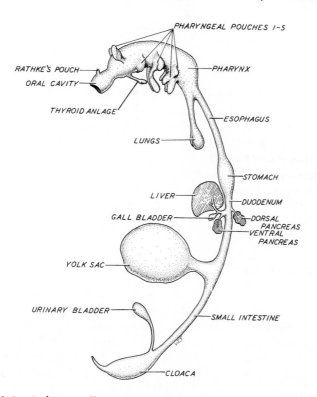

Figure 8–3. A diagram illustrating the parts and outgrowths of the embryonic digestive tube.

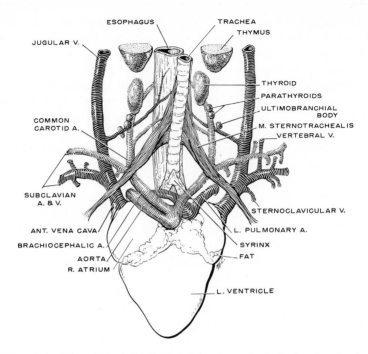

Figure 8–4.   Dissection of the thorax of the domestic fowl, showing the thyroids, parathyroids, and ultimobranchial bodies in relation to the heart and major blood vessels.

ultimobranchial tissue (Fig. 8–5). Since the ultimobranchial bodies originate as paired outgrowths from the caudal end of the pharynx, and often possess a follicular structure, there has been a feeling among investigators that they may share some of the functional competence of other pharyngeal derivatives. Sehe has made a careful study of these bodies in fishes, amphibians, reptiles, and birds, and found no evidence of thyroidal activity in them. Rather than concluding that they are functionless, it appears more correct to state that they have not been convincingly demonstrated to perform any function.[38, 39]

Comparative Anatomy

Parathyroid glands have not been identified in cyclostomes and teleost fishes, and appear not to develop in neotenous amphibians. Two pairs of parathyroids are typically found in amphibians; they are small rounded bodies lying posterior to the thyroids in close association with branches of the external jugular vein. Since they are spatially separated from the thyroids, they may be removed without interfering with the thyroid glands. Most reptiles have two pairs of parathyroids (Fig. 8–5), though as mentioned earlier, three pairs or one pair may be found in certain species. Birds often have two separate parathyroids, located caudad of each thyroid lobe; in other

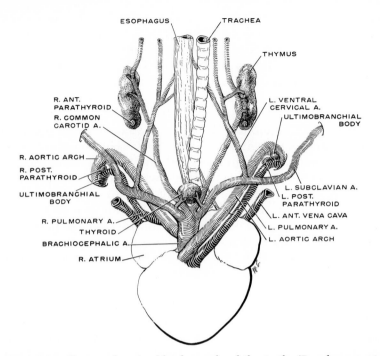

Figure 8–5. Heart and major blood vessels of the turtle *(Pseudemys scripta)*, showing the thyroid gland and the usual locations of parathyroid glands and ultimobranchial bodies.

species, the parathyroids on each side tend to fuse. When the parathyroids of the chicken are approached by ventral dissection, each seems to be a double structure; dorsal dissection, however, reveals that they are fused to form a single structure on each side (Fig. 8–4).

One or two pairs of parathyroids may be present in mammals, and at least one pair is commonly associated with or embedded within the thyroid tissue. In certain species (*e.g.*, rabbit, sheep, and ox) some or all of the parathyroids may be spatially separated from the thyroid lobes. Four parathyroids are present in man, and in many other species such as the dog, cat, rabbit, horse, guinea pig, and opossum. Only two parathyroids are normally present in the rat, mouse, mole, pig, seal, shrew, and certain other species. Aberrant parathyroid rests are difficult to detect anatomically, and one cannot be certain about the frequency of their occurrence.

BIOCHEMISTRY RELATED TO PARATHYROID FUNCTION

Parathyroid Hormone (PTH)

The first active extracts of parathyroid tissue were prepared by Collip in 1924. While it soon became apparent that PTH might be a polypeptide, not much progress was made in isolating and purifying the active principle until rather recently. The revival of interest in problems of calcium metabolism and parathyroid physiology during the last decade correlates with the introduction of new fractionation methods, improvements in organ perfusion and tissue culture techniques, the availability of radioisotope Ca[45] for the study of bone metabolism, and the development of more refined bioassay procedures.

The amino acid sequence of PTH has not been fully determined, but current studies indicate that it is a straight chain polypeptide having a molecular weight of about 9000. The molecule contains two methionine, one tryptophan, and one tyrosine residues, but no cystine. Biologic activity is lost following oxidation by hydrogen peroxide or performic acid. Treatment of the molecule with dilute acid splits it into smaller polypeptide fragments, consisting of 30 to 50 amino acids, and some of these have considerable calcium-mobilizing and phosphaturic activities. Since several peptides can be identified in bovine extracts which have biologic properties resembling the one generally considered to be the parathyroid hormone, it is not yet possible to decide whether the gland actually secretes one peptide or a complex of peptides.[29, 31, 36, 37]

The U.S.P. unit for the standardization of commercial parathyroid extracts is defined as the amount required to elevate the serum calcium of normal dogs an average of 1 mg. per 100 ml. within 18 hours after subcutaneous injection. The Hanson unit is 0.01 of the amount required to elevate the serum calcium 1 mg. per 100 ml. within six hours after being injected into parathyroidectomized dogs. Another method is based on the rise in serum calcium of young rats six hours after parathyroidectomy and the subcutaneous administration of the material being tested. The animals are generally maintained on a calcium-free diet for several days before the parathyroids are removed. The increased urinary excretion of inorganic phosphate by 2-month-old male rats during the first six hours after parathyroidectomy provides another end point. There is an increase in the excretion of administered P[32] by thyroparathyroidectomized rats under the influence of parathyroid hormone, and some have used it in assaying their preparations. Activity may be determined *in vitro* by measuring the hormone-induced oxidation of succinate by liver mitochondria. Radioimmunoassay is used to determine antigenic potency of the parathyroid hormone derivatives obtained by chemical or enzymatic methods.

Whether "calcitonin" represents another hormone which the parathyroids elaborate to correct hypercalcemia remains an unsettled issue (see page 213). The chemical nature of calcitonin is not known. The problem is somewhat confused by the fact that hypocalcemic activity can be demonstrated in extracts prepared from a number of organs including the thymus, adrenals, liver, kidney, and thyroid.[10,11]

Mineral Metabolism

The parathyroid hormone (PTH) is primarily involved in the metabolism of calcium and phosphorus, the principal mineral constituents of the skeleton. Over 99 per cent of the total body content of calcium and about 90 per cent of the total body content of phosphorus are found in the skeleton. Therefore it is not surprising to find that PTH modifies the osseous system. Without attempting to give a detailed and exhaustive treatment of the subject, some aspects of calcium and phosphorus metabolism in relation to the skeletal system are presented as an aid to understanding parathyroid physiology.

Calcium Metabolism

The human body contains more calcium than any other cation. A human adult of average size contains 1200 to 1400 gm. of calcium: most of this is found in the skeleton; about 12 gm. is present in the soft tissues and is chiefly intracellular; less than 1 gm. is found in blood and extracellular fluid. Although the concentration of calcium ions in the body fluids is low, it performs a vital role in neuromuscular excitability, membrane permeability, enzyme activity, the clotting of blood, and the responses of the organism to fluctuations in acid-base balance. The normal organism carefully regulates the amount of calcium in the blood, and even minor variations in its concentration may produce profound effects on neuromuscular irritability. Tetany, or tonic spasms of the skeletal muscles, occurs when the Ca^{++} in the body fluids falls too low. The magnitude of contraction of the isolated frog's heart is directly proportional to the amount of Ca^{++} present, up to a certain concentration. In the absence of Ca^{++} the heart remains in diastole, but if the concentration is too great it goes into a state of sustained contraction or rigor. Potassium and magnesium ions antagonize the effects of Ca^{++} on contraction of the heart.

By using radiocalcium (Ca^{45}) and radiophosphorus (P^{32}) it is possible to follow the movement of these elements from the blood into the tissues. Intravenous Ca^{45} leaves the blood very rapidly and is deposited in the skeleton. Long-term studies on the retention of Ca^{45} indicate that the turnover of total bone calcium is very slow.

Calcium is absorbed largely from the upper part of the small intestine, and factors that hasten the passage of intestinal contents through this part of the tract reduce the amount of calcium that can be absorbed. Since hydrochloric acid has a solubilizing effect on dietary calcium, the efficiency of calcium absorption may be influenced by the reservoir function of the stomach and its frequency of emptying (Fig. 8–6). Vitamin D promotes the intestinal absorption of calcium. The presence of alkali and an excess of fat interfere with

A   *B*

Figure 8–6. Homogeneous osteoporosis produced in the dog by the surgical removal of the stomach. The animal on the left *(A)* was gastrectomized at 103 days of age and appeared as in this sketch 510 days after the operation. The animal on the right *(B)* is an unoperated control. Both puppies were given the same opportunities for feeding. The bowing of the front legs and the swayed condition of the back become pronounced after gastrectomy in this species and are indicative of a weakened skeleton. (Drawn from taxidermic mounts provided by Dr. A. C. Ivy.)

calcium absorption. A high calcium to phosphorus ratio in the diet impedes the absorption of calcium and raises the requirement for vitamin D. An excess of dietary phosphate has no striking effect on the absorption of calcium. Factors that reduce calcium absorption also impair phosphate absorption. Since parathyroidectomy reduces the intestinal absorption of calcium, it is probable that PTH has some effect on calcium metabolism at this level.

The human erythrocyte does not contain calcium. The normal level of serum calcium is about 10 mg. per 100 ml. with a range from 9 to 11 mg. per 100 ml.; in infants and during early childhood the range is slightly higher. Approximately 55 to 60 per cent of the calcium in the serum in ultrafiltrable and diffusible; the remaining 40 to 45 per cent is bound to serum proteins, largely to the albumin fraction. The diffusible fraction of serum calcium is generally considered to be ionized, although some of the diffusible calcium may be in the nonionized form. Citrate forms a nonionized compound with diffusible calcium. If the citrate levels of the serum are high, all of the serum calcium may become diffusible although not ionized. The serum appears to be supersaturated with calcium and phosphate, more being present than can be dissolved in water at the same pH. A partial precipitation of serum calcium occurs when the serum is shaken with pieces of cartilage. An excess of phosphate in the serum diminishes the amount of calcium that can be held in solution; a reduction of serum phosphate has the opposite effect. The cerebrospinal fluid contains about 5 mg. per 100 ml. of calcium, and this is the diffusible fraction since the protein-bound portion is not free to leave the circulation.

The blood plasma of laying hens contains both "ionic" (diffusible) and organically bound (nondiffusible) calcium. The latter is bound to phosphoprotein and forms a readily dissociable complex. While the egg is in the shell gland, the region of the oviduct that secretes the shell, the protein-bound fraction is appreciably reduced, whereas the diffusible calcium varies only slightly. It is probable that the "ionic" calcium leaves the blood stream by diffusion as the shell is formed and its concentration in the plasma is maintained by a dissociation of the organically bound fraction. During the egg-laying cycle the diffusible fraction increases cyclically relative to the total calcium, but the increment is relatively small.

The amount of calcium in the blood depends on a balance between the amount received by intestinal absorption and by the resorption of bone, and the amount lost by excretion in the urine and feces and by deposition in bone salt. Bone resorption in the young animal occurs principally in the areas where growth and remodeling are occurring, but some deposition of new bone takes place in the normal adult. Despite the large and variable movements of calcium in and out of the blood, the level of serum calcium is held remarkably constant. Within a few hours after parathyroidectomy the total calcium level falls to 5 to 7 mg. per 100 ml., whereas hyperparathyroidism elevates it above 10 mg. per 100 ml.

An interesting syndrome may be produced experimentally by gastrectomy of puppies. After surgical removal of the stomach of the dog, skeletal deformities similar to those of rickets become apparent as the animal ages (Fig. 8–6). The achlorhydria consequent upon gastrectomy interferes with the absorption of calcium from the upper intestine. Furthermore, in the absence of the stomach incompletely digested food passes so rapidly along the intestine that insufficient amounts of calcium and phosphorus are absorbed. An acidosis ensues in such gastrectomized animals after the ingestion of food, and increased amounts of calcium and phosphate are excreted in the urine. While the levels of serum calcium and phosphate are within normal limits, the animals are not absorbing and retaining sufficient minerals to permit proper hardening of the skeletal system. The skeleton therefore is exceptionally spongy, a condition called "homogeneous osteoporosis."[2]

Phosphorus Metabolism

The phosphate radical is present in every cell in the organism, and it performs an important role in the energy transfer mechanisms involved in cell metabolism. Besides its intracellular role in intermediary metabolism, this radical is an important ingredient of bone salts. It also serves as a buffer in the preservation of normal acid-base balance. In infants and young children, the inorganic phosphorus of the serum ranges from 5 to 7 mg. per 100 ml. This diminishes with age and 3 to 4.5 is the range generally stated for normal adults. Practically all of the inorganic phosphorus of the serum is diffusible. Phosphorus is also present in the blood as a constituent of lipids and of acid-soluble organic phosphate esters; these are more abundant in the red cells than in the serum. The level of serum phosphate is a poor reflection of the rapid phosphate exchanges that go on continuously within the living organism.

Phosphorus in the form of inorganic phosphate is absorbed from the small intestine, and this is facilitated by acids. In alkaline media there is a tendency for it to be precipitated as insoluble phosphates, such as calcium phosphate. Phosphate absorption is improved by diets low in calcium; insoluble phosphates are formed if there is an excess of calcium in the diet. Since vitamin D promotes calcium absorption, it indirectly facilitates phosphate absorption. The phosphate that reaches the circulation may be stored in bone or in the form of such compounds as nucleic acid, phospholipids, nucleoprotein, and phosphoproteins. Phosphate excretion occurs chiefly through the kidneys, about two-thirds of the ingested phosphorus appearing in the urine. Fecal excretion accounts for the remainder. The kidneys are important organs in controlling phosphate balance. Hyperphosphatemia is characteristic of kidney failure, since phosphate continues to be absorbed from the intestine and is retained.

Severe skeletal defects develop in rats when they are maintained on a phosphorus-deficient diet. There may be little or no change in the serum calcium level, but the serum phosphate may reach a value of less than 1 mg. per 100 ml. Despite the negative phosphorus balance, the phosphorus in the liver, muscle, and other soft tissues remains normal. The requirements of the soft tissues are met at the expense of the skeleton, and this leads to a progressive osteoporosis. The ribs and vertebrae become very thin and low in mineral, but the teeth are relatively unaffected.

The Solubility Product

The bone salts consist chiefly of calcium phosphate, calcium carbonate, fluoride, hydroxide, and citrate. The bone matrix is elaborated by osteoblasts or results from the degeneration of cartilage cells, and this is impregnated by the calcium salts. The tissue fluids appear to be saturated with respect to calcium and phosphate. Any increase either in calcium-ion concentration or phosphate-ion concentration tends to precipitate insoluble calcium phosphate. Thus, within certain limits, there is a reciprocal relationship between the serum calcium and phosphate levels. $(Ca^{++}) \times (HPO_4^{=})$ expressed in milligrams per 100 milliliters is called the solubility product. This may be illustrated by taking a few arbitrary figures as examples. If the serum calcium is 10 mg. per 100 ml. and the serum phosphate is 5 mg. per 100 ml., the solubility product is 50; an equilibrium prevails and bone deposition and resorption occur at equal rates. *In vitro* and *in vivo* studies have shown that products less than 30 bring about the decalcification of bone. Slices of uncalcified bone immersed in solutions containing varying concentrations of calcium and phosphorus do not calcify unless the calcium-phosphorus product is above 30. A number of endocrine and nutritional factors are known to influence the elaboration of bone matrix, and thus exert indirectly an effect on calcification of the skeleton.

Bone Structure and Metabolism

Bone consists of an organic matrix (35 per cent) and inorganic material (65 per cent). If the mineral component of bone is removed by letting it stand in dilute acid, there remains a strong flexible matrix of organic material, which retains the shape of the original bone. The matrix consists chiefly of a protein that appears to be identical to the collagen fibers of tendon or cartilage. In addition to calcium and phosphate, bone contains small quantities of magnesium, potassium, sodium, fluorine, and strontium. The same minerals are found in teeth, but the water content is lower than in bone. Dentine and enamel contain more calcium phosphate and less calcium carbonate than bone. The mineral matter of the skeleton is in the form of crystals, and this suggests that it is deposited as a consequence of precipitation. The mineral appears to exist as an apatite, a double salt of calcium phosphate and calcium carbonate. These crystals are oriented with reference to the fibrous latticework of the matrix and to the mechanical stresses and strains applied to the bone in performing its function. Disuse of the skeleton may cause a loss of minerals and matrix from the bones that normally bear the weight of the body. Complete bed rest in a previously active individual may cause enough demineralization of the skeleton to elevate the calcium levels of the blood. This effect may result in part from an increased flow of blood through the bones in relation to function.

The skeleton may be regarded as a mass of protein that has become heavily impregnated with mineral crystals. It contains a syncytium of osteocytes and a meshwork of collagen and elastic fibers, both set in a background of cement substance. The cement is a gelatinous material similar to the ground substance of mesenchyme. In adults, as well as in young organisms, the skeletal system undergoes constant structural and metabolic changes. Bone is being formed in some areas and is simultaneously resorbed from other areas, the two processes taking place side by side. The whole skeleton is in a state of dynamic equilibrium, matrix formation and calcium salt deposition adding to it and matrix destruction and calcium salt removal subtracting from it. Thus the bones are rather plastic structures and are able to undergo a certain degree of remodeling in accordance with the everyday stresses to which they are subjected.[28]

Since the introduction of radioactive isotopes, it has been amply demonstrated that the mineral salts of bone are metabolically active. There is a continuous and rapid exchange of calcium and phosphate between the tissue fluids that bathe the bone trabeculae and the crystals of calcium phosphate that compose the bone. The greatest exchange occurs in the areas of the bone where the circulation is greatest. Furthermore, the rate of exchange between body fluids and bone varies in different sites in the bone and in different bones of the body. For example, the rate of renewal of calcium in the ribs and sternum of the dog is much more rapid than that of the calvarium or of the diaphysis of the femur or tibia. Radioactive phosphorus has been found to remain in the body of an adult rat for about two months; 30 per cent of the P^{32} taken up by the skeleton is lost within 20 days. Even the molar teeth, which do not grow in the adult rat, take up small amounts of P^{32} and lose it very slowly. These and many other observations show that the mineral matter of bone is constantly changing.

Bone Formation and Resorption

The areas of new bone formation are characterized by the presence of many osteoblasts. These cells are thought to lay down matrix in apposition to the calcified bone and to produce the enzyme, alkaline phosphatase. After the organic matrix has been elaborated by the osteoblasts, bone crystals appear in the cement substance, their alignment appearing to be determined by the network of collagen fibers. The bone surfaces are bathed by the body fluids, hence it is difficult to explain how bone deposition and resorption can occur simultaneously in adjacent regions. An important factor appears to be a local increase in phosphate ions in those regions where deposition is occurring.

The enzyme alkaline phosphatase is invariably present in the regions of active mineralization, and this suggests that it may be related to the process (Fig. 8–7). The osteoblasts are known to contain high concentrations of this enzyme. Most of the alkaline phosphatase present in blood plasma emanates from the skeleton, and the blood titers may be used clinically as an estimate of osteoblastic activity. It has been proposed that alkaline phosphatase hydrolyzes organic esters of phosphoric acid and thereby produces a high local concentration of inorganic phosphate, which causes the deposition of

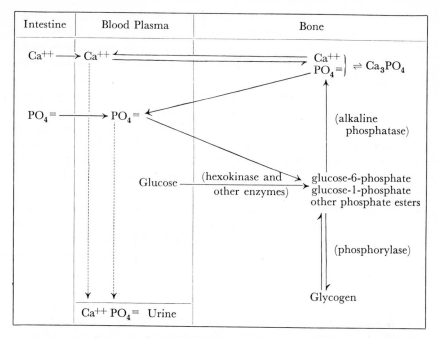

Figure 8–7. Diagram of some factors thought to be involved in bone deposition. (Modified from Bell, Davidson, and Scarborough: Textbook of Physiology and Biochemistry.)

insoluble calcium phosphate. *In vitro* studies have shown that phosphate esters, in the presence of this enzyme, may provide the phosphate ions necessary for bone calcification. However, it is questionable whether or not such esters are present *in vivo* at the sites of active mineralization in amounts sufficient to produce the effect. Alkaline phosphatase does appear to be involved in some manner in new bone formation, but some workers feel that it is concerned more with the formation of organic matrix than with the deposition of bone salt.

There is also the possibility that glycolysis is involved in bone deposition (Fig. 8–7). The enzyme phosphorylase has been found in growing cartilage and bone but not in articular cartilage. Cartilage cells accumulate exceptionally large stores of glycogen, and this disappears abruptly before or during the period when bone salts are being deposited. Phosphorylase, in the presence of plasma inorganic phosphate, could break down glycogen to glucose-1-phosphate, glucose-6-phosphate, and related esters; these could be hydrolyzed by bone phosphatase to free high concentrations of phosphate ions in localized areas. As a consequence of the local supersaturation, calcium phosphate may be precipitated. The exact manner in which glycolysis influences bone formation has not been clarified: it may provide esters of phosphoric acid as substrate for phosphatase, as described above, or it may function to provide energy for some phase of the mechanism of bone formation. While cartilage may undergo calcification *in vitro* after the enzymes have been inactivated, there are important quantitative differences which suggest that glycolysis is involved under normal conditions in the living organism.

Since large numbers of osteoclasts accumulate in the regions of bone resorption, it is generally agreed that they perform some role in the process. Their exact manner of operation has not been conclusively demonstrated. Studies on the medullary bone of laying birds have led to the conclusion that osteoblasts, osteocytes, and osteoclasts are temporary functional states of the same cell type.

It is possible that local increases in citrate concentration may be a factor of considerable importance in promoting the dissolution of bone salt. Resorbing bone tissue *in vitro* has been shown to release citrate into the culture medium. Parathyroidectomy lowers the citrate level of the plasma, as well as the total calcium level. The administration of parathyroid hormone to normal animals elevates both the serum citrate and total calcium. Some of the current theories of parathyroid hormone action postulate that the demineralization of the skeleton after hormone administration is correlated with an increased production of citrate by the bone.

PHYSIOLOGY OF THE PARATHYROID GLANDS

The current concept is that parathyroid hormone acts principally upon two end organs, bone and kidney. The hormone causes the breakdown of apatite crystal in bone, releasing both calcium and phosphate into the circulation; the level of calcium is thus raised beyond that which would obtain through the normal physicochemical equilibrium of bone salts and tissue fluids. The hormone simultaneously stimulates the kidney to excrete phosphate; this prevents the saturation of the plasma with calcium and phosphate ions, a condition which might lead to the deposition of this salt in soft tissues. In addition, there is evidence that PTH increases the absorption of calcium from the intestine. It is not known whether the various physiologic activities of the parathyroids are attributable to one or several hormones.

The Effects of Parathyroidectomy

The most important changes after removal of the parathyroid glands are: (1) diminished levels of serum calcium, involving largely if not exclusively the diffusible fraction; (2) reduced blood citrate; (3) reduced urinary excretion of calcium; (4) increased levels of inorganic phosphorus in the serum; and (5) diminished urinary elimination of inorganic phosphorus. The diminished calcium content of the extracellular fluids produces hyperexcitability of the neuromuscular system, and this eventuates in involuntary twitchings of the muscles. Unless calcium ions are elevated in the tissue fluids, the fibrillary twitchings progress into generalized tremors, clonic and tonic spasms, and violent convulsions. Death often results from asphyxiation consequent upon spasm of the laryngeal muscles. Certain defects also occur in the cardiovascular, gastrointestinal, and urinary systems.

Mammals

The dog and cat have been used extensively in experimental studies involving extirpation of the parathyroids. In these species the external parathyroids are usually accessible, and the animals are susceptible to tetany because of the high phosphorus and relatively low calcium content of their meat rations. In general, herbivores tolerate the operation better than carnivores.[9, 27]

Total parathyroidectomy of the dog produces a characteristic train of disturbances that increase in severity after the operation. Within a day or two the animal refuses food (anorexia), and the temperature of the body may be subnormal. Little water is consumed and anuria may develop. Vomiting, salivation, and diarrhea are characteristic of chronic stages. The calcium content of the blood serum falls rapidly, but this is not due to an increased urinary excretion of calcium; the urinary calcium is reduced, and the fecal calcium is not increased appreciably. The serum calcium drops from a normal of about 10 mg. per 100 ml. to 7 to 5 mg. per 100 ml. This hypocalcemia is accompanied by a reduced excretion of phosphorus and a consequent elevation of inorganic phosphorus in the blood (hyperphosphatemia). Muscular twitchings (tetany) appear within two or three days after parathyroidectomy and result from the low concentration of calcium ions in the body fluids. Fibrillary twitchings are first noted in the muscles of the head, face, and back. These become more conspicuous with the lapse of time, and clonic and tonic spasms of the appendicular muscles set in.

The manifestations of tetany in the dog lead to an elevation of the body temperature (hyperpyrexia). This in turn excites the respiratory centers, and breathing becomes deep and rapid (hyperpnea). Carbonic acid is removed to such an extent that the blood becomes more alkaline than normal and inhibits the ionization of calcium. The hypocalcemia results in an epileptiform convulsion during which death may occur from asphyxiation owing to spasticity of the respiratory muscles. The violent muscular contractions and the breathing of carbon dioxide may suffice to increase the hydrogen ion concentration of the blood and thus make possible an elevation of calcium ions, which leads to a temporary remission of the symptoms. The convulsions can be forestalled by the production of uranium nephritis or by any other procedure which provokes an acidosis. If the animal does not die during the first seizure and remains untreated, subsequent attacks eventually prove fatal.[5]

Tetany can be brought on in the parathyroidectomized dog by raising the body temperature artificially, as by forced exercise or by drugs. The respiratory centers are probably more easily excited than in the normal animal, and the elevated temperature of the body provokes a hyperpnea. The resulting alkalosis suffices to produce tetany in the parathyroidectomized animal, although it would not do so in dogs having a normal level of serum calcium.

Goats usually do not show tetany after removal of the parathyroids, but definite muscular tremors are seen in some cases. The train of symptoms that follows parathyroidectomy in the monkey is similar to that in the dog but develops somewhat less rapidly. Although accessory parathyroids are reported to be unusually frequent in rabbits, these animals succumb promptly when all of the parathyroid tissue is removed.

Parathyroidectomy in the rat is usually not fatal, and this animal has been used most extensively in order to determine the effects of prolonged parathyroid deprivation. It is not known to what extent this ability to tolerate parathyroidectomy is due to the presence of accessory parathyroid tissue, but in some strains accessory tissue is said to be very infrequent. The majority of animals operated on suffer tetany, especially if they are maintained on rations low in calcium and high in phosphorus. Deficiency of the parathyroid hormone in this species eventually leads to decalcification of the bones and to disorganization of the enamel of the teeth. Owing to the mobilization of salts, the teeth become opaque, brittle, and distorted out of position. On chemical analysis the bones are found to contain a relatively high content of magnesium, but to be low in ash and deficient in calcium and phosphorus. Abnormal osseous projections from the surfaces of alveolar bones (exostoses) are frequently encountered after prolonged deficiency.

Cataractous lenses have been associated with parathyroid deprivation in both dogs and rats. Among human subjects, cataracts are present in almost all long-standing cases of hypoparathyroidism. Thyroidectomy in the human subject occasionally results in tetany because of the inadvertent or unavoidable removal of the parathyroid bodies. Disturbances resulting from a deficiency of the parathyroid hormone in man are not so profound as in purely carnivorous laboratory mammals. Slight twitching, nervousness, or spasm of the facial or appendicular muscles is usually the only manifestation. In some persons the tetany remains in a latent form and is detectable only by special physiologic tests.

Since the tetanic state can be alleviated by regulating the amounts and the ratio of calcium and phosphorus in the diet, parathyroidectomy is not invariably fatal. The severity of the symptoms is conditioned not only by the dietary intake of calcium and phosphorus, but also by the demands of the organism for these essential elements. The growing organism needs abundant calcium for the differentiation of the skeleton, and parathyroidectomy proves fatal unless adequate calcium is provided. Similarly, in pregnant and lactating animals the demand for mineral salts exceeds that of nongravid or nonlactating ones, and susceptibility to parathyroprivic tetany is increased.

Although experimental and clinical evidence is sufficient to establish the fact that hypocalcemia prevails during active tetany, there is no definite level at which tetany invariably occurs. It may be present with a total calcium level of 8 mg. per 100 ml. or absent at 4 mg. per 100 ml. It is apparent that the hyperexcitability of the neuromuscular system during parathyroid deficiency correlates with the ionized calcium rather than with the total concentration of serum calcium. Hypocalcemia and tetany may occur without a concomitant rise in the inorganic phosphorus of the serum, but there is evidence that these conditions are accentuated by the retention of acid-soluble phosphorus in the blood. Tetany is ameliorated by factors that facilitate the excretion of phosphate. For example, phosphate diuresis may be caused by the administration of hypertonic solutions of saline or glucose, and this has been shown to relieve tetany in certain species.

Birds, Reptiles, and Amphibians

In birds the parathyroid glands have been demonstrated to share in the regulation of calcium and phosphorus metabolism. Removal of the parathyroids in the pigeon is followed by a decrease in serum calcium and an increase in the serum phosphorus. The untreated animals may become tetanic and die in convulsions. Certain large breeds of pigeons (*e.g.*, white Carneau) are particularly suitable for studies of this type, since the two pairs of parathyroids lie 5 to 12 mm. posterior to the thyroids. Thus parathyroidectomy involves no injury whatever to the thyroid glands. Parathyroidectomized birds may be maintained for long periods by the administration of dihydrotachysterol and calcium gluconate or by feeding gelatinous aluminum hydroxide.

Calcium deficiency in birds produces enlargement of the parathyroids. Bovine parathyroid extract is effective in causing hypercalcemia in avian species. It is known that the administration of ovarian hormone (estrogen) increases tremendously the level of blood calcium in the domestic fowl and other birds. Estrogens may produce serum calcium levels of 30 to 100 mg. per 100 ml. in the domestic fowl, whereas heavy doses of bovine parathyroid extract elevate the blood calcium only 2 to 8 mg. per 100 ml.

Removal of both pairs of parathyroid glands from fresh-water turtles was found not to alter the serum levels of calcium and phosphate.[7]

Parathyroidectomy of amphibians leads to diminished levels of blood calcium in all species studied. Tetany does not follow parathyroid removal in *Rana pipiens* and several species of urodeles; it has been reported in the bullfrog (*R. catesbeiana*) and in the toad (*Bufo viridis*).[4, 12]

The blood serum of cyclostomes and elasmobranchs, organisms having no bone and presumably no parathyroid glands, contains an exceptionally high concentration of calcium ions.[48]

The Action of Parathyroid Hormone

In general, the metabolic changes observed in hyperparathyroidism are opposite to those that characterize parathyroid deficiency. The condition may occur spontaneously or be produced experimentally by the injection of parathyroid hormone. An excess of the hormone brings about hypercalcemia, hypophosphatemia, an increased urinary excretion of phosphate and calcium, frequent metastatic deposits of calcium in organs and tissues, hyposensitivity of the neuromuscular system, and demineralization of the skeleton. The alkaline phosphatase concentration of the serum is increased, indicating heightened osteoblastic activity. In advanced stages cysts and giant cell tumors may be present in bones.[26]

The administration of PTH to a parathyroidectomized animal results in a characteristic sequence of physiologic adjustments. One of the first changes to occur is an increase in the renal excretion of phosphate and a diminished loss of calcium through the urine. The serum citrate level rises. As the amount of phosphate in the plasma falls, there is a gradual rise in the concentration of serum calcium. When the hypercalcemia becomes established, the renal loss of calcium is progressively increased. The magnitude of the hypercalcemia and phosphaturia is proportional to the dose of PTH administered. The hypercalcemia results principally from the mobilization of bone calcium, and, to a lesser extent, from an increased intestinal absorption of calcium and increased reabsorption of calcium from the renal tubules. The main organs responding to this hormone are the kidneys and bones, and the evidence indicates that these are direct effects. The renal response occurs promptly, whereas the skeletal changes are slower in their onset. This difference in promptness of response may correlate with the striking differences in the rate of blood flow through the two organs, or it may be that the bone changes are dependent upon cellular elements which require time to differentiate.

The manner in which PTH induces bone resorption is poorly understood. A current concept is that the hormone acts in some manner to increase the number of osteoclasts, specialized cells which are thought to play a role in bone destruction. Studies indicate that the osteoclasts differentiate from other types of bone cells, and that they are prevalent in areas undergoing active remodeling. Whether they initiate the process of resorption or merely phago-cytize wastes in these areas remains unknown. The number of osteoclasts in the metaphysis of the rat's femur has been used as an index of parathyroid activity. The parathyroids of the rat are markedly stimulated by removal of the kidney (nephrectomy), and, within 48 hours after this operation, the number of osteoclasts in the femur has doubled. Parathyroid stimulation may also be induced in the rat through the use of calcium-free rinses, in the peritoneal lavage technique, and this is reflected by an increased osteoclast count in the femur. The number of osteoclasts provides a morphologic indication of parathyroid activity, but their manner of action has not been clarified.[8, 43, 45, 46]

Since the osteoclasts are phagocytic cells, attempts have been made to destroy them through the radiation emitted by engulfed plutonium and to determine whether PTH effectively mobilizes bone mineral in their absence. In short-term experiments, it was found that plutonium prevented the differentiation of osteoclasts from mesenchymal cells, but did not impair the function of existing osteoblasts and osteoclasts. While the increased production of osteoclasts in response to endogenous PTH was prevented, the hormone was still effective in controlling calcium homeostasis for 5 days.[15]

Actinomycin D prevents the calcium-mobilizing action of PTH on bone, but does not alter its effects upon the renal elimination of phosphate and calcium. This antibiotic is known to interfere with protein synthesis by preventing the formation of ribonucleic acids; it is thought to block DNA-directed RNA synthesis by binding at specific sites on the DNA primer. When actinomycin D is given to parathyroidectomized rats 2 hours before an effective dose of PTH, the plasma phosphate falls as would be expected, but the serum calcium is not normally elevated. The actinomycin has apparently blocked the action of PTH on bone, but not its action on the kidney. This suggests that the process of bone destruction, promoted by PTH, depends in some manner upon the synthesis of ribonucleic acids and proteins. Careful histologic and cytologic studies on bone cells following the use of this antibiotic have been made.[35, 40]

After giving repeated injections of PTH to the dog, the serum calcium may rise to a peak of 20 mg. per 100 ml. There is a diuresis and an increased excretion of phosphate and calcium. Increased coagulability of the blood and decreased excitability of the nerves parallel the hypercalcemia. The calcium content of the soft tissues of the body is increased, and metastatic deposits are frequently found in the uriniferous tubules, the gastric and intestinal walls, the heart, lesser arteries, liver, bronchi, and lungs. Prolonged administration of sublethal amounts of the hormone produce profound effects upon the osseous system. This produces an osteodystrophy characterized by resorption of both spongy and cortical bone and consequent deformation of the limbs. The marrow cavity, as well as the areas denuded of calcium, is replaced by fibrous tissue and giant cells, a condition closely simulating osteitis fibrosa cystica, which is met with clinically.

Generalized osteitis fibrosa, or von Recklinghausen's disease, is a clinical syndrome associated with parathyroid hyperplasia and excessive release of the parathyroid secretion. In severe cases the skeletal system is softened so greatly by the withdrawal of minerals that fractures and disabling deformities are unavoidable. In advanced stages distorting tumefactions occur on the bones. The vertebral column may be curved abnormally, either in the dorsal (kyphosis) or lateral (scoliosis) direction, and thus lead to a hump-backed condition. Bowing of the long bones is common. Distortion of the skeleton modifies the posture and gait of the person, and the height of the body may decrease as much as a foot during the course of a few days.

Regulation of the Parathyroids

The functional status of the parathyroids is closely linked with calcium metabolism in the organism. The parathyroids of the rat become smaller after large doses of parathyroid extract. The glands enlarge during rickets, and there is greater enlargement in low calcium than in low phosphate rickets. Parathyroid hypertrophy occurs in birds deprived of sunlight. The pituitary gland appears to exert no direct control over parathyroid function, and there is general agreement that the level of serum calcium is the chief regulatory factor.[14]

Hypocalcemia may be experimentally produced by a variety of procedures, and all of them demonstrate the amazing capacity of the organism to restore and maintain normal levels of serum calcium through the mobilization of skeletal stores. Hypocalcemia may be produced by the intravenous infusion of disodium ethylene-diaminetetraacetate (Na_2-EDTA). This substance removes calcium by forming a chelate complex with it. In normal fasted dogs, the intravenous infusion of EDTA at a continuous rate for one hour may lower the serum calcium from 10 mg. per 100 ml. to around 4 mg. per 100 ml. at the end of this period. Serum phosphorus is slightly diminished during the infusion period. After discontinuation of the EDTA the serum calcium rises rapidly and normal levels are restored after a few hours. The rate of calcium mobilization from the skeleton is proportionate to the lowering of the serum calcium, and this suggests that an equilibrium exists between these two calcium fractions.

Total parathyroidectomy of the dog reduces the serum calcium to 6 or 7 mg. per 100 ml. within 24 hours. The infusion of EDTA reduces the calcium level still further in these animals and, after it is withdrawn, enough calcium can be mobilized from the skeleton to restore the serum calcium to the new equilibrium value of 7 mg. per 100 ml. The administration of parathyroid extract to parathyroid-ectomized animals raises the serum calcium to 10 mg. per 100 ml. or above. It appears that an equilibrium exists between the serum calcium and the mobilizable calcium pool of the skeleton, and that this equilibrium can operate in the dog to maintain a serum calcium level of 5 to 7 mg. per 100 ml. in the absence of parathyroid tissue. It thus seems that bone can supply calcium to the extracellular fluid compartments in the absence of parathyroids, but that these glands are essential for elevating the serum calcium above a certain level.

The *calcium replacement* concept of PTH action has been proposed by Talmage and his co-workers largely on the basis of their peritoneal lavage studies on the rat. Following parathyroid-ectomy, the serum calcium falls to 4 mg. per 100 ml., and at this point a basic equilibrium prevails between the body fluids and specific areas of bone. The kidney threshold for calcium is normally 6 mg. per 100 ml., but it falls slightly below 4 mg. per 100 ml. after removal of the parathyroids. Two competitive processes appear to operate in the normal animal. The basic equilibrium mechanism deposits calcium salts on bone, but diminished calcium in the blood stimulates the parathyroids to release PTH. This hormone acts to break down apatite crystal in bone and thus returns calcium to the plasma. The basic equilibration phenomenon does not depend upon PTH and is capable of sustaining serum calcium levels at approximately 4 mg. per 100 ml. in the parathyroidectomized animal.[42, 44]

Neuromuscular Irritability and Tetany

When the concentration of calcium ion in the extracellular fluid falls below normal, the nervous system becomes progressively more excitable and this may lead to tetany. This manifests itself first as generalized hypertonicity of muscles and then as fibrillary twitchings that may progress to clonic and tonic spasms and violent convulsions. Tetany varies in severity and may be produced experimentally by a variety of procedures.

There are numerous forms of tetany that are not accompanied by a deficiency of the parathyroid hormone. One form is encountered frequently in rickets, a disease resulting from a deficiency of vitamin D in young animals. There is an insufficient deposition of calcium and phosphorus in the osseous system; consequently the bones are soft and easily deformed. The hypersensitivity of the neuromuscular system in rickets, as in parathyroprivia, is correlated with an insufficiency of calcium ions in the blood. Tetany also occurs in osteomalacia, an Oriental disease essentially the same as rickets. Sprue is a rare disease characterized by the impaired absorption of calcium from the gastrointestinal tract. This results in hypocalcemia and frequently produces tetany.

Another form of tetany is due to magnesium deprivation. The "grass tetany" among cattle apparently results from diets deficient in this element. Rats and dogs deprived of magnesium exhibit hyperexcitability and tetanic convulsions. A deficiency of magnesium apparently decreases the solubility of lime salts in the blood and leads to the excretion of the insoluble fraction. Since hypocalcemia is not a constant finding in the tetany owing to magnesium deprivation, it is possible that the nervous hyperirritability results directly from the deficiency of magnesium ions rather than from a deficiency of calcium ions.

Overventilation by means of forced breathing produces a carbon dioxide deficit and a consequent alkalosis. The increase in pH apparently interferes with the ionization of calcium and thus produces tetany. In this instance, however, the total calcium and phosphorus in the serum are within the normal range. A comparable alkalosis and consequent tetanic seizures may result from the administration of large amounts of sodium bicarbonate. The loss of hydrochloric acid through persistent vomiting gives rise to "gastric" tetany.

The early experiments of Jacques Loeb indicated that excised skeletal muscles become hyperirritable and exhibit clonic twitchings when maintained in fluids lacking or deficient in calcium ions. Curare does not prevent the transmission of impulses in the nerve itself, but it impairs the motor endings and thus prevents the activation of effector organs. The fact that parathyroprivic tetany in the dog is abolished by subparalytic doses of curare suggests strongly that the immediate disturbance that produces tetany is the hyperirritability of the motor nerves rather than the increased sensitivity of the muscles. On the other hand, similar doses of curare do not abolish the tetany that results from a deficiency of magnesium. Little is known about the exact mechanisms that participate in the onset of tetany. It appears that no single etiologic factor is involved, and no systemic alteration has been detected that occurs invariably in tetany.

Some investigators have emphasized the importance of the central nervous system. The spasm of a particular muscle is abolished by the complete section of the peripheral nerve that supplies it. That the tremors are associated with impulses transmitted from the central system by the efferent portion of the reflex arc is indicated by the fact that section of the dorsal roots only does not prevent the tremors. Transection of the spinal cord and decerebration abolish the convulsive seizures of manifest tetany but do not prevent the "involuntary" tremors. Ether anesthesia prevents tetany in the parathyroidectomized dog. Studies on the rat indicate that the central nervous system is involved in the syndrome of tetany. Through the use of barbiturates, curare, and spinal transections, it has been shown that the integrity of the central nervous system at a level higher than the spinal cord is necessary for the onset of tetany in this species.

The increased irritability of the motor nerves in parathyroprivic animals may be determined by the application of electrical and mechanical stimuli. Several methods for the clinical determination of latent tetany are based upon the lowered threshold of nervous stimulation necessary for eliciting muscular responses. In normal human infants a current of approximately 5 milliamperes is required to produce a tonic contraction of the skeletal muscles on cathodal closure, whereas in severe tetany a current of 0.5 to 0.9 milliampere may be sufficient to elicit the response. The nervous system is somewhat more excitable in normal adult human beings than in children under 5 years of age, but muscular responses obtained with galvanic currents of less than 2 milliamperes are often indicative of latent tetany.

Other Factors Affecting Bone Metabolism

Vitamin D (Calciferol)

This vitamin is formed in the skin through the action of ultraviolet light upon such sterols as ergosterol. Its absence or deficiency impairs the utilization of calcium and phosphorus and produces rickets. The bones of rachitic animals are imperfectly calcified and consequently are easily twisted out of shape by the weight of the body. The serum calcium and phosphate are usually deficient, but both may be restored to normal levels by physiologic doses of the vitamin. Dihydrotachysterol, also obtained by the irradiation of ergosterol, has similar effects. Both substances increase the intestinal absorption of calcium and, in addition, promote the excretion of phosphate in the urine. Massive doses of calciferol lead to the mobilization of calcium and phosphorus from the skeleton and have an effect similar to excessive parathyroid hormone. While both calciferol and dihydrotachysterol

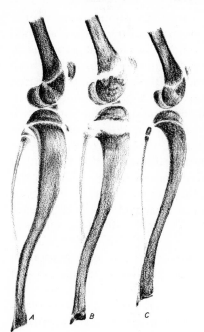

Figure 8–8. Sketches from roentgeno-grams of the hindlimbs of rats. *A,* Bones from a rat that had received a rachitogenic diet plus vitamin D for 45 days. *B,* Rachito-genic diet for 45 days plus daily injections of parathyroid extract during the last 20 days. *C,* An animal of the same age that had received a high calcium ration throughout life. By comparing *A* and *B* it becomes apparent that vitamin D encourages the closure of the epiphysial cartilages in rachitic rats, whereas parathyroid extract does not.

may be successfully employed in treating hypoparathyroidism, there is no known physiologic connection between them and the parathyroid hormone. The skeletal defects in vitamin D deficiency are not ameliorated by the parathyroid hormone (Fig. 8–8).[13, 41]

Adenohypophysial Hormones

That hypophysectomy of the young animal causes a cessation of skeletal growth is well known. Growth is resumed when such animals are given somatotrophin, and if the hormone is continued for long periods, gigantism results. Thyrotrophin also influences growth through its regulation of thyroid function. Observations on the rat indicate that thyroxine and somatotrophin function syn-ergistically in promoting skeletal growth. Large amounts of thyroxine accelerate the maturation of bone, whereas thyroidectomy delays bone development. By promoting the secretion of adrenal cortical hormones, ACTH tends to suppress the formation of new bone, but does not interfere with resorption of bone.

Estrogens in Birds

As birds approach the laying period, the ovarian follicles enlarge and the level of estrogen production is increased. Under the influence of this ovarian hormone large amounts of calcium are stored in the intramedullary deposits that appear in the cavities of the long bones.

New bone is added from the endosteum and reduces or obliterates the marrow cavities. This is the avian method of storing large amounts of calcium for eggshell deposition. The hen's egg contains about 2.0 gm. calcium in the shell and approximately 30 mg. in the yolk. Radioactive isotope techniques have shown that 40 to 50 per cent of the calcium in the shell is turned over from the skeleton and that the remainder is passed from the intestine through the blood plasma to the shell gland. The long bones of young chicks and cocks contain little if any intramedullary bone, and it becomes very sparse in resting hens or in hens at the end of a long period of egg production. The deposition of intramedullary bone in cocks and young birds may be induced by the administration of estrogens. No other hormone has this effect. The intramedullary bone is promptly resorbed upon withdrawal of the hormone. The intramedullary formation may be regarded as a secondary sex characteristic in birds, since it is formed and maintained under the influence of estrogen. It serves as a special substrate for the rapid turnover of calcium required for the addition of shells to the eggs.[51]

In the laying hen, the intramedullary bone is cyclically deposited and resorbed in connection with the storage and liberation of calcium. During early stages of shell formation the intramedullary bone contains many osteoblasts and osteoclasts, but during advanced stages of calcification of the shell there are huge numbers of osteoclasts surrounding the bone trabeculae but osteoblasts are sparse. Submicroscopic crystallites of bone have been detected in the osteoclasts by electron microscopy. This suggests that the osteoclasts perform some role in the destruction of bone. It is probable that the intramedullary bone of laying hens is resorbed in some areas and simultaneously replaced in others. Thus there are cyclic increases and decreases in intramedullary bone during shell deposition, but it is never totally removed. The volume of intramedullary bone present at any particular time depends on the level of estrogen production, the utilization of calcium for shell production, and the amount of calcium consumed in the food.[3, 30, 47, 50]

The mechanism whereby estrogens induce intramedullary bone formation in birds and certain mammals remains obscure. Such bone changes are not produced by any other hormone, and it should be noted that estrogens cause new bone formation only in the interior of the bones. This localized action may correlate with the vascularity of these areas. Estrogens have little or no effect on the periosteal surfaces of the long bones. They may produce localized vascular reactions in bone similar to their effects on the small blood vessels of the uterine endometrium.

Adult chickens can maintain a total serum calcium level of 10 mg. per 100 ml. for at least a month when deprived of calcium in the diet. This is accomplished by resorption of bone mineral, especially from the flat bones of the body. Around 25 per cent of the total bone mass may be lost in this manner, though the long bones of the appendages are not severely affected except in prolonged calcium deficiency. Rapidly growing chicks cannot survive long in the absence of calcium. In hens deprived of both calcium and vitamin D, egg production is discontinued within five days.

Estrogens produce comparable skeletal modifications in mice. The effect is proportional to the amount of estrogen administered, and new spongy bone may entirely fill the marrow cavities. Estrogen does not have this effect in adult rats, but in young animals, there may be some increase in the spongy bone below the growing epiphysis.[49]

PHYSICOCHEMICAL PROPERTIES OF BONE

Considerable progress has been made in understanding the physicochemical nature of bone mineral, and radioactive isotopes have assisted in clarifying some of the interrelationships involving calcium and phosphate. The bone crystals are extremely small, and this results in a large surface area in bone. They are deposited in an organic matrix consisting chiefly of collagen fibers and mucopolysaccharides. There is a close relationship between the crystals and the collagen fibers, and the fibers themselves probably determine the crystallization of bone salt from the serum. Specific groups in the collagen fiber molecules may serve as templates or "seed" upon which crystal formation occurs. The bone crystals are composed chiefly of calcium, phosphate, hydroxyl, and citrate, with traces of many other ions. The bone mineral is thought to be similar to hydroxy apatite and, like minerals of the apatite series, its calcium-phosphate ratios are highly variable.[28]

Ionic exchanges can occur readily on the bone crystals, and this may have important effects on the solubility of the modified crystal. When radioactive calcium or phosphate is given intravenously to an animal, the radioactivity disappears quickly from the blood as the radioactive ions are taken up by the bone in exchange for similar, nonradioactive ions. Different kinds of ions in the body fluids may displace calcium and phosphate ions from bone crystal. For example, calcium ions can be displaced by strontium or sodium, and phosphate ions by carbonate or citrate. It has been demonstrated that citrate may be exchanged for phosphate on the surface of the bone crystal and that high concentrations of phosphate may cause the release of citrate from bone crystal. The citrate-phosphate competition for sites on the surface of bone crystals appears to be an important aspect of bone metabolism.

Some calcium and phosphate can be removed from blood serum by shaking it with dried bone, indicating that serum is supersaturated with bone mineral. It appears that PTH must exert some specific effect on "living" bone that enables the bone mineral to be released into serum that is already supersaturated. Various lines of evidence indicate that the hormone maintains the serum calcium at a level above that which can be produced by a physicochemical equilibrium prevailing between the bone surfaces and the extracellular fluids.

When PTH is administered to an animal, it causes dissolution of the organic matrix and bone crystals. Consequently calcium, phosphate, and other ionic constituents of the crystals are released into the body fluids. Many observations indicate that there is a relationship between PTH, citrate metabolism, and bone resorption. The citrate content of bone is relatively high (1 to 2 per cent), whereas marrow and cartilage contain much less. Resorbing bone grown *in vitro* has been found to release citrate into the culture medium. Parathyroidectomy lowers the level of blood citrate as well as the blood calcium. The subcutaneous administration of PTH, which is more effective than the intravenous, elevates both the serum citrate and calcium. It has also been found that the rise in serum citrate precedes the rise in serum calcium in the dog. The administration of citrate to young animals causes bone resorption and elevates the serum calcium. Since the kidney is the main site of citrate oxidation, bilateral nephrectomy causes an accumulation of citrate and results in demineralization of the skeleton and hypercalcemia. This effect, however, does not occur if the parathyroid glands are removed prior to removal of the kidneys. With the technique of peritoneal lavage, it has been found that PTH and exogenous citrate act similarly in removing Ca^{45} from bone.

It is quite obvious that, when bone crystal *per se* is broken down, both calcium and phosphate must be released in the same proportions as they are combined in the crystal. On an atom basis this is three calcium atoms to two atoms of phosphorus, and by weight a ratio of 2:1. Studies utilizing radioactive isotopes indicate that dissolution of bone crystal by PTH does yield atoms in this proportion and suggest very strongly that PTH acts in bone at the level of the bone crystal. By acting at the level of the bone crystal, the parathyroid hormone affects both calcium and phosphate, and both ions are probably influenced by PTH effects on the kidney.[17-19]

The Mechanism of Action of Parathyroid Hormone

Human patients suffering from primary hypoparathyroidism are known to have low serum calcium levels and high serum phosphate levels. Parathyroid extracts, administered to these patients, promote a phosphate diuresis that is followed by diminished levels of serum phosphate and elevated levels of serum calcium. An early concept of parathyroid hormone action was that it acted primarily upon the kidney to promote the excretion of phosphate, thus lowering the serum phosphate level. The mobilization of bone mineral, with a concomitant rise in serum calcium, was supposed to be a secondary phenomenon resulting from a reduction of the calcium-phosphate ion product in the serum. The *renal theory* explained all of the data available at the time, but it is no longer considered adequate.

Parathyroid transplants have a direct resorptive effect on parietal bone. When pieces of parietal bone together with parathyroid tissue are transplanted to the cranial cavity of mice, bone resorption occurs contiguous to the parathyroid transplant, whereas bone deposition occurs on the opposite side. Bone resorption accompanied by osteoclasts has been demonstrated by placing parathyroid grafts against the parietal bones of mice and rats; other tissues do not produce this effect. Direct parathyroid-induced bone absorption has been obtained by culturing parathyroid tissue *in vitro* in close contact with parietal bone. These experiments show very convincingly that the hormone of the parathyroid gland acts directly on bone. Furthermore, it has been established in a variety of species that PTH stimulates the release of calcium from bone to the extracellular fluid after the kidneys have been removed. Without denying that PTH has an effect on the kidneys and intestine, the great weight of evidence supports the view that its primary effect is upon the skeletal system, to increase the effective solubility of bone mineral.[1, 6, 23, 24, 26]

By use of the technique of peritoneal lavage, it is possible to show that PTH can release calcium from bone after any influence of the kidney or of intestinal absorption of calcium has been ruled out. After nephrectomy of the rat, an isotonic solution of saline containing 3 per cent glucose and no calcium or phosphorus was introduced into the peritoneal cavity and allowed to remain there for one hour to attain equilibrium with the body fluids. After this time the wash was removed and analyzed for calcium and phosphate. In nephrectomized animals the wash contained 7 mg. per 100 ml. calcium; after parathyroidectomy of the nephrectomized animal the value fell to 3.5 mg. per 100 ml., along with a fall in phosphorus and citric acid. Small amounts of parathyroid extract restored all three values to original levels. Such experiments leave no doubt that the parathyroid glands can exert their effects in the absence of the kidneys. It is also apparent that in the absence of parathyroids the bone can supply calcium to the fluid compartments over long periods of time. The equilibrium level between bone and extracellular fluid in the parathyroidectomized animal is between 3 and 4 mg. per 100 ml., and most of this is assumed to be in the ionized form. It has been suggested that this equilibrium may be purely a physical phenomenon, assuming that the apatite crystals of bone are sufficiently soluble at the pH of the body fluids to give this effect.

This equilibrium between bone calcium and the extracellular fluid can be raised by PTH even in the absence of the kidneys.[45]

There is general agreement that a close association exists between citric acid in bone and the action of PTH on calcium metabolism. It has been suggested that the increased production of citrate under the influence of PTH is somehow related to the function of osteoclasts. Possibly one action of the hormone is to cause a release of citrate from bone cells, possibly osteoclasts, for the localized demineralization of bone, thus raising the calcium of the fluid compartments to the required levels.

There are suggestions that high levels of parathyroid hormone in the system stimulate the utilization of pyruvate and glucose by bone for the production of citrate and lactate. Similar trends have been noticed in tissues other than bone after PTH administration. One hypothesis is that tissues in general may respond to the hormone by forming increased amounts of citrate and lactate over the well-known biochemical pathways, but since bone contains relatively little isocitric dehydrogenase, the citrate accumulates in bone instead of being oxidized readily. Therefore the main effect of PTH upon citrate production is seen in bone rather than in other tissues. The accumulated citrate in bone supposedly leads to the replacement of phosphate in the bone crystal by citrate, the freed phosphate accounting for the elevated serum phosphate that occurs in the blood shortly after the blood citrate is raised. The dissolution of calcium citrate in the extracellular fluid leads to the rise in serum calcium. According to this theory, the basic mechanism of PTH action is to increase the utilization of pyruvate, and possibly of glucose, for the production of citrate, which acts on the bone crystal. It is not known whether this effect results from permeability changes or from some influence on intracellular enzyme systems.[20, 33, 34]

While the exact mechanism of parathyroid hormone action awaits clarification, there is general agreement that the hormone maintains a constant level of serum calcium by removing calcium and phosphate from the bone and simultaneously raising the renal threshold for calcium and lowering the threshold for phosphate. It appears established that PTH acts primarily on some phase of bone metabolism, but secondarily affects the kidneys, the intestine, and perhaps other tissues.[16, 21, 22, 32]

REFERENCES

1. Barnicot, N. A.: The local action of the parathyroid and other tissues on bone in intracerebral grafts. J. Anat., 82:233, 1948.
2. Bassabarger, R. A., Freeman, S., and Ivy, A. C.: The experimental production of severe homogeneous osteoporosis by gastrectomy in puppies. Amer. J. Physiol., 121:137, 1938.
3. Bloom, M. A., Domm, L. V., Nalbandov, A. V., and Bloom, W.: Medullary bone of laying chickens. Amer. J. Anat., 102:411, 1958.

4. Boschwitz, D.: The parathyroid glands of *Bufo viridis* Laurenti. Herpetologia, *17*:192, 1961.

5. Bryan, W. R., and Garrey, W. E.: Contributory factors in parathyroid tetany in dogs. High temperature, panting and overventilation. Amer. J. Physiol., 98:194, 1931.

6. Chang, H.: Localized resorption of bone adjacent to parathyroid grafts. Anat. Rec., *106*:266, 1950.

7. Clark, N. B.: Experimental and histological studies of the parathyroid glands of fresh-water turtles. Gen. & Comp. Endocrinol., 5:297, 1965.

8. Cooper, C. W., Yates, C. W., Jr., and Talmage, R. V.: Some endogenous parathyroid effects manifested by bone *in vitro*. Proc. Soc. Exp. Biol. & Med., *119*:81, 1965.

9. Copp, D. H.: Calcium and phosphorus metabolism. Amer. J. Med., 22:275, 1957.

10. Copp, D. H.: Parathyroids, calcitonin, and control of plasma calcium. Recent Prog. Hormone Research, *20*:59, 1964.

11. Copp, D. H., and Cameron, E. C.: Demonstration of a hypocalcemic factor (calcitonin) in commercial parathyroid extract. Science, *134*:2038, 1961.

12. Cortelyou, J. R., Hibner-Owerko, A., and Mulroy, J.: Blood and urine calcium changes in totally parathyroidectomized *Rana pipiens*. Endocrinol., 66:441, 1960.

13. Crawford, J. D., Gribetz, D., Diner, W. C., Hurst, P., and Castleman, B.: The influence of vitamin D on parathyroid activity and the metabolism of calcium and citrate during calcium deprivation. Endocrinol., *61*:59, 1957.

14. Doty, S. B., and Talmage, R. V.: Stimulation of parathyroid secretion in the absence of the adrenal, thyroid, or pituitary gland. Gen. & Comp. Endocrinol., 4:545, 1964.

15. Doty, S. B., Yates, C. W., Lotz, W. E., Kisecleski, W., and Talmage, R. V.: Effect of short term alpha irradiation on parathyroid activity and osteoclast numbers. Proc. Soc. Exp. Biol. & Med., *119*:77, 1965.

16. Egawa, J., and Neuman, W. F.: Effect of parathyroid extract on the metabolism of radioactive phosphate in kidney. Endocrinol., 74:90, 1964.

17. Elliott, J. R., and Freeman, S.: Parathyroid function and the plasma citric acid and calcium response to nephrectomy. Endocrinol., 59:181, 1956.

18. Elliot, J. R., and Talmage, R. V.: Influence of parathyroids on removal of citric acid administered by peritoneal lavage. Proc. Soc. Exp. Biol. & Med., 94:596, 1957.

19. Elliott, J. R., and Talmage, R. V.: Removal of Ca^{40} and Ca^{45} from bone by citrate as influenced by parathyroids. Endocrinol., 62:709, 1958.

20. Firschein, H. E., Neuman, W. F., Martin, G. R., and Mulryan, B. J.: Studies on the mechanism of action of parathyroid hormone. Recent Prog. Hormone Research, *15*:427, 1959.

21. Forscher, B. K., and Cohn, D. V.: *In vitro* carbohydrate metabolism of bone: Effect of treatment of intact animal with parathyroid extract. *In* R. F. Sognnaes (ed.): Mechanisms of Hard Tissue Destruction. Washington, D.C., American Association for the Advancement of Science, 1963, p. 577.

22. Foulks, J. G., and Perry, F. A.: Alterations in renal tubular phosphate transport during intravenous infusion of parathyroid extract in the dog. Amer. J. Physiol., *196*:567, 1959.

23. Gaillard, P. J.: Parathyroid gland tissue and bone *in vitro*. Exp. Cell Research, Suppl. 3:154, 1955.

24. Gaillard, P. J.: Parathyroid and bone in tissue culture. *In* R. O. Greep and R. V. Talmage (eds.): The Parathyroids. Springfield, Ill., Charles C Thomas, 1961, p. 20.

25. Gaillard, P. J., Talmage, R. V., and Budy, A. (eds.): The Parathyroid Glands; Ultrastructure, Secretion and Function. Chicago, Ill., University of Chicago Press, 1965.

26. Greep, R. O., and Talmage, R. V. (eds.): The Parathyroids. Springfield, Ill., Charles C Thomas, 1961.

27. Howard, J. E.: Calcium metabolism, bones and calcium homeostasis. A review of certain current concepts. J. Clin. Endocrinol., *17*:1105, 1957.

28. McLean, F. C., and Urist, M. R.: Bone: An Introduction to the Physiology of Skeletal Tissue. Chicago, University of Chicago Press, 1955.

29. Munson, P. L., Hirsch, P. F., and Tashjian, A. H., Jr.: Parathyroid gland. Ann. Rev. Physiol., 25:325, 1963.
30. Polin, D., Sturkie, P. D., and Hunsaker, W.: The blood calcium response of the chicken to parathyroid extracts. Endocrinol., 60:1, 1957.
31. Potts, J. T., Jr., and Aurbach, G. D.: The chemistry of parathyroid hormone. *In* P. J. Gaillard, R. V. Talmage, and A. M. Budy (eds.): The Parathyroid Glands; Ultrastructure, Secretion and Function. Chicago, Ill., University of Chicago Press, 1965, p. 53.
32. Pullman, T. N., Lavender, A. R., Aho, I., and Rasmussen, H.: Direct renal action of a purified parathyroid extract. Endocrinol., 67:570, 1960.
33. Raisz, L. G., Au, W. Y. W., and Tepperman, J.: Effect of changes in parathyroid activity on bone metabolism *in vitro*. Endocrinol., 68:783, 1961.
34. Ranney, R. E.: The effect of estrone and parathyroid extract on bone citrate metabolism. Endocrinol., 67:166, 1960.
35. Rasmussen, H., Arnaud, C., and Hawker, C.: Actinomycin D and the response to parathyroid hormone. Science, 144:1019, 1964.
36. Rasmussen, H., and Craig, L. C.: Parathyroid hormone, the parathyroid polypeptides. Recent Prog. Hormone Research, 18:269, 1962.
37. Rasmussen, H., Sze, Y.-L., and Young, R.: Further studies on the isolation and characterization of parathyroid polypeptides. J. Biol. Chem., 239:2852, 1964.
38. Sehe, C. T.: Radioautographic studies on the ultimobranchial body and thyroid gland in vertebrates: fishes and amphibians. Endocrinol., 67:674, 1960.
39. Sehe, C. T.: Comparative studies on the ultimobranchial body in reptiles and birds. Gen. & Comp. Endocrinol., 5:45, 1965.
40. Talmage, R. V., Cooper, C. W., and Neuenschwander, J.: The effect of actinomycin D on parathyroid-induced changes in bone and kidney. Gen. & Comp. Endocrinol., 5:475, 1965.
41. Talmage, R. V., and Dodds, B. F.: Comparative study of some effects of administration of dihydrotachysterol and calciferol to rats. Endocrinol., 57:236, 1955.
42. Talmage, R. V., and Doty, S. B.: The effect of sodium fluoride on parathyroid function in the rat as studied by peritoneal lavage. Gen. & Comp. Endocrinol., 2:473, 1962.
43. Talmage, R. V., Elliott, J. R., and Enders, A. C.: Parathyroid function as studied by continuous peritoneal lavage in nephrectomized rats. Endocrinol., 61:256, 1957.
44. Talmage, R. V., and Kraintz, F. W.: The effect of sodium chloride acidosis on parathyroid function in the rat as studied by peritoneal lavage. Gen. & Comp. Endocrinol., 1:341, 1961.
45. Talmage, R. V., and Toft, R. J.: The problem of the control of parathyroid secretion. *In* R. O. Greep and R. V. Talmage (eds.): The Parathyroids. Springfield, Ill., Charles C Thomas, 1961, p. 224.
46. Toft, R. J., and Talmage, R. V.: Quantitative relationship of osteoclasts to parathyroid function. Proc. Soc. Exp. Biol. & Med., 103:611, 1960.
47. Urist, M. R.: The effects of calcium deprivation upon the blood, adrenal cortex, ovary, and skeleton in domestic fowl. Recent Prog. Hormone Research, 15:455, 1959.
48. Urist, M. R.: Calcium and phosphorus in the blood and skeleton of the elasmobranchii. Endocrinol., 69:778, 1961.
49. Urist, M. R., Budy, A. M., and McLean, F. C.: Endosteal-bone formation in estrogen-treated mice. J. Bone & Joint Surg., 32A:143, 1950.
50. Urist, M. R., Deutsch, N. M., Pomerantz, G., and McLean, F. C.: Interrelations between actions of parathyroid hormone and estrogens on bone and blood in avian species. Am. J. Physiol., 199:851, 1960.
51. Winget, C. M., and Smith, A. H.: Dissociation of the calcium-protein complex of laying hen's plasma. Am. J. Physiol., 196:371, 1959.

9

THE PANCREATIC
ISLETS

The mammalian pancreas is a compound gland consisting of exocrine and endocrine tissues (Fig. 9–1). The exocrine constituent secretes pancreatic juice which is poured into the duodenum via the pancreatic duct; the islets of Langerhans are aggregations of endocrine cells which liberate their hormones directly into the circulation. The human pancreas contains a million or more individual islets scattered widely throughout the acinar tissues; the total islet tissue constitutes only 1 or 2 per cent of the pancreatic mass. The cells of the islets are arranged in irregular cords which are separated by a very rich system of capillary vessels or sinusoids (Fig. 9–2). While the exocrine cells receive sympathetic and parasympathetic fibers, it is doubtful whether the nervous system performs any important role in regulating the secretory functions of the islets.

The pancreas and liver originate as outpocketings of the duodenal entoderm, at a point just caudad to the pylorus (Fig. 8–3). There are generally three main pancreatic buds, one dorsal and two ventral. The dorsal primordium constricts from the duodenum and thus forms the duct of Santorini, which may persist in the adult as the accessory pancreatic duct. The ventral outgrowth, originally paired, is drained by Wirsung's duct, which persists in the adult as the pancreatic duct proper. The dorsal and ventral anlagen of the human embryo fuse during the seventh week to form the pancreas. In birds, the three pancreatic outgrowths do not fuse so completely, and the adult gland consists of three completely or partially separated lobes (Fig. 9–3).

270

INTERLOBULAR SEPTUM   PANCREATIC ACINUS

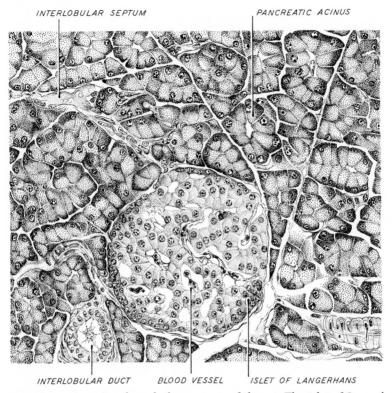

INTERLOBULAR DUCT   BLOOD VESSEL   ISLET OF LANGERHANS

Figure 9–1. A section through the pancreas of the rat. The islet of Langerhans is a gland of internal secretion, whereas the surrounding acinar tissue forms an exocrine gland.

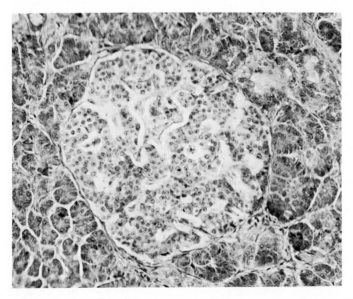

Figure 9–2. Section of the human pancreas showing a pancreatic islet. Note the sinusoidal spaces separating the cords and masses of islet cells.

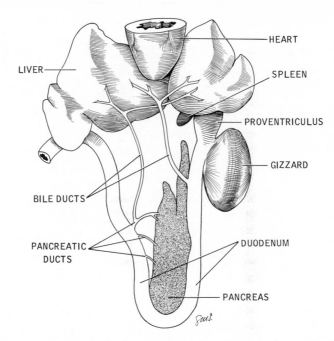

Figure 9–3. Pancreas and adnexa of the pigeon *(Columba livia)*. The liver lobes are retracted cranially; one lobe of the pancreas does not show since it is behind the descending limb of the duodenum. The three pancreatic ducts enter the right limb of the duodenal loop. Notice the absence of a gall bladder.

The endocrine cells of the islets arise from the duct epithelium and often seem to remain connected to its finer ramifications; however, neither insulin nor glucagon is present in pancreatic juice. There is no clear evidence that acinar cells ever transform into islet tissue. Since the islets bud off from the duct epithelium, and the duct itself is an outgrowth of the duodenal entoderm, the islets can be regarded as endocrine specializations of the duodenal mucosa. The gastrointestinal hormones, such as secretin, arise from the mucosal lining of the stomach and intestine.

Two hormones, insulin and glucagon, are known to derive from the islets of Langerhans. Both of these hormones act mainly, but not exclusively, upon the liver. Since the pancreas is drained by the hepatic portal vein, the hormones must traverse the liver before they can reach the systemic circulation. The islet hormones are enzymatically inactivated by liver tissue, and thus attain higher concentrations in the blood of the portal vein than in the systemic circulation. It is possible that large doses of exogenous hormones, added to peripheral blood, have certain effects which are pharmacologic rather than physiologic. The gastrointestinal hormones (*e.g.*, secretin, cholecystokinin) confine their actions to the gastrointestinal tract and its appendages, and the islet hormones show this same tendency.

ANATOMY OF THE PANCREATIC ISLETS

Microscopic Anatomy

Several types of cells are identifiable in islet tissue.[27] There is very good evidence that insulin is a product of the β-cells, and that the α-cells are the source of glucagon. In mammals, the β-cells are more abundant and contain granules which are soluble in alcohol and acetic acid; since these cells contain insulin, they may be specifically stained with pseudoisocyanin. The α-cells are less abundant, and tend to be arranged about the periphery of the islet. C-cells, appearing nongranular under the light microscope, have been described. The ultrastructure of the α- and β-cells, as determined by electron micros-copy, demonstrates that they are different cell types (Fig. 9–4). The β-cells of neonatal hamsters are biochemically competent before the appearance of distinct islets of Langerhans.[48] The pancreas of larval frogs does not become important in glucose regulation until mid-metamorphosis.[16]

Comparative Morphology

No structure comparable to the pancreas is found among the invertebrates. In the ammocoetes larva of the lamprey, small clusters of cells are found in the submucosa of the intestinal wall, at the junction of the foregut and midgut. These structures (follicles of Langerhans) were described by Langerhans in 1873 and are presumed to be islet tissue. The administration of glucose to these larvae causes certain follicle cells (probably β-cells) to become vacuoloated and hydropic, just as in mammals. Cells appearing to correspond to the exocrine pancreas are present in the epithelium of the anterior intestine. As the larval lamprey undergoes metamorphosis the islet follicles give rise to a compact tissue at the blind end of the intestinal caecum. Encapsulated follicles of islet tissue have been found in adult hagfishes near the point where the bile duct enters the intestine. It appears that both endocrine and exocrine constituents of the pancreas are present in cyclostomes, but these remain separate from each other. These observations suggest that islet tissue arose very early in vertebrate evolution as a derivative of the intestinal tract.

Much diversity is encountered among teleost fishes, but, in some of them (*e.g., Ameiurus, Lophius, Cottus*), most of the islet tissue is concentrated into a "principal islet" which is separate from the exocrine pancreas (Fig. 9–5). In the initial attempts to prepare effec-tive extracts of mammalian pancreas, it was learned that proteolytic enzymes from the exocrine pancreas promptly destroyed the insulin. It was possible to obtain potent extracts from the principal islets of

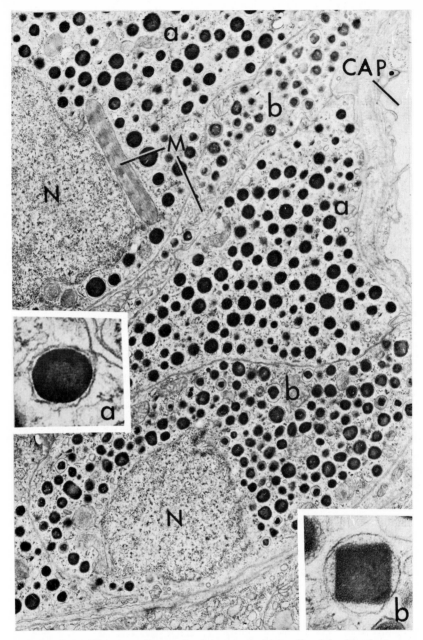

Figure 9–4. Electron micrograph of pancreatic islet cells of the lizard, *Eumeces fasciatus.* Alpha (a) and beta (b) cells are clustered about a capillary (CAP) and can be distinguished by structural differences in their secretion granules and mitochondria. An alpha granule (left inset) is homogeneously dense and has a round profile, whereas a beta granule (right inset) is crystalline when fully condensed. The density of the beta granules depends on their degree of condensation. Many alpha cell mitochondria (M) possess tubular cristae oriented longitudinally, as shown beside the nucleus (N) in the upper left corner of the figure, whereas beta cell mitochondria are typical in appearance. Golgi elements and endoplasmic reticulum are usually more abundant in the beta cells. Micrograph × 12,000; insets × 54,000. (Courtesy of Dr. Paul R. Burton, University of Kansas.)

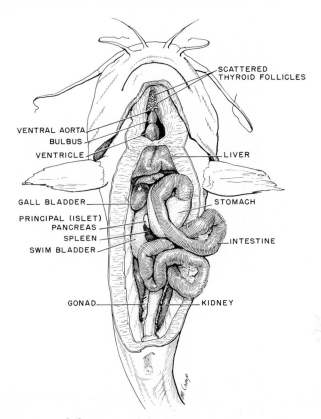

Figure 9–5. Ventral dissection of the catfish *(Ameiurus)*, showing the location of the principal (islet) pancreas with reference to other organs. Scattered thyroid follicles are shown diagrammatically around the ventral aorta.

the anglerfish (*Lophius*), since these organs contain very little exocrine tissue. Although some fishes show a tendency to concentrate islet tissue into separate nodules, the two kinds of tissue are intermingled in the great majority of species.

Pancreatic cytology is very confused in the poikilothermic vertebrates and the situation needs to be reinvestigated, by means of modern cytochemical methods and electron microscopy, and by extending such studies to a larger variety of species. It appears that β-cells are present in the pancreas of all vertebrates, but the α-cells seem to be more variable.[53] Some urodeles are said to possess only β-cells in their islets and to be much more sensitive than reptiles and birds to exogenous insulin. The small islets of *Ambystoma* are reported to contain only α-cells, whereas the larger islets contain both types of cells. The anurans that have been studied carefully seem to have both α- and β-cells in their islets. The islets of reptiles contain both cell types, though the α-cells are generally the more numerous (Fig. 9–6). The α-cells are very abundant in birds, and in some species at least, there seem to be two kinds of islets, some containing only α-cells and others only β-cells. Extraction studies indicate that the avian

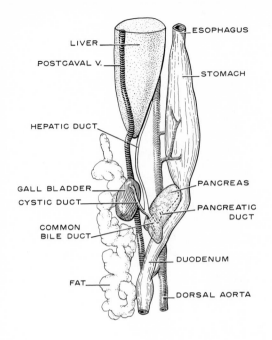

Figure 9-6. Dissection of the pancreas and adnexa of the snake *(Natrix)* from ventral view.

pancreas yields about 10 times more glucagon than comparable quantities of mammalian gland. Exogenous insulin generally lowers the level of blood sugar (hypoglycemia), but in species having a high α-cell count (some lizards and birds), this treatment produces an initial hypoglycemia which is followed by a more lasting elevation of blood sugar (hyperglycemia). This probably means that the hypoglycemia produced by insulin stimulates the α-cells to release glucagon which has the reverse effect.

SOME FUNDAMENTALS OF CARBOHYDRATE METABOLISM

The primary function of carbohydrates in most organisms is to provide a source of energy for the various metabolic transformations. While animals can and do derive energy from fats and proteins, they are first converted to carbohydrate, or an intermediate in carbohydrate metabolism, before the energy is made available. Energy for the maintenance of life is obtained by the degradation of compounds of relatively high potential energy into products of low potential energy, and these transformations are catalyzed by enzymes. In order to understand the general pattern of carbohydrate metabolism and the mechanisms that are involved in integrating and controlling it, the functional importance of enzyme systems must be kept in mind.

General Properties of Enzymes

Enzymes are proteins that catalyze the reactions in living systems. Although they are produced by living cells, they are capable of functioning separately from the cell. Many have been obtained in crystalline form, and the probable sequence of amino acids has been worked out for salivary amylase, ribonuclease, and several others. Like other proteins, they are subject to denaturation, and most of them are easily destroyed by heat; they are active over a limited pH range and are generally destroyed by acids or alkalies. The enzymic transformations of the body occur under extremely mild conditions. In higher animals, for example, the body temperature remains close to 37.5° C., and in many parts of the body the pH cannot vary far from neutrality. There is an optimum temperature and an optimum pH for each enzyme. The latter value usually lies close to that of the environment in which the enzyme normally functions within the organism. Most intracellular enzymes of higher animals have a pH optimum near neutrality, but alkaline phosphatase, found in many tissues, has an optimal pH near 9; pepsin normally acts in the acid medium of the gastric juice and functions best at a pH of 2.7. Many plant enzymes show optimal activities at pH ranges from 4 to 6.

The substance acted upon by an enzyme is known as its *substrate*. Many enzymes are named by adding the suffix "ase" to the names of the substrates upon which they act. Enzymes for proteins are proteases and peptidases; for lipids, lipases; for esters, esterases; and for nucleic acids, nucleases. The name may refer to function rather than substrate; thus oxidases catalyze oxidations, dehydrogenases bring about the removal of hydrogen, hydrolases catalyze the reaction of hydrolysis, and so on.

Although all enzymes are the products of living cells, they may function within the cell (intracellular) or outside of the cell (extracellular) that produced them. The exocrine glands of the alimentary tract, for example, secrete enzymes that are necessary for the digestion of food before it can be absorbed. Microorganisms, such as molds and bacteria, often liberate enzymes that break down the tissues of the host into soluble materials they can utilize. The intracellular enzymes remain inside the cell and function there. Many enzyme systems, especially those concerned with the provision of energy, are widely distributed among organisms; intermediary metabolism, whether occurring in a yeast cell, a bacterium, or a mammalian muscle, seems to be based upon enzyme reactions that are not radically different. There are some indications that enzyme systems functioning in certain sequences may be confined to specific cell structures. The mitochondria, for example, possibly contain a full complement of enzymes necessary for catalyzing the reactions of the tricarboxylic acid cycle. The intracellular enzymes are frequently quite difficult to isolate.

It is generally believed that there is a temporary union of the substrate with some active group on the surface of the enzyme molecule. This active group may be merely a special arrangement of amino acids, or it may be a special grouping of nonprotein nature, in which case it is called a *prosthetic group.* Such groups are called *coenzymes* if they are loosely attached and form dissociable complexes with the enzyme protein. The protein part of the enzyme is known as the *apoenzyme* and it becomes a *holoenzyme* after association with a coenzyme. Many coenzymes are derivatives of the vitamin B complex, and play important roles in biologic oxidations; some of them act in association with appropriate apoenzymes by accepting and subsequently giving up pairs of hydrogen atoms. Adenosine di- and triphosphate (ADP and ATP) are coenzymes of importance in the transfer of phosphate. A particular coenzyme may associate with different apoenzymes and participate in several enzyme systems.

Enzymes often accelerate the attainment of equilibrium in reversible reactions by catalyzing both the breakdown of a substance and its synthesis. This may be illustrated by the action of phosphorylase:

$$\text{Glycogen} + H_3PO_4 \underset{\xleftarrow{\hspace{4cm}}}{\overset{\text{phosphorylase}}{\xrightarrow{\hspace{4cm}}}} \text{Glucose-1-phosphate}$$

Phosphorylase may therefore be used for the preparation of glucose-1-phosphate or, by varying the conditions, for the synthesis of glycogen. In such reversible reactions, the point of equilibrium depends upon a number of factors, such as the concentration of the reacting substances. When great changes in potential chemical energy are involved, the reactions are usually not reversible, the enzyme promoting a "one-way" reaction leading to a decrease in free energy. The conversion of glucose to glucose-6-phosphate by hexokinase proceeds in one direction only because of the high energy level of adenosine triphosphate:

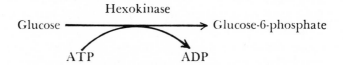

Most of the proteolytic and amylase enzymes of the alimentary tract are hydrolytic and hence do not catalyze reversible reactions.

The velocity of enzymatic reactions may be influenced by temperature, pH, and the concentration of enzyme, substrate, and cofactors. It is assumed that molecules of substrate become absorbed onto the surface of the enzyme molecule and that the products of the reaction are liberated, leaving the enzyme unaltered. An enzyme molecule can thus participate in a reaction repeatedly and, provided that an excess of substrate is present, the velocity will, within limits, be proportional to the concentration of the enzyme. Certain enzymes are confined to discrete particles in the cell, and the rate of metabolic reactions may be limited by the ability of substrate to reach the enzymes. If more substrate is present than is required to saturate the enzyme surface, the provision of additional substrate does not increase the reaction velocity. In many instances, the rate diminishes if the products of the reaction are allowed to accumulate. In cases in which the enzyme requires a dissociable cofactor, such as a coenzyme or an inorganic ion, the reaction rate will vary with the presence of these materials.

Enzyme Inhibitors

Many substances are known to inhibit or antagonize the action of enzymes. The enzyme-substrate complex tends to be quite unstable, and it often happens that foreign substrates can temporarily or permanently occupy the active sites on the enzyme molecule and block its normal function. Acetylcholine from cholinergic nerves is quickly destroyed by the enzyme choline esterase, but eserine (physostigmine) forms a completely stable complex with this enzyme and blocks its activity. Instances of this type are irreversible and are examples of *noncompetitive* inhibition. *Competitive* inhibitors may remain on the surface of the enzyme at the sites normally occupied by the true substrate and thus prevent the access of true substrate molecules. To use a simile, the competitive inhibitor is like a key that enters a lock, but the fit is not perfect and it jams the lock instead of turning it. Succinic dehydrogenase (succinoxidase) normally catalyzes the oxidation of succinic acid, but malonic acid is a competitive inhibitor. When the two acids are present together, they compete for active sites on the enzyme surface. The sulfonamides may interfere with enzymatic reactions requiring *p*-aminobenzoic acid, a true competition existing between the two substances. Since the enzymes are proteins, they may be irreversibly destroyed by heat, radiations, heavy metals, protein precipitants, and many other agents that adversely affect proteins.

Anti-enzymes

The repeated administration of small amounts of pure enzymes to an animal may cause the formation of specific anti-enzymes. The enzymes in snake venom, for example, elicit the formation of anti-enzymes when administered to sheep or horses, and these are used therapeutically in the treatment of snake bite. The cells of the gastrointestinal mucosa contain anti-enzymes that protect them against the action of proteolytic enzymes involved in the digestion of food. Parasites such as *Ascaris* contain similar substances that enable them to withstand the digestive enzymes of the alimentary tract. Intestinal round worms may be digested alive by ficin, a proteinase from the fig tree not ordinarily encountered by such parasites.

General Pattern of Carbohydrate Metabolism

Carbohydrate metabolism is a large field with many special ramifications, and only general aspects of the subject are discussed here as an aid in understanding hormone effects.[7] The oxidation of muscle glycogen to carbon dioxide and water provides the energy for muscular work. There is at first a series of reversible reactions that can occur in the absence of oxygen (anaerobic); these pathways convert muscle glycogen to pyruvic and lactic acids. This process is called *glycolysis.* A second series of reactions occurs in the presence of oxygen (aerobic) and results in the oxidation of pyruvic acid to carbon dioxide and water. The excess of lactic acid is conveyed by the blood to the liver where it is reconverted to glycogen. Blood glucose is the only material that muscles can utilize for the synthesis of glycogen. The quantities of glucose taken out of the blood for utilization by the tissues are compensated by the release of glucose into the blood by the liver. The blood sugar levels are held relatively constant by a regulatory system that depends largely upon the synthesis and storage of glycogen by the liver. The liver is capable of synthesizing glycogen from dietary sugars and proteins, and possibly from dietary fats. The main aspects of carbohydrate metabolism are summarized in Figures 9–7 and 9–8.

Several metabolic pathways of great importance occur in the liver: (1) *glycogenesis,* the synthesis of glycogen from glucose; (2) glycogenolysis, the conversion of glycogen to glucose; and (3) *gluconeogenesis,* the synthesis of glucose from noncarbohydrate precursors, such as certain amino acids, glycerol, etc. Gluconeogenesis is

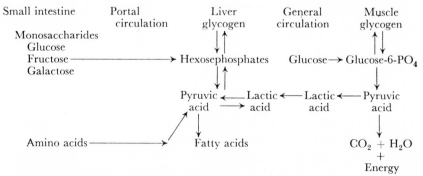

Figure 9–7. Schema showing the major transformations in the metabolism of carbohydrates. (After L. S. Fosdick, 1959.)

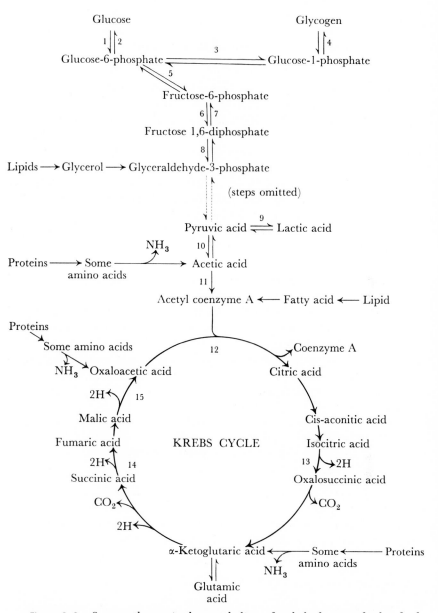

Figure 9–8. Some pathways in the metabolism of carbohydrates and other foodstuffs. Enzymes: 1, Hexokinase; 2, Glucose-6-phosphatase; 3, Phosphoglucomutase; 4, Phosphorylase; 5, Phosphohexose isomerase; 6, Phosphofructokinase; 7, Diphosphofructose phosphatase; 8, Aldolase; 9, Lactic dehydrogenase; 10, Carboxylase; 11, Acetylkinase; 12, Condensing enzyme; 13, Isocitric dehydrogenase; 14, Succinic dehydrogenase; 15, Malic dehydrogenase.

of especial importance during fasting or when low carbohydrate diets are being consumed.

The Origin of Blood Sugar

The digestive enzymes convert starches and disaccharides of the diet into the monosaccharides, glucose, fructose, and galactose; these are absorbed into the portal system. Fructose and galactose are quickly converted by the liver into glycogen and generally are absent from the systemic circulation. Glucose is present in the blood at all times and is the principal source of energy for all cells. The usual concentration in the human subject is 70 to 100 mg. per 100 ml. during fasting, but after a meal rich in carbohydrate the blood glucose may rise to 140 or 150 mg. per 100 ml. When the blood sugar becomes too high (hyperglycemia), as in diabetes mellitus, glucose filters through the renal glomeruli at a rate that exceeds the capacity of the tubules to reabsorb it, hence appreciable quantities "spill over" into the urine (glycosuria). The blood glucose level at which sugar appears in the urine is termed the *renal threshold.* This is extremely variable but is usually stated to be 160 to 180 mg. per 100 ml.

There is a constant drain of blood glucose to the tissues and, if this is not compensated by dietary intake, liver glycogen must be converted to blood glucose. The enzymes phosphorylase and phosphoglucomutase will catalyze the breakdown of glycogen to glucose-6-phosphate, and the latter will be converted to glucose by the enzyme glucose-6-phosphatase. The glycogen stored in muscle is not directly convertible to blood glucose.

The Fate of Blood Glucose

The glucose of the blood may be dealt with in several different ways: (1) stored as glycogen in the liver, muscles, and to a lesser extent in other tissues; (2) converted to fat, certain amino acids, or other carbohydrates; and (3) oxidized by the tissues to carbon dioxide and water with the production of heat and energy.

Storage as Glycogen

If there are no urgent physiologic needs for oxidative energy or for conversion to special products, the excess of glucose in the blood is stored in the form of glycogen. Glycogenesis proceeds in essentially the same manner in liver and muscle. Muscles, however, can form glycogen only from glucose; the liver can synthesize it from lactic acid, pyruvic acid, citric acid, glycerol, and certain amino acids, as well as from glucose. The essential steps in glycogenesis may be summarized:

hexokinase
(1) Glucose $+$ ATP $\xrightarrow{\hspace{2cm}}$ Glucose-6-PO$_4$ $+$ ADP

phosphoglucomutase
(2) Glucose-6-PO$_4$ $\rightleftharpoons$ Glucose-1-PO$_4$

phosphorylase
(3) Glucose-1-PO$_4$ $\rightleftharpoons$ Glycogen $+$ PO$_4$

(4) ADP $+$ PO$_4$ $\longrightarrow$ ATP

Adenosine triphosphate serves as a phosphate donor in reaction (1), but it is reconstituted in reaction (4). Fructose and a number of other compounds that can be converted to glucose-6-phosphate are brought into the glucose pathway. Any compound that can be converted to glucose-6-phosphate is a potential source of liver glycogen and blood glucose.

Conversion to Fat and Amino Acids

The liver is capable of converting excessive glucose to fatty acids, which are stored as triglycerides in the fat depots. By the use of isotopic methods it has been shown that a large proportion of glucose is converted to fatty acids before its final degradation to carbon dioxide and water. Many of the metabolites of glucose may give rise to nonessential amino acids. A small amount of glucose may be converted to other compounds containing sugar residues such as nucleic acids, glycoproteins, and mucopolysaccharides.

Oxidation

The main function of monosaccharides is to provide a source of energy, chiefly in the form of energy-rich phosphate bonds. All tissues have the capacity of converting glucose to carbon dioxide and water. Nervous tissue, unlike muscle and liver, does not form glycogen, and hence is completely dependent upon blood glucose as a source of energy. Most other tissues can use amino acids and fat to meet a portion of their metabolic needs. Nerve cells can oxidize glucose directly to pyruvic acid, carbon dioxide, and water. This means that the brain and other components of the nervous system must have uninterrupted supply of blood glucose. When the blood sugar falls too low (hypoglycemia), the metabolism of nervous tissue is impaired. This occurs after an overdose of insulin and is characterized by loss of consciousness.

Muscles must maintain a constant supply of stored glycogen to meet their energy requirements. Muscles form glycogen in essentially the same way as the liver, but the reaction is not reversible in muscles. Muscle glycogen is broken down to hexosephosphate, rather than to glucose. The oxidation of muscle glycogen to carbon dioxide and water occurs in two steps: (1) an "explosive" conversion of glycogen to lactic acid, an anaerobic phase called *glycolysis*; and (2) an aerobic phase during which pyruvic acid is converted to carbon dioxide and water. Since the anaerobic phase is more rapid than the aerobic phase, lactic acid tends to accumulate in the muscle. The lactic acid reaches the liver, where it is reconverted to glycogen (glyconeogenesis) and subsequently released as glucose (glycogenolysis):

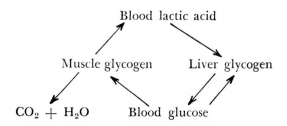

Heart muscle utilizes carbohydrate through the same metabolic pathways as skeletal muscle, and it is probable that lactic acid is the most important fuel for the heart under ordinary conditions.

Intermediary Metabolism

As glucose is withdrawn from the blood to meet the requirements of the tissues, the liver makes good the deficit by converting stored glycogen to glucose (glycogenolysis) or by producing glucose from noncarbohydrate sources (gluconeogenesis). Glycogenolysis is accomplished by reversing the enzyme-catalyzed steps of glycogenesis. The actual utilization of carbohydrates involves their degradation to pyruvic and lactic acids and is generally termed *anaerobic glycolysis*. The oxidation of pyruvate to carbon dioxide and water is termed the "aerobic phase," the "tricarboxylic acid cycle," the "citric acid cycle," or the "Krebs cycle."

Glycolysis

This phase of metabolism may start from glycogen, glucose, or fructose. It has been demonstrated to occur in a great variety of organisms, and the main steps are similar, whether they occur in microörganisms, plants, or higher animals. Glycolysis is a complicated process that takes place in many stages, and these cannot be discussed here. The participation of oxygen is not required in any of the reactions. However, if the end product of glycolysis, pyruvic acid, is not burned, it accumulates and prevents the completion of glycolytic reactions. Only a small fraction of the energy contained in a glucose molecule is liberated by its conversion to pyruvic acid. The energy released by the oxidation of pyruvic acid is much greater than that released during the stages of glycolysis.

The Tricarboxylic Acid Cycle of Krebs

Under aerobic conditions, pyruvic acid undergoes a series of stepwise reactions that liberate a large amount of energy (Fig. 9–8). It first combines with coenzyme A and is decarboxylated, the hydrogen being passed to nicotinamide adenine dinucleotide (NAD). The two-carbon fragment (acetyl) unites with phosphorylated coenzyme A to produce acetylcoenzyme A. This reaction may be considered irreversible. "Acetyl" is the name given to two-carbon fragments derived from various kinds of molecules during their metabolism. Carbohydrates, fats, and proteins can give rise to an acetyl, which then enters a final common metabolic pathway. Acetyl coenzyme A, in the presence of oxaloacetic acid and an appropriate enzyme, forms citric acid and coenzyme A. Citric acid undergoes internal rearrangements and then is dehydrogenated and decarboxylated, giving rise to α-ketoglutaric acid. The latter is decarboxylated to form succinic acid. A considerable amount of energy is liberated in each oxidative decarboxylation, and a part of it is stored in high energy phosphate bonds. Succinic acid undergoes a series of dehydrogenations eventually yielding oxaloacetic acid, which again becomes a receptor for an acetyl fragment. Acetyl coenzyme A is formed in the liver as well as in muscle, and in the liver the acetyl may participate in a number of reactions other than oxidation through the Krebs cycle. It may give rise to acetoacetic acid or it may be utilized in the synthesis of fatty acids and cholesterol.

Fragments from all types of foodstuffs are eventually channeled through the tricarboxylic acid cycle. It is a means whereby the organism can effectively utilize fragments of organic compounds derived from the degradation of carbohydrates, fats, and proteins. For example, the amino acids that an animal derives through the digestion of plant proteins may not be in the correct proportions for the synthesis of animal proteins. The extra amino acids may be deaminated and the residues passed through the Krebs cycle to contribute to the formation of high energy phosphate bonds. It is obviously easier for an organism to store high energy phosphates than it would be to store and utilize the odd assortment of catabolic fragments. The Krebs cycle is of great importance biologically, since it is the common meeting ground for the metabolism of the three major classes of foodstuffs.

BIOCHEMISTRY OF THE PANCREATIC HORMONES

Insulin

When the methods of protein fractionation were applied to pancreatic extracts, it became possible in 1922 to produce crude preparations of insulin that could be used for animal experimentation and for the treatment of diabetic patients. Crystalline insulin preparations became available in 1926. The complete amino acid sequence in the insulin molecule was established in 1954, and was a great achievement in protein chemistry because it was the first time that a well-defined protein had been totally elucidated in terms of structure.[49, 50] Insulin was synthesized in 1963 by Katsoyannis and his colleagues, and this represented the first synthesis of a naturally occurring protein. It was also the first time that the proposed primary structure of a protein was confirmed by chemical synthesis. The two polypeptide chains were synthesized separately, and the protein produced by the combination of the two chains duplicated the biologic activity possessed by the natural hormone. As usually happens, other groups of workers in Europe and China had made progress toward the same accomplishment.[23-25]

The structure of a molecule of ox insulin is shown in Figure 9–9. It consists of an A chain containing 21 amino acid residues with glycine as the N-terminal residue, and a B chain containing 30 residues with phenylalanine as the N-terminal amino acid. The two chains are linked by two disulfide bridges at positions 7 and 20 in the A chain and 7 and 19 in the B chain. A disulfide bridge in the A chain links the cysteine residues at positions 6 and 11.

The molecular weight of ox insulin, calculated from the amino acid composition, is 5734. Under most conditions, molecules of this weight undergo polymerization to give molecular weights in multiples of 12,000 in the range of 12,000 to 48,000. It is not known what group or groups in the molecule are responsible for its biologic activity. The molecule is irreversibly inactivated by proteolytic enzymes or by acid hydrolysis; no satisfactory method has yet been found to protect insulin from hydrolysis in the alimentary tract, and consequently it must be administered by injection. Potency is lost following disruption of the disulfide bridges or following the iodination of tyrosine residues within the molecule.

The examination of insulins from different vertebrate species indicates that there are slight variations in the sequence of amino acids (Table 9–1). The most common species variations occur at positions 4, 8, 9, and 10 in the A chain, and positions 1, 3, 29, and 30 in the B chain. Two chemically different insulin molecules have been identified in the rat, even when a single pancreas is used. There are wide-

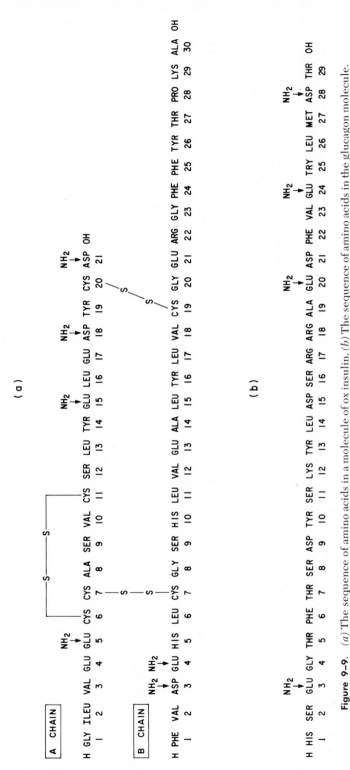

Figure 9-9. (a) The sequence of amino acids in a molecule of ox insulin. (b) The sequence of amino acids in the glucagon molecule.

Table 9 – 1.   Variations in Amino Acid Sequences in Insulins from Different Species as Compared with Ox Insulin

Animal	Positions in A chain				Positions in B chain				
	4	8	9	10	1	3	29	30	31
Ox	Glu	Ala	Ser	Val	Phe	Asp (NH$_2$)	Lys	Ala	0
Human	---	Thr	---	Ileu	---	-------	---	Thr	0
Sheep	---	---	Gly	---	---	-------	---	---	0
Dog	---	Thr	---	Ileu	---	-------	---	---	0
Horse	---	Thr	Gly	Ileu	---	-------	---	---	0
Pig	---	Thr	---	Ileu	---	-------	---	---	0
Rabbit	---	Thr	---	Ileu	---	-------	---	Ser	0
Sei whale	---	---	---	Thr	---	-------	---	---	0
Sperm whale	---	Thr	---	Ileu	---	-------	---	---	0
Rat 1	Asp	Thr	---	Ileu	---	Lys	---	Ser	0
Rat 2	Asp	Thr	---	Ileu	---	Lys	Met	Ser	0
Bonito 1*	?	?	?	?	Leu	?	?	?	0
Bonito 2*	?	?	?	?	Ala	?	Lys	0	0
Cod*	?	?	?	?	Ser	?	?	?	Lys

*Bonito 2 insulin contains one less residue than ox insulin, and cod insulin contains one more. The bonito and cod insulins have not been fully elucidated.

spread differences between fish and mammalian insulins. The B chain of cod insulin contains one more residue than is found in known mammalian insulins, but it does not differ significantly in biologic activity from ox insulin. Two insulins are extractable from the pancreas of the bonito fish. Bonito-2 insulin has one less residue in the B chain than is found in the ox; 12 positions in the A chain and five positions in the B chain are different from those of ox insulin. It may eventually be found that multiple insulins are present even in mammals; unfortunately, there is no information on the chemistry of these hormones in amphibians, reptiles, and birds.[43, 47]

The indications are that the antibody-combining sites in the insulin molecule are different from those that are responsible for biologic activity. This is important in the immunoassay of insulin and in dealing with diabetics who become resistant to the hormone owing to the development of antibodies. The amino acid sequences of pig and human insulins are the same, except for the amino acid at the C terminal of the B chain. Pig insulin is antigenic in man, and remains antigenic even if the last amino acid or the last eight amino acids are removed from the C terminus of this chain.[4]

Insulin is rapidly degraded in the body and only traces appear in the urine of normal subjects. The inactivation and degradation of insulin by homogenates and slices of liver have been shown to be accomplished by an enzyme system, insulinase, which is relatively specific in catalyzing the hydrolysis of this hormone. An insulin-degrading enzyme has been isolated in a highly purified state from beef liver. Liver extracts also contain a factor that can competitively inhibit the action of insulinase both *in vitro* and *in vivo*. This has been referred to as "insulinase inhibitor." The effectiveness of insulin depends upon the balance between these two principles, the binding of insulin to circulatory protein, and various factors that compete with or antagonize the action of the hormone at the cellular level.[1, 11, 37, 40, 59]

It has been shown that insulin becomes firmly bound to certain target tissues. The metabolic effects of insulin on the diaphragm, mammary gland, and adipose tissue may be demonstrated after a short immersion of each tissue in a solution of the hormone, and prolonged washings do not remove the hormone from the tissues. These results have been confirmed by using isotopic insulin, and the indications are that the hormone becomes chemically bound to the tissues as a prerequisite to its action.[18, 26]

Glucagon

This hyperglycemic-glycogenolytic factor is found in extracts of the pancreas and of the gastric mucosa of certain species. It causes a rise in blood sugar upon intravenous injection and is frequently present in insulin preparations as an impurity. Biochemically and physiologically it is quite different from insulin. The glucagon molecule is a straight-chain polypeptide containing 29 amino acid residues and has a molecular weight of 3485 (Fig. 9–9). It may be noted that only a few dipeptide sequences are similar to insulin and that disulfide bridges are lacking in the glucagon molecule. It does not contain cystine and this probably accounts for its relative resistance to alkali treatment, a property that facilitates the preparation of glucagon solutions free from insulin activity.[2, 3, 5, 6]

Glucagon may be bioassayed by either *in vivo* or *in vitro* methods. A satisfactory method is to determine the height and duration of the hyperglycemic response after administering the test preparation intravenously to fasted, anesthetized cats. By using the cat assay, a unit of glucagon is defined as the amount capable of causing a blood sugar rise of 30 mg. per 100 ml., and this is about equal to the activity of 0.1 microgram of cystalline glucagon per kilogram of body weight. The rate of glycogenolysis in liver slices and the reactivation of phosphorylase in liver slices or homogenates provide sensitive *in vitro* methods of assay.[57]

Hyperglycemic materials similar to glucagon have been extracted from the gastric mucosa, spleen, tongue, skin, and other tissues. The distribution of the glucagon-like material in the gastric mucosa of the dog is said to parallel the distribution of argentaffin cells, which are similar in some respects to the α-cells of the islets. It is by no means certain that these extrapancreatic agents are glucagon; there are some indications the hyperglycemic material found in the gastrointestinal tract is serotonin. It is obvious that hyperglycemic agents from miscellaneous sources should not be called "glucagon" until chemical and biologic studies indicate that they are the same substance. The functional significance of glucagon in the economy of the organism is far from clear. Present evidence does not prove that it is an antagonist, a synergist, or a regulator of insulin action.

Glucagon loses its biologic activity when perfused through the liver or when incubated with extracts of liver, kidney, or muscle. It is also inactivated by incubation with blood. The indications are that glucagon is destroyed by the same enzyme system that destroys insulin and other proteins.[42]

THE PHYSIOLOGY OF INSULIN

Insulin is essentially an anabolic hormone produced by the β-cells of the pancreatic islets, and its main actions favor the formation and storage of materials that are essential for growth. In addition to affecting carbohydrate metabolism, it has important regulatory actions on the metabolism of fats and proteins. When the normal source of insulin is cut off by removing the pancreas (pancreatectomy), the blood sugar rises and the glycogen stores of the liver are reduced. The administration of insulin to such an animal reduces the blood sugar and prevents further loss of liver glycogen. An excess of insulin lowers the blood sugar and produces convulsions and death unless the effect is counteracted quickly by sugar from either an exogenous or endogenous source. Insulin increases the uptake of glucose by the cells and facilitates its conversion to fat, protein, glycogen, or carbon dioxide and water. Since diabetics cannot convert glucose to other substances effectively, much of it leaves the body through the urine and hence is wasted. The hormone moderates hepatic gluconeogenesis and favors the conversion of glucose to glycogen, the latter being stored in liver and muscles. The synthesis of fatty acids ceases after the source of insulin is removed by pancreatectomy, whereas an excess of insulin increases fat synthesis. Certain actions of pituitary growth hormone (somatotrophin) and testosterone on protein synthesis, positive nitrogen balance, and growth require the presence of insulin.

Although nervous factors may be involved in the regulation of pancreatic secretion, it appears that humoral factors are the more important. This is indicated by the fact that denervated or grafted pancreas releases insulin at the proper times in response to fluctuations in the levels of blood sugar. The blood sugar level is controlled by insulin and, reciprocally, the output of insulin by the pancreas is conditioned by the blood sugar levels. Hyperglycemia elicits the release of insulin from the islets, but hypoglycemia diminishes it. In all forms of diabetes mellitus there is a relative or absolute deficiency of insulin, and this condition may be duplicated in experimental animals by pancreatectomy and other procedures.

Experimental Diabetes Mellitus

Diabetic states, simulating those that occur spontaneously in the human subject, may be produced by a number of experimental procedures. Since insulin is produced by the β-cells of the pancreatic islets, total pancreatectomy produces an immediate onset of diabetes. The Thiroloix-Sandmeyer type of diabetes may follow subtotal removal of the pancreas. The diabetic symptoms are mild immediately after the operation, but increase in severity with the lapse of time, or else gradually subside. The β-cells may be selectively damaged by the administration of toxic agents, such as alloxan, although it is doubtful whether such agents can completely prevent the production of insulin. The administration of excessive glucose for prolonged periods may result in exhaustion atrophy of the β-cells.[12] There is also evidence that damage to the β-cells may result from the prolonged administration of excessive insulin. Temporary or permanent damage to the β-cells, resulting in diabetic states, may be produced by the repeated administration of large doses of anterior pituitary, adrenocortical, or thyroid hormones.

Total Pancreatectomy

Total removal of the pancreas has been accomplished in many vertebrates, and the intensity of the diabetic state is quite variable.[45] Herbivorous mammals appear to tolerate pancreatectomy better than the carnivores, and some of them may live for long periods without insulin. In some species of birds (*e.g.,* duck) only a transitory hyperglycemia follows pancreatectomy and a hypoglycemia may occur. A diabetic syndrome, however, develops in geese in the absence of the pancreas.[39] Lizards are quite sensitive to glucagon and severe hypoglycemia may occur after the removal of the pancreas. A severe diabetes with hyperglycemia and glycosuria develops in the pancreatectomized tortoise. Very severe diabetes follows ablation of the pancreas in dogs, cats, and rats.

Though diabetes mellitus was known to the Romans, the disease was not correlated with a hypofunction of the pancreas until 1889. In this year von Mering and Minkowski found that pancreatectomy in the dog produces functional disturbances simulating those of human diabetics.[60] While the most obvious disorder appearing in the diabetic animal is impaired utilization of carbohydrate, it must be remembered that the metabolism of fat and protein, and indeed the total food metabolism, is impaired. The metabolic defects occurring in the pancreatectomized dog will be considered in some detail since they are essentially the same as those appearing in the human diabetic.

HYPERGLYCEMIA AND GLYCOSURIA.   Shortly after the supply of insulin is cut off by pancreatectomy, the blood sugar begins to rise and sugar appears in the urine after the renal threshold (160 to 180 mg. per 100 ml.) is surpassed. The hyperglycemia and glycosuria in the pancreatectomized dog may be severe, blood sugar levels reaching 300 to 400 mg. per 100 ml. and the animals losing 3 to 4 gm. per kg. glucose through the urine per day. Even when the animals are fasted, the blood sugar generally remains above the renal threshold and glycosuria occurs continuously. The diabetic animal passes abnormally large amounts of urine (polyuria) and consequently is thirsty and consumes much fluid (polydipsia). Since the tissues cannot utilize glucose normally, although they need fuel, the diabetic animal is constantly hungry and tends to eat excessively (polyphagia). There is an increased urinary elimination of nitrogen, and the continued loss of water from the body results in a state of dehydration together with profound disturbances in tissue electrolytes. Ketone bodies in the blood and urine are at a high level. Wounds are easily infected in the diabetic subject. The untreated animal gradually becomes weaker and loses weight, despite a voracious appetite, and, in diabetic coma, the plasma volume decreases and shock and kidney failure develop. Pancreatectomized dogs usually do not live for more than one or two weeks without insulin. Even when given adequate insulin they do not live indefinitely; they eventually develop a fatty infiltration of the liver, which is fatal. This liver defect in the depancreatectomized dog can be prevented or cured by feeding lipotropic factors such as choline, methionine, or betaine.

The glycogen stores of the diabetic liver are low, and little if any increase occurs after the administration of glucose. The hyperglycemia is largely a consequence of increased liver glycogenolysis and deficient glycogenesis by muscle. While the tissues of the diabetic subject receive a generous supply of glucose, they are unable to utilize it properly. The muscle glycogen falls during exercise, as in normal animals, but the resynthesis of glycogen occurs at a very slow rate in the pancreatectomized dog. In such animals, however, glycogen deposition may occur in such tissues as heart muscle, kidney tubules, and leukocytes. The so-called hydropic degeneration of the β-cells of the islets appears to be an actual deposition of glycogen in the cytoplasm. The subnormal utilization of glucose by the diabetic is indicated by reduced glucose tolerance, decreased respiratory quotient (R.Q.), and fasting hyperglycemia and glycosuria. When extra glucose is injected into a diabetic subject, the R.Q. does not rise as it does in normal animals, and there is a prolonged hyperglycemia and glycosuria. Excised organs from diabetic animals consume some glucose, though at a much slower rate than comparable tissues from normal animals. That the diabetic animal produces excessive glucose from protein (gluconeogenesis) is indicated by the negative nitrogen balance and the elevated urinary G:N ratio.

The hyperglycemia so characteristic of pancreatic diabetes is due in large measure to metabolic defects in the liver. No type of pancreatic diabetes can be produced after removal of the liver (hepatectomy). In the pancreatectomized-hepatectomized dog, the blood sugar levels fall rapidly and severe hypoglycemia develops.

FAT AND PROTEIN UTILIZATION. Since the diabetic organism cannot use glucose properly, the fat and protein stores of the body are drawn upon as a source of energy. As the fat stores are mobilized, the fat content of the blood rises; the blood cholesterol is also elevated. When a sample of blood from a severe case of diabetes is allowed to stand, a thick creamy layer of fatty material may be detectable. Protein is also utilized excessively by the diabetic and as a consequence there is severe tissue-wasting. The antiketogenic amino acids derived from dietary and tissue proteins are converted to glucose, but this cannot be stored as glycogen or utilized properly by the tissues and hence is eliminated through the urine. In the diabetic, there is also a diminished capacity to convert sugar into fatty acids. In severe diabetes, fatty acid synthesis ceases and such compounds cannot be completely oxidized to carbon dioxide. Thus an abnormal type of fatty acid oxidation ensues that results in an excessive production of ketone bodies; these appear in the blood (ketonemia) and in the urine (ketonuria). The ketone bodies are acetoacetic acid, β-hydroxybutyric acid, and acetone, and the process of their formation is called "ketogenesis." In human patients in diabetic coma, the breath and urine may have the odor of acetone. Since two of the ketone bodies are acids, the alkali reserve of the blood is reduced and the carbon dioxide combining power is diminished. The breathing becomes slow and deep (air hunger) and the alveolar CO_2 tension falls. The content of ammonium salts increases in the urine; the pH of the urine remains normal if the acidosis is compensated or falls if the acidosis is uncompensated.

From the foregoing it appears that the main defect consequent upon insulin deficiency is the reduced ability to utilize extracellular glucose for oxidation to CO_2 and for the synthesis of fatty acids, and probably also for the deposition of glycogen. Body fats and to some extent proteins are then utilized to an increased extent, but a part of these materials is lost in the urine as ketone bodies and glucose. Lipogenesis is seriously impaired in the diabetic animal. It is possible that the inability to synthesize fatty acids and to oxidize them completely results secondarily from impaired glucose metabolism, but some evidence has accumulated indicating that insulin deficiency causes a defect in fat metabolism *per se*. The body economy of the untreated diabetic resembles that prevailing during chronic starvation, and even if acidotic crises are avoided, death eventually results from tissue wastage.

Subtotal Pancreatectomy

If one-eighth of the dog's pancreas is left intact, the animal maintains normal blood sugar and does not become diabetic. After surgical reduction of the pancreas, the intact fragment is less resistant than the whole pancreas and can be damaged easily by the administration of anterior pituitary extracts or adrenocortical or thyroid hormones, thus producing diabetes. After such an operation in the cat, permanent diabetes can be produced by the prolonged administration of excessive glucose. The elevated blood sugar overworks the remaining β-cells in the fragment, causing them to undergo functional exhaustion and destruction. Such lesions in the pancreatic islets of the intact fragment do not develop if hyperglycemia is prevented by giving insulin along with the glucose.

When more than seven-eighths of the dog's pancreas is removed, Thiroloix-Sandmeyer diabetes ensues. This is a mild type of diabetes that is not stationary. The β-cells of the fragment may degenerate progressively and cause the diabetic state to increase in severity until death results, or the islet cells may increase in number and volume and eventually secrete enough insulin to return the blood sugar level to normal.

Diabetes in the Rat

Methods have been perfected for total pancreatectomy of the rat, and such animals die within two days from diabetic coma unless replacement therapy is employed.[52] When about 5 per cent of the rat's pancreas is left intact, a very slow type of diabetes develops. For one or two months after the operation there are no apparent indications of diabetes. An incipient state develops during which blood sugar levels are normal during fasting, but hyperglycemia and glycosuria become apparent after feeding. A manifest diabetes eventually develops and becomes more severe until the animals succumb. This slow and gradually developing type of diabetes facilitates the study of certain problems, such as factors that tend to ameliorate the condition or factors that cause it to increase in severity. It has been found that the incidence of this type of diabetes in rats is less in females than in males. Ovariectomy increases the incidence of diabetes after subtotal pancreatectomy of the female, and the opposite effect is obtained by administering estrogens.[21]

Estrogens and adrenocortical steroids may at first increase the severity of the diabetic state, and later exert a preventive effect on the diabetes of subtotally pancreatectomized rats. Estrogens have a curative effect when administered to rats made diabetic with alloxan; the hormone causes an increase in the number of pancreatic islets and of β-cells. This stimulating action of estrogen on the pancreas is especially pronounced when it acts in the presence of insulin.

Alloxan Administration

Alloxan provides a quick and convenient method for producing experimental diabetes in a variety of vertebrates. Three phases are generally observed after the administration of alloxan: transitory periods of hyperglycemia and hypoglycemia followed by permanent hyperglycemia and other diabetic symptoms. Alloxan is thought to act directly and specifically on the β-cells, causing them to undergo degeneration and resorption; the α-cells and the acinar tissue remain relatively unaffected. The alloxan diabetic animal, however, is not totally deprived of insulin. Dehydroascorbic and dehydroisoascorbic acids resemble alloxan in chemical structure and produce similar diabetogenic effects.

Progressive hyperglycemia and β-cell destruction have been observed in alloxanized catfish.[41] Permanent diabetes occurs in a small percentage of turtles treated with alloxan, and typical β-cell lesions are observed. Alloxan apparently does not produce diabetes in birds, such as ducks, chickens, pigeons, and owls. The β-cells of the avian pancreas generally do not seem to show such conspicuous changes as in mammals, although there may be some slight indications of hydropic degeneration. The islets of the alloxanized duck may show necrotic lesions, but diabetic symptoms do not appear. Among mammals, alloxan diabetes has been studied most extensively in rats, mice, hamsters, and guinea pigs.

There are certain very conspicuous differences between the diabetes produced by alloxan and that produced by removal of the pancreas. In alloxan diabetes, the hyperglycemia and glycosuria are generally more severe than in totally pancreatectomized animals. Alloxanized animals survive longer without insulin than do the pancreatectomized animals, and the ketonemia and ketonuria may be mild and transitory. When dogs are made diabetic with alloxan and then pancreatectomized, the glycosuria is reduced and less insulin is required to maintain normal blood sugar levels. In these animals, however, ketonuria and coma supervene promptly when insulin is discontinued. It may well be that some of these differences are due to the fact that the alloxanized animal is not deprived of glucagon from the α-cells, whereas the totally pancreatectomized animal lacks both insulin and glucagon.

Adrenal Cortex and Diabetes

Metabolic processes are regulated by a complicated interplay of multiple hormones, and in the organism, one hormone never acts completely alone. The metabolism of carbohydrates is related to that of fats and proteins, and these processes are regulated by a balance of hormones from the pancreas, anterior pituitary, adrenal cortex and medulla, and thyroid, and, in some instances, the gonadal steroids. It has been known for a long time that the diabetic symptoms of pancreatectomized dogs and cats tend to clear up if the adrenal glands are also removed.[33] In certain human diseases, such as Cushing's syndrome, where there is an increased secretion of 11-oxygenated steroids by the adrenal cortex, a diminished tolerance to glucose or even overt diabetes is frequently found. These diabetic symptoms are ameliorated or cured by surgical removal of the adrenal.

The 11-oxygenated steroids of the cortex probably influence blood glucose in two ways. They inhibit the incorporation of amino acids into protein and stimulate protein mobilization, thus augmenting the supply of gluconeogenic materials. There is also evidence that these steroids retard the utilization of glucose by peripheral tissues, though the mechanism of this effect remains unknown. The net effect of administering cortisol and similar cortical hormones is an elevation of the blood sugar. Conversely, in adrenalectomized animals, the blood sugar falls to low levels when food is withheld.

A transitory (corticoid) diabetes can be produced in normal rats, rabbits, and guinea pigs by the administration of adrenocortical oxysteroids; resistance to insulin is increased and the blood sugar rises. While some lesions may develop in the pancreatic islets of these species after this treatment, a permanent diabetic state does not ensue. Dogs and cats may be made sensitive to diabetogenic agents by removing 80 to 85 per cent of the pancreas, the intact fragment being capable of maintaining normal blood sugar levels under usual conditions. Temporary (corticoid) or permanent (metacorticoid) diabetes may be produced in these animals by administering such adrenal cortical hormones as cortisol or cortisone. At first, these hormones appear to cause islet hypertrophy or hyperplasia that probably results in an augmented output of insulin; after prolonged administration, the β-cells are permanently damaged and meta-corticoid diabetes results.

Thyroid Administration

The general effect of thyroid hormones is to enhance many catabolic pathways and to augment oxidative processes in the body. Hyperthyroidism in man increases the intensity of the diabetic state. The administration of thyroxine to laboratory animals may lead to a complete absence of glycogen in the liver. Toxic goiters are often accompanied by a picture of mild diabetes. Permanent (metathyroid) diabetes can be produced in subtotally pancreatectomized dogs by the repeated administration of thyroid hormone. As with other hormones that produce a hyperglycemic state, there is an increase in insulin production at first, but this decreases later as the islet cells are damaged.

Anterior Pituitary and Diabetes

Corticotrophin (ACTH), acting to promote the secretion of adrenal cortical hormones, may increase the supply of carbohydrate as a consequence of augmented gluconeogenesis. Another hormone of anterior hypophysial origin, probably somatotrophin, elevates the blood glucose by some mechanism that remains unexplained.

Transitory (hypophysial) or permanent (metahypophysial) diabetes may be produced in a variety of vertebrates by the administration of pituitary extracts or hormones to the intact animal. The prolonged administration of excessive somatotrophin to normal dogs or cats cause irreversible damage to the β-cells and a permanent diabetes follows withdrawal of the hormone. This pancreatic lesion, leading to permanent diabetes, is a direct consequence of the prolonged hyperglycemia rather than of the hypophysial hormone itself. After surgical reduction of the pancreas in cats and dogs, transitory or permanent diabetes may be produced by the injection of corticotrophin or prolactin. This is a pancreatic diabetes resulting from exhaustion and degeneration of the β-cells, the source of insulin. There are indications that the production of insulin is not completely suppressed in any type of metahormonal diabetes.

The role of the anterior hypophysis in carbohydrate metabolism and diabetes has been extensively studied by a number of workers. The main facts are: (1) Hypophysectomized animals tend to develop hypoglycemia when fasted. Sensitivity to insulin is greatly increased; that is, a given dose of insulin produces a larger fall of blood sugar than it does in normal animals. The ability of the hypophysectomized animal to release glucose from the liver in response to hypoglycemia is impaired. (2) Removal of the hypophysis from an animal rendered diabetic by total pancreatectomy diminishes the intensity of the diabetic state ("Houssay animals"). (3) Certain anterior pituitary hormones increase the resistance of normal, hypophysectomized, or pancreatectomized animals to the hypoglycemic action of insulin. There appears to be some degree of antagonism between the pancreas and the anterior hypophysis; this is indicated by the fact that hypophysectomized subjects are strikingly sensitive to insulin, whereas certain anterior lobe hormones produce insulin resistance. (4) Pituitary extracts or partially purified hormones increase the intensity of the diabetic state when administered to pancreatectomized or pancreatectomized-hypophysectomized animals. (5) Prolonged administration of certain anterior lobe hormones can produce pancreatic diabetes in intact or partially pancreatectomized animals.

THE HOUSSAY EFFECT IN ANIMALS. Work with the pancreatectomized-hypophysectomized dog emphasizes the physiologic importance of a balance between insulin on the one hand and the anterior hypophysial hormones on the other. Although the diabetic condition is attenuated, the Houssay animal is far from normal; it seems to be precariously balanced between hypoglycemia and hyperglycemia. There are wide fluctuations in the levels of blood sugar; whereas the administration of carbohydrate causes marked hyperglycemia. As compared with animals lacking pancreas only, the doubly operated animal survives longer without insulin and is more resistant to infections. In the Houssay animal the nitrogen balance is not so profoundly negative, and there is less tissue wastage than in the pancreatectomized subject. Blood sugar may remain within normal limits for prolonged periods, and the glycosuria and polyuria are diminished or occasionally absent. Ketosis is less severe than in singly operated animals. Liver and muscle glycogen may be within normal limits and, after the injection of glucose, the R.Q. may be increased almost as in normal animals. Like animals lacking pituitary glands only, the Houssay animal is extremely sensitive to insulin. The ameliorating effects of hypophysectomy on pancreatic diabetes are mainly due to reduced gluconeogonesis and ketogenesis and to the increased ability of the tissues to utilize glucose when the blood sugar is held to lower levels.

THE HOUSSAY PHENOMENON IN VITRO. Liver slices from normal cats, pancreatectomized cats, and pancreatectomized-hypophysectomized cats (Houssay animals) have been studied for their capacity to incorporate isotopic acetate into the higher fatty acids. Fat synthesis by the liver slices from pancreatectomized animals is reduced to a very low level; removal of the pituitary in addition to the pancreas restores the synthesis of fatty acid to normal range. Liver slices from pancreatectomized cats also produce large quantities of ketone bodies *in vitro,* but similar slices from Houssay cats produce almost none. *In vitro* measurements have shown that the uptake of glucose by liver from diabetic animals is below normal. It may be increased until it approximates the normal level by removing the pituitary gland or by injecting insulin at suitable times before removing the liver for the *in vitro* measurements. Livers from diabetic animals lose glucose faster than those from normal subjects. Apparently in the intact organism certain metabolic processes proceed under the balanced influence of insulin and pituitary factors; imbalance results when the animal is deprived of one or the other, and in the Houssay animal the balance is reinstated by reducing the hormones from both sources to zero.

The Principal Actions of Insulin

The pancreatectomized animal can be kept in good health for long periods by the administration of insulin, provided it is given a suitable diet. Insulin has been of great value in treating diabetes mellitus in man, especially in those cases in which the islets are damaged and cannot secrete insulin. It should be stressed, however, that not all cases of diabetes are due to defects in the islets of Langerhans and an insufficiency of insulin production by the pancreas.[38] Many factors other than pancreatic defects can enter into human diabetes, and these extrapancreatic features of the disease have not been fully clarified. Insulin is acidic and is fairly soluble in plasma and tissue fluids and hence rapidly diffuses away from the site of injection. Much progress has been made in preparing slowly absorbed insulins that exert prolonged effects. The rate of absorption can be reduced by combining insulin with a basic protein, protamine from fish sperm, and the addition of zinc makes it still less soluble in tissue fluids. Zinc preparations of insulin have also been devised in which the duration of effectiveness in the body is correlated with the form and size of the particles in suspension.

When insulin is administered to a pancreatectomized animal, the principal effects are: (1) reduction of the blood sugar and a consequent disappearance of the glycosuria and polyuria; (2) increased utilization of glucose by the tissues; (3) increased conversion of glucose to fat; (4) increased rate of protein synthesis; (5) inhibition of excessive ketogenesis; (6) reduced gluconeogenesis by the liver; (7) increased storage of glycogen by the liver and muscles; and (8) decreased concentration of potassium and inorganic phosphate in the blood. This electrolyte effect is probably a consequence of an increased uptake of glucose and other hexoses into the tissue cells and of the deposition of potassium and phosphate with glycogen in the liver and muscles. The concentration of these electrolyes (K and PO_4) closely parallels the blood glucose, suggesting that their titers in the circulation are dependent upon metabolic mechanisms involving phosphorylation.

The increased oxidation of glucose in the tissue and its utilization for the synthesis of fat and glycogen encourage its removal from the circulation. Furthermore, in the presence of insulin, the liver is more competent to retain glycogen. Whether insulin exerts a direct effect on the synthesis of hepatic glycogen or whether it opposes the glycogenolytic action of other hormones has not been clearly determined. In any case, insulin facilitates the utilization of glucose and diminishes its production, and these two phenomena serve to reduce the blood sugar levels. That extrapancreatic hormonal factors are involved in the regulation of blood sugar has already been indicated.

After an overdose of insulin the blood sugar may fall to levels low enough to produce convulsions and coma. A comparable condition occurs in hyperinsulinism in which the pancreatic islets liberate an excess of insulin. When the blood sugar drops to about 40 mg. per 100 ml., there are likely to be symptoms such as headache, a feeling of apprehension, inability to concentrate, tremor, sweating, and eventual coma. The condition can be relieved by giving sugar orally or by injecting glucose or epinephrine. The action of epinephrine depends upon the presence of ample stores of glycogen in the body from which glucose can be formed. Some of the symptoms of hypoglycemia are due to the increased secretion of epinephrine from the adrenal medulla.

The Mechanism of Insulin Action

While hormones exert multiple effects, and these have been rather thoroughly elucidated at the level of the organism, there is interest in determining what primary events they trigger at the molecular level. It is generally assumed that homeostatic efficiency has increased during the evolution of organisms through the addition of chemical messengers which supplement basic or fundamental means of regulation. The implication is that hormones do not initiate new biochemical reactions, but function at the cellular level to condition the speed of pre-existing reactions. Four general concepts have been proposed to explain how hormones may act: (a) they may have direct effects upon intracellular enzyme systems, (b) they may control the permeability of plasma membranes or have similar effects upon the membrane system within the cell, (c) they may act through an energy-conferring metabolic agency, or (d) they may act directly upon the chromosomes to activate or inhibit particular genes. Biochemical information on insulin action has been derived mainly from *in vitro* systems employing the diaphragm muscle and epididymal fat bodies of the rat, and the perfused rat heart.

One of the earliest concepts was that insulin acted at one or more steps in the intermediary metabolism of carbohydrate. Hexokinase catalyzes the formation of glucose-6-phosphate from glucose, with the production of ADP from ATP, and this is probably an obligatory step in the utilization of glucose by all tissues. This theory proposed that insulin acted in some manner to release hexokinase from the depressive influence of pituitary and adrenocortical hormones, thus permitting this essential step to occur. Since insulin enhances the utilization of glucose in animals whose pituitaries and adrenals have been removed, the concept as originally proposed loses validity.[31, 65]

The "glucose transfer" theory, supported strongly by Levine and

Goldstein and by Park, has aroused widespread interest and stimulated a large amount of experimentation, but it does not accommodate all of the information now available. According to this view, insulin acts in some undetermined manner to promote the transfer of glucose across the cell membranes, particularly those of skeletal muscles. Sugar entry is regarded as the rate-limiting step in glucose metabolism; once the sugar molecules get into the cells they can be phosphorylated or put to other relevant uses. After it was found that insulin also increases the transport of certain amino acids into the cell, it was thought by some that the effects of the hormone upon both carbohydrate and protein metabolism might be accounted for by postulating a single locus of action at the cell surface. Since it has been shown that insulin enhances the synthesis of messenger RNA in diaphragm muscle and other tissues, and this effect is independent of substrates, it is obvious that the hormone does not act solely by conditioning the entrance of glucose and amino acids into the cells.[19, 29, 30, 44, 54, 56]

Studies on the mechanism of action of vasopressin suggest that the disulfide bond of the hormone may react with a thiol site at the surface of the receptor cells. Since the A chain of the insulin molecule also possesses an intrasulfide bridge, it has been postulated that this SS-SH interchange mechanism might be an important aspect in the cellular action of this hormone.[51]

Wool first proposed that insulin might produce its effect by activating one or more gene loci within the chromosomes.[62, 63] He found that insulin increases the formation of messenger RNA in muscle, an accomplishment which would presumably promote the synthesis of enzymes and structural proteins. Puromycin is an antibiotic which blocks the synthesis of proteins without preventing RNA synthesis. When tested upon rat diaphragms, this antibiotic has an inhibitory effect upon protein synthesis, whereas the net synthesis of glycogen is not significantly impaired. Actinomycin D, an antibiotic which selectively inhibits the DNA-directed synthesis of RNA, has been found to prevent certain insulin actions in diabetic rats.[17] Although actinomycin does not modify the hypoglycemic action of insulin in diabetic rats, it does prevent insulin from repairing the enzymatic defects in the synthesis of fatty acids by adipose tissue. It also prevents the repair of enzymes essential for the restoration of liver glycogen in response to insulin. These and other bits of information suggest that insulin does promote enzyme synthesis by stimulating the renewal of RNA from nuclear DNA. They suggest, however, that the transport of glucose molecules across cell membranes, a process stimulated by insulin, does not depend upon the synthesis of new enzyme protein. It is not necessary to assume that a hormone acts to trigger the same molecular event in every target tissue; much depends upon the specific specializations of the target cells, and many hormonal effects may be secondary rather than primary.[8, 19, 36]

Though we still do not know the complete story of how insulin acts, or for that matter, of how any hormone acts, rapid progress is being made. The problem of hormone action at the cellular and molecular levels is a difficult one, but the answer is of such importance as to justify the expenditure of time and effort.

The Hypoglycemic Sulfonamides and Diabetes

Diabetes mellitus in man has turned out to be a much more complicated disease than was formerly supposed, and the whole problem has undergone a thorough "shake up" because of the re-discovery of certain hypoglycemic sulfonamide derivatives that are active by mouth. There were suggestions that guanidine derivatives might be useful in the treatment of diabetes, but some were found to have many toxic side effects. Interest in the sulfonamides began in 1941 when it was fortuitously observed that certain ones produced hypoglycemic effects in man and experimental animals with a mini-mum of undesirable side reactions. Loubatiéres and others extended these observations, and some progress has been made in analyzing the mechanism of action of such compounds. The sulfonylureas were originally produced and tested as more soluble sulfa drugs that would give prolonged chemotherapeutic effects; their hypoglycemic actions in diabetes were unexpected or accidental findings. The potentialities of this discovery as an approach to the oral treatment of diabetes were quickly appreciated by investigators all over the world, and the problem has been studied very intensively since 1954. One important aspect of the research on hypoglycemic compounds has been a reinvestigation of the etiology of diabetes mellitus and the recognition that there are different forms of the disease.[10, 34, 35, 61]

Middle-aged obese diabetics (maturity-onset type) often have normal levels of pancreatic insulin and adequate amounts in the blood, but for unknown reasons this insulin does not reach the tissues and act in the normal way.[64] Young diabetics (growth-onset type), on the other hand, more frequently have little if any insulin in the blood or in pancreatic tissue, reflecting an absolute deficiency of the hor-mone. Some diabetic patients require much more insulin than is necessary to maintain a totally pancreatectomized person. Many middle-aged and elderly diabetics are relatively insensitive to in-sulin as compared to most juvenile diabetics, and this suggests that contrainsulin factors may play a role in the etiology and course of the maturity-onset type.

With the development of isotope techniques it has become pos-sible to introduce small amounts of labeled insulin into living organisms and trace its distribution and eventual fate. I^{131}-labeled insulin generally disappears less rapidly from the blood of diabetics who have taken insulin for long periods than from the blood of normal persons. This and other observations suggest the presence of a plasma-binding factor in many insulin-treated persons that hinders the entry of the hormone into the tissues and depresses its enzymatic degradation. It has been proposed that the plasma factor binding insulin may be an antibody that arises as a consequence of insulin therapy. Among the factors that may interfere with the normal action of insulin are: (1) hormones from the pituitary and adrenal glands that antagonize the action of insulin, (2) enzymatic destruction of insulin, (3) development of antibodies to exogenous or even endogenous insulin, and (4) extracellular factors that may interfere with the distribution of insulin to the peripheral tissues.[9, 13, 22, 28]

It is of great interest that the hypoglycemic sulfonamide derivatives act almost exclusively in the maturity-onset type of diabetes, in which there is available, but non-useful, insulin emanating from the pancreatic islets. The mechanisms whereby the sulfonamides act have not been established with certainty. There is considerable evidence that such compounds act primarily on the β-cells to promote the production of endogenous insulin; thus their effectiveness depends upon the number of β-cells remaining in the islets or the number that can be regenerated. Significant effects have not been demonstrated in pancreatectomized mammals. Since the effectiveness of exogenous insulin is potentiated by the sulfonamides, it is possible that they prevent insulin degradation by inhibiting the insulinase action of the liver. Under certain conditions, sulfonylurea-like drugs may suppress the production of glucose by the liver. Destruction of the α-cells, with a decrease in glucagon production, has been suggested as a possible mechanism of action of these drugs. The response of the duck to sulfonamides appears not to be altered by either total pancreatectomy or enterectomy. This suggests that hypoglycemic compounds may act by different mechanisms in birds and in mammals. Studies on the domestic fowl indicate that tolbutamide reduces the level of blood sugar by acting mainly through extrapancreatic and extrahepatic mechanisms. Thus it appears that no one action can explain the antidiabetic effects of these drugs in man and animals.

The treatment of diabetes is a complicated problem for the clinician and cannot be elaborated here. There is general agreement that the hypoglycemic sulfonamides are valuable adjuncts in the treatment of selected cases of diabetes, that they may not be entirely devoid of toxicity, and that continued research may develop new compounds having the essential properties of the sulfonamides but lacking their undesirable features.

THE PHYSIOLOGY OF GLUCAGON

Source and Secretion

Glucagon was first discovered in commercial preparations of insulin and workers experienced difficulty in separating it from insulin. Available evidence indicates that the α-cells of the islets are the principal source of this polypeptide. Alloxan destroys the β-cells of the islets, markedly diminishing the amount of extractable insulin, but this treatment does not reduce the amount of glucagon that can be recovered from the pancreas. The hormone is also present in fetal pancreas before the acinar tissue has developed, and in the pancreas of adults after the induction of acinar atrophy by ligation of the pancreatic ducts. Various degrees of destruction of the α-cells can be produced in the guinea pig by administering cobalt chloride; if a high percentage of the α-cells is obliterated, extractable glucagon is diminished or absent. The islets of reptiles and birds contain a preponderance of α-cells, and much glucagon can be extracted from the pancreas of these forms.

Since the use of the immunoassay method to determine glucagon in blood, strong evidence has been found to support the concept that it is secreted in response to low levels of blood sugar. It has been shown through cross-circulation experiments that insulin-induced hypoglycemia causes the appearance of glucagon in the blood leaving the pancreas. It is probable that the pancreas releases insulin when blood sugar is high and glucagon when blood sugar is low, and that the two hormones are mutually balanced through their effects on the level of blood glucose. Both hormones have to be considered as integral components of the blood sugar regulating mechanism.

Physiologic Effects of Glucagon

When pure insulin-free glucagon is administered to an animal, the most outstanding effect is an elevation in the concentration of blood glucose. The concentration of potassium in the blood plasma rises, probably as a consequence of glycogen breakdown in the liver. The severity and duration of the hyperglycemia depend upon the amount of hormone given, the manner of administration, and the nutritional status of the test animal. Glucagon is more effective when given intravenously or intraperitoneally than when given subcutaneously or intramuscularly. The most effective way to administer the hormone is to inject it into the portal vein, which carries it directly to the liver. Glucagon has no effect on blood sugar after circulation through the liver is blocked or after the liver is removed. The capacity of the hormone to produce hyperglycemia is reduced by prolonged fasting, diabetic acidosis, or other conditions that lower the glycogen reserves of the liver.[15]

The main action of glucagon is to promote hepatic glycogenolysis.[55] This has been demonstrated in perfused livers, liver slices, and liver homogenates. The hormone also promotes gluconeogenesis from protein. The liver cannot hold glycogen and the blood glucose rises sharply. Glucagon-treated animals fail to gain weight, and this correlates with the protein catabolic effect of the hormone and with a diminished consumption of food. Prolonged treatment results in increased nitrogen excretion, a negative nitrogen balance, and a reduced concentration of amino acids in the blood. Under glucagon treatment, the volume of gastric juice is reduced and its content of hydrochloric acid is quite low. Motility of the gastrointestinal tract is reduced, and practically no pancreatic juice is secreted.[14]

Intensive treatment of young rabbits with glucagon results eventually (about five months) in a true metaglucagon diabetes. The pancreatic islets decrease in size and the β-cells undergo hydropic degeneration. The hyperglycemia, glycogenolysis, and negative nitrogen balance persist after the glucagon is discontinued, and these disturbances are due to insulin deficiency consequent upon destruction of the β-cells.[32]

The Mechanism of Action of Glucagon

We have seen that the principal action of glucagon is to raise the blood sugar by promoting the glycogenolytic processes of the liver. When liver slices are incubated with glucagon, glycogen diminishes and glucose-1-phosphate accumulates. This is the rate-limiting step and is catalyzed by the enzyme phosphorylase. This enzyme exists in the liver and other tissues as active (phosphorylase "a") and inactive (phosphorylase "b") forms. The active phosphorylase contains phosphate and its inactivation involves the removal of phosphate to form dephosphophosphorylase. Inactivation is accomplished by phosphorylase phosphatase, and activation by dephosphophosphorylase kinase, both enzymes being present in liver tissue. All of the phosphorylase kinases require a nucleotide, 3',5'-cyclic adenosine monophosphate (3',5'-AMP), as cofactor or activator. The enzyme adenyl cyclase, in the presence of Mg^{++}, generates 3',5'-AMP from ATP. The generation of 3',5'-AMP is accelerated by glucagon in the liver, by epinephrine in liver and muscle, and by ACTH in adrenocortical tissue. Thus, the over-all effect of glucagon is to facilitate the activation of phosphorylase, the enzyme which catalyzes the first step in the breakdown of liver glycogen to form blood glucose. Stated in the simplest terms, (a) glucagon acts by facilitating the formation of 3',5'-AMP; (b) this is required as a cofactor by the enzyme dephos-

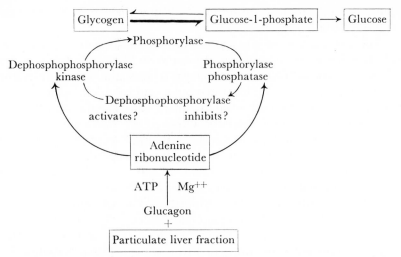

Figure 9–10. Diagram showing the locus of action of glucagon in glycogenolysis. (From Behrens and Bromer: Vit. & Horm., *16*, 1958.)

phophosphorylase kinase; (c) the latter enzyme is necessary to pro-duce active phosphorylase from the inactive form; and (d) the active phosphorylase catalyzes the transformation of glycogen to glucose-1-phosphate (Fig. 9–10).

The formation of liver phosphorylase "a" by dephosphophosphory-lase in cell-free homogenates of dog and cat liver is increased mark-edly by the addition of small amounts of glucagon or epinephrine. This is one of the few instances in which hormones are found to affect enzyme systems in the absence of intact cell structure.

It is now known that enzymes from different tissues of the *same animal* may possess different chemical structures, but still exert the same catalytic activities. Both glucagon and epinephrine activate liver phosphorylase, but muscle phosphorylase is activated only by epinephrine. Tissue differences in the enzyme apparently explain why phosphorylase of liver responds to glucagon, whereas phos-phorylase of muscle does not. It is a curious fact that two hormones as different in chemical structure as glucagon and epinephrine share the common ability of activating liver phosphorylase.[14, 20, 46, 58]

REFERENCES

1. Antoniades, H. N.: The state of transport of insulin in blood. Endocrinol., 68:7, 1961.
2. Behrens, O. K., and Bromer, W. W.: Biochemistry of the protein hormones. Ann. Rev. Biochem., 27:57, 1958.
3. Behrens, O. K., and Bromer, W. W.: Glucagon. Vit. & Horm., 16:263, 1958.
4. Berson, S. A., and Yalow, R. S.: Antigens in insulin: determinants of specificity of porcine insulin in man. Science, 139:844, 1963.

5. Bromer, W. W., Sinn, L. G., and Behrens, O. K.: The amino acid sequence of glucagon. J. Amer. Chem. Soc., 79:2807, 1957.
6. Bromer, W. W., Sinn, L. G., Staub, A., and Behrens, O. K.: The amino acid sequence of glucagon. Diabetes, 6:234, 1957.
7. Cantarow, A., and Schepartz, B.: Biochemistry, 3rd ed. Philadelphia, W. B. Saunders Company, 1962.
8. Chain, E. B.: Recent studies in carbohydrate metabolism. Brit. Med. J., 2:709, 1959.
9. Colwell, A. R., Jr., and Colwell, J. A.: Pancreatic action of the sulfonylureas. J. Lab. & Clin. Med., 53:376, 1959.
10. Cox, R. W., Henley, E. D., Fergus, E. B., and Williams, R. H.: Sulfonylureas and diabetes mellitus: clinical evaluation. Diabetes, 5:358, 1956.
11. De Bodo, R. C., and Altszuler, N.: Insulin hypersensitivity and physiological insulin antagonists. Physiol. Rev., 38:389, 1958.
12. Dohan, F. C., and Lukens, F. D. W.: Experimental diabetes produced by the administration of glucose. Endocrinol., 42:244, 1948.
13. Duncan, L. J. P., and Clarke, B. F.: Pharmacology and mode of action of the hypoglycaemic sulphonylureas and diguanides. Ann. Rev. Pharmacol., 5:151, 1965.
14. Foà, P. P.: Glucagon. In G. Pincus, K. V. Thimann, and E. B. Astwood (eds.): The Hormones, Vol. 4. New York, Academic Press, 1964, p. 531.
15. Foà, P. P., Galansino, G., and Pozza, G.: Glucagon, a second pancreatic hormone. Recent Prog. Horm. Research, 13:473, 1957.
16. Frye, B. E.: Metamorphic changes in the blood sugar and the pancreatic islets of the frog, Rana clamitans. J. Exp. Zool., 155:215, 1964.
17. Gellhorn, A., and Benjamin, W.: Insulin action in alloxan diabetes modified by actinomycin D. Science, 146:1166, 1964.
18. Haugaard, N., Haugaard, E. S., and Stadie, W. C.: Combination of insulin with cells. J. Biol. Chem., 211:289, 1954.
19. Hechter, O., and Halkerston, I. D. K.: On the action of mammalian hormones. In G. Pincus, K. V. Thimann, and E. B. Astwood (eds.): The Hormones, Vol. 5. New York, Academic Press, 1964, p. 697.
20. Henion, W. F., and Sutherland, E. W.: Immunological differences of phosphorylases. J. Biol. Chem., 224:477, 1957.
21. Houssay, B. A.: Comparative physiology of the endocrine glands. In A. Gorbman (ed.): Comparative Endocrinology. New York, John Wiley & Sons, 1959, p. 639.
22. Houssay, B. A., Penhos, J. C., Urgoiti, E., Teodosio, N., Apelbaum, J., and Bowkett, J.: The role of insulin in the action of the hypoglycemic sulfonyl compounds. Ann. N. Y. Acad. Sci., 71:25, 1957.
23. Katsoyannis, P. G.: On the problem of the chemical synthesis of proteins with special reference to insulin. Metabolism, 13 (Part 2):1059, 1964.
24. Katsoyannis, P. G.: The synthesis of insulin chains and their combination to biologically active material. Diabetes, 13:339, 1964.
25. Katsoyannis, P. G.: Synthetic studies on the A and B chains of insulin. Vox Sanguinis, 9:227, 1964.
26. Krahl, M. E.: The Action of Insulin on Cells. New York, Academic Press, 1961.
27. Lacy, P. E.: Electron microscopic identification of different cell types in the islets of Langerhans of the guinea pig, rat, rabbit and dog. Anat. Rec., 128:225, 1957.
28. Levine, R., et. al.: The effects of sulfonylureas and related compounds in experimental and clinical diabetes. Ann. N. Y. Acad. Sci., 71:1, 1957.
29. Levine, R., and Goldstein, M. S.: On the mechanism of action of insulin. Recent Prog. Horm. Research, 11:343, 1955.
30. Levine, R., and Goldstein, M. S.: The action of insulin. Sci. American, 198 (5):99, 1958.
31. Litwack, G., and Kritchevsky, D., (eds.): Actions of Hormones on Molecular Processes. New York, John Wiley & Sons, 1964.
32. Logothetopoulos, J., Sharma, B. B., Salter, J. M., and Best, C. H.: Glucagon and metaglucagon diabetes in rabbits. Diabetes, 9:278, 1960.

33. Long, C. N. H., and Lukens, F. D. W.: Effects of adrenalectomy and hypophysectomy on experimental diabetes in the cat. J. Exp. Med., *63*:465, 1936.
34. Loubatières, A.: The hypoglycemic sulfonamides: history and development of the problem from 1942 to 1955. Ann. N. Y. Acad. Sci., *71*:4, 1957.
35. Loubatières, A.: The mechanism of action of the hypoglycemic sulfonamides: a concept based on investigations in animals and in human beings. Ann. N. Y. Acad. Sci., *71*:192, 1957.
36. Manchester, K. L.: The action of insulin on protein biosynthesis in muscle. Memoirs Soc. Endocrinol., No. 11, 113, 1961.
37. Mirsky, I. A.: The role of insulinase and insulinase inhibitors. Metabolism, *5*: 138, 1956.
38. Mirsky, I. A.: Insulinase, insulinase-inhibitors, and diabetes mellitus. Recent Prog. Horm. Research, *13*:429, 1957.
39. Mirsky, I. A., and Gitelson, S.: The diabetic response of geese to pancreatectomy. Endocrinol., *63*:345, 1958.
40. Mirsky, I. A., Perisutti, G., and Diengott, D.: Effect of fasting on insulinase activity and on hypoglycemic response to insulin. Endocrinol., *60*:303, 1957.
41. Murrell, L. R., and Nace, P. F.: Experimental diabetes in the catfish: normal and alloxan-diabetic blood glucose and pancreatic histology. Endocrinol., *64*: 542, 1959.
42. Narahara, N. T., and Williams, R. H.: Degradation of glucagon-I[131] by rat tissues *in vitro*. Endocrinol., *60*:285, 1957.
43. Nicol, D. S. H. W., and Smith, L. F.: Amino-acid sequence of human insulin. Nature, *187*:483, 1960.
44. Park, C. R., and Johnson, L. H.: Effect of insulin on transport of glucose and galactose into cells of rat muscle and brain. Amer. J. Physiol., *182*:17, 1955.
45. Penhos, J. C., and Lavintman, N.: Total pancreatectomy in toads: effect of hypophysectomy and glucagon. Gen. & Comp. Endocrinol., *4*:264, 1964.
46. Rall, T. W., Sutherland, E. W., and Berthet, J.: The relationship of epinephrine and glucagon to liver phosphorylase. J. Biol. Chem., *224*:463, 1957.
47. Randle, P. J.: Insulin. *In* G. Pincus, K. V. Thimann, and E. B. Astwood (eds.): The Hormones, Vol. 4. New York, Academic Press, 1964, p. 481.
48. Sak, M. F., Macchi, I. A., and Beaser, S. B.: Postnatal development of beta cells and ILA secretion in the pancreatic islets of the golden hamster. Anat. Rec., *152*:25, 1965.
49. Sanger, F.: Chemistry of insulin. Science, *129*:1340, 1959.
50. Sanger, F., Thompson, E. O. P., and Kitai, R.: The amide groups of insulin. Biochem. J., *59*:509, 1955.
51. Schwartz, I., Rasmussen, H., Schoessler, M. A., Silver, L., and Fong, C. T. O.: Relation of chemical attachment to physiological action of vasopressin. Proc. Natl. Acad. Sci., U. S. A., *46*:1288, 1960.
52. Scow, R. O.: "Total" pancreatectomy in the rat: operation, effects, and postoperative care. Endocrinol., *60*:359, 1957.
53. Sivadas, P.: The occurrence of β-cells in the islets of Langerhans of *Tilapia mossambica* (Peters) (Teleostei). Gen. & Comp. Endocrinol., *4*:295, 1964.
54. Smith, G. H., Randle, P. J., and Battaglia, F. C.: The mechanism of action of insulin on muscle. Memoirs Soc. Endocrinol., No. 11, 124, 1961.
55. Sokal, J. E., Sarcione, E. J., and Henderson, A. M.: Relative potency of glucagon and epinephrine as hepatic glycogenolytic agents. Endocrinol., *74*:930, 1964.
56. Stadie, W. C.: The "permeability" hypothesis of the action of insulin. Diabetes, *6*:446, 1957.
57. Sunderman, F. W., and Sunderman, F. W., Jr. (eds.): Measurements of Exocrine and Endocrine Functions of the Pancreas. Philadelphia, J. B. Lippincott Co., 1961.
58. Sutherland, E. W.: The effect of the hyperglycemic factor and epinephrine on enzyme systems of liver and muscle. Ann. N. Y. Acad. Sci., *54*:693, 1951.
59. Tomizawa, H. H., and Halsey, Y. D.: Isolation of an insulin-degrading enzyme from beef liver. J. Biol. Chem., *234*:307, 1959.
60. Von Mering, J., and Minkowski, O.: Diabetes Mellitus nach Pankreasextirpation. Arch. exper. Path. u. Pharmakol., *26*:371, 1889.

61. Williams, R. H., and Tucker, B. W.: Hypoglycemic actions of tolbutamine and carbutamide. Metabolism, 5:801, 1956.
62. Wool, I. G.: Effect of insulin on nucleic acid synthesis in isolated rat diaphragm. Biochim. Biophys. Acta, 68:28, 1963.
63. Wool, I. G.: Insulin and protein biosynthesis. *In* G. Litwak and D. Kritchevsky (eds.): Actions of Hormones on Molecular Processes, New York, John Wiley & Sons, 1964, p. 422.
64. Yóung, F. G.: Insulin and insulin antagonism. Endocrinol., 73:654, 1963.
65. Young, F. G., Broom, W. A., and Wolff, F. W. (eds.): The Mechanism of Action of Insulin: A Symposium. Springfield, Ill., Charles C Thomas, 1960.

10_____

THE ADRENAL GLAND: MEDULLA: CHROMAFFIN TISSUE

The adrenal glands were first described in man by Eustachius in 1563. Other anatomists, dissecting poorly preserved cadavers, identified these organs along the anterior borders of the kidneys and were impressed by the fact that they were generally filled with fluid. Not appreciating the effects of post-mortem decay, the term suprarenal "capsules" was used to describe them. Cuvier (1805) recognized that each gland consists of an inner and outer region, now referred to as the medulla and cortex, respectively. The first hint that these glands might be of functional significance came from Thomas Addison's description (1849) of a clinical condition resulting from their deterioration, a syndrome now bearing his name.

ANATOMY OF THE ADRENALS

The Mammalian Adrenal

This gland is a compound structure consisting of an outer *cortex* and an inner *medulla*. The hormones of the cortex are steroids, whereas those of the medulla are amines. The two components of the organ originate from different embryonic primordia. The cortex is derived from mesoderm in close association with the developing gonads. The medulla is ectodermal, since it differentiates from neural

310

crest cells along with the sympathetic ganglia. The medullary cells are modified ganglion cells and remain in intimate contact with the preganglionic fibers of the sympathetic system. Secretion of the medulla is regulated very largely by means of these nerves. The cortex, on the other hand, resembles the anterior hypophysis in being practically devoid of secretory nerve terminals.

Like other endocrine glands, the adrenals receive a rich blood supply (Fig. 10–1). The human organs are flattened bodies situated in the retroperitoneal tissue along the cranial ends of the kidneys. They vary considerably in shape, but are usually described as triangular or crescentic. Accessory deposits of cortical tissue are frequently found in many mammalian species, most commonly in the perirenal fat and along the path of descent of the gonads.

During the third month of intrauterine life, the human adrenal reaches its maximum relative size and exceeds that of the kidney. This large size of the fetal adrenal is due to the presence of a thick *boundary zone* (fetal cortex or X zone) between the *definitive* cortex

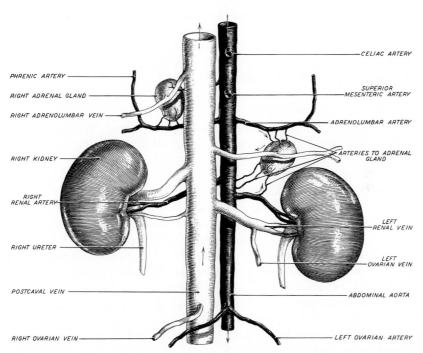

Figure 10–1. A dissection of the kidneys and adnexa of the cat, showing the position of the adrenal glands and their blood supply. The adrenals receive blood through numerous small arteries arising from the adrenolumbar arteries, the aorta, and the renal arteries. The venous drainage of the cat's adrenal is into the adrenolumbar vein, which passes over or through the gland. The arterial system is indicated in black.

and the medulla. During late prenatal and early postnatal life the fetal zone involutes and is not present to any appreciable extent in the glands of normal adults. In the adult human the adrenal is only one-thirtieth as large as the kidney. Studies have shown that the fetal cortex is capable of secreting adrenal steroids, and there are suggestions that chorionic gonadotrophin may perform a role in the development and maintenance of this zone, possibly by influencing the release of ACTH from the fetal pituitary.[32] A comparable zone has been described in the adrenals of mice, hamsters, and certain other mammalian species.[27]

The mammalian gland is surrounded by a relatively heavy connective tissue capsule from which trabeculae extend into the substance of the cortex. The epithelioid cells of the cortex are supported by a loose framework of reticular tissue. Histologically, the cells of the cortex are arranged into three vaguely defined layers: the *zona glomerulosa, zona fasciculata,* and *zona reticularis* (Fig. 10–2). The glomerulosa is a thin layer lying immediately below the capsule and is composed of irregular groups of cells. The fasciculata, the widest layer of the cortex, is composed of radially disposed cords of polyhedral cells. The reticularis is the innermost layer of the cortex, and the radial arrangement of its cells is usually not so obvious as in the fasciculata. The zona glomerulosa is little affected by hypophysectomy and is probably the source of the steroid hormones that function in the regulation of electrolyte metabolism. The fasciculata and reticularis are highly dependent on the presence of the pituitary gland and are thought to be responsible for the formation of carbohydrate-regulating steroids. Studies on the bovine adrenal suggest that the zones of the cortex possess different enzyme systems and hence can effect the biosynthesis of different steroid hormones.

Although the cortical cells are particularly susceptible to injury, they have a marked capacity for regeneration. One method of producing demedullated animals is to sever the capsule and express as much of the contents as possible; a complete cortex is regenerated from the capsule and the few glomerulosa cells that adhere to it. Like nervous tissue, the medullary cells are highly differentiated and there is no provision for their replacement. Mitotic divisions may be observed in all zones of the cortex, but there is a tendency for them to occur most frequently in the outermost regions of the zona fasciculata. Whether or not there is normally a centripetal movement of cells from the outer fasciculata into the inner reticularis remains a contended point.[10, 43]

Unlike the cortex, the medulla is not essential for life, since demedullated animals survive quite well under the sheltered conditions of laboratory environments. The medulla is composed of irregular strands and masses of cells separated by sinusoidal vessels.

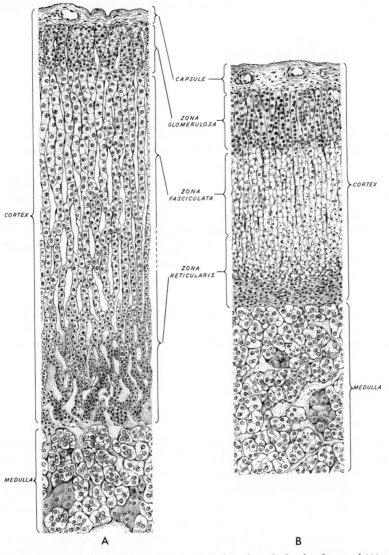

Figure 10–2. Comparable sections through the adrenal glands of normal *(A)* and hypophysectomized *(B)* rats. Since the functional capacity of the adrenal cortex is conditioned by the release of ACTH, hypophysectomy results in tremendous shrinkage of the cortex. The medulla is not influenced by hypophysectomy. Both sections are drawn to scale.

Most of the medullary cells contain fine cytoplasmic granules that stain with chromates and hence are called "chromaffin cells." They also give a green color reaction when treated with ferric chloride. Sympathetic ganglion cells, occurring singly or in groups, may be found interspersed among the medullary cells. In aging birds, the medullary cells may undergo structural modifications in the direction of ganglion cells.[38]

There are widely scattered accumulations of cells in both verte-brate and invertebrate organisms that resemble the medullary cells in origin, structure, and staining reactions. These include the para-ganglia found within or adjacent to the capsules of the sympathetic ganglia; the carotid glands located near the bifurcation of the common carotid arteries; the organs of Zuckerkandl near the origin of the in-ferior mesenteric artery; and scattered chromaffin cells within the liver, heart, kidney, gonads, and elsewhere. Chromaffin cells and catecholamines have been identified in the mantles of certain mol-luscs, the nervous system of leeches, and the cutaneous glands of certain amphibia. Serotonin is an indole amine that, like epinephrine, originates in chromaffin cells.

The adrenal medullary cells are generally regarded as modified postganglionic neurons, and their functional activity seems to be controlled largely by nervous mechanisms. Secretion by the medul-lary cells may be prevented by sectioning the splanchnic nerve or by applying nicotine directly to the gland itself. Stimulation of the splanchnic nerve elicits a marked outpouring of medullary hormones. Centers in the posterior hypothalamus are known to relay impulses to the adrenal medulla by way of the splanchnic nerves.

Comparative Morphology

Adrenal tissues are present in all vertebrates from cyclostomes to mammals, but profound differences are encountered in the arrange-ment of the functional components, *i.e.,* steroid-producing cells and catecholamine-producing cells. Histologic studies indicate that the two kinds of adrenal tissue coexist in cyclostomes: cells, presumed to be steroidogenic, are scattered along the walls of the postcardinal veins and in the mesonephric kidneys; small clusters of chromaffin cells are found in the same areas, and these occasionally come in contact with the steroidogenic cells. In elasmobranchs, the steroido-genic tissue is condensed into several well-formed bodies lying between the caudal ends of the kidneys; these are the *interrenal glands*. Paired aggregations of chromaffin cells are present between the kidneys, the more posterior ones being embedded in the kidneys (Fig. 10–3). The two components of the chondrichthyean adrenal are typically separated, though small islets of chromaffin cells have been described in the interrenal glands of the ray *Raja clavata.* It should be noted that the chondrichthyes are the only vertebrates having an adrenal component which is accurately described as an "interrenal" gland, meaning located between the kidneys, and these fishes are not in the main evolutionary line leading to tetrapods.[4, 9]

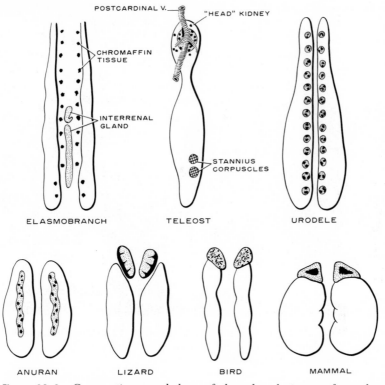

Figure 10–3. Comparative morphology of the adrenal tissues of vertebrates. Solid black indicates chromaffin tissue; stippling indicates steroidogenic tissue. Note that chromaffin tissue and steroidogenic tissue (interrenal gland) are spatially separate in the elasmobranch. The adrenal tissues of bony fishes are typically found in the "head" kidneys, around branches of the postcardinal veins; there may be some spatial separation of the two kinds of tissues, but they are usually intermingled. Note that a cortex (steroidogenic tissue) and medulla (chromaffin tissue) are present only in mammalian adrenals. (Based on Gorbman, A., and Bern, H. A.: Textbook of Comparative Endocrinology. New York, John Wiley & Sons, 1962.)

Great variation is found among actinopterygian fishes with respect to the condensation and dispersal of the adrenal tissues. These are generally located within or just anterior to the "cephalic kidneys," and occur around the postcardinal veins and their branches (Fig. 10–4). In many species, the so-called "cephalic kidneys" consist largely of lymphoid or myeloid tissue, or both, and hence are blood-forming organs. The two types of adrenal cells are entirely separated in certain species *(Salmo)*, but in others they are intermingled *(Cottus)*. Branches of the postcardinal veins may be lined with chromaffin cells which are surrounded by steroidogenic cells.[34, 37]

The corpuscles of Stannius are bodies within the mesonephric kidneys of some teleosts and are thought to arise as proliferations from the urinary ducts (Fig. 10–3). Some workers have detected

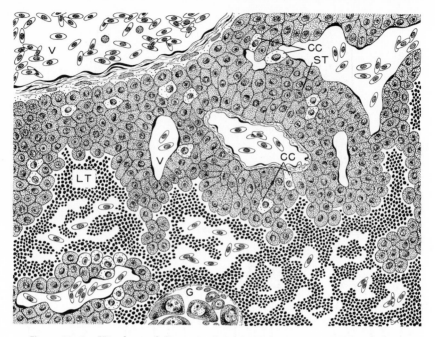

Figure 10–4. Histology of the carp adrenal gland. CC, chromaffin cells; G, ganglion; LT, lymphoid tissue of "head" kidney; ST, steroidogenic tissue; V, vein containing red corpuscles. Camera lucida, × 540.

adrenocortical steroids in these corpuscles and regard them as holocrine glands which play a physiologic role comparable to the adrenal cortices of mammals. Other workers have not been able to identify steroids in these bodies. The fact that they differ in embryonic origin and mode of secretion from established steroidogenic tissue in teleosts has led many investigators to abandon the view that they are comparable to adrenal cortices.[20]

The amphibian adrenal consists of rather discrete bodies along the ventral surfaces of the kidneys, and the chromaffin and steroidogenic cells are interspersed (Fig. 10–3). At certain points, the adrenal tissue may be completely buried within the kidney. The steroidogenic cells are organized into cords which are separated by conspicuous blood sinuses; the chromaffin cells occur singly or in small clusters; and many neurons are present throughout the gland. A very characteristic feature of the adrenals of aquatic anurans is the presence of many "Stilling cells" scattered throughout the organs. These cells resemble mast cells and are PAS-positive and eosinophilic (Fig. 10–5). The functional role of the Stilling cells is unknown, but they are said to be absent in three genera of terrestrial toads.[31]

The adrenal glands of reptiles and birds are more compact than in lower forms, and the two types of tissue are intermingled. The adrenals of turtles are discrete bodies located on the anterior ventral

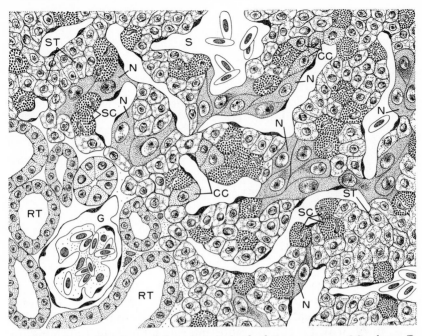

Figure 10–5. Histology of the adrenal gland of *Rana pipiens*. CC, chromaffin cells; G, glomerulus of kidney; N, neuron; RT, renal tubule; S, sinusoid containing red corpuscles; SC, Stilling cells; ST, steroidogenic tissue. Camera lucida, × 540.

surfaces of the kidneys; in snakes, the adrenals are some distance anterior to the kidneys (Figs. 10–6 and 10–7). In certain lizards and snakes, the chromaffin cells aggregate to form a distinct band of tissue at the periphery of the organ, partly surrounding the central mass of steroidogenic tissue (Fig. 10–3). The avian adrenals are located near

Figure 10–6. Ventral view of the adrenal glands of the turtle *(Pseudemys scripta)*, showing the main blood vessels of the kidney region.

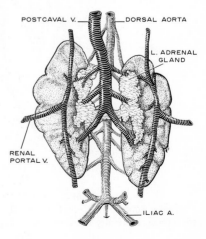

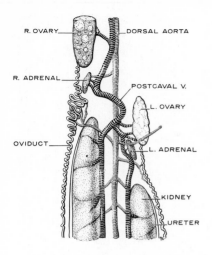

Figure 10–7. Adrenal glands and adnexa of the snake *(Natrix)*, from ventral view.

the anterior poles of the kidneys and consist of cords of steroidogenic tissue and clusters of chromaffin cells (Figs. 10–8 and 9). It is only in mammals that distinct cortices and medullae are present, and even here, there may be considerable interdigitation and intermingling of the two kinds of tissue.[8, 21, 44, 49, 50]

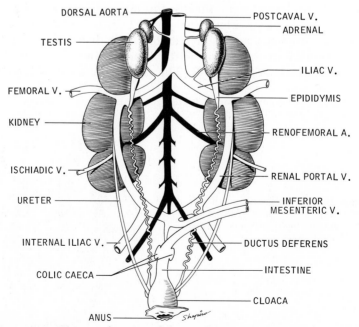

Figure 10–8. Urogenital organs of the male pigeon *(Columba livia)*. Both testes are retracted laterally to expose the adrenal glands.

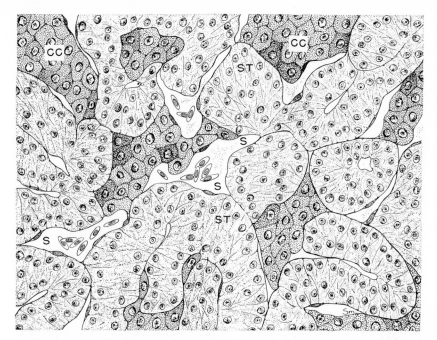

Figure 10–9. Histology of the chicken adrenal gland. CC, chromaffin cells; S, sinusoids containing red corpuscles; ST, steroidogenic tissue. Camera lucida, × 540.

Studies on the adrenal gland of the rat suggest that the production of epinephrine by the medullary cells is regulated by the pituitary-adrenocortical system. The conversion of norepinephrine to epinephrine requires the transfer of a methyl group, and this process is catalyzed by the enzyme phenylethanolamine-N-methyl transferase (PNMT). The activity of this medullary enzyme is markedly reduced after hypophysectomy, but may be restored by administering either ACTH or glucocorticoids. The ACTH produces its effect by increasing the availability of glucocorticoids from the steroidogenic tissue. Since the glucocorticoids are known to promote protein synthesis in a variety of tissues, it is probable that they elevate PNMT activity by regulating the conditions which are necessary for its synthesis. The evolutionary trend has been toward a closer association of catechol-amine-producing tissue and steroid-producing tissue, and, in light of the above observations, this relationship may have some functional significance.[51] The ability of chromaffin cells, and possibly adrenergic neurons, to form epinephrine through the methylation of norepinephrine might conceivably be enhanced by their nearness to the cells that secrete adrenal steroids.

Adrenal Terminology

These glands have been named with reference to their positions with respect to the kidneys, using such prefixes as *ad* (to or near), *inter* (between), *intra* (within), and *supra* (above or over). Confusion often arises through the establishment of a morphologic nomenclature suitable for mammals, before anything is known about the lower vertebrate classes. Since the steroid-producing constituent of the adrenal forms a cortex only in mammals, it is misleading to refer to it as "adrenocortical tissue" in submammalian forms where there is no cortex. Furthermore, *interrenal glands* are present only in chondrichthyean fishes, and, even though they secrete some of the same steroids as the mammalian cortex, it is equally misleading to apply the term "interrenal tissue" to this component in teleosts, amphibians, reptiles, birds, and mammals, where the adrenals are not between the kidneys, and where the glands are a composite of both chromaffin and steroidogenic tissues. There can be no doubt that the interrenal glands of elasmobranchs are homologous and analogous to the adrenal cortices of mammals; and that the scattered aggregations of chromaffin cells in elasmobranchs and other fishes are homologous and analogous to the mammalian medullae. As the situation stands at present, there is no adequate morphological designation for the steroid-producing tissue in the adrenals of teleosts, amphibians, reptiles, and birds. Perhaps the time has come when it would be desirable to describe the two adrenal components in physiologic terms such as the "steroidogenic adrenal" and the "amineogenic adrenal."

It is probable that there are extra-adrenal deposits of chromaffin cells in all vertebrates. Catecholamine-containing cells stain brownish with bichromate solutions, and this is generally called the "chromaffin reaction." Other reactions have been used such as a green color following ferric chloride, a blue stain with ferric-ferricyanide, blackening with osmium tetroxide, and reduction of silver salts and gold chloride. Though there have been recent improvements in staining techniques, there remains some doubt as to how specifically these procedures are capable of identifying epinephrine and norepinephrine in cells.[18, 25] Since the identification of chromaffin cells presents difficulties and yields results which can be doubted, it seems that more extensive use should be made of the sensitive biologic and chemical assay methods which are now available for the identification of catecholamines in tissue extracts. The cytochemical procedures for identifying "chromaffin cells" are not ideal, and they may stain other elements (mastlike cells) which are capable of storing dopamine and other catecholamines, but probably do not synthesize them. As information accumulates, it may be advantageous to replace the term "chromaffin cells" by more precise terms such as "amineogenic cells" or "catecholamine-containing" cells.

There is no justification for calling the adrenal glands of teleosts, amphibians, reptiles, and birds "interrenal glands," nor does it make sense to refer to the steroid-producing tissue in these groups as "interrenal" or "adrenocortical" tissue. "Steroidogenic" would seem to be a more precise designation for this tissue, though the terms "interrenal tissue" and "adrenocortical tissue" could be retained for chondrichthyeans and mammals, respectively. The term "amineogenic tissue" could be safely applied to the chromaffin cells which comprise integral parts of the adrenal glands.

BIOCHEMISTRY OF THE CATECHOLAMINES

The cells of the adrenal medulla elaborate epinephrine and norepinephrine, often referred to collectively as *catecholamines.* Both hormone molecules contain an asymmetric carbon atom and therefore can exist in two optically active forms. The hormones secreted by the gland are levorotatory (L-forms), whereas those produced by laboratory synthesis are racemic (DL-forms). The mixture is resolved after preparation and the L-form is supplied for clinical use. The L-isomer of epinephrine is about 15 times more active than the D-isomer in elevating the blood pressure of the spinal cat. Commercial preparations made from ox adrenals may contain as much as 20 per cent of norepinephrine. The two hormones are very similar in chemical properties, but the presence of an additional methyl group in epinephrine changes the side chain from a primary amine (norepinephrine) to a secondary amine (epinephrine) (Fig. 10–10). Considerable quantities of ascorbic acid are present in the medulla, and it is thought to play an important role in maintaining the medullary hormones in the reduced state. It has been shown that the vitamin acts *in vitro* to protect these pressor amines from oxidation.

Adrenal extracts contain both epinephrine and norepinephrine, the proportions of which are fairly constant and characteristic for the species. Dopamine, a precursor of norepinephrine, is also found in medullary extracts. The adult human adrenals secrete about 10 times more epinephrine than norepinephrine; the adrenergic nerves of the sympathetic division release only traces of epinephrine. During prenatal life the human adrenals and the organs of Zuckerkandl contain only norepinephrine. Epinephrine appears after birth, and at 1 year of age the two hormones are present in about equal proportions. The amount of epinephrine gradually increases until it becomes the major amine of the adult adrenal. The reverse appears to be true in chickens; during early life the adrenal contains mostly epinephrine, whereas norepinephrine predominates in the adult. Chromaffin tumors sometimes appear in the adrenal medulla or wherever chromaffin tissue is found in the body, and in these cases, the

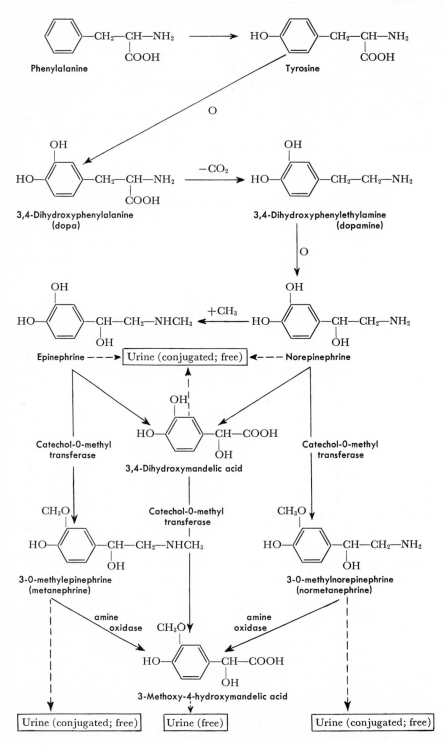

Figure 10–10. Biosynthesis and metabolism of adrenal medullary hormones. (From Cantarow, A., and Schepartz, B.: Biochemistry, 3rd ed. Philadelphia, W. B. Saunders Co., 1962).

quantities of pressor amines in the blood may be increased tremendously.

Since norepinephrine is a transmitter substance released by
certain nerve terminals, its distribution in the body is not limited
to the adrenal medulla and chromaffin deposits.[41] It has been demonstrated in almost all mammalin tissues except the placenta, which
lacks nerve fibers. Norepinephrine is present in the central nervous
system and attains a relatively high concentration in the hypothalamus. The norepinephrine content is highest in nerves that are rich
in adrenergic fibers, such as the sympathetic trunk and the splenic
and splanchnic nerves. The amount of norepinephrine present in
the splenic nerves increases from the proximal toward the distal
portion. The amine is synthesized by the nerve cell and stored in the
axonic terminals whence it is passed to the exterior.[11, 13, 17, 19]

Spindle-shaped cells giving the chromaffin reaction have been
described in various tissues and are especially abundant in the
skin and lungs. There is little direct information regarding the
capacity of chromaffin cells outside the adrenal medulla to produce
catechol hormones. After degeneration of the adrenergic nerves to
an organ, almost all of the norepinephrine in the organ disappears,
whereas the epinephrine content may be slightly increased. If the
adrenergic fibers regenerate and re-establish connections with the
organ, the level of norepinephrine in the organ is restored. This may
indicate that chromaffin cells within the organ do not degenerate after
denervation and continue to secrete epinephrine. Section of the
preganglionic sympathetic fibers does not diminish the norepinephrine content of an organ, showing that the synthesis of
norepinephrine by the postganglionic neuron is not dependent on
impulses delivered to it over the preganglionic fibers. The norepinephrine content of sympathetic effectors is closely correlated with
the number of adrenergic fibers that supply them. Since adrenergic
nerves can release norepinephrine continuously on repeated stimulation over long periods, it must be synthesized rapidly and there
would appear to be some provision for the intra-axonal storage of
the neurohumor.

Cellular Origin of the Hormones

Electron microscopic studies of chromaffin cells have demonstrated that they contain large numbers of dense osmiophilic
granules, ranging in diameters from 100 to 400 mμ. These granules
are surrounded by membranes, and appear to originate in the Golgi
region of the cell. They contain a very high content of catecholamines
and adenosine triphosphate (ATP). The hormones are liberated
rapidly when the granules are placed in hypotonic solutions. Exposure of the granules to high temperatures also causes a prompt

release of pressor amines. It is probable that the granules do not leave the cell but only discharge their contents on stimulation. The normal stimulus for the discharge of medullary hormones is acetylcholine, which is liberated by the splanchnic nerve terminals that come in contact with the medullary cells. However, acetylcholine does not induce the liberation of pressor amines when added to a suspension of granules in isotonic sucrose solution. By comparing denervated adrenals with normal, it has been found that nerve impulses arriving at the gland do not appreciably change the distribution of pressor amines between the granules and the nongranular cytoplasm.[5, 15, 26]

As with other endocrine glands secreting multiple hormones, the question arises of whether both hormones are secreted by the same cell or whether there are separate cells for the production of each hormone. Evidence favoring the view that there are two cell types is based on: (a) histochemical studies indicating that different cells in the medulla stain selectively for either norepinephrine or epinephrine; (b) the isolation of granules from medullary extracts differing in their relative content of the two amines; and (c) the capacity of different stimuli to release epinephrine or norepinephrine selectively. Studies on human subjects indicate that active aggressive emotional displays are associated with the urinary excretion of norepinephrine, while tense, but passive, emotional displays increase the excretion of epinephrine without affecting the excretion of norepinephrine.[7, 16, 29]

The adrenal venous blood of the cat contains more norepinephrine than epinephrine. Stimulation of the sciatic nerve or the application of other painful stimuli encourages the secretion of epinephrine; clamping the carotid arteries produces a reflexive vasoconstriction and the adrenal medullae secrete mostly norepinephrine. After denervation of the cat's adrenal the output of norepinephrine is reduced to very low levels. Reducing the blood sugar by administering insulin causes an augmented release of epinephrine, but the intravenous injection of excessive glucose diminishes the secretion of epinephrine without affecting the secretion of norepinephrine. Stimulation of a particular area of the hypothalamus causes mainly epinephrine to appear in the adrenal venous blood; stimulation of another area promotes the appearance of norepinephrine in the venous effluent. These observations indicate that epinephrine and norepinephrine may be released separately by the medulla and support the concept that the hormones arise from different medullary components.

Whether the two hormones originate from one or two cell types cannot be answered at present. The various histochemical techniques lack absolute specificity. Furthermore, studies on depleted glands show that norepinephrine reappears in advance of epinephrine, and this suggests that previous functional activity would have an effect on the proportions of the two hormones extractable from them. Granular fractions containing mostly norepinephrine may represent immature stages that would eventually form epinephrine.[24, 30]

Biosynthesis and Metabolism of the Catecholamines

The amino acids are extremely important compounds, since the body uses them for numerous purposes. The protein complex of the organism is constantly changing; some proteins are continuously being broken down and new tissue proteins are being synthesized. The products of tissue protein breakdown and the amino acids derived from dietary proteins produce a common metabolic pool of nitrogen from which the tissues may withdraw the necessary amino acids for their repair, maintenance, and growth. Unless the amino acids are rather promptly incorporated into tissue or other proteins, they undergo deamination and are lost so far as protein synthesis is concerned. Amino acids, therefore, are essential for the repair and growth of tissues, as well as for the synthesis of normal supplies of hormones, vitamins, and other substances. Tyrosine or phenylalanine, for example, are essential for producing such hormones as thyroxine and epinephrine. The synthesis of insulin, glucagon, and the various hormones of the pituitary gland makes heavy demands on the amino acid pool of the body.[36]

The amino acids phenylalanine and tyrosine are generally regarded as precursors of epinephrine. The main biosynthetic pathway is phenylalanine → tyrosine → dopa → dopamine → norepinephrine → epinephrine, and this is shown in Figure 10–10. Tyrosine is oxidized to dopa, and this is decarboxylated to dopamine, which is oxidized to norepinephrine. The latter is methylated to form epinephrine.[1] In nervous tissue, where norepinephrine functions as a chemical transmitter, very little, if any, epinephrine is formed. It is believed by some workers that the end-product of catecholamine biosynthesis may be dopamine in certain tissues (*e.g.*, lungs, intestine, liver) where it acts as a local hormone. Epinephrine and norepinephrine may exist in the blood plasma in the free form or undergo conjugation with sulfate or glucuronide; most of the circulating epinephrine is bound to blood proteins, mainly albumin. Norepinephrine does not bind to blood proteins to such a great extent.

The catecholamines disappear very rapidly from the circulation. Both may be present in the urine as free or conjugated forms. Their metabolic degradation involves methylation, effected by the enzyme catechol-O-methyl transferase, and deamination and oxidation, effected by amine oxidase. The metabolites appearing in the blood and urine are inactive, and the most abundant ones are 3-methoxy-4-hydroxymandelic acid, metanephrine, and normetanephrine (Fig. 10–10).[2, 3, 14, 23, 39]

The Neurohumors

Evidence has accumulated to demonstrate convincingly that nerve cells release a variety of physiologically active agents. We have divided these into two classes: (a) *neurohormones* are considered to be the products of neurosecretory cells which are discharged into the circulation to act as hormones upon distant target tissues and organs, and (b) *neurohumors* are the transmitter agents released at the synapse and are largely destroyed before reaching the blood.

Although epinephrine and norepinephrine are hormones of chromaffin tissue, norepinephrine is also released as a neurohumor by most postganglionic sympathetic nerve endings. It is possible that adrenergic nerves may release small amounts of epinephrine, but the great mass of evidence indicates that norepinephrine is the neurotransmitter. The postganglionic neurons in the splenic nerves contain large quantities of norepinephrine, but almost no epinephrine. Extracts of organs that receive sympathetic innervation usually contain both epinephrine and norepinephrine, but the latter amine disappears from these organs after the nerves are sectioned and allowed to degenerate. Epinephrine continues to be produced by such denervated organs and probably emanates from chromaffin cells within the organ rather than being contained in the neurons. These observations indicate that the transmitter agent of adrenergic nerves is norepinephrine only and not actually a mixture of norepinephrine and epinephrine. Some dopamine may be present with norepinephrine at the nerve terminals.[59]

Bilaterally adrenalectomized human beings excrete practically no epinephrine in the urine, but the urinary levels of norepinephrine remain within normal limits. The norepinephrine must come from some extra-adrenal source, most probably from the adrenergic nerves. Furthermore, in adrenalectomized subjects there continues to be a diurnal variation in the excretion of norepinephrine. More of the amine appears in the urine during wakefulness than during sleep, as in normal subjects. Even changes from the recumbent to the standing position increase the urinary output of norepinephrine. These observations strengthen the concept that norepinephrine, rather than epinephrine, is the neurohumoral transmitter of the sympathetic nervous system.

Mechanism of Epinephrine Action

The catecholamines initiate a great variety of adjustments when administered to test animals; among these may be mentioned an elevation of blood sugar through the mobilization of both liver and muscle glycogen, increased nonesterified fatty acids in the blood plasma, and various effects upon cardiac and smooth muscles. It is probable that many of these effects are secondary to some basic, or primary, action exerted by the hormones. When biochemical effects can be demonstrated in *in vitro* systems, where secondary actions are ruled out, there is strong presumptive evidence that the agent is exerting a primary action. It is known that epinephrine, like pancreatic glucagon, is a potent agent in promoting the activation of phosphorylase. Norepinephrine is much less effective, and this correlates with its relative ineffectiveness in producing hyperglycemia *in vivo*. Facilitation of this enzyme system explains how epinephrine might affect carbohydrate metabolism, but it remains to be determined whether or not this basic action can account for all the multiple effects of the hormone.[33, 35, 42, 45]

Both epinephrine and glucagon increase cyclic-3',5'-AMP in particulate fractions of the liver; epinephrine has the same effect in muscle preparations, but glucagon is ineffective in muscle. This basic reaction may be shown graphically as follows:

$$\text{ATP} \xrightarrow[\text{Mg}^{++} \text{ and epinephrine}]{\text{adenyl cyclase}} 3',5'\text{-AMP}$$

$$\underset{\text{(inactive)}}{\text{PHOSPHORYLASE ``b''}} \xrightarrow[\text{ATP, Mg}^{++}, 3',5'\text{-AMP}]{\text{dephosphophosphorylase kinase}} \underset{\text{(active)}}{\text{PHOSPHORYLASE ``a''}}$$

PHYSIOLOGY OF THE CHROMAFFIN CELL HORMONES

Comparative Effects of Epinephrine and Norepinephrine

Although these two medullary hormones are similar in some of their biologic actions, there are important differences in the nature and degree of their effects (Table 10–1). Both hormones increase the heart rate, although epinephrine is the more potent in this respect. Both increase systolic blood pressure, whereas epinephrine has no effect on diastolic pressure. The hypertensive effect of norepinephrine is a consequence of increased peripheral resistance; that of epinephrine results from an increased cardiac output in spite of decreased total peripheral resistance. Epinephrine increases the blood flow through skeletal muscle, liver, and brain, whereas norepinephrine has no effect or decreases it. Both hormones produce constriction of the skin capillaries and cause pallor. Renal blood flow is diminished by both hormones. The net peripheral vascular effect

Table 10–1.   Contrasted Actions of Epinephrine and Norepinephrine

System	Function	Effect		Relative Activity, E/N*
		Epinephrine	Norepinephrine	
Cardio-vascular	Peripheral resistance	Decreased	Increased	—
	Systolic B. P.	Increased	Increased	0.5
	Diastolic B. P.	No effect	Increased	—
	Heart rate	Increased	Slightly increased	20
	Cardiac output	Increased	No change	—
	Blood vessels in denervated limb	Vasodilatation	Vasoconstriction	—
	Coronary vessels	Vasodilatation	Vasodilatation	—
	Pulse rate	Increased	Decreased	—
	Eosinophil count	Increased	No effect	—
	Net peripheral vascular effect	Vasodilatation	Limited vasodilator actions; over-all vasoconstriction	—
Blood flow through individual organs	Skeletal muscle	100% increase	Unaltered or decreased	—
	Liver	100% increase	No material effect	—
	Brain	20% increase	Slight decrease	—
	Kidney	40% decrease	20% decrease	2
Respiratory system	Bronchial muscle	Inhibition	Inhibition	20
Carbohydrate metabolism	Blood sugar	Increased	Increased	4
Eye	Pupillary dilators	Excitation	Excitation	15
Intestine	Small	Inhibition	Inhibition	2
	Large	Inhibition	Inhibition	1
Genital system	Nonpregnant uterus (rat, cat)	Inhibition	Inhibition	100
Central nervous system (man)	Mental state	Anxiety	No effect	—

* E = epinephrine; N = norepinephrine.

of epinephrine is to cause vasodilation; norepinephrine exerts limited vasodilator actions, but its over-all effect is to produce vasconstriction. Epinephrine is very potent in increasing oxygen consumption and glucose output from the liver, but norepinephrine is relatively weak in these respects.

The adrenal medulla functions in conjunction with the sympathetic nervous system and is intimately concerned with emotional adjustments. The medullary hormones are released in response to sympathetic stimulation, and this division of the autonomic system is integrated by components involving the cerebral cortices, midbrain, and hypothalamus. Although the two amines are related chemically and biologically, they appear to be released independently and to perform separate and distinct roles in the economy of the organism. Anticipatory states tend to elevate the release of norepinephrine more than epinephrine, but in intense emotional reactions both amines are elevated. The actions of epinephrine seem suitable to equip the organism to meet certain kinds of emergency situations: it acts to prevent hypoglycemia by stimulating metabolism and mobilizing glycogen as glucose; it redistributes the blood, draining it out of the skin and forcing it into important organs, such as skeletal muscle, liver, and brain. Norepinephrine is predominantly present at sympathetic endings and seems to function largely as a pressor hormone normally required for the maintenance of blood pressure. With the exception of the coronary arteries, norepinephrine produces general vasoconstriction and stimulates the heart but is relatively impotent in its metabolic actions.

Actions of the Epinephrines

Carbohydrate Metabolism

Epinephrine increases the blood sugar level and is one of the most important factors in the normal organism for counteracting the hypoglycemic action of insulin[22] (Fig. 10–11). Emotional excitement, injury, and exercise, as well as the administration of certain anesthetics (ether, morphine), cause an augmented release of epinephrine and a consequent elevation of blood sugar. A low level of blood sugar, resulting from any cause, has a stimulatory effect on the adrenal medulla, and epinephrine operates to bring the glucose level back to normal. Epinephrine exerts its hyperglycemic action by increasing the rate of glycogenolysis in the liver and muscles. Under the influence of the hormone, both liver and muscle glycogen are converted to hexose phosphates and, in the liver, glucose is formed by the action of a phosphatase. Muscle lacks this phosphatase and completes the glycolytic process with the formation of lactic acid. The muscle may resynthesize some of the lactic acid to glycogen, but much of it escapes into the blood and is carried to the liver, where it is converted to glycogen or glucose. After the injection of epinephrine, the hepatic glycogen stores are generally higher than normal owing to the synthesis of glycogen from lactate that had been released from the muscles.

Epinephrine also influences carbohydrate metabolism indirectly by stimulating the adenohypophysis to release ACTH. It is not known whether epinephrine activates the pituitary gland directly, or indirectly through connections in the hypothalamic portion of the brain. In any case, the ACTH augments the release of steroids from the adrenal cortex, and the 11-oxygenated hormones are extremely potent in promoting the synthesis of carbohydrate from protein.

Some workers have found that epinephrine depresses the rate at which the tissues use glucose. Epinephrine reduces glucose tolerance and the arteriovenous glucose difference is slight even when

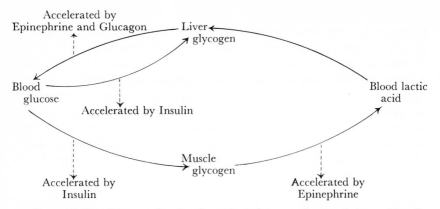

Figure 10–11. Diagram showing the major influences of epinephrine and insulin on the distribution of carbohydrate in the body. (After West and Todd: Textbook of Biochemistry.)

the arterial blood contains much glucose. If there is an actual inhibition of glucose utilization, it may be due in part to the action of adrenocortical steroids. There is also some evidence that epinephrine may act at the level of the cell membrane and reduce the rate of entry of glucose into the cells.

Epinephrine exerts more marked effects on carbohydrate metabolism in some mammalian species than in others, the rabbit being much more sensitive than the human being, dog, cat, or rat. Hyperglycemia may result from doses that do not produce any elevation of blood pressure. Norepinephrine, in contrast to epinephrine, produces very slight changes in carbohydrate metabolism. Animals deprived of the adrenal medulla recover very slowly from hypoglycemia, which is probably accounted for on the basis of the relative inability of norepinephrine to mobilize glycogen stores. Muscle glycogenolysis fails to occur in demedullated animals even when they are subjected to operative trauma or severe hypoglycemia. This suggests that the medulla is the principal source of circulating epinephrine and that the norepinephrine released by adrenergic nerves does not attain circulatory titers sufficient to have this effect.

Epinephrine increases oxygen consumption and basal metabolic rate when given in moderate amounts; large doses may produce the opposite effect. Cold-adapted rats have an increased ability to produce heat by means other than muscular contraction. Although norepinephrine has little calorigenic effect in warm-adapted rats, it markedly elevates the oxygen consumption of cold-adapted rats without producing a hyperglycemia.[28] Hyperkalemia, or a rise in serum potassium, typically follows epinephrine treatment.

In summary, epinephrine elevates the blood sugar in three ways: (1) by mobilizing the carbohydrate stores of the liver; (2) by encouraging the transformation of muscle glycogen into lactic acid, from which the liver manufactures new carbohydrate; and (3) by stimulating the adenohypophysis to secrete ACTH, which causes the release of adrenal cortical hormones having an effect on glyconeogenesis. There is evidence that epinephrine acts in some manner to depress the utilization of carbohydrate by the tissues. Since hypoglycemia elicits the secretion of epinephrine and hyperglycemia stimulates the secretion of insulin, it is apparent that these two hormones are important in the homeostatic regulation of blood sugar levels (Fig. 10–11).

Cardiovascular System

The catecholamines affect the heart and blood vessels in many different ways, but it should be understood that these effects can be influenced by many factors, such as compensatory reflex adjustments, dosage, manner and rate of administration, and the species. Epinephrine is a powerful heart stimulant, increasing the frequency, force, and amplitude of contraction. Systolic blood pressure, pulse rate, and cardiac output are increased. Small doses of epinephrine can increase the cardiac output without elevating the blood pressure. Norepinephrine, in contrast, is a powerful vasoconstrictor and raises both the systolic and diastolic pressures, but it does not produce much change in the cardiac output (Table 10–1). Tachycardia typically follows epinephrine treatment, but bradycardia often follows norepinephrine injections. The elevated blood pressure resulting from norepinephrine usually causes a reflexive increase in vagal tone and a slowing of the heart. These differences in the cardiovascular effects of the two amines are due largely to the fact that epinephrine reduces peripheral resistance by producing dilatation of the vascular bed of the skeletal muscles; norepinephrine causes a rise in total peripheral resistance by constricting the vessels in the muscles, skin, and viscera. When applied locally to the skin and mucous membranes, both hormones produce pallor by diverting blood away from the smaller capillaries and into a few main vascular channels.

The pharmacologic actions of the epinephrines may be demonstrated by applying them to isolated organs, or strips of organs, suspended in physiologic solutions. When they are applied to isolated mammalian hearts, the contractions increase in rate and amplitude. The denervated mammalian heart is accelerated by as little as 1 part of epinephrine in 1,400,000,000 parts of fluid. Muscular contractions in intestinal strips from the rabbit are inhibited by the addition of small quantities of epinephrine or norepinephrine. It must be recognized that the reactions elicited in excised organs or in anesthetized animals are not necessarily indicative of the responses that would be obtained in the normal intact subject in which compensatory adjustments may be accomplished by nervous reflexes.

Nervous System

The injection of epinephrine to normal human subjects produces a feeling of restlessness and anxiety and a sense of fatigue, whereas norepinephrine does not produce such symptoms. Hence the two hormones have different effects on the central nervous system.

It has been known for a long time that tissues and organs supplied by the sympathetic nerves are made more sensitive to the catechol hormones by denervation, but there is no satisfactory explanation of this phenomenon. Possibly the concentrations of enzymes that destroy the adrenergic transmitter (norepinephrine) may diminish in the organs after the nerves have degenerated. Ephedrine has been reported to inhibit the action of amine oxidase and thereby to potentiate the effects of the catechol hormones and also to increase the effects produced by stimulation of the adrenergic nerves.

Thyroid

There is general agreement that hyperthyroidism causes an increased sensitivity to epinephrine and that hypothyroidism causes tolerance to epinephrine. The ability of epinephrine to elevate the blood sugar in guinea pigs is strikingly reduced by thyroidectomy. There are reports that the level of amine oxidase in the liver and in blood is decreased by thyroxine injections and increased by thyroidectomy or the administration of antithyroid agents. This may account in part for the exaggerated effects of the catecholamines when they are administered to hyperthyroid animals.

Pigmentary Effectors

The pigment cells of many teleost fishes and reptiles are richly supplied with autonomic nerve fibers, and color changes may be effected by stimulating or sectioning these fibers. The release of neurohumoral agents by the nerve terminals appears to be the most important factor in regulating the chromatophores in those forms in which the chromatophores are directly innervated. Epinephrine-like compounds generally produce a concentration of pigment granules when applied to chromatophores, and acetylcholine usually has an opposing action.

Some Miscellaneous Actions

Epinephrine generally reduces the level of circulating eosinophils by its action on ACTH release and a consequent increase in the production of adrenocortical hormones. Mitotic activity in tissues *in vitro* is suppressed by epinephrine.[6] The clotting time of blood is reduced by exogenous epinephrine, but the mechanism of this action is poorly understood. The medullary hormones have important effects on water and electrolyte metabolism, but these reactions are complex and varied.

Nonesterified fatty acids are produced from rat adipose tissue when it is incubated *in vitro* with either epinephrine or norepinephrine. The hormones presumably promote the hydrolysis of neutral fats within the tissue. The L-isomers are much more active than the D-isomers, which suggests that this is the type of response that might occur within the organism.[48] Epinephrine differs from ACTH in not requiring ionized calcium for this lipolytic effect.

THE AUTONOMIC NERVOUS SYSTEM

Some general features of the autonomic nervous system are mentioned here as an aid to understanding the roles performed by the catecholamines in the economy of the organism.

Anatomic Organization

The peripheral nervous system is composed of the craniospinal nerves and the components of the autonomic system. The latter is an aggregation of ganglia, nerves, and plexuses through which efferent innervation is supplied for the heart, glands, and smooth muscle in diverse locations. The autonomic fibers are connected so intimately with the central nervous system that the two cannot be delimited anatomically. The autonomic system is controlled mainly by the hypothalamic portion of the brain. Hence the autonomic nerves constitute a functional rather than an anatomic division of the nervous system. The general anatomic features are indicated in Figure 10–12. The sympathetic division, or the thoracolumbar outflow, is shown on the right side of the figure, while the parasympathetic division, or craniosacral outflow, is shown on the left.

SYMPATHETIC DIVISION. The sympathetic ganglia are of two types, vertebral and collateral. The vertebral group consists of approximately 22 pairs of ganglia united by intervening fiber tracts in such a manner as to form a chain along the right and left sides of the vertebral column. These sympathetic chains extend from the level of the first cervical vertebra to the anterior surface of the coccyx. The largest of the collateral (prevertebral) ganglia are the celiac, superior mesenteric, and inferior mesenteric. The *preganglionic neurons* extend from the gray matter of the central nervous system to one of the ganglia where they make synaptic connections with *postganglionic neurons* that extend from the ganglia to the effector organs. The cell bodies of the preganglionic neurons of the thora-

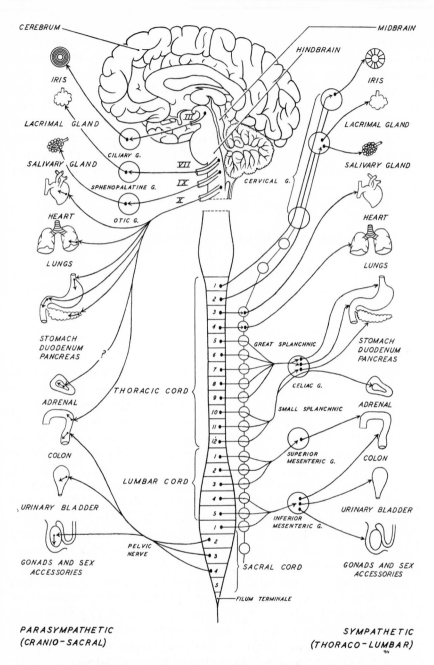

Figure 10–12. A diagram of the autonomic nervous system. The parasympathetic division is shown on the left, the sympathetic division on the right. Roman numerals refer to cranial nerves.

columbar outflow are contained within the gray matter of the thoracic and lumbar regions of the spinal cord. These fibers, together with ordinary somatic efferent fibers, emerge from the cord through the anterior roots of the spinal nerves. The preganglionic fibers soon separate from the somatic efferent fibers of the anterior roots and terminate in a ganglion.

Most of the spinal nerves emerging from these regions of the cord are connected with the vertebral ganglia by means of the *white rami communicantes*. The preganglionic neurons may form synapses with postganglionic neurons within the vertebral ganglia that they first enter, may pass through one or more ganglia and form synapses within other vertebral ganglia at higher or lower levels, or may pass uninterruptedly through the vertebral ganglia and establish synapses within one of the collateral ganglia. The cell bodies of the postganglionic neurons, together with their dendritic ramifications, are within the sympathetic ganglia. The axons of the postganglionic neurons, unlike the preganglionic neurons, are usually unmyelinated. The postganglionic axons either course through the sympathetic nerves to the viscera or enter spinal nerves to reach the body wall and skin. All the spinal nerves are connected to corresponding ganglia of the sympathetic chains by means of the *gray rami communicantes* through which they receive fibers from the sympathetic trunks.

There are usually many more postganglionic fibers leaving the sympathetic ganglia than there are preganglionics coming to them. The numerous synaptic connections in the sympathetic system make possible an extensive dissemination of impulses. The preganglionic sympathetic fibers to the adrenal are unusual, inasmuch as they make no ganglionic connections before terminating in the medullary portion of the gland.

PARASYMPATHETIC DIVISION. The cell bodies of the preganglionic neurons of the parasympathetic system or craniosacral outflow are situated within the midbrain, hindbrain, and sacral region of the spinal cord. The preganglionic fibers of the cranial component of the parasympathetic system are contained within the oculomotor, facial, glossopharyngeal, and vagus nerves. The preganglionic fibers of the sacral constituent emerge in the anterior roots of the corresponding sacral nerves and proceed to the pelvic organs as the pelvic nerves. It will be noted that the preganglionic fibers of the parasympathetic system are long and end within terminal ganglia located in or close to the effector organs. Thus the postganglionic axons of the parasympathetic are relatively short. Like the fibers of the sympathetic system, the preganglionics are myelinated, whereas the postganglionics are unmyelinated.

VISCERAL SENSORY NERVE SUPPLY. While it has been the tradition to consider the autonomic system as purely efferent, it should not be inferred that the visceral organs lack a sensory or afferent nerve supply. The afferent fibers from the viscera transmit impulses from the various internal organs to the brain and spinal cord. Their cell bodies are located in the dorsal root ganglia or in similar cranial ganglia, and they have no synapses in either the spinal or sympathetic ganglia.

General Actions of the Autonomic System

Most of the visceral organs are doubly innervated, and in general, the sympathetic and parasympathetic components exert antagonistic actions. Thus stimulation of the parasympathetic fibers within the vagi slows the rhythmic contractions of the heart, whereas sympathetic stimulation accelerates heart action. The contractility of the heart is due basically to a mechanism within its own walls, but the autonomic system modifies its activity. The parasympathetic fibers to the stomach and small intestine augment gastrointestinal processes, whereas the sympathetic fibers to the same organs are inhibitory. The term "autonomic" is not entirely appropriate when applied to this portion of the peripheral nervous system, since it is dependent on the brain and cord and is unable to function as an independent unit. The term signifies, however, that this system of neurons is concerned with the regulation of physiologic processes that are beneath consciousness and hence proceed in the absence of voluntary control.

In spite of the diversified functions of the sympathetic division, it is not essential for life. Large parts of it have been surgically removed from human subjects without serious impairment of function. Sympathectomized animals, particularly cats, have been maintained in good health for long periods under laboratory conditions, but the effects of the operation become evident when such animals are subjected to emergencies and unfavorable environments. Obviously, these animals would succumb if forced to struggle for existence in a hazardous environment. They are incapable of arduous physical work, do not adjust properly to changing temperatures, and are unable to become physically aroused when attacked by enemies.

It is a common practice to designate autonomic neurons as *adrenergic* or *cholinergic*. Neurons that release norepinephrine are adrenergic; those that release acetylcholine and similar agents are cholinergic. Most of the postganglionic neurons of the sympathetic system are adrenergic; all of the preganglionic neurons of both sympathetic and parasympathetic divisions are cholinergic. Most of the postganglionic neurons of the parasympathetics, as well as the ordinary somatic motor neurons terminating in skeletal muscles, are cholinergic.

In addition to the catecholamines and acetylcholine, 5-hydroxy-tryptamine and a number of other substances have been identified as neurohumoral substances. If neurons are to be identified on the basis of the kind of neurohumor they produce, more categories than adrenergic and cholinergic are needed.[46]

Since the isolation of epinephrine in 1901, many similarities between the systemic effects of exogenous epinephrine and those produced by stimulation of the sympathetic nerves have been recognized. However, certain discrepancies between the two became apparent and could not be accounted for until norepinephrine became available for experimental purposes in 1948. For example, stimulation of the splenic nerve of the cat stimulates the denervated heart, but it does not cause relaxation of the uterus; small amounts of exogenous epinephrine produce both effects. It appears that this nerve produces norepinephrine in quantities sufficient to affect the denervated heart, but this amine is known to have very weak effects on the uterus of the cat. Norepinephrine is the only neurohumor convincingly demonstrated to be produced by the adrenergic terminals of mammals. Though traces of epinephrine are also present at these endings, it remains to be determined whether this amine arises from the nerve cells themselves or from extra-axonal chromaffin cells which may be closely associated with them.[17]

FUNCTIONAL UTILITY OF THE CATECHOLAMINES

Progress in understanding the functional role of the adrenal medulla has been slow for a number of reasons. Among these are: (1) the presence of extramedullary chromaffin deposits that presumably secrete catecholamines, (2) the production of no profound disturbances by removal of the adrenal medulla, (3) the former belief that the adrenal medulla secreted only epinephrine, (4) the uncertainty regarding the nature of the adrenergic neurohumor, and (5) the fact that the actions of exogenous epinephrine may be modified or reversed by several means. Although norepinephrine was synthesized in 1904, its importance as a medullary hormone and as a sympathetic neurohumor was not recognized until 1948. Since then the functional roles of the adrenal medulla and sympathetic division have become clearer, though there are still many gaps.

The adrenal medulla is the source of two or more hormones and its functional state is regulated by a direct nerve supply. Centers in the hypothalamus control medullary secretion via the splanchnic nerves. While it is not known that the hormones are elaborated by separate medullary cells, they can be released independently.

Since the medulla is under constant stimulation by nerve impulses originating throughout the body, it is generally agreed that there is a basal level of production of hormones. This basal rate of secretion fluctuates with normal body activities and is tremendously increased during emergencies. Medullary activity is accelerated chiefly by hypoglycemia and by exposure to stressor stimuli, such as severe temperature changes, trauma, hemorrhage, combat, attack, and so on.[3, 12]

There is much evidence to support the emergency theory of epinephrine function, as proposed by Cannon, and the concept appears to be generally accepted. The adrenal medulla usually secretes more epinephrine than norepinephrine, and the actions of the former hormone seem well suited to equip an organism for emergencies. Coping with a sudden emergency requires a massive response of the autonomic nervous system. The sympathetic division can produce a massive, widespread reaction, but the responses to parasympathetic stimulation are highly localized. Activation of the sympathicoadrenal system results in the release of large quantities of catecholamines. Since the preganglionic sympathetic fibers to the adrenal medulla are cholinergic, a comparable outpouring of medullary hormones may be induced by the administration of acetylcholine. Under these conditions the animal shows typical signs of heightened emotions: cardiac acceleration, deep respiration, gastrointestinal inhibition, sweating, pallor of the skin, increased pilomotor activity, elevated blood sugar, and increased flow of blood through the muscles. All of these changes may occur to varying degrees under different circumstances.

There can be no doubt that noxious stimuli promote the secretion of medullary hormones and that many of the responses to epinephrine (*e.g.*, accelerated heart action, increased flow of blood through muscles) are of utility to the hard-pressed organism. It is not certain, however, that all of the physiologic actions of epinephrine are necessary to enable an organism to adjust to environmental changes. Much of the earlier work attempting to prove the emergency theory of epinephrine action failed to take into consideration the importance of the adrenal cortical hormones in emergency adjustments. It is known that epinephrine may operate under certain conditions to promote the release of ACTH from the anterior hypophysis, with a consequent release of certain adrenal cortical steroids, although pituitary activation may be only a minor function of epinephrine under stressful conditions. The mechanisms involved in the neuroendocrine adjustments to stressor stimuli are extremely complicated and await full clarification. Both norepinephrine and epinephrine are involved in stress adjustments, but the latter medullary hormone is regarded as being of more importance in this respect.

Norepinephrine is the chief neurohumor that mediates adrenergic impulses, and it acts mainly at these terminals. Though small amounts of it may diffuse from the nerve endings into the general circulation, and some is released from the adrenal medulla, this hormone is less well suited than epinephrine for promoting emergency adjustments. Norepinephrine is currently regarded as functioning in the normal organism in the maintenance of vascular tone and hence blood pressure. It is probably secreted continuously by the sympathetic endings and acts locally to effect rapid adjustments essential for the maintenance of blood pressure. Various lines of evidence indicate that the release of norepinephrine is increased or decreased in response to conditions that threaten to alter normal blood pressure levels.

In summary, the chief functions of the catecholamines are to maintain blood pressure, to bring about alterations in carbohydrate metabolism, and to assist in systemic adjustments to certain kinds of stress. Norepinephrine is the transmitter substance of adrenergic nerves, and the neurohumor arising from this source can maintain normal vasomotor tone in the absence of adrenal medullary tissue. The differential release of the catechol hormones from the medulla probably depends on the functional requirements of the organism. Thus, norepinephrine is released in response to needs for circulatory adjustments, while epinephrine is of primary importance in metabolic adjustments and in the regional supply of blood to certain organs. Although both norepinephrine and epinephrine are involved in emotional expressions, epinephrine conforms more nearly to Cannon's concept of an emergency hormone.[47] Many actions of the catecholamines do not occur in the absence of adrenocortical hormones, the latter being necessary to maintain the integrity and responsiveness of the tissues.[40] Unlike the adrenal cortex, where emphasis is on adjustments to nonspecific stress, the adrenal medulla may be considered as a component of the sympathetic system and its hormones participate in specific emotional reactions.

REFERENCES

1. Axelrod, J.: Enzymatic formation of adrenaline and other catechols from monophenols. Science, *140*:499, 1963.
2. Axelrod, J., and Tomchick, R.: Enzymatic O-methylation of epinephrine and other catechols. J. Biol. Chem., *233*:702, 1958.
3. Axelrod, J., and Whitby, L. G.: Effect of psychotic drugs on the uptake of H³-norepinephrine by tissues. Science, *133*:383, 1961.
4. Bern, H. A., deRoos, C. C., and Biglieri, E. G.: Aldosterone and other corticosteroids from chondrichthyean interrenal glands. Gen. & Comp. Endocrinol., *2*:490, 1962.
5. Blaschko, H., Hagen, P., and Welch, A. D.: Observations on the intracellular granules of the adrenal medulla. J. Physiol., *129*:27, 1955.
6. Bullough, W. S.: A study of the hormonal relations of epidermal mitotic activity *in vitro*. III. Adrenalin. Exp. Cell Res., *9*:108, 1955.

7. Burgos, M. H.: Histochemistry and electron microscopy of the three cell types in the adrenal gland of the frog. Anat. Rec., *133*:163, 1959.

8. Chester Jones, I.: The Adrenal Cortex. London, Cambridge University Press, 1957.

9. Chester Jones, I., Phillips, J. G., and Bellamy, D.: Studies on water and electrolytes in cyclostomes and teleosts with special reference to *Myxine glutinosa* L. (the hagfish) and *Anguilla anguilla* L. (the Atlantic eel). Gen. & Comp. Endocrinol., Suppl. 1:36, 1962.

10. Chester Jones, I., and Spalding, M. H.: Some aspects of zonation and function of the adrenal cortex. J. Endocrinol., *10*:251, 1954.

11. Chidsey, C. A., Kaiser, G. A., and Braunwald, E.: Biosynthesis of norepinephrine in isolated canine heart. Science, *139*:828, 1963.

12. Coleman, B., and Glaviano, V. V.: Tissue levels of norepinephrine and epinephrine in hemorrhagic shock. Science, *139*:54, 1963.

13. De Robertis, E., and vaz Ferreira, A.: Submicroscopic changes in the nerve endings in the adrenal medulla after stimulation of the splanchnic nerve. J. Biophys. Biochem. Cytol., 3:611, 1957.

14. De Schaepdryver, A. F., and Kirshner, N.: Metabolism of adrenaline after blockade of monoamine oxidase and catechol-O-methyltransferase. Science, *133*:586, 1961.

15. Eade, N. R.: The distribution of the catechol amines in homogenates of the bovine adrenal medulla. J. Physiol., *141*:183, 1958.

16. Elmadjian, F., Hope, J. M., and Lamson, E. T.: Excretion of epinephrine and norepinephrine in various emotional states. J. Clin. Endocrinol., *17*:608, 1957.

17. von Euler, U. S.: Distribution and metabolism of catechol hormones in tissues and axones. Recent Prog. Hormone Research, *14*:483, 1958.

18. von Euler, U. S.: Chromaffin cell hormones. *In* U. S. von Euler (ed.), Comparative Endocrinology. Vol. 1. New York, Academic Press, 1963, p. 258.

19. von Euler, U. S., and Fänge, R.: Catecholamines in nerves and organs of *Myxine glutinosa*, *Squalus acanthias* and *Gadus callarias*. Gen. & Comp. Endocrinol., *1*:191, 1961.

20. Fontaine, M.: Evolution of form and function of endocrine organs with special reference to the adrenal gland. Proc. 16th Internat. Cong. Zool., Washington, D.C., 3:25, 1963.

21. Gabe, M., and Martoja, M.: Contribution à l'histologie de la glande surrénale des Squamata (reptiles). Arch. Anat. Microscop. Morphol. Exp., *50*:1, 1961.

22. Goldfien, A., Zileli, M. S., Despointes, R. H., and Bethune, J. E.: The effect of hypoglycemia on the adrenal secretion of epinephrine and norepinephrine. Endocrinol., *62*:749, 1958.

23. Guyton, A. C., and Gillespie, W. M., Jr.: Constant infusion of epinephrine: rate of epinephrine secretion and destruction in the body. Amer. J. Physiol., *165*:319, 1951.

24. Hagen, P.: The storage and release of catecholamines. Pharmacol. Revs., *11*:361, 1959.

25. Hale, A. J.: Observations on the nature of the chromaffin reaction. J. Physiol., *141*:193, 1958.

26. Hillarp, N. A., Lagerstedt, S., and Nilson, B.: The isolation of a granular fraction from the suprarenal medulla, containing the sympathomimetic catechol amines. Acta Physiol. Scandinav., *29*:251, 1953.

27. Holmes, W. N.: Histological variations in the adrenal cortex of the golden hamster with special reference to the X-zone. Anat. Rec., *122*:271, 1955.

28. Hsieh, A. C. L., and Carlson, L. D.: Role of adrenaline and noradrenaline in chemical regulation of heat production. Amer. J. Physiol., *190*:243, 1957.

29. Kirshner, N.: Uptake of catecholamines by a particulate fraction of the adrenal medulla. Science, *135*:107, 1962.

30. Kopin, I. J.: Storage and metabolism of catecholamines: the role of monoamine oxidase. Pharmacol. Revs., *16*:179, 1964.

31. Lakshman, A. B.: A descriptive study of the cytology of the adrenal glands of South Indian anurans. Endocrinologica Japonica, *11*:169, 1964.

32. Lanman, J. T.: The adrenal fetal zone: its occurrence in primates and a possible relationship to chorionic gonadotropin. Endocrinol., *61*:684, 1957.

33. Leonard, S. L., and Crandall, M.: Hormonal stimulation of phosphorylase activity in the rat uterus *in vitro*. Endocrinol., *73*:807, 1963.
34. Mahon, E. F., Hoar, W. S., and Tabata, S.: Histophysiological studies of the adrenal tissues of the goldfish. Candian J. Zool., *40*:449, 1962.
35. Malmejac, J.: Activity of the adrenal medulla and its regulation. Physiol. Revs., *44*:186, 1964.
36. Meister, A.: Biochemistry of the Amino Acids. New York, Academic Press, 1957.
37. Nandi, J.: New arrangement of interrenal and chromaffin tissues in teleost fishes. Science, *134*:389, 1961.
38. Payne, F.: Adrenal ganglia and medullary cells in hypophysectomized and ageing fowl. J. Exp. Zool., *128*:259, 1955.
39. Poole, T. R., and Watts, D. T.: Peripheral blood epinephrine levels in dogs during intravenous infusion. Amer. J. Physiol., *196*:145, 1959.
40. Ramey, E. R., and Goldstein, M. S.: The adrenal cortex and the sympathetic nervous system. Physiol. Revs., *37*:155, 1957.
41. Richardson, J. A., and Woods, E. F.: Release of norepinephrine from the isolated heart. Proc. Soc. Exp. Biol. & Med., *100*:149, 1959.
42. Vaughan, M.: Effect of hormones on phosphorylase activity in adipose tissue. J. Biol. Chem., *235*:3049, 1960.
43. Walker, B. E., and Rennels, E. G.: Adrenal cortical cell replacement in the mouse. Endocrinol., *68*:365, 1961.
44. Wassermann, G., and Tramezzani, J. H.: Separate distribution of adrenaline- and noradrenaline-secreting cells in the adrenal of snakes. Gen. & Comp. Endocrinol., *3*:480, 1963.
45. Weiner, N.: The catecholamines: biosynthesis, storage and release, metabolism, and metabolic effects. *In* (G. Pincus, K. V. Thimann, and E. B. Astwood (eds.), The Hormones. Vol. 4. New York, Academic Press, 1964, p. 403.
46. Welsh, J. H.: Neuroendocrine substances. *In* A. Gorbman (ed.): Comparative Endocrinology. New York, John Wiley & Sons, 1959, p. 121.
47. West, G. B.: The comparative pharmacology of the suprarenal medulla. Quart. Rev. Biol., *30*:116, 1955.
48. White, J. E., and Engel, F. L.: A lipolytic action of epinephrine and norepinephrine on rat adipose tissue *in vitro*. Proc. Soc. Exp. Biol. & Med., *99*:375, 1958.
49. Wright, A., and Chester Jones, I.: The adrenal gland in lizards and snakes. J. Endocrinol., *15*:83, 1957.
50. Wright, A., Chester Jones, I., and Phillips, J. G.: The histology of the adrenal gland of Prototheria. J. Endocrinol., *15*:100, 1957.
51. Wurtman, R. J., and Axelrod, J.: Adrenaline synthesis: Control by the pituitary gland and adrenal glucocorticoids. Science, *150*:1464, 1965.

11 _____

THE ADRENAL CORTEX: STEROIDOGENIC TISSUE

STRUCTURE AND NOMENCLATURE OF STEROID HORMONES

Steroid hormones are secreted by the adrenal cortex, testis, ovary, and placenta, and some knowledge of their structure and nomenclature is essential. The steroids comprise a group of biologically active organic compounds which includes such substances as cholesterol, ergosterol, and the bile acids, as well as the adrenal corticoids, androgens, estrogens, and progestogens. The steroids have in common a cyclopentano-perhydro-phenanthrene nucleus consisting of a fully hydrogenated phenanthrene (rings A, B, and C) to which is fused a five-carbon cyclopentane ring (D). The constituents in the nucleus and on the commonly occurring side chains are numbered as shown in Fig. 11–1b. Steroid chemists do not ordinarily write in all the carbon and hydrogen atoms as in Fig. 11–1a, but use a kind of shorthand for the steroid nucleus and indicate only the most important characteristics of the compound. It is understood that the full complement of valence bonds for each carbon atom is satisfied by carbon or hydrogen atoms, or both. The angular methyl groups are indicated by straight lines at the junctures of the respective rings, and the unsaturated carbons are shown by double bonds.

By reference to Fig. 11–1a, it may be seen that there are six asymmetric carbon atoms which are common to two different rings.

342

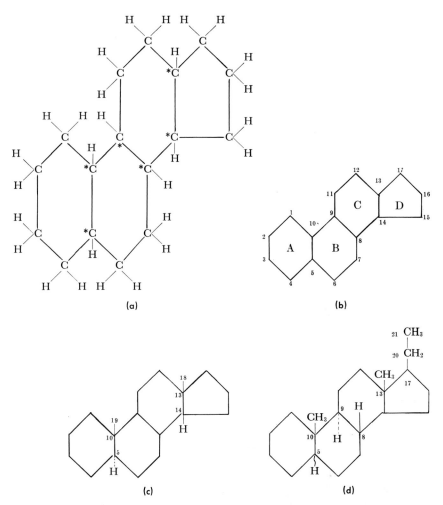

Figure 11-1. (*a*) Complete structural formula of the steroid nucleus; the six asymmetric carbon atoms are indicated by asterisks. (*b*) Numbering of the 17 carbon positions and designation of the four rings in gonane, a hypothetical parent compound. (*c*) Angular methyl groups (numbered 18 and 19) are attached to carbons 10 and 13; these groups are indicated by a solid line since they project toward the observer (*cis* or β position). The hydrogen at carbon 5 is attached by a broken line since it projects away from the observer (*α* or *trans*); the hydrogen at carbon 14 is *cis* or β. (*d*) In addition to the angular methyl groups (carbons 18 and 19), an ethyl group is attached at carbon 17, and its carbons are numbered 20 and 21. The H at position 5 is attached by a wavy line, indicating that it may be *cis* or *trans*.

The nucleus contains three types of carbon atoms: those which are linked with two adjacent carbons and carry two hydrogen atoms (carbons 1, 2, 3, etc.); four of the six asymmetric carbon atoms are linked to three carbon atoms and carry only one hydrogen atom (carbons 5, 8, 9, and 14); and finally carbons 10 and 13, to which the angular methyl groups are attached, are linked to four carbon atoms and carry no hydrogen atoms.

The naturally occurring steroid molecules may be visualized as essentially flat structures, with some substituents projecting below it (away from the observer) and others projecting above it (toward the observer). The angular methyl groups are important for reference and may be regarded as arising from the nucleus and projecting above it. The positions of the two methyl groups above the plane of the molecule are indicated by using solid lines to attach them to carbons 10 and 13. When substituent groups are connected to the nucleus by solid lines, this means that they lie on the same side of the molecule as the angular methyl groups. If a substituent is attached by a broken valence bond, it means that it projects downward below the plane of the nucleus and hence is on the opposite side with respect to the angular methyl groups. Groups that project in the same direction from the plane of the nucleus are said to be *cis* to each other; if they project in different directions they are *trans* to each other. Groups that are *cis* to the methyl reference points are designated as "*β*" and are indicated by solid valence lines; those that are *trans* to the same points are designated as "*α*" and are shown by broken valence lines. Wavy lines may be used when substituents may be either *cis* or *trans*.

Unfortunately, steroid nomenclature is quite confusing because a great variety of schemes have been followed by different workers. The common or trivial name for a compound has the advantage of being easy to remember, but it does not reveal anything about the nature of the substituents on the nucleus, their positions, or their spatial arrangements. The basic hydrocarbons upon which nomenclature is based are shown in Fig. 11-2. In addition to the stereoisomerism, often encountered at carbon atoms 3, 5, 11, and 17, nuclear modifications also occur and these have to be designated. The basic hydrocarbons are all saturated (no double bonds) and end with the suffix "*ane.*" They may become unsaturated by losing hydrogens, and this is indicated in the nucleus by double bonds, and in the nomenclature by changing the suffix "*an(e)*" to "*en(e).*" Two double bonds make the suffix "*dien(e),*" and three make it "*trien(e).*" In naming unsaturated compounds, the position of the double bond must be indicated; this is done by giving the number of the carbon atom where the double bond starts. Thus, "*-3*" indicates that the double bond extends between carbons 3 and 4. When double bonds exist between carbon atoms which are not numbered consecutively, as between carbons 9 and 11, both carbons are indicated. This double bond would be indicated as "*-9(11),*" the numbers being placed before part of the hydrocarbon name and followed by the suffix "*ene.*"

The basic hydrocarbon may be further modified by substituting oxygen for hydrogen. The suffix "*ol*" is used to indicate an alcohol or hydroxyl group, and this is preceded by the number of the carbon

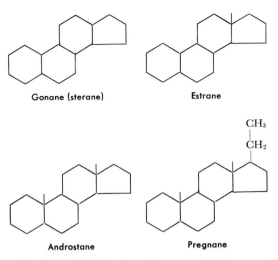

Figure 11-2. Four hypothetical hydrocarbons upon which nomenclature is based. Gonane lacks side chains and is a C_{17} steroid. Estrane has an angular methyl group at carbon 13, giving a total of 18 carbons; androstane has an additional methyl group at carbon 10, giving a total of 19 carbon atoms; and pregnane has both methyl groups plus an ethyl side chain at carbon 17, making a C_{21} steroid.

atom to which it is attached. This may also be shown by placing the term "*hydroxy*" before the name of the hydrocarbon. Ketone groups are indicated by the suffix "*one*," or by the prefix "*oxo*" preceding the hydrocarbon name. The prefix "*nor*" indicates shortening of a side chain or the contraction of a ring.

Four naturally occurring steroid hormones are shown in Figure 11–3, and both trivial and systematic names are given for each. The systematic name for estradiol-17β is estra-1,3,5(10)-triene-3,17β-diol; testosterone is 17β-hydroxyandrost-4-en-3-one; progesterone is pregn-4-ene-3,20-dione; and cortisol is 11β,17α,21-trihydroxypregn-4-ene-3,20-dione.

The steroid hormones are conveniently classified according to the number of carbon atoms present in the nucleus and side chains. The androgens, estrogens, progestogens, and corticoids are derived from the basic hydrocarbons shown in Fig. 11–2. The estrogens are derivatives of estrane and are C_{18}-steroids and generally have a high degree of unsaturation in the A ring; androgens derive from androstane and are C_{19}-compounds; progestogens and corticoids have the pregnane nucleus and are C_{21}-compounds.

Stereoisomerism

Steroid hormones may have the same molecular and structural formulas but different spatial or configurational formulas. Differences in molecular shape, produced by the attachment of substituents in *cis* or *trans* positions, may have very important effects upon biologic

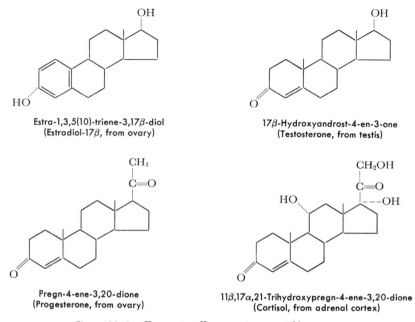

Estra-1,3,5(10)-triene-3,17β-diol
(Estradiol-17β, from ovary)

17β-Hydroxyandrost-4-en-3-one
(Testosterone, from testis)

Pregn-4-ene-3,20-dione
(Progesterone, from ovary)

11β,17α,21-Trihydroxypregn-4-ene-3,20-dione
(Cortisol, from adrenal cortex)

Figure 11-3.   Four naturally occurring steroid hormones.

activity. Isomerism at carbon atoms 3, 5, 11, and 17 is quite common
among the steroid hormones. Isomerism at carbon 3 is illustrated by
the first two compounds in Fig. 11–4: 5 α-androstan-3 α-ol has a
hydroxyl group at carbon 3 in the *trans* position, but in 5 α-androstan-3
β-ol the hydroxyl group is in the *cis* position. In both compounds, the
hydrogens at positions 5 are *trans* (α) with respect to the angular
methyl groups. Among the adrenocortical steroids, a hydroxyl group
is frequently found at carbon 11; it is generally *cis* to the angular
methyl groups and is therefore the β configuration. When a hydroxyl
group is present at position 17 it may take the α or β form, depending
on whether or not an ethyl side chain is present at the same position.
If there is an ethyl side chain at position 17, the hydroxyl group will
be of the α type; if it is absent, the hydroxyl group has the β configuration.

Study the compounds shown in Figs. 11–3 and 11–4. Notice how
the chemical names used for the compounds allude to the parent
hydrocarbon and designate the kind of change, the place of change,
and the stereoisomerism involved in the change.

HORMONES FROM THE STEROIDOGENIC TISSUE
OF THE ADRENAL GLAND

Nearly fifty steroids have been obtained from the cortical component of the mammalian adrenal gland. This mixture includes

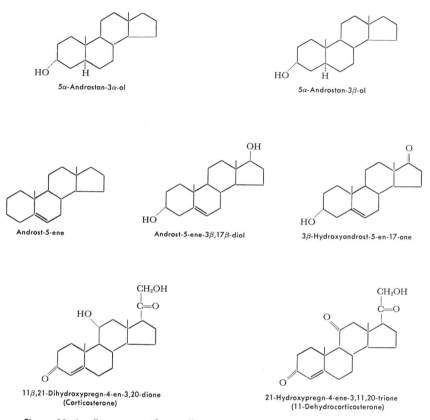

Figure 11–4. Some steroids to illustrate isomerism, substitutions and nomenclature.

corticoids, possessing glycogenic and electrolytic activities, androgens, progestogens, estrogens, and in addition, a large number of apparently inactive steroids that are precursors or metabolites of the active hormones. The adrenal cortex is a very versatile organ and it is possible that more hormones of physiologic importance will be discovered in adrenal extracts and venous blood as better procedures are developed to test them.[22, 50, 57]

The most important adrenal corticoids, excluding androgens, estrogens, and progestogens, are shown in Fig. 11–5. All of these are derivatives of pregnane and contain a total of 21 carbon atoms. Structures essential for activity are: (a) a double valence bond at C-4, (b) a ketonic group (C=O) at carbon 3, and (c) a ketonic group at carbon 20. The corticoids have profound effects on carbohydrate and mineral metabolism. Such compounds are sometimes called "glucocorticoids" and "mineralocorticoids," respectively. A hydroxyl group (OH) at carbon 21 enhances the capacity of the compound to en-

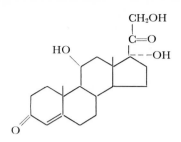

Cortisol (Compound F)

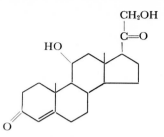

Corticosterone (Compound B)

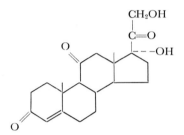

Cortisone (Compound E)

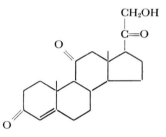

Dehydrocorticosterone (Compound A)

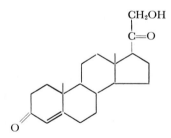

Deoxycorticosterone (DOC)

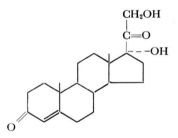

11-Deoxycortisol (Compound S)

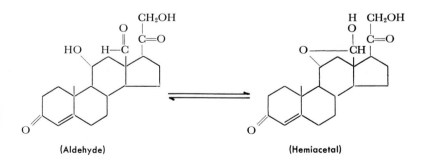

(Aldehyde)   (Hemiacetal)

Aldosterone

Figure 11–5. Some biologically active C_{21} adrenal cortical steroids.

courage sodium retention and must be present for an effect on carbohydrate metabolism. Action on carbohydrate metabolism is heightened by the presence of a hydroxyl group at carbon 17. Corticoids having oxygen at carbon 11, either as hydroxyl or ketonic groups, exert major activity in carbohydrate metabolism. An oxygen function at position 11 generally decreases the capacity of the steroid to cause sodium retention, but aldosterone is an exception.

On the basis of chemical structure and biologic activity the hormones of the adrenal cortex may be grouped into four categories:

1. The 11-oxygenated corticosteroids possess oxygen at carbon 11 and are especially potent in affecting carbohydrate and protein metabolism, but have relatively little effect on water and electrolyte metabolism. The most important natural steroids of this class are cortisol, corticosterone, 11-dehydrocorticosterone, and cortisone.

2. Corticoids that lack oxygen at position 11 have major effects on electrolyte and water metabolism without much action on the metabolism of carbohydrate and protein. 11-Deoxycorticosterone (DOC) and 11-deoxycortisol belong to this class. 11-Deoxycorticosterone was prepared in 1937 from the plant steroid stigmasterol, long before it was known to be present in *trace* amounts in adrenal tissue, and was the first adrenal steroid to be made available commercially.

3. Aldosterone, the most effective adrenocortical steroid in electrolyte metabolism, was finally isolated from the amorphous fraction of adrenal extracts. The distinguishing chemical feature of this steroid is the presence of an aldehyde group at carbon 18 instead of a methyl group. When in solution, the hormone exists in hemiacetal and aldehyde forms.

4. Both androgens and estrogens, as well as progesterone, are elaborated by the adrenal cortex. Since these sex hormones may arise from the adrenal, there is considerable overlapping between adrenocortical and gonadal functions.

Phyletic Distribution

There is much evidence to support the view that a pituitary-adrenal axis operates in all vertebrates, and that the steroidogenic tissue of the adrenal secretes similar hormones from fishes to mammals. Either corticosterone or cortisol, or both, have been identified as major adrenal hormones in cyclostomes, elasmobranchs, teleosts, lungfish, amphibians, reptiles, and birds. The glucocorticoids must be very ancient molecules since they are secreted by adrenal tissue of cyclostomes, the most primitive living vertebrates. Both cortisol and corticosterone have been found in the peripheral blood of two hagfishes (*Myxine* and *Polistotrema*) and in a fresh-water lamprey

(*Petromyzon*). If aldosterone is present in the Cyclostomata, it is in very minute concentrations and has not been identified. Aldosterone is secreted by all mammalian adrenals that have been examined and is known to occur in low concentrations in many nonmammalian vertebrates. It has been detected in the adrenal venous blood of birds and in the peripheral blood of the salmon. By use of *in vitro* incubation methods, aldosterone has been identified in three species of elasmobranchs and in several species of teleosts, amphibians, snakes, lizards, and birds. Cortisol is a consistent product of the teleost adrenal, but reptiles and birds appear to secrete a preponderance of corticosterone. The adrenals of the toad (*Bufo marinus*) and bullfrog (*R. catesbeiana*) are known to secrete corticosterone and aldosterone; the salamander (*Amphiuma*) is known to produce both cortisol and corticosterone; and only cortisol has been identified in the African frog (*Xenopus*). Cortisol is the predominant glucocorticoid in man, monkey, dog, and hamster, whereas rats, mice, and rabbits secrete mainly corticosterone.[7, 11, 15-17, 49, 58]

Artificial Corticoids

A variety of new compounds has been produced in the laboratory by modifying the molecular structure of cortisone, cortisol, and deoxycorticosterone (Fig. 11–6). Some of these unnatural substances possess biologic properties and potencies that are quite different from the parent steroids. 9α-Fluoro-, chloro-, bromo- and iodo-cortisol acetate have been prepared. Halogenation at the 9α position not only enhances mineralocorticoid activity but the glucocorticoid activity is about 10 times greater than that of cortisone acetate. When cortisol is dehydrogenated at positions C-1 and C-2, the glucocorticoid function is exaggerated, but the sodium-retaining activity appears to be diminished. Perhaps the most potent corticoid that has been prepared is 2α-methyl-9α-fluorocortisol acetate. This compound is 60 to 90 times more potent than DOCA in sodium-retaining activity and is about 40 times more active than cortisone acetate in the liver glycogen deposition test in rats.[54]

Microbial Transformations

Certain bacteria, yeasts, molds, and protozoans are known to possess enzyme systems that can effect certain oxidative and reductive changes in the steroid molecule. These enzymic changes are of great interest, since they may be models of those that operate in tissues at the vertebrate level. In the synthetic manufacture of cortisone and other adrenal steroids, one of the most difficult operations is the introduction of an oxygen atom at position 11. Certain plants

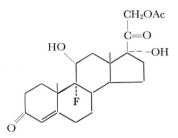

9α-Fluorocortisol acetate

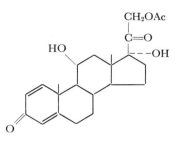

Prednisolone acetate

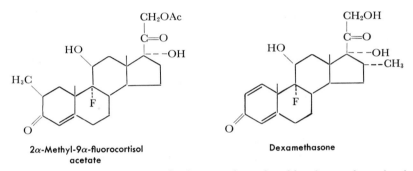

2α-Methyl-9α-fluorocortisol acetate

Dexamethasone

Figure 11–6. Four potent artificial corticoids produced by altering the molecular structure of cortisol.

provide raw material for the manufacture of progesterone, a compound having some of the required structure of cortisone and cortisol but no 11-oxo-group. When progesterone is used as substrate, certain molds (*e.g., Rhizopus, Aspergillus, Streptomyces*) introduce the 11-hydroxyl group. Much progress has been made in the isolation and culture of pure strains of microorganisms that are capable of effecting specific hydroxylations in steroid molecules.[19]

Assay Methods

The bioassay procedures are based on the capacity of the adrenocortical hormones to restore various functions in the adrenalectomized animal. The 11-oxysteroids may be bioassayed on the basis of their ability to promote the deposition of glycogen in the liver, to prolong life during exposure to cold, or improve tolerance to traumatic injury. The abilities of corticoids to reduce the number of circulating eosinophils and to kill the lymphocytes in lymph nodes *in vitro* have also been used as bioassay parameters. Other tests, measuring principally mineralocorticoid activity, are the maintenance of life in adrenalectomized subjects, improvement in muscular work performance, and effects on the Na:K ratio of the urine.

The bioassays played an important part in the isolation of the active hormones and still find application in the testing of new analogues. However, for routine purposes, they have been largely supplanted by less-laborious and cheaper chemical (colorimetric) methods. Partition chromatography makes it possible to identify minute quantities of closely related steroids in adrenal extracts and to detect such hormones as aldosterone which appear in the body fluids in very low concentrations. Chromatographic techniques, in conjunction with radioactive steroids, have been used extensively in studies on the metabolism of adrenocorticoids.

The Release of Adrenal Steroids

Almost any kind of stress to which the animal is subjected can cause an outpouring of adrenal cortical hormones. In man and other mammals there are strong indications of a daily rhythm in the release of 11-oxygenated hormones from the adrenal. In male and female mice, the level of eosinophils in the blood is higher at noon than at night, whereas mitotic divisions are more frequent in the adrenal cortices at night than at noon. Since these adrenal hormones act to depress the eosinophils, it is probable that the mouse adrenal discharges mostly at night. The levels of 11-oxygenated steroids in the blood of nocturnal mice, as compared with the predominantly diurnal human subject, differ in environmental phase relations. It may be that there are species differences in the manner in which the daily rhythms of hormone release are synchronized.[6, 30]

The adrenals of wild and domesticated Norway rats are strikingly different. The cortices of wild rats are not only larger but contain more lipid, aldehyde, ketonic carbonyl groups, and a richer blood supply. When the wild animals are tamed, the adrenals gradually diminish in size. The cortex of the wild rat apparently continues in a state of heightened secretory activity. There are sex differences in the size of the adrenal cortices. For example, the female rat has a larger adrenal than the male, but in the hamster this sexual dimorphism is reversed. The adrenal glands of birds seem to be less reactive to various stimuli than those of laboratory mammals.[15, 23, 48, 70]

Increased population densities, acting to increase the number of aggressive confrontations between individuals, frequently correlate with an augmented production of adrenocortical hormones. The degree of response to changes in population size depends upon the behavioral aggressiveness of the strain or species. The house mouse (*Mus musculus*) is very aggressive, whereas the deer mouse (*Peromyscus maniculatus*) is much less so. Population increases have much more effect on the adrenals of the former species than on the latter. The adrenal cortices of the two species respond equally well when subjected to trained fighters of their own species, or when exposed to cold. Brief encounters of adult male mice with trained fighters increase the size of the adrenals and elevate the amount of corticosterone in the plasma. This response occurs in the absence of physical injury, indicating that the stimulus is sociopsychologic or "emotional." It has been observed that in growing populations of mice the most submissive members, no longer offering any resistance, may be completely ignored by dominant individuals, and their adrenals diminish in size and release only small amounts of corticosterone.[5, 10]

Biosynthesis and Metabolism of Adrenal Steroids

The main sequence of biosynthetic steps from acetate through cholesterol and pregnenolone to the adrenocortical and gonadal hormones can be traced. Although much remains to be determined with reference to alternative pathways and the specific enzymes that effect the transformations, this work represents one of the most significant contributions to endocrinology. The important concept has emerged that all of the organs that synthesize steroid hormones, *viz.*, adrenal cortices, testes, ovaries, and placenta, possess the same enzyme systems. Although the enzymes that catalyze particular transformations at particular times may predominate in specific steroid-hormone-producing tissues, the others are not necessarily completely absent. These accomplishments have been made possible largely through the use of radioactive isotopes, combined with paper chromatography and improved perfusion and *in vitro* techniques.[18, 32, 33]

Adrenal Corticoids

The biosynthesis of these compounds is illustrated in Fig. 11–7, and the pathways are common to all species that have been studied. Acetate and cholesterol are known to be the important precursors, although the possibility exists that cholesterol is not an obligatory intermediate. Pregnenolone is the first C-21 compound to be produced from cholesterol, and it is oxidized to progesterone. Three enzyme systems, the 11β, 17α, and 21-hydroxylases, catalyze the reactions leading to cortisol and corticosterone. Aldosterone may arise from cholesterol, progesterone, deoxycorticosterone, or corticosterone, hydroxylation being accomplished at carbon atom 18. The conversion of androgens to estrogens involves hydroxylation at carbon 19. A separate hydroxylating system appears to be present for each position, and molecular oxygen and reduced nicotinamide adenine dinucleotide phosphate (NADPH) are used in the hydroxylations.[34, 61]

There are many indications that the pituitary-adrenal axis begins

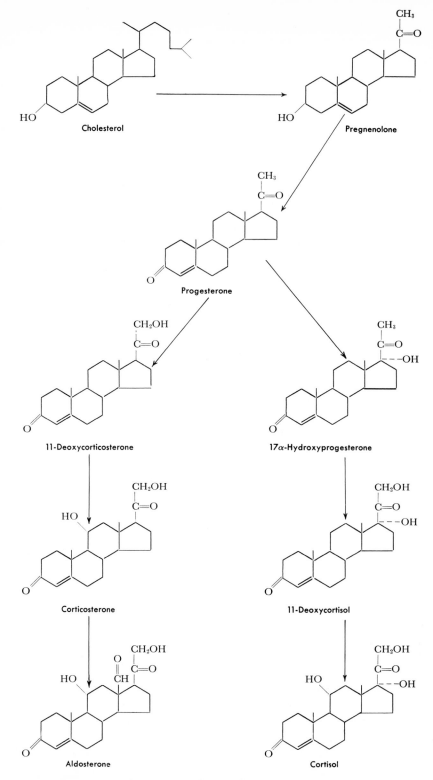

Figure 11–7. Some main pathways of corticosteroid biosynthesis.

to function before birth. Human fetal adrenals appear to possess the necessary enzyme equipment for the synthesis of cortical steroids. When homogenates of such adrenals are incubated *in vitro* with a NADPH generating system, with progesterone or α-hydroxyprogesterone used as substrate, cortisol is formed.[45, 64, 67]

Adrenal Androgens

The adrenal androgens arise from the C-21 corticoids and also directly from cholesterol (Fig. 11–8). Incubation and perfusion

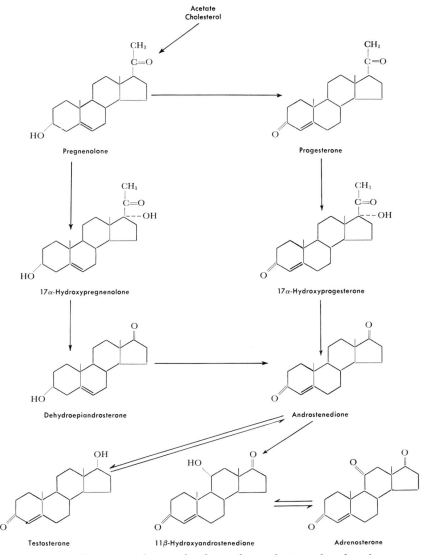

Figure 11–8. Common pathways of androgen biosynthesis in the adrenal cortex.

experiments leave no doubt that C-21 steroids can be converted to androgens by adrenal tissue. When labeled progesterone is perfused through an adrenal, labeled androstenedione and 11β-hydroxy-androstenedione may be isolated from the perfusate. Trace amounts of these two androgens have been detected in human adrenal venous blood. There are reasons for believing that a significant percentage of the total adrenal androgen may be formed directly from choles-terol via pregnenolone. For instance, the adrenal cortices of the human fetus contain androgens before significant amounts of corti-coids can be detected. In patients with masculinizing tumors of the adrenal cortices, the output of dehydroepiandrosterone and other androgens is increased tremendously, but the secretion of C-21 steroids may not increase proportionately. On the other hand, in patients with Cushing's syndrome there is an excessive production of cortisol with no increase in androgens other than those that may arise through the catabolism of C-21 corticoids. In conditions of stress, there is a profound increase in corticoids, but the 17-keto-steroids tend to diminish. These facts suggest that androgens in the adrenal may arise indirectly from corticoids or be synthesized directly from cholesterol.

Catabolism of Adrenal Steroids

The steroid hormones are rapidly catabolized in the organism and excreted in the urine as conjugates of glucuronic acid, or in the case of androgens, of sulfuric acid. Few of the steroids are excreted without change. The liver is the main site of steroid hormone catabo-lism, although the kidneys and perhaps other tissues may function in this capacity to some extent. Biologic inactivity of the compound correlates with the loss of the α,β-unsaturated ketone grouping at position 3 and, in some cases, with loss of the α-ketol side chain at carbon 17. Much information is available concerning the catabolic transformations, so that it is possible to predict what hormones the adrenal cortex is secreting from the metabolites that can be isolated from the urine. The secretory behavior of the cortex may be evaluated by measuring the urinary metabolites in the resting subject or after the administration of ACTH.[53]

The 17-ketosteroids of the urine may be determined colorimet-rically by the Zimmermann reaction, and this gives an indication of the metabolites that are derived from the adrenocortical and testicular hormones. The total of neutral 17-ketosteroids is about 33 per cent less in normal women than in men. The daily output for women is 5 to 15 mg. and that for young men ranges from 10 to 22 mg. The difference is presumably due to the testicular steroids. Complete failure of the adrenal cortices may cause the output to fall to zero in the female and below 5 mg. in the male. Although most of the neutral

17-ketosteroids are derived from adrenal cortical hormones, it must be emphasized that quantitation of these substances as a group is no infallible measure of either testicular or adrenal function. Not all of the ketones that are determined by the Zimmerman reaction are necessarily 17-ketosteroids. For example, 17-ketosteroids appear to rise during pregnancy when large amounts of pregnenolone are being produced; this compound is a C-20 ketone and the Zimmerman reaction does not differentiate it from a 17-ketosteroid.[36]

Enzymatic Defects and Adrenal Androgens

During embryonic life, the adrenal cortices originate in close association with the gonadal primordia. Clinicians have known for a long time that tumorous conditions of the adrenals and gonads may lead to the release of hormones that simulate the action of the other gland. For example, certain hyperplasias and malignant tumors of the adrenal cortices may release large quantities of androgen or estrogen, thus resembling the normal action of the testes and ovaries. Although the older pathologists suggested that "embryonic rests" of the other tissue might be carried over from embryonic life and account for these conditions, the theory never received confirmation. In the light of present knowledge, it is more probable that such defects result from alterations in the functioning of enzyme systems that are normally present in all steroid-hormone-producing organs.

The adrenogenital syndrome is a human disease characterized by bilateral hypertrophy of the adrenal cortices or a cortical neoplasm. Tremendous amounts of androgen are secreted, but the production of cortisol remains within normal limits or is slightly decreased. The masculinizing influences depend on the age of onset and the sex of the patient. The adrenal has a limited ability to produce cortisol in response to ACTH injections but a marked ability to produce androgens. Thus, ACTH treatment increases the already high levels of urinary 17-ketosteroids. The production of adrenal androgen may be diminished by the administration of cortisol, this naturally occurring corticoid being a powerful inhibitor of ACTH release by the pituitary. Two different enzymatic deficiencies in the biosynthetic sequence of adrenal cortical steroids have been suggested, either of which may lead to this syndrome. The fundamental adrenal defect in the adrenogenital syndrome seems to be a relative deficiency of either the 21-hydroxylase system or the 11β-hydroxylase system. With these enzymic defects there is a piling up of "unfinished corticoids" such as 17-hydroxyprogesterone and 11-deoxycortisol. Since the adrenal does not add enough cortisol to the circulation to inhibit the pituitary release of ACTH, the adrenal responds to the continuing high titers of ACTH by producing androgens. Several other adrenal diseases have been explained as abnormalities of specific enzyme systems.[4]

REGULATION OF ADRENOCORTICAL SECRETION[73]

Glucocorticoids

Adrenalectomy results in an increased release of ACTH by the pituitary, and, in the hypophysectomized animal, the adrenal output of glucocorticoids is reduced to a very low level. The administration of ACTH to intact or hypophysectomized subjects is followed by adrenocortical hypertrophy and a consequent increase in the production of glucocorticoids such as cortisol and corticosterone. The levels of ascorbic acid in the cortex are depleted under conditions of heightened secretory activity. The cholesterol content of the cortex falls after ACTH treatment, whereas the concentration of glucocorticoids in adrenal venous blood and of their metabolites in the urine are strikingly increased. The prolonged administration of glucocorticoids to normal animals causes the adrenal cortices to regress until they are equivalent to the cortices of hypophysectomized animals (Fig. 11–9). The pituitary releases increasing amounts of ACTH when the blood levels of glucocorticoids are low, and diminishes the output as the plasma glucocorticoids are elevated. Certain enzymatic reactions in the cortex may be blocked by such nonsteroidal agents as amphenone and metopyrone (SU 4885), thus preventing the biosynthesis of cortisol and corticosterone, and, in the absence of these steroid inhibitors, the pituitary releases large amounts of ACTH. Insecticides of the DDT type produce a selective necrosis

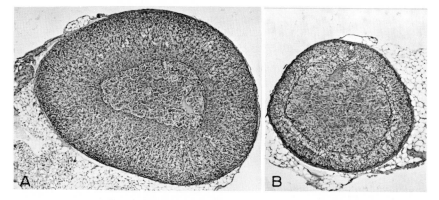

Figure 11–9.   Effect of prolonged administration of cortisone on the adrenal cortex of the adult mouse. *A*, Adrenal gland of the normal mouse, showing medullary and cortical components. *B*, Adrenal gland of an adult mouse following the administration of 1 mg. of cortisone daily for 30 days. Note that the cortex has diminished in width until it is structurally equivalent to that of a hypophysectomized animal; the medulla remains normal. The circulating steroid acts by way of the hypothalamus and anterior pituitary to inhibit the production of ACTH, a trophic hormone required for normal functioning of the cortex. Both glands are at the same magnification.

of the dog's adrenal cortex; this reduces the synthesis of steroids and augments the release of ACTH.

In vitro studies have shown that adrenal grafts of the rat, consisting only of regenerated cortex, are capable of secreting corticosterone, deoxycorticosterone and aldosterone. Under *in vivo* conditions of deliberately imposed stress, the grafts respond to ACTH stimulation, but circulatory failure seems to prevent the grafts from releasing their hormones in normal quantities.[42, 46]

Nonfunctional enlargement of the adrenal cortex follows the administration of estrogens, particularly the synthetic ones such as stilbestrol and hexestrol. This response is dependent on the integrity of the pituitary. It is probable that the estrogens act in some manner to block the synthesis of corticoids, and as these diminish in the blood, the pituitary releases increased amounts of ACTH to stimulate the cortex.[68]

There is general agreement that a negative feedback mechanism operates to control the levels of glucocorticoids in the blood. The concentration of these hormones in the blood depends on how rapidly the adrenal releases them, and on how rapidly they are inactivated and eliminated from the system. Only negligible amounts of active adrenal steroids are lost through the urine and bile, and the liver is the main organ that possesses the enzymatic equipment for their inactivation.

A sexual dimorphism in adrenal size is known to occur in the rat, the females having larger adrenals than the males. A parallel relationship between the capacity of the liver to inactivate adrenal steroids *in vitro* and the size of the adrenals has been found. An enzyme system has been identified in liver homogenates of rats, and the concentration of the enzyme is three to ten times higher in females than in males. Even the rapid enlargement of the rat's adrenal during estrus is associated with an increase in this liver enzyme. The hepatic and adrenal sex differences in rats may be abolished by castration at an early age. These differences can be re-established or reversed in young castrates by giving androgens or estrogens. Since the liver of the female rat inactivates corticoids at a high rate, the adenohypophysis must release large amounts of ACTH to stimulate the adrenal cortex to maintain adequate blood levels of corticoids. These results show that the rate of hepatic inactivation of the circulating steroids is an important determinant of ACTH release and adrenocortical secretion rate, and lend support to the feedback hypothesis.[2, 27, 41, 66, 72]

Although ACTH is the main hormone that stimulates adrenocortical secretion, other hormones probably act in conjunction with it. It has been reported that synthetic vasopressin, applied by direct arterial infusion, stimulates the adrenal glands of the dog to secrete cortisol. This seems to be a direct effect of the vasopressin, and not one mediated by the adenohypophysis or any other organ.[35]

Aldosterone

This steroid from the adrenal cortex functions primarily in the regulation of electrolyte and water metabolism. The factors which control its synthesis and discharge are highly involved and remain largely unsettled. Although ACTH may have some capacity to promote the release of aldosterone from the cortex, it is relatively independent of anterior pituitary control. Even before aldosterone was discovered, it was known that hypophysectomized animals survived quite well without serious impairment of their electrolyte metabolism, whereas adrenalectomized animals died unless additional salt was provided. Histologic studies of adrenals from hypophysectomized animals revealed that most of the adrenocortical involution occurs in the fasciculata-reticularis areas, the glomerulosa appearing unaffected by the absence of ACTH. The postulate that the zona glomerulosa is the source of a salt-regulating hormone, the production of which does not depend entirely upon ACTH, has been amply confirmed. ACTH seems to be one factor among many which can stimulate the adrenal to produce and discharge aldosterone.[3, 8, 14]

In the beef adrenal it is possible to separate the outer capsule and glomerulosa from the underlying fasciculata with considerable accuracy, thus making it possible to test the separate zones for their capacity to produce steroids. When ACTH is incubated with glomerulosa strippings, it does not promote the conversion of cholesterol to aldosterone; if fasciculata-reticularis slices are used, ACTH causes the conversion of cholesterol to cortisol. This indicates that ACTH has no effect, or a very insignificant effect, on aldosterone biogenesis.

When progesterone, deoxycorticosterone, and corticosterone are used as substrate for beef adrenal slices, they are metabolized in radically different ways depending on whether the adrenal tissue consists of glomerulosa or fasciculata-reticularis. When these steroids are added to glomerulosa, they are converted to aldosterone. Progesterone enhances the production of cortisol only when it is added to fasciculata-reticularis tissue. From these studies it has been concluded that cortisol is produced almost entirely from the fasciculata-reticularis, aldosterone from the glomerulosa, and corticosterone from both the glomerulosa and the two inner zones of the cortex. It is becoming apparent that specific pathways of corticosteroid biosynthesis occur within different zones of the adrenal cortex, which implies that there is a corresponding zonation of the enzyme systems involved. This would explain how it is possible for cortical cells from different zones to synthesize different kinds of hormones from an identical precursor. Thus, it appears that the glomerulosa is the site of 18-oxygenation, but the fasciculata-reticularis is not; 17-hydroxylase activity occurs in the fasciculata-reticularis, but not in the glomerulosa; and 3 β-dehydrogenase and 11- and 21-hydroxylase activities occur in both areas of the gland.[25, 26, 63, 65]

Farrell and his associates have isolated a substance ("glomerulotrophin") from the pineal gland which selectively stimulates the zona glomerulosa to secrete aldosterone. Glomerulotrophin is chemically related to melatonin and is said to exert no effect on cortisol production. A second factor, also of pineal origin, is claimed to be present in such extracts and to exert an anti-ACTH effect, thus inhibiting both aldosterone and cortisol secretion. Other workers have reported that pinealectomy of the rat causes adrenal hypertrophy and that pineal extracts induce adrenal atrophy.[20, 21, 71]

Angiotensin, a potent vasopressor substance produced in the blood under the influence of the kidneys, may be another factor which operates to release aldosterone. Synthetic angiotensin, administered to normal human subjects, releases aldosterone, cortisol, and corticosterone. It has the same effect in dogs deprived of their kidneys and pituitary glands. Minute amounts of angiotensin stimulate aldosterone release from adrenocortical tissue *in vitro*.[24, 47, 52]

Sodium-loading diminishes the release of aldosterone, whereas sodium deprivation increases it. Changes in blood volume also influence the output of this hormone, reduced volumes increasing and increased volumes decreasing its production. In dogs, stretching of the right atrium, but not the left atrium, causes a marked fall in aldosterone production. Pregnancy and various kinds of stress increase the urinary excretion of aldosterone, and this suggests that central nervous mechanisms are involved in the regulation of its production. The problem is a very difficult one since so many factors seem to be involved, and final conclusions are not warranted at this time.

Mechanism of ACTH Action

Since ACTH peptides have been synthesized, and the main biosynthetic pathways in the adrenal cortices have been determined, many attempts are being made to elucidate the structure-function relationships through the use of *in vitro* systems. Although the Haynes-Berthet theory of ACTH action probably is not the final story, it has aroused interest and stimulated research in this area.[31] They suggested that ACTH might stimulate steroidogenesis (a) by regulating enzyme activity at "key" points, (b) by making cofactors available, or (c) by conditioning the availability of substrates. Stated briefly, the current theory is that ACTH acts on adenyl cyclase to make cyclic 3',5'-AMP available for the activation of phosphorylase. The activated enzyme would facilitate glycogenolysis and, with the aid of other enzymes, make glucose-6-phosphate available. Since the latter compound is metabolized largely by dehydrogenation, increased amounts of reduced nicotinamide adenine dinucleotide phosphate (NADPH) would be formed. The NADPH would serve as a source of energy for steroidogenesis and enable the adrenal hormones to be synthesized at an increased rate.

PHYSIOLOGY OF THE STEROIDOGENIC ADRENAL

The Effects of Bilateral Adrenalectomy

Bilateral removal of the adrenals produces a series of metabolic disturbances which are identical with those appearing in patients with Addison's disease. If the adrenals have been completely removed and there are no accessory cortical deposits, the animals invariably die within a week or two. The fact that adrenalectomized animals may be maintained indefinitely in normal physiologic condition by the administration of cortical steroids, in the absence of exogenous epinephrine, is direct proof that the cortical portion of the gland is essential for life. The symptoms appearing in untreated animals include extreme muscular weakness, a variable degree of hypoglycemia, gastrointestinal disturbances, hemoconcentration, reduced blood pressure and body temperature, and failure of the kidneys. Growth ceases in young animals, and older ones generally lose weight. Adrenalectomized subjects are unable to tolerate stresses of any type; exposure to trauma, cold, heat, toxins, infections, fasting, forced exercise, etc., is likely to prove fatal. In some mammalian species the survival period after total adrenalectomy is prolonged by pregnancy and pseudopregnancy. Comparable results are obtained by the administration of progesterone, a hormone of the corpus luteum.

After adrenalectomy, the thymus and lymph nodes tend to become enlarged and the blood lymphocytes are elevated. Regression of these tissues in response to stress does not occur normally. Blood sugar levels tend to be low and the liver is deficient in glycogen. The amount of nitrogen lost from the body during fasting is below normal, suggesting that in cortical deficiency there is a reduced capacity to draw on body protein in order to maintain the blood glucose and liver glycogen.

In the absence of adrenal cortices, there is an excessive loss of sodium, chloride, and bicarbonate through the kidneys, but there is a diminished clearance of potassium. The excretion of sodium is accompanied by a diuresis which leads to hemoconcentration; the loss of bicarbonate decreases the pH of blood, a condition of acidosis. It is well known that life may be prolonged in adrenalectomized subjects or in those with Addison's disease by simply administering large amounts of salt solution. Restricting the consumption of salt precipitates the crisis of adrenal insufficiency. It should be understood, however, that salt therapy merely corrects some of the symptoms, without repairing the basic defects.

Electrolytes and Fluid Shifts

The main action of mineralocorticoids is to regulate the body electrolytes and water. Though traces of deoxycorticosterone are found in cortical tissue and in adrenal vein blood, it is probably a precursor of aldosterone, the most important mineralocorticoid. The principal action of aldosterone in mammals is to reduce the amount of sodium lost from the body through the urine. This is accomplished by the enhanced reabsorption of sodium from the glomerular filtrate through the walls of the renal tubules. The reabsorption is an active process since the ions are moved against an electrochemical potential gradient. Although glucocorticoids as cortisol and corticosterone are potent factors in the regulation of carbohydrate metabolism, they are also capable of enhancing or inhibiting the excretion of water and sodium. The neurohypophysial peptides also exert important influences upon the kidney tubules, and thus influence the osmolarity of the body fluids.

Though other hormones such as thyroxine, insulin, estrogens, parathyroid hormone, and somatotrophin are known to affect particular ions or alter the water content of specific tissues, the adrenocortical steroids and neurohypophysial peptides (vasopressin, vasotocin) are most profoundly concerned with salt and water balance of the body. It has been pointed out earlier that these hormones are widely distributed among the vertebrates. Aldosterone, cortisol, and corticosterone are present in all of the major groups from fishes to man. The neurohypophysial octapeptides emanating from the posterior pituitary have undergone only minor changes in structure during vertebrate evolution. Both the pituitary peptides and the adrenal steroids act upon targets which are essentially epithelial surfaces capable of allowing the transcellular movement of water and osmotic solutes. Such targets include the kidney tubules, gills, skin, gastrointestinal mucosa, urinary bladder, and various types of exocrine glands.

Animals may be divided into two categories with reference to their methods of meeting osmotic stress: (a) the *osmoconformers* are osmotically labile and change their body fluids in accordance with the medium in which they live, and (b) the *osmoregulators* are independent of their environments and maintain their body fluids at remarkably constant osmotic concentrations regardless of the medium in which they live. All gradations are found between these two extremes, but the great majority of vertebrates are osmoregulators.

The body fluids of vertebrates are about one-fourth to one-third the salinity of sea water. Although not all osmoregulations are under direct hormonal control, the endocrine system clearly performs an important role in adjusting body fluids in response to environmental changes.[38]

Mammals

These highest vertebrates have radiated into a variety of ecologic niches; they are found in fresh water, in sea water, and in moist or dry air, and are able to tolerate a wide range of temperatures. By being able to regulate the salt and water concentrations of their body fluids, they have become relatively independent of their environments. Perfection of the kidney tubules, coupled with hormonal and neural controls, permits the mammals to discharge urine which is hyperosmotic to the blood.

Reptiles and Birds

Nasal (supraorbital) glands are present in all birds and are especially well developed in marine species.[40, 59] Their only known function is to serve as osmoregulatory organs. Certain marine species (*e.g.*, albatross) consume only salt water, and this can be tolerated since the nasal glands secrete a fluid containing high concentrations of salt, principally sodium chloride. Marine birds are known to have larger adrenals than those which are strictly terrestrial. Sea birds are difficult to maintain under laboratory conditions, and the domestic duck has been used as an experimental animal for studies on the nasal glands. The glands of this species are of intermediate size, but they enlarge and secrete hypertonic salt solutions after salt-loading. Forcing the ducks to drink salt water, instead of fresh water, induces hypertrophy of the steroidogenic part of the adrenal gland and causes a concentrated salt solution to drip from the external nares. The urine decreases in volume after salt-loading and contains less sodium and more potassium than when fresh water is consumed. Bilateral adrenalectomy prevents the extrarenal response to salt loads, and the administration of corticosterone or cortisol restores normal excretory patterns in both kidneys and nasal glands.[55] Although it is possible that the nasal glands are partly regulated by parasympathetic innervation, as has been suggested, these experiments on the duct indicate that adrenal steroids and possibly neurohypophysial octapeptides are also involved. Although the exact mechanisms controlling the activation of the nasal glands are unknown, it is probable that the first step is triggered by the increased osmolarity of the blood; this could affect the secretion of the pituitary gland as well as the steroidogenic adrenal. Since corticosteroids influence the secretion of the nasal glands of the duck, the adrenals probably function naturally in regulating these glands in marine birds.[37, 38]

Marine reptiles, as well as certain terrestrial species, also possess nasal salt glands and can secrete significant quantities of salt extrarenally. No careful studies have been made on reptiles with respect to the possible involvement of hormones in regulation of the nasal glands. Studies on the tropical lizard (*Iguana iguana*) have shown that secretion of the nasal salt gland is stimulated by the intraperitoneal injection of sodium chloride.[60] Many turtles have a large, bilobed bladder, and large quantities of water are reabsorbed from it. Aldosterone increases the active transport of sodium across the bladder of the tortoise, but spirolactone has the reverse effect.[1]

The amount of finished urine eliminated from the cloaca in birds and reptiles is small and may be in the form of a viscous paste of uric acid crystals. There is considerable evidence that large amounts of water, together with sodium and potassium, are reabsorbed from the cloacae of birds and reptiles. It has been suggested that the appearance of an extrarenal mechanism for the excretion of salt (nasal glands) in these classes is related to their ability to reabsorb water from the cloaca.[60] Relatively little is known about the mechanisms that may be involved in regulating the permeability of cloacal and bladder membranes in reptiles and birds.

Amphibians

Permanently aquatic amphibians are surrounded by a hypotonic medium and actively absorb salts through the kidneys, urinary bladder, gills, skin, and intestinal mucosa in order to maintain the ionic concentration of their body fluids. When not in water, amphibians conserve water by decreasing its evaporative loss through the skin. The neurohypophysial hormones exert antidiuretic effects by reducing the glomerular filtration rate, increasing the reabsorption of fluid from the kidney tubules and urinary bladder, and by enhancing the uptake of water and salt through the skin.

Excessive hydration may be a threat to amphibians living in hypotonic (freshwater) environments, and it appears that the adrenal steroids may be involved in these adjustments. Adrenalectomy of *Rana temporaria* results in an accumulation of water in the tissues and a loss of sodium.[9] The administration of ACTH or adrenocorticoids to amphibians promotes the uptake of sodium from their freshwater environments. Aldosterone is the only adrenal steroid capable of stimulating active sodium transport by the isolated toad bladder *in vitro*.[12, 13] Cortisol and corticosterone have no effect on such bladder preparations when they are used alone, but they do block the effects of aldosterone. Pretreatment of amphibians with

ACTH or adrenal steroids increases sodium influx through the isolated skin. These various studies suggest that the neurohypophysial principles are of especial importance when amphibians are threatened by dehydration, and that the adrenal steroids bring about adjustments which are essential for life in hypotonic environments where hydration is a threatening factor.

Fishes

The stenohaline fishes are unable to tolerate salinities differing from their normal environments (freshwater or marine), whereas the euryhaline species can adjust to a variety of salinities. Many teleosts live continuously in fresh water or sea water, whereas others (salmon) return to fresh water to spawn, or, like the eels, breed in the sea and become adults in fresh water. Freshwater fish do not drink water, but water enters osmotically through the gills and perhaps through the skin; since the renal tubules reabsorb salts from the glomerular filtrate, large volumes of dilute urine are excreted. Certain ions are actively taken in through the gills to assist in maintaining the proper osmotic and ionic equilibrium. Marine teleosts drink sea water and excrete large amounts of sodium and chloride through the gills; the urine flow is much reduced.

Osmoregulatory mechanisms are poorly understood among the stenohaline fishes. Most workers have found that hypophysectomy has no effect upon their metabolism of water and electrolytes. The killifish (*Fundulus*) is a euryhaline species and adjusts well to either fresh or sea water. Hypophysectomized *Fundulus* do not live long in fresh water, and the blood chloride falls rapidly; prolactin partially restores their ability to adjust to fresh water. It is known that depletion of neurosecretory material from the preoptic nucleus and neurohypophysis occurs when certain species are exposed to increased salinities. Bioassay procedures have demonstrated that the neurohypophysis is deficient in antidiuretic potency under these conditions. This would seem to indicate that the neurohypophysial hormones are involved in osmoregulation; however, most workers have been unable to demonstrate that these principles have an antidiuretic effect in fish.

Studies on euryhaline fishes strongly suggest that the adrenal steroids, together with other factors, are involved in the physiologic adjustments which promote the excretion of sodium. Aldosterone reduces the rate of sodium influx by the gills of the eel (*Anguilla anguilla*) in fresh water. The administration of corticosterone, cortisol, or aldosterone to the freshwater trout (*Salmo gairdneri*) reduces the concentration of sodium in the plasma. This over-all effect results from a diminished loss of sodium through the kidneys and accelerated efflux of this ion through the gills. When untreated trout are transferred to sea water, there is a temporary increase in blood sodium followed by a progressive decline to a level slightly above that of fish in fresh water. The decline is due to the accelerated loss of sodium through the gills. During smoltification (preparation for life in the sea) in salmonid fishes there is heightened activity of the steroidogenic adrenal, and the animals adjust rapidly to increased salinities. Thyroidal and gonadal hormones also play an important role in initiating smoltification and migration to salt water.[38]

The elasmobranchs are unusual among vertebrates in that their blood osmoconcentration is higher than that of their environment, whether fresh water or sea water. The urine contains large quantities of urea, but is hypoosmotic to the blood. The rectal gland of sharks is an intestinal diverticulum specialized for the excretion of sodium chloride. These glands are much smaller in freshwater species than in species living in marine habitats. The secretion from the rectal gland of *Squalus* is isosmotic with the blood, but contains about twice as much sodium chloride, and practically no urea. There is no information on the functional regulation of the rectal glands.[51]

Carbohydrate Metabolism

The disturbances in carbohydrate metabolism occurring in the adrenalectomized animal are due chiefly to removal of the cortex and are similar in many respects to those that follow hypophysectomy. In the fasted, untreated, adrenalectomized animal, severe depletion of liver glycogen, low blood glucose levels, and decreased intestinal absorption of glucose ensue. Muscle glycogen is lost during the terminal stages of cortical insufficiency. These changes may be prevented by giving sufficient carbohydrate and are largely corrected by the administration of sodium salts. Adrenalectomized animals excrete less nitrogen during fasting than do normal subjects, which suggests a decrease in the rate of formation of glucose from tissue protein (gluconeogenesis). The adrenalectomized animal, like the hypophysectomized animal, utilizes carbohydrate at an accelerated rate. Muscle glycogen is oxidized at an increased rate and this leads to depletion of the liver glycogen stores. In the absence of cortical hormones, the animal cannot replenish liver glycogen by gluconeogenesis from protein. The adrenalectomized animal is known to be very sensitive to the action of insulin. Adrenalectomy, like hypophysectomy, alleviates the symptoms of pancreatic diabetes; blood sugar is lowered, and the urinary excretion of glucose, ketone bodies, and nitrogen decreases. The two fundamental defects in carbohydrate metabolism consequent upon adrenalectomy are (1) excessive oxidation of glucose and (2) decreased gluconeogenesis from body protein.[29, 44, 69]

Although the 11-oxygenated adrenal hormones have some effect on electrolytes and fluid shifts, they are especially potent in correcting the defects in carbohydrate metabolism that follow adrenalectomy. Cortisol (compound F) is three to five times more potent in this respect than corticosterone (compound B) or 11-dehydrocorticosterone (compound A); cortisone (compound E) is two to three times more potent than compounds A and B. Aldosterone has about one-third the activity of cortisone in causing liver glycogen deposition, but is about 30 times more effective than DOC in this respect.

The administration of 11-oxygenated corticoids to fasting normal or adrenalectomized animals causes a rise in blood sugar and a striking increase in liver glycogen and total body carbohydrate, but muscle glycogen stores are not appreciably changed. The increased carbohydrate stores are the result of diminished oxidation of glucose and accelerated gluconeogenesis from tissue protein. The latter is indicated by an increased urinary elimination of nitrogen. In adrenalectomized animals the respiratory quotient (R.Q.) is increased, but the adrenal cortical hormones lower it, indicating that the hormones have an inhibitory effect on glucose utilization. The phosphorylation of glucose to glucose-6-phosphate, catalyzed by hexokinase, is the first reaction in the utilization of glucose, and it appears that the cortical steroids exert an inhibitory influence at this point. There are indications that the corticoids may act at this level by potentiating the inhibitory effect of pituitary somatotrophin on the hexokinase reaction. Both the accelerated gluconeogenesis and diminished utilization of glucose, effected by the 11-oxygenated corticoids, are antagonized by the action of insulin.

When hypophysectomized rodents are fasted, the liver glycogen is soon exhausted and the blood sugar drops to low levels. These changes may be prevented by administering adrenal corticoids or restored to normal if the levels are already low. The muscle glycogen stores are not appreciably affected by this treatment.

Diabetes, produced by pancreatectomy or alloxan, is aggravated by administering cortical hormones. Insulin convulsions in mice and rats may be prevented by giving 11-oxygenated corticoids, the adrenal hormones acting to provide sugar by stimulating gluconeogenesis.

The cortical steroids exert three main effects on carbohydrate metabolism: they discourage the utilization of carbohydrate, presumably by acting with somatotrophin to inhibit the hexokinase reaction; they promote the formation of glucose from tissue protein; and they cause the deposition of glycogen in the liver.

Protein and Fat Metabolism

The 11-oxygenated steroids cause an increased deposition of hepatic glycogen that is accompanied by an increased elimination of urinary nitrogen. Although such steroids can influence the nitrogen balance of the body, it has not been determined how this is accomplished; they may diminish the rate of protein synthesis or they may increase the rates of breakdown of tissue proteins and amino acids. There are suggestions that the adrenal steroids may reduce the rate of protein synthesis by antagonizing the effects of insulin, thus reducing the rate of energy production through the breakdown of glucose. It is also possible that cortical hormones may retard protein synthesis by an effect on the metabolism of nucleic acids.

Studies have been made on the effects of cortical steroids on the mobilization of protein nitrogen from lymphoid tissues (spleen, thymus, lymph nodes) and from liver. The administration of cortical extracts to adrenalectomized mice or of ACTH to hypophysectomized mice leads to a rapid liberation of nitrogen from these tissues when they are tested *in vitro*. Tissues taken from adrenalectomized animals release relatively little protein nitrogen.[28, 43]

The conversion of carbohydrate to fat is markedly increased in the adrenalectomized rat. The 11-oxycorticoids depress the synthesis of fat from carbohydrate. The administration of cortisol or cortisone to rats suppresses the ketosis that occurs during fasting or that is consequent upon cold exposure. Increased ketosis results from the administration of purified somatotrophin or of purified ACTH. The latter hormone has a ketogenic effect even in the absence of the adrenal cortices. It appears that these two pituitary hormones (*i.e.*, STH and ACTH) accelerate the breakdown of fatty acids. Either directly, or indirectly through the adrenal cortex, they act antagonistically to insulin not only in carbohydrate metabolism but in fat metabolism as well.

Miscellaneous Effects

A striking action of 11-oxycorticoids, whether injected or produced endogenously, is to diminish the number of eosinophils (eosinopenia) and lymphocytes (lymphopenia) in the peripheral circulation. Aldosterone is about half as active as cortisone in causing eosinopenia. Deoxycorticosterone does not produce eosinopenia unless very high doses are used.

Although the cortical hormones can fully restore the resistance of adrenalectomized animals to various kinds of stressors, such as toxins, temperature changes, trauma, etc., there is no clear evidence that they can augment the resistance of intact animals to such stresses. In the cold stress test, often used for the bioassay of cortical steroids, the animals are adrenalectomized and then subjected to low temperatures. Aldosterone and cortisone are about equal in their capacity to enable adrenalectomized animals to tolerate cold; the 11-deoxy-corticoids are weak in this respect.

The oxysteroids of the adrenal profoundly influence the inflammatory reactions of the tissues. Local inflammatory responses to irritating substances are reduced or delayed as are the hypersensitivity reactions to most antigens. Such cortical hormones also delay the healing of wounds and may reduce the capacity of the tissues to wall off infectious agents. They are known to have important effects on antibody formation. The symptomatic relief provided by cortisol, cortisone, or ACTH may be helpful in certain diseases but distinctly deleterious in other circumstances.

Reproductive functions are arrested during periods of chronic adrenal insufficiency. The failure of lactation that occurs after adrenalectomy is attributable, in part at least, to generalized disturbances in the vascular system, in the distribution of inorganic ions and water and in the metabolism of carbohydrate, fat, and protein.

Considerable evidence has accumulated indicating that the adrenocortical hormones have important influences on the excitability of the brain and on the metabolism of nervous tissue.

Stress and Disease

It is an established fact that adrenalectomized animals have very little ability to tolerate stressors, such as temperature extremes, prolonged muscular activity, trauma, infections, intoxications, etc. This inability to withstand damaging stimuli may be repaired by the administration of adrenal cortical hormones. Furthermore, when intact animals are stressed, the pituitary-adrenal axis is activated, and a rather stereotyped sequence of reactions occurs in response to an outpouring of secretions from these glands. The response of the organism to nonspecific stress has been called the "General Adaptation Syndrome." The endocrine adjustments that occur during stress must be of utility to the organism in its attempt to maintain homeostasis.

Selye has proposed the hypothesis that the adaptive mechanisms that are called into operation during exposure to nonspecific stress may derail and cause disease.[62] For example, the secretion of large amounts of ACTH and anti-inflammatory adrenal steroids during stress may be useful in enabling an organism to survive during the emergency by suppressing excessive inflammatory reactions; but, on the other hand, the same response may be harmful inasmuch as it permits the spread of infections. By administering pituitary and adrenal hormones to "sensitized" laboratory animals, Selye and his co-workers have been able to induce a variety of pathologic changes, such as hypertension, arthritis, arteriosclerosis, nephrosclerosis, gastrointestinal ulcers, and many others. Most of the work has involved the administration of overdoses of hormones to animals sensitized by unilateral nephrectomy and by a high dietary load of sodium chloride. These pathologic changes have been interpreted as simulating human diseases. According to Selye's concept of "adaptation diseases," maladjustments to stress may play an etiologic role in certain diseases of man. Although an enormous amount of research has been published on the physiologic effects of stress, there is a paucity of evidence showing that diseases can be produced in normal subjects by exposing them to naturally occurring stressors.

The "permissive" action of adrenal cortical hormones has been emphasized by a number of workers.[39] According to this view, the adrenocortical hormones are essential for the full-blown manifestation of certain responses to stress, but they are not direct causative agents of the responses. A number of situations have been studied in which a hormone acts to produce the necessary environment for other biologic substances to exercise the full scope of their functions.

That adaptive mechanisms in response to stress may derail and produce disease by hormonal excesses or imbalances is an interesting concept, but the supporting evidence is largely indirect and not sufficient to establish it as a fact. (For an excellent evaluation of the stress concept and its significance in disease, see Rosch.[56])

REFERENCES

1. Bentley, P. J.: Studies on the permeability of the large intestine and urinary bladder of the tortoise (*Testudo graeca*) with special reference to the effects of neuro-hypophysial and adrenocortical hormones. Gen. & Comp. Endocrinol., 2:323, 1962.
2. Bernstein, D. E.: Autotransplantation of the adrenal of the rat to the portal circulation: Effect of administration of testosterone in male rats. Endocrinol., 67:685, 1960.
3. Blair-West, J. R., Coghlan, J. P., Denton, D. A., Goding, J. R., Wintour, M., and Wright, R. D.: The control of aldosterone secretion. Recent Prog. Hormone Research, 19:311, 1963.
4. Bongiovanni, A. M., and Eder, W.: *In vitro* hydroxylation of steroids by whole adrenal homogenates of beef, normal man, and patients with the adrenogenital syndrome. J. Clin. Invest., 37:1342, 1958.
5. Bronson, F. H., and Eleftheriou, B. E.: Chronic physiological effects of fighting in mice. Gen. & Comp. Endocrinol., 4:9, 1964.
6. Brown, H. E., and Dougherty, T. F.: The diurnal variation of blood leucocytes in normal and adrenalectomized mice. Endocrinol., 58:365, 1956.
7. Carstensen, H., Burgers, A. C. J., and Li, C. H.: Demonstration of aldosterone and corticosterone as the principal steroids formed in incubates of adrenals of the American bullfrog (*Rana catesbeiana*) and stimulation of their production by mammalian adrenocorticotropin. Gen. & Comp. Endocrinol., 1:37, 1961.
8. Chester Jones, I.: The role of the adrenal cortex in the control of water and salt-electrolyte balance in vertebrates. Memoirs Soc. Endocrinol., 5:102, 1956.
9. Chester Jones, I., Phillips, J. G., and Holmes, W. N.: Comparative physiology of the adrenal cortex. *In* A. Gorbman (ed.): Comparative Endocrinology. New York, John Wiley & Sons, 1959, p. 582.
10. Christian, J. J., and Davis, D. E.: Endocrines, behavior, and population. Science 146:1550, 1964.

11. Cortés, J. M., Péron, F. G., and Dorfman, R. I.: Secretion of 18-hydroxydeoxy-corticosterone by the rat adrenal gland. Endocrinol., *73*:713, 1963.
12. Crabbé, J.: Stimulation of active sodium transport across the isolated toad bladder after injection of aldosterone to the animal. Endocrinol., *69*:673, 1961.
13. Crabbé, J.: Effects of adrenocortical steroids on active sodium transport by the urinary bladder and ventral skin of Amphibia. *In* P. C. Williams (ed.): Hormones and the Kidney. New York, Academic Press, 1963, p. 75.
14. Davis, J. O.: Mechanism regulating the secretion and metabolism of aldosterone in experimental hyperaldosteronism. Recent Prog. Hormone Research, *17*:293, 1961.
15. deRoos, R.: *In vitro* production of corticoids by chicken adrenals. Endocrinol., *67*:719, 1960.
16. deRoos, R.: The corticoids of the avian adrenal gland. Gen. & Comp. Endocrinol., *1*:494, 1961.
17. deRoos, R.: The Physiology of the Avian Interrenal Gland: A Review. *In* C. G. Sibley (ed.): Proc. 13th Internat. Ornithological Congress, Vol. 2. 1963, p. 1041.
18. Dorfman, R. I.: Biosynthesis of adrenocortical steroids. Cancer, *10*:741, 1957.
19. Eppstein, S. H., Meister, P. D., Murray, H. C., and Peterson, D. H.: Microbiological transformations of steroids and their applications to the synthesis of hormones. Vit. & Horm., *14*:359, 1956.
20. Farrell, G.: Adrenoglomerulotropin. Circulation, *21*:1009, 1960.
21. Farrell, G., and McIsaac, W. M.: Adrenoglomerulotrophin. Arch. Biochem. & Biophysics, *94*:543, 1961.
22. Fieser, L. F., and Fieser, M.: Steroids. New York, Reinhold Publishing Corp., 1959.
23. Flickinger, D. D.: Adrenal responses of California quail subjected to various physiologic stimuli. Proc. Soc. Exp. Biol. & Med., *100*:23, 1959.
24. Ganong, W. F.: The central nervous system and the synthesis and release of adrenocorticotropic hormones. *In* A. V. Nalbandov (ed.): Advances in Neuroendocrinology. Urbana, University of Illinois Press, 1963, p. 92.
25. Giroud, C. J. P., Stachenko, J., and Piletta, P.: *In vitro* studies on the functional zonation of the adrenal cortex and of the production of aldosterone. *In* A. F. Muller and C. M. O'Connor (eds.): An International Symposium on Aldosterone. London, J. & A. Churchill, 1958, p. 56.
26. Giroud, C. J. P., Stachenko, J., and Venning, E. H.: Secretion of aldosterone by the zona glomerulosa of rat adrenal glands. Proc. Soc. Exp. Biol. & Med., *92*:154, 1956.
27. Glenister, D. W., and Yates, F. E.: Sex difference in the rate of disappearance of corticosterone-4-C^{14} from plasma of intact rats: further evidence for the influence of hepatic Δ^4-steroid hydrogenase activity on adrenal cortical function. Endocrinol., *68*:747, 1961.
28. Glenn, E. M., Bowman, B. J., Bayer, R. B., and Meyer, C. E.: Hydrocortisone and some of its effects on intermediary metabolism. Endocrinol., *68*:386, 1961.
29. Greengard, O., Weber, G., and Singhal, R. L.: Glycogen deposition in the liver induced by cortisone: dependence on enzyme synthesis. Science, *141*:160, 1963.
30. Halberg, F., Peterson, R. E., and Silber, R. H.: Phase relations of 24-hour periodicities in blood corticosterone, mitoses in cortical adrenal parenchyma, and total body activity. Endocrinol., *64*:222, 1959.
31. Haynes, R. C., Jr., Sutherland, E. W., and Rall, T. W.: The role of cyclic adenylic acid in hormone action. Recent Prog. Hormone Research, *16*:121, 1960.
32. Hechter, O., Jacobsen, R. P., Schenker, V., Levy, H., Jeanloz, R. W., Marshall, C. W., and Pincus, G.: Chemical transformation of steroids by adrenal perfusion: perfusion methods. Endocrinol., *52*:679, 1953.
33. Hechter, O., and Pincus, G.: Genesis of the adrenocortical secretion. Physiol. Rev., *34*:459, 1954.
34. Hechter, O., Solomon, M. M., Zaffaroni, A., and Pincus, G.: Transformation of cholesterol and acetate to adrenal cortical hormones. Arch. Biochem. & Biophysics, *46*:201, 1953.

35. Hilton, J. G., Scian, L. F., Westermann, C. D., and Kruesi, O. R.: Direct stimulation of adrenocortical secretion by synthetic vasopressin. Proc. Soc. Exp. Biol. & Med., *100*:523, 1959.
36. Hirschmann, H., de Courcy, C., Levy, R. P., and Miller, K. L.: Adrenal precursors of urinary 17-ketosteroids. J. Biol. Chem., *235*:PC48, 1960.
37. Holmes, W. N., Phillips, J. G., and Butler, D. G.: The effect of adrenocortical steroids on the renal and extra-renal responses of the domestic duck (*Anas platyrhynchus*) after hypertonic saline loading. Endocrinol., 69:483, 1961.
38. Holmes, W. N., Phillips, J. G., and Chester Jones, I.: Adrenocortical factors associated with adaptation of vertebrates to marine environments. Recent Prog. Hormone Research, *19*:619, 1963.
39. Ingle, D. J.: Permissibility of hormone action: a review. Acta Endocrinol., *17*:172, 1954.
40. Inoue, T.: Nasal salt gland: independence of salt and water transport. Science, *142*:1299, 1963.
41. Kitay, J. I.: Pituitary-adrenal function in the rat after gonadectomy and gonadal hormone replacement. Endocrinol., 73:253, 1963.
42. Kolthoff, N. J., Macchi, I. A., and Wyman, L. C.: Isotopic determinations of blood volume in intact and regenerated rat adrenals during cold stress. Endocrinol., 73:27, 1963.
43. Kostyo, J. L.: *In vitro* effects of adrenal steroid hormones on amino acid transport in muscle. Endocrinol., 76:604, 1965.
44. Landau, B. R., Mahler, R., Ashmore, J., Elwyn, D., Hastings, A. B., and Zottu, S.: Cortisone and the regulation of hepatic gluconeogenesis. Endocrinol., 70:47, 1962.
45. Lanman, J. T., and Silverman, L. M.: *In vitro* steroidogenesis in the human neonatal adrenal gland, including observations on human adult and monkey adrenal glands. Endocrinol., 60:433, 1957.
46. Macchi, I. A., and Wyman, L. C.: Qualitative characterization of corticoids produced by adrenal autografts in the rat. Endocrinol., 73:20, 1963.
47. Marieb, N. J., and Mulrow, P. J.: Role of the renin-angiotensin system in the regulation of aldosterone secretion in the rat. Endocrinol., 76:657, 1965.
48. Mosier, H. D.: Comparative histological study of the adrenal cortex of the wild and domesticated Norway rat. Endocrinol., 60:460, 1957.
49. Nandi, J., and Bern, H. A.: Chromatography of corticosteroids from teleost fishes. Gen. & Comp. Endocrinol., 5:1, 1965.
50. Oertel, G. W., and Eik-Nes, K. B.: Isolation and identification of 11-ketoprogesterone, 11-hydroxyprogesterone and 11-hydroxyandrostenedione in canine adrenal vein blood. Endocrinol., 70:39, 1962.
51. Oguri, M.: Rectal glands of marine and fresh-water sharks: comparative histology. Science, *144*:1151, 1964.
52. Peart, W. S.: The renin-angiotensin system. Pharmacol. Revs., *17*:143, 1965.
53. Pechet, M. M., Hesse, R. H., and Kohler, H.: The metabolism of aldosterone: isolation and characterization of two new metabolites. J. Amer. Chem. Soc., *82*:5251, 1960.
54. Perrine, J. W., Bortle, L., Heyder, E., Partridge, R., Ross, E. K., and Ringler, I.: adrenal cortical activities of 9α-fluoro-11β,16α,17α-21-tetrahydroxy-1, 4-pregnadiene-3,20-dione. Endocrinol., *64*:437, 1959.
55. Phillips, J. G., Holmes, W. N., and Butler, D. G.: The effect of total and subtotal adrenalectomy on the renal and extra-renal release of the domestic duck (*Anas platyrhynchus*) to saline loading. Endocrinol., 69:958, 1961.
56. Rosch, P. J.: The growth and development of the stress concept and its significance in clinical medicine. *In* Gardiner-Hill (ed.): Modern Trends in Endocrinology. London, Butterworth, 1958, p. 278.
57. Samuels, L. T., and Reich, H.: The chemistry and metabolism of the steroids. Ann. Rev. Biochem., *21*:129, 1952.
58. Sandor, T., Lamoureux, J., and Lanthier, A.: Adrenocortical function in birds: *in vitro* biosynthesis of radioactive corticosteroids from pregnenolone-7-H³ and progesterone-4-C¹⁴ by adrenal glands of the domestic duck (*Anas platyrhynchos*) and the chicken (*Gallus domesticus*). Endocrinol., 73:629, 1963.
59. Schmidt-Nielson, K.: The salt-secreting gland of marine birds. Circulation, *21* (Part 2):955, 1960.

60. Schmidt-Nielson, K., Borut, A., Lee, P., and Crawford, E., Jr.: Nasal salt excretion and possible function of cloaca in water conservation. Science, *142*:1300, 1963.

61. Seltzer, H. S., and Clark, D. A.: Evidence for conversion of corticosterone to aldosterone in man. Proc. Soc. Exp. Biol. & Med., *98*:674, 1958.

62. Selye, H.: Perspectives in stress research. Perspectives in Biol. & Med., *2*:403, 1959.

63. Sheppard, H., Swenson, R., and Mowles, T. F.: Steroid biosynthesis by rat adrenal: functional zonation. Endocrinol., *73*:819, 1963.

64. Solomon, S., Lanman, J. T., Lind, J., and Lieberman, S.: The biosynthesis of Δ^4-androstenedione and 17α-hydroxyprogesterone from progesterone by surviving human fetal adrenals. J. Biol. Chem., *233*:1084, 1958.

65. Stachenko, J., and Giroud, C. J. P.: Functional zonation of the adrenal cortex: pathways of corticosteroid biogenesis. Site of ACTH action. Endocrinol., *64*:730, 1959.

66. Urquhart, J., Yates, F. E., and Herbst, A. L.: Hepatic regulation of adrenal cortical function. Endocrinol., *64*:816, 1959.

67. Villee, D. B., Engel, L. L., and Villee, C. A.: Steroid hydroxylation in human fetal adrenals. Endocrinol., *65*:465, 1959.

68. Vogt, M.: The effects of hexoestrol and of "Amphenone B" on morphology and function of the rat adrenal cortex. Yale J. Biol. & Med., *29*:469, 1957.

69. Winternitz, W. W., Dintzis, R., and Long, C. N. H.: Further studies on the adrenal cortex and carbohydrate metabolism. Endocrinol., *61*:724, 1957.

70. Woods, J. W.: The effects of acute stress and of ACTH upon ascorbic acid and lipid content of the adrenal glands of wild rats. J. Physiol., *135*:390, 1957.

71. Wurtman, R. J., Roth, W., Altschule, M. D., and Wurtman, J. J.: Interactions of the pineal and exposure to continuous light on organ weights of female rats. Acta Endocrinol., *36*:617, 1961.

72. Yates, F. E., Herbst, A. L., and Urquhart, J.: Sex difference in rate of ring A reduction of Δ^4-3-keto-steroids *in vitro* by rat liver. Endocrinol., *63*:887, 1958.

73. Yates, F. E., and Urquhart, J.: Control of plasma concentrations of adrenocortical hormones. Physiol. Rev., *42*:359, 1962.

12 _____

THE BIOLOGY OF
SEX AND
REPRODUCTION

All groups of living organisms can reproduce in some manner, and the continuity of the species depends upon this capacity. Unlike reproduction, sexual dimorphism is by no means a universal attribute of organisms. Since monoecious, or hermaphroditic, organisms are capable of producing both sperms and eggs, it is obvious that the ability to produce a particular kind of gamete is not dependent upon the differentiation of specific sexual characters. In sexual reproduction, two cells (gametes) fuse to form a new individual (zygote), and the significance of this event is that it promotes genetic diversity.

Many lower organisms form gametes of like size and shape (isogametes), and the fusion of these is suggestive of sexuality. However, the isogametes cannot be designated as "male" or "female" since they are morphologically indistinguishable and, in many instances, seem capable of performing either role. The most basic feature of this cellular union (syngamy) is the succession of haploid and diploid phases. The chromosome number is doubled at fertilization and halved by the meiotic process. Even the behavior of chromosomes during meiosis is suggestive of "sex." Homologous chromosomes of a diploid set make contact with each other and the chrommeres and gene loci are lined up with remarkable precision (conjugation); this is followed by divisions which reduce the number of chromosomes. Polyploidy may occur in certain species, giving rise to more than two full sets of homologous chromosomes.

375

At the chromosomal level there is some kind of opposing polarity in the molecular patterns and forces which direct their movements, and this may lie at the very core of the "sex" problem.[50] Among bacteria (*Escherichia coli*), a single chromosome passes from one conjugant into the other, and the alignment of the two chromosomes is suggestive of that occurring during meiosis.[25] These facts indicate that reproduction through the fusion of cells is not necessarily dependent upon male-female differentiation. The great majority of vertebrates are dioecious, the anisogametes being proliferated by dimorphic individuals of the species.

SEX DETERMINATION AND ONTOGENETIC DIFFERENTIATION

In the vertebrates a sex-determining mechanism is established at fertilization (sex determination), and this directs and controls all of the later ontogenetic processes involved in male-female differentiation of the genital system (postgenetic differentiation). The genetic determination is not final and irrevocable; many external and

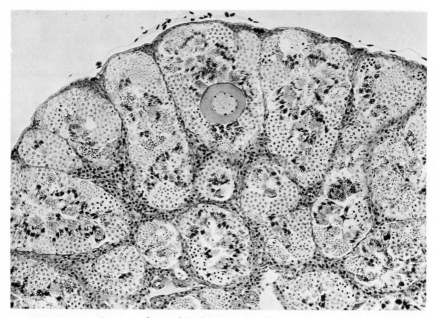

Figure 12–1. Section of an adult frog's testis showing an oöcyte within one of the seminiferous tubules. It is possible that this egg cell migrated, at an early stage, from the cortex into the medulla and became confined within a seminiferous tubule; it is also possible that an indifferent spermatogonium might have escaped the masculinizing influence of the medulla and differentiated into an egg instead of a sperm. Genetically, it is not known whether this abortive cell was determined as an egg or a sperm. It is known that the early germ cells of vertebrates are bipotential. (Courtesy of Robert R. Cardell, Jr., and General Biological Supply House.)

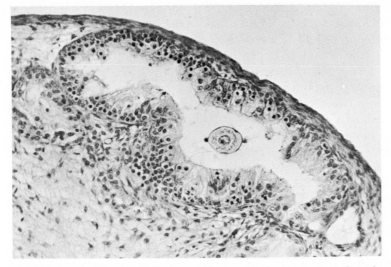

Figure 12–2. An oöcyte within a seminiferous tubule of a testis graft in the rat. A fetal testis and a fetal ovary were transplanted next to each other below the kidney capsule of an adult host; the double graft was removed after 40 days. The early germ cells of the ovary are capable of ameboid movement; at this early stage, many oögonia may migrate from the ovary into the tubules of the contiguous testis graft. (C. D. Turner and H. Asakawa, unpublished.)

internal environmental factors may come into operation during the developmental process and modify or completely reverse the genetic constitution of the individual. Germ cells, presumably of identical genetic constitution, may lie close together and differentiate as sperms or ova within the same individual (Figs. 12–1 and 12–2). This is encountered very often among hermaphroditic invertebrates and lower vertebrates, and suggests that male-determining and female-determining territories arise in the body during ontogenesis.

Genotypic sex is established at fertilization and depends upon the "sex" chromosomes which are contributed by the parents. For simplicity the two major types of sex determination may be called the *mammalian* and *avian* types. The XX-XY type of determination is characteristic of mammals, most frogs, some fishes, and dipterous insects. The whole problem of sex determination in man remains uncertain, but it appears to differ in some respects from that of *Drosophila*, which has been used so frequently as a model. Improved methods of chromosome identification indicate that the human being has 46 chromosomes, instead of 48 as believed for many years: there are 22 pairs of autosomes and a pair of sex chromosomes. While the Y chromosome of *Drosophila* is necessary for male fertility, it is essentially inert with reference to the differentiation of phenotypic sex. Recent studies indicate that the Y chromosome is strongly "male determining" in man, in contrast to the same chromosome in *Drosophila*. In mammals and the other groups mentioned, the male is the heterogametic (XY) sex, half of the spermatozoa being X bearers and the other half Y bearers.[33, 37, 39]

In the avian type of determination the female is the heterogametic sex. The small chromosome, equivalent to the Y in mammals, is designated by the letter W, and the X chromosome is designated in these cases as Z. Half of the eggs carry a W chromosome and the other half a Z chromosome; all of the sperms carry a Z chromosome. The homozygous (ZZ) condition produces males, and the heterozygous (ZW) produces females. This is the type of mechanism that operates in birds, most reptiles and salamanders, and in some fishes and insects. In certain species the inert Y and W chromosomes are absent and the mechanism may be designated XO and ZO. The W chromosome is then not present in birds, and the Y is lost in certain mammals (*e.g.*, Japanese mouse).

Sex mosaics, or gynandromorphs, are infrequently found among vertebrate groups. This condition probably occurs occasionally in man, though it has not been proved by sex chromosome studies. In gynandromorphism, known to result from an abnormality of the sex chromosomes, sharply delimited fractions of the body show male characteristics and the rest female. The condition has been studied most carefully in insects, in which the secondary sex characters are fixed by the genes. In *Drosophila*, half of the body may be male and the other half female, the line of division splitting the fly lengthwise. A frequent cause of this abnormality is the loss of an X (or Z) chromosome from an early cleavage cell derived from an XX (or ZZ) zygote. Other cases apparently result from the parthenogenic development of an ovum followed by the fertilization of an early blastomere.

There is abundant proof that individuals from many vertebrate species, without changing their chromosomes and genes, may differentiate in a direction opposite to their genotypic sex. Sexual characters, like other somatic characters determined by multiple genes, are subject to extreme variability. When populations are analyzed, some individuals are found to be weighted heavily in the male or in the female direction, with many individual variations between these two extremes. This suggests the existence of a quantitative relationship, or balance, between the set of genes determining maleness and the set determining femaleness.

Sex Chromatin

While studying the structural features of nerve cells in cats, Barr and his associates discovered a characteristic mass of chromatin in the nuclei of such cells from genetic females.[5] The chromatin mass is Feulgen-positive, measures about 1μ in diameter, and usually

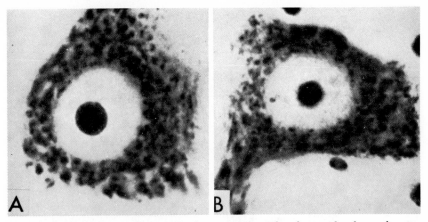

Figure 12–3. Ventral horn cells from spinal cords of normal calves, showing absence of sex chromatin in the normal male *(A)* and the presence of a sex chromatin mass in the nucleus of the cell from a normal female *(B)*. (From Moore, Graham, and Barr: J. Exp. Zool., *135*, 1957.)

lies on the inner surface of the nuclear membrane (Fig. 12–3). This sexual dimorphism has been found in man and numerous other mammals. The Barr test is now widely used in analyzing sex abnormalities in man. Skin biopsies, leukocytes, exfoliate cells from the vagina, or scrapings from the oral or nasal epithelia all provide readily available material for execution of the test. In intersexes, where there is an admixture of male and female characters, knowledge of the genetic sex may be valuable in deciding which direction the hormonal or surgical therapy should take. The genetic sex of very young embryos can be determined long before this would be possible by histologic study of the gonads. The sex chromatin is even present in the gonocytes, or primordial germ cells, before they reach the gonadal primordia.

The general inference is that the presence of sex chromatin is diagnostic of a genetic female (XX) and its absence is diagnostic of a genetic male (XY). This chromatin body is thought to arise from the fused heteropyknotic portions of two X chromosomes. The presence of a drumstick-like appendage on the nucleus of female polymorphonuclear leukocytes has been found useful in determining genetic sex in man and several other vertebrates.[14]

ANATOMY OF THE REPRODUCTIVE SYSTEM

The *primary* sex characters are the gonads, *i.e.*, testes in the male and ovaries in the female. The higher vertebrates have evolved elaborate systems of ducts and glands for the conveyance of viable germ cells toward the exterior of the organism (Figs. 12–4 and 12–5).

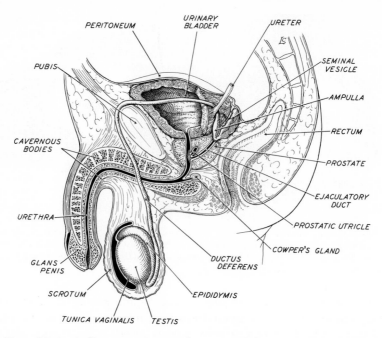

Figure 12–4. A diagrammatic sagittal section of the male pelvis, showing the genital organs and their relations to the bladder and urethra.

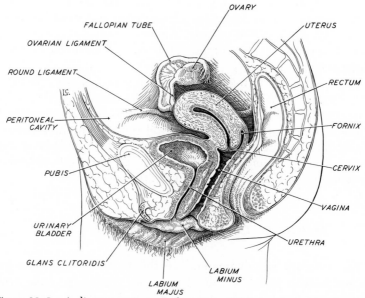

Figure 12–5. A diagrammatic sagittal section of the female pelvis, showing the genital organs and their relations to the bladder and urethra.

These systems of ducts and glands involved in the transmission of gametes or developing zygotes constitute the *sex accessories*. The gonads not only proliferate gametes but also secrete hormones that condition the functional state of the accessory sex organs and, to some extent at least, influence the psychobiologic phenomena involved in the mating reactions. The proliferation of gametes and the mating reaction are basically rhythmic processes, and it is recognized that both are controlled or conditioned by a wide variety of intrinsic and extrinsic factors.

The *secondary* sex characters are more or less external specializations that are not essential for the proliferation and movement of germ cells but are concerned chiefly with mating and with the birth and nutrition of the young. These characters are more highly developed and diversified in birds than in any other vertebrate class. The ornamental secondary characters in birds, such as the dimorphic differentiation of feathers, head furnishings, and various other types of integumentary derivatives, are physiologically conditioned and serve to bring the sexes together during the reproductive periods. In mammals the secondary sex characters are less pronounced than in many of the fishes, amphibians, reptiles, and birds. Among these characters are the differential conditioning of the mammary glands in the two sexes, pelvic modifications for the facilitation of parturition, reddening and swelling of the circumanal "sex skin" during the follicular phase of the menstrual cycle in some primates, and differences in the size and shape of the larynx.

THE VERTEBRATE TESTIS

Mammals

In man and most other mammals the testes of the adult are lodged in an integumentary pouch, the *scrotum*. Many types of experiments have shown that this organ is an adaptation for regulating the internal temperature of the testes. The spontaneous or experimental retention of the testes in the abdominal cavity in species in which they normally descend into the scrotum is called *cryptorchism* and is associated with profound damage to the seminiferous tubules. In seasonally breeding mammals the testes ascend through the inguinal canals and remain in the body cavity during the nonbreeding period. Scrota are lacking in a few mammals, *e.g.*, the whale, elephant, seal, and rhinoceros, and the testes remain permanently in the abdominal cavity. There is no scrotum in the armadillo, but the testes descend to the entrance into the inguinal canal.[41] The human testes usually assume scrotal positions during the terminal month of fetal life, and the inguinal canal becomes sealed off shortly after birth.

The stratified lining of the seminiferous tubules constitutes an epithelium from which the spermatozoa are proliferated. The tubule is limited by a thin basement membrane and a small amount of lamellated connective tissue. Contractile epithelial cells have been described in the limiting membrane of the seminiferous tubules of the rat, and these may play a role in the release of spermatozoa from the epithelium and their movement into the rete testis.[13] Pressure effects produced by accumulating cells may also be a factor involved in the movement of spermatozoa through the tubules. The *spermatogonia,* lying next to the basement membrane, exhibit a series of mitotic divisions leading to the formation of *primary spermatocytes.* These undergo the first meiotic division and give rise to haploid cells called *secondary spermatocytes.* The latter begin the second meiotic division almost immediately and produce smaller cells which are the *spermatids.* The transformation of spermatids into spermatozoa involves principally cytoplasmic loss and the differentiation of tailpieces. These cells are displaced toward the lumen of the tubule by the appearance of further generations of maturing spermatogonia. Spermatogonial mitoses do not occur at random; groups of cells at comparable stages of development burst into mitosis in unison. Well-defined cellular associations succeed each other in time in any given region of the tubule, and the sequence is repeated indefinitely. Three different processes are distinguishable therefore in the seminiferous epithelium: (1) increase in the number of cells by mitosis, (2) reduction in the number of chromosomes by meiosis, and (3) the production of sperms from spermatids by spermiogenesis.

The sustentacular cells of Sertoli are relatively large elements extending from the basement membrane toward the lumen. They are regarded as supporting cells, which probably provide nourishment for the spermatids with which they are intimately associated. In some species, the sperm heads remain embedded in the Sertoli cells for relatively long periods. The release of spermatozoa from the Sertoli cells is termed *spermiation,* and this process is analogous to ovulation in the female.

In immature males the seminiferous tubules are solid and contain only spermatogonia and undifferentiated cells. The testes of seasonally breeding males involute at the end of the breeding season and become comparable to those of the sexually immature animal. The human testes are almost stationary in growth during the first 10 years of life. Although wide variations are found among individuals, by the age of 12 the tubules have become luminal and the epithelium contains many spermatogonia, Leydig cells, primary and secondary spermatocytes, and spermatids. Spermatogenic function is generally well established by the age of 15. Although there is generally a decrease in spermatogenic activity in aging men, it is known that complete spermatogenesis may continue later than the ninth decade.[38]

The interspaces between the seminiferous tubules are occupied by blood vessels, connective tissue, and the *interstitial cells of Leydig*. The latter cells are of mesenchymal origin and appear singly or in clusters of varying sizes. Although some investigators feel that the problem has not been settled, a wealth of circumstantial evidence points to the Leydig cells as the source of testicular androgen and possibly of testicular estrogen. In aging men there is generally a decline in androgen secretion, but the production of estrogen is preferentially retained.

There are as yet no satisfactory microscopic criteria for assessing the functional activity of the Leydig cells. The apparent number of such cells appearing in histologic preparation may give a very misleading picture of the secretory capacity of the testis. The number appears to vary within normal individuals and also among species. For example, the testes of mature cocks contain fewer Leydig cells than those of younger, growing birds; but there is no evidence that the mature cock secretes less androgen than it did previously. Massive deposits of interstitial cells are present in the testis of the boar, whereas relatively scanty aggregates of Leydig cells occur in normal human and bovine testes.[34]

The testes of the horse, seal, giraffe, and elephant are strikingly enlarged at birth, and shrink greatly during the first few days of postnatal life. The large size of the testis is due to a remarkable proliferation of the interstitial cells, which compose the bulk of the organ. The response must be due to the action of circulating maternal hormones upon the fetus.

The testes of the human infant are enlarged at birth owing to the extensive intertubular deposits of Leydig cells. These cells, which developed *in utero*, disappear promptly after birth and do not reappear again until the boy reaches the age of 11 to 13 years. There is normally little evidence of the presence of testicular hormone during childhood. Although small amounts of 17-ketosteroids are present in the urine, these compounds may emanate from the adrenal cortex rather than from the testis. At puberty the testes secrete effective amounts of androgen, and the accessory sex organs undergo rapid growth and maturation. Secondary sex characters, such as deeper voice, beard, and body hair, begin to appear.

NONMAMMALIAN VERTEBRATES

The Leydig cells of most mammalian species constitute a permanent secretory unit but, in wild birds, the interstitium becomes

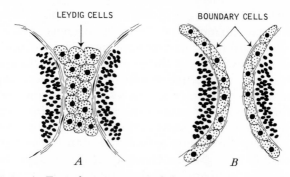

Figure 12–6. *A*, Typical arrangement of the interstitial cells of Leydig in the vertebrate testis. *B*, The Leydig cell homologue (boundary cells) in the walls of the testicular lobules of certain teleost fishes. (After Marshall and Lofts, 1956.)

exhausted *en masse* at the end of the breeding season. A new crop of Leydig cells promptly begins to differentiate from the intertubular connective tissue cells in preparation for the next season's sexual activities. Special histologic methods are required to distinguish connective tissue cells from young Leydig cells: this appears to account for many of the erroneous statements in the literature that Leydig cells are absent at certain periods of the avian cycle.[28]

The tubules of the anuran testis contain nests of cells which undergo spermatogenesis nonsynchronously. The segmented testes of mature urodeles consist of active lobes filled with sperms, and quiescent lobes from which the next crop of spermatozoa will arise. The testes of teleostean fishes are generally organized into lobules which contain cysts of differentiating germ cells. In some teleosts, urodeles, and turtles, tubule-boundary cells are observed instead of typical interstitial cells of Leydig. Most teleosts possess interstitial cells in the typical vertebrate position, but, in a few species such as the pike (*Esox lucius*), boundary cells originate in the lobule wall.[29] The boundary cells are homologous to the Leydig cells and apparently have the same endocrine function. They disintegrate after the spermatozoa are shed and are renewed from fibroblasts in the wall of the lobule (Fig. 12–6).

THE VERTEBRATE OVARY

Mammals

The human ovaries are flattened glands lying on the sides of the pelvic cavity and are attached by the mesovaria and the ovarian ligaments. The free surface of the organ is covered by a single layer of cuboidal cells, the gonadal epithelium. The gland is roughly divisible into a *cortex*, which extends over the entire surface except at the hilus, and an inner *medulla*. Although these two regions appear to contain distinct structures, there is no sharp line of demarcation between them in the mature organ. *Follicles* and *corpora lutea* in various stages of differentiation and destruction characterize the cortex of the sexually mature individual, whereas the medulla contains the larger blood vessels of the organ. In many species the stroma is pervaded by epithelioid elements, the interstitial cells, which probably arise from the theca interna of *atretic* follicles or from stromal cells proliferated during earlier life. Distinct masses of interstitial cells are not present in the human ovary but, in the rabbit, cells of this type fill all the space not occupied by follicles, corpora lutea, rete cords, and blood vessels.

During late fetal life, as well as in the postnatal female, clusters of cells arise from the ovarian epithelium. One cell in the cluster enlarges more rapidly than the others and is called the oögonium, whereas the remaining cells constitute the early follicle. After the oögonium enlarges and becomes distinguishable from its neighbors, it is called a *primary oöcyte*. A homogeneous membrane, the *zona pellucida* appears between the primary oöcyte and the follicular cells. The latter cells increase rapidly, forming many layers, the thecal layers are differentiated, and the follicle assumes a deeper position in the substance of the ovary. The primary oöcyte divides, giving off the first polar body, and becomes a secondary oöcyte.[17] The germ cell becomes a mature ovum after the second polar body is released. The polar bodies are entrapped within the zona pellucida, this membrane remaining with the ovum until its implantation or death. Under the influence of pituitary gonadotrophins a fluid-filled space, the antrum, appears in the membrana granulosa and the structure becomes a *vesicular* or *graafian* follicle (Fig. 12–7). Although there is general agreement that the vesicular follicle is the main source of ovarian estrogen, the exact cells responsible for its production have not been unequivocally determined. Some workers attribute estrogen production to the cells of the theca interna; others feel that it is a function of the granulosa.

Both ovaries of the human infant may contain as many as 500,000 primary follicles, but there is little likelihood that any additional germ cells can be formed postnatally. It is generally estimated that not more than 400 eggs could be ovulated from puberty (age 12 to 15) to menopause (age 40 to 50). This means that there is normally a progressive and rapid rate of follicular degeneration or *atresia*. Follicles at all stages of development are subject to atresia, signs of impending follicular degeneration generally being observed first in the germ cell itself.

In vespertilionid bats, vesicular follicles are known to persist in the ovaries for unusually long periods. Such follicles may be well

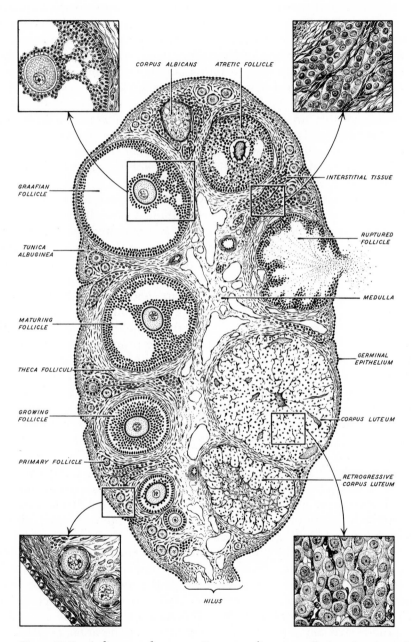

CORPUS ALBICANS

ATRETIC FOLLICLE

GRAAFIAN FOLLICLE

TUNICA ALBUGINEA

MATURING FOLLICLE

THECA FOLLICULI

GROWING FOLLICLE

PRIMARY FOLLICLE

INTERSTITIAL TISSUE

RUPTURED FOLLICLE

MEDULLA

GERMINAL EPITHELIUM

CORPUS LUTEUM

RETROGRESSIVE CORPUS LUTEUM

HILUS

Figure 12–7. A diagram of a composite mammalian ovary. Progressive stages in the differentiation of a graafian follicle are indicated on the left. The mature follicle may become atretic (top) or ovulate and undergo luteinization (right).

developed in October, as much as six months before ovulation occurs at the end of hibernation. The cells of the cumulus oöphorus of these long-lived follicles undergo marked hypertrophy and accumulate enormous quantities of glycogen.[46] This cumulus mass surrounds the ovum and is regarded as an adaptation that makes possible the long survival of the follicle under conditions of drastically reduced metabolism in the individuals as they hang torpid in hibernation (Fig. 12–8).

The endocrine aspects of reproduction need to be studied more carefully in the Insectivora, *i.e.*, hedgehogs, shrews, and moles. In the European mole (*Talpa europaea* L.) there is a deposit of interstitial tissue massed separately from the ovigenous part of the ovary, and the former shrinks in size during heat and pregnancy. In the shrews (*e.g., Blarina, Elephantus*) luteinizing granulosa cells obliterate the antrum and push the ovum and its surrounding ball of cumulus cells out of the follicle. It thus appears that in these species preovulatory luteinization is a major factor in freeing the egg from the follicle.

The vesicular follicles of the sow are semitransparent and stand out from the surface of the ovary like a bunch of grapes. The follicles that are about to rupture measure 7 to 10 mm. in diameter. Rather

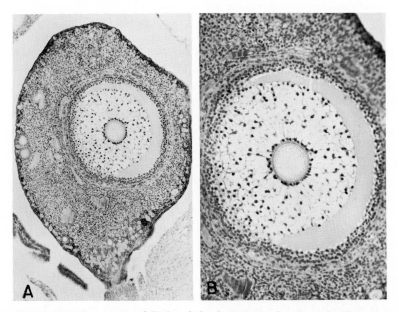

Figure 12–8. An ovarian follicle of the bat *Myotis lucifugus lucifugus* at two levels of magnification. The cumulus cells hypertrophy and accumulate enormous quantities of glycogen, an adaptation which enables the follicle to survive the prolonged period of hibernation. *A,* Lower magnification showing the follicle in relation to the whole ovary; *B,* the same follicle at higher magnification. (From Wimsatt, W. A., and Kallen, F. C.: Anat. Rec., *129,* 1957.)

large quantities of liquor folliculi are lost at ovulation and a slight oozing of blood may occur. The ovaries of the horse are kidney-shaped, the depression being called the "ovulation fossa." It was formerly thought that ovulations occurred only from this fossa, but it is known now that they may occur elsewhere as well. The vesicular follicle of the mare may reach a diameter of 2 inches and contain from 60 to 80 cc. of fluid.[2] The ovaries of the new-born seal weigh 32 to 36 gm. and those of the mother weigh 25 to 28 gm. Several weeks after birth the ovaries are fully involuted and weigh only 2 to 4 gm. Ovulation is usually suppressed during pregnancy, but it has been said to occur occasionally in women, cattle, sheep, rats, rabbits, hamsters, rabbits, and other species.

Another ovarian component of endocrine importance is the *corpus luteum*, a yellow-colored body that typically differentiates from the wall of the postovulatory follicle. Although clotted blood, forming a *corpus hemorrhagicum*, accumulates in the newly ruptured follicles of rodents and certain other mammals, such a structure is not conspicuous in primates. In human ovaries the collapsed follicle is promptly filled with proliferating cells, which grow inwardly from the theca interna and membrana granulosa. Changes in the follicular wall, signifying impending luteinization, are observable in most species a short time before the follicle actually ruptures. The corpora lutea are an important source of progesterone and, since estrogens can be extracted from luteal tissue, it is probable that they synthesize both types of steroid hormones. During the human menstrual cycle the corpora lutea remain functional for 7 to 11 days but, if pregnancy occurs, functional activity is prolonged for several months. Vesicular follicles sometimes undergo extensive luteinization without having ovulated and give rise to the *corpora atretica*, or pseudolutein bodies.

Reproduction in the armadillo (*Dasypus novemcinctus*) is characterized by a specific polyembryony, which normally results in the formation of identical quadruplets. Only one egg is ovulated during each reproductive cycle. Within the ruptured follicle is formed a single, huge corpus luteum, which accounts for about 90 per cent of the volume of this ovary.[41]

It appears that ovulations and the formation of *accessory* corpora lutea are the rule in the pregnant mare, African elephant, Indian antelope (nilgai), and perhaps other mammals. The corpora lutea of pregnancy seem to be very short-lived in the pregnant mare and begin to regress by the end of the first month.[2] During the second and third months of pregnancy ovarian activity attains a high peak, and it is probable that ovulations occur and new corpora lutea are formed in order to maintain the gestational requirements. By the end of the sixth month of pregnancy the mare's ovary contains neither corpora lutea nor large follicles. In the mare and many other species, the placenta acts as an adjunct to the ovary and assumes the function of supplying the hormones that are necessary for the continuation of pregnancy (Fig. 15–2).

Corpora lutea may be considered as adaptations that have made possible the evolution of viviparity. Although they have reached their highest degree of functional specialization in mammals, luteal structures are known to occur in the ovaries of other vertebrate classes. They have been described in both oviparous and ovoviviparous selachians, teleosts, and reptiles.[32] Corpora lutea are present in the ovaries of egg-laying mammals (*e.g.,* duck-billed platypus), and it has been suggested that their secretions may perform a role in lactation and in nursing behavior. In general it seems probable that the hormones of the corpus luteum are concerned with the retention of embryos in the uterus or with the storage of eggs in the oviduct.

The Avian Ovary

In the great majority of birds only the left ovary and oviduct are functional. The right ovary is present in the chick embryo and remains macroscopically visible for a short time after hatching, but in the mature bird, it is a rudiment that can be identified only by microscopic procedures. The right rudiment undergoes development if the functional ovary is destroyed by disease or is removed surgically.

The avian ovary differs anatomically from that of mammals in several important respects. The larger avian follicles are not contained within the ovarian stroma. The egg cells that are destined to reach ovulatory size, as well as those that become atretic in the process, are borne on follicular stalks (Fig. 12–9). There is no antrum and no collection of follicular fluid. The egg itself is surrounded by the vitelline membrane, the membrana granulosa, and the theca folliculi; all of these are quite comparable to their mammalian counterparts. The *stigma* (cicatrix), the area that ruptures at ovulation to permit the exit of the egg from the follicle, develops on the follicular wall opposite the stalked attachment. Although the follicular sac is gradually absorbed after ovulation, the calyx and stalk are nondeciduate structures and are retained. Each follicular stalk bears a large number of follicles; these range in size from microscopic structures too small to be seen with the unaided eye to an egg just ready to be ovulated. After ovulation the abandoned stalk continues to be used by the younger follicles; the largest one dominates and grows to ovulatory size.

Avian ova are among the most rapid-growing structures to be found among higher vertebrates. Tremendous quantities of yolk are accumulated quickly. In the domestic fowl, ova weighing less than 100 mg. reach mature size and attain a weight of 18 to 20 gm. in nine days. A very complicated vascular supply develops in connection

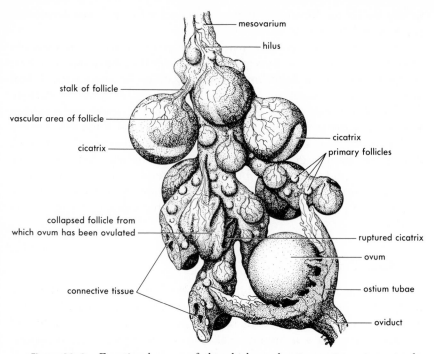

Figure 12–9. Functional ovary of the chicken, showing various stages in the maturation of the ova. A mature ovum has just been released and is entering the ostium of the oviduct. (From Nelsen, O. E.: Comparative Embryology of the Vertebrates. New York, McGraw-Hill Book Co., 1953.)

with each growing follicle. This consists of an extensive complex of veins, arranged in three concentric layers in the follicular wall and terminating in a fine meshwork of venules enveloping the growing ovum. In contrast, the arterial supply to the follicle is relatively meager. This venous stasis apparently permits blood to remain in the follicle long enough for the yolk antecedents to be transferred to the egg. The main part of this vascular arrangement is used in succession by other follicles on the same stalk that are awaiting their turn to grow to ovulatory size.[34]

Mammalian species ovulate one or a few eggs at certain periods of the reproductive cycle. In contrast to this the bird may release eggs from the ovary day after day over protracted periods. Only a single follicle, the largest of the series, responds to the ovulation stimulus but, at the same time, many others accumulate yolk and continue toward maturity.

Corpora lutea are not found in avian ovaries. As in mammals, follicles may become atretic at any stage and these have sometimes been mistakenly described as "avian corpora lutea." There is evidence, however, that both estrogen and progesterone are necessary for the normal integration of the reproductive cycles in birds. Blood from laying hens has progesterone activity as assayed by the Hooker-Forbes test, and there are indications that progesterone, or a hormone of equivalent effect, is present in the ovarian follicles of such animals. There is also ample evidence that the ovary of the domestic fowl secretes androgen. In the chicken and certain other species, the postovulatory follicle remains visible for a considerable time and it may well be that it performs some endocrine function. In fowl ovaries, clusters of interstitial cells, similar to those found in the rudimentary gonad, may be present in the vicinity of the theca. Such cells may secrete androgen or some other steroid hormone, but there is not enough experimental evidence to prove it.

The Amphibian Ovary

The amphibian ovary is essentially a hollow structure; no fluid collects in the growing follicles; and after ovulation, luteal bodies do not typically differentiate in the collapsed follicles. The ovary of the frog is composed of six or seven lobes, which contract separately. Since these spontaneous contractions occur rather constantly in both sexually mature and immature specimens, they do not seem to be associated with ovulation except as this process may be influenced by the circulation of blood.

The ovary is essentially a two-layered pouch with the eggs situated between the two layers. As the eggs leave the ovarian epithelium, they become surrounded by a single layer of follicle cells. The follicles grow and bulge into the cavities of the lobes, but the stalked attachments to the ovarian wall are retained. Outside the follicular cells is a layer of smooth muscle that constitutes the cyst wall. This wall of muscular tissue does not completely enclose the egg but is reflected around the stalk that attaches the follicle to the outer surface of the ovary. The inner epithelial membrane covers the exterior of the follicle and, like the cyst wall, is anchored on all sides of the stalked attachment. Thus at the stalk there is a region where the egg, together with its surrounding follicle cells, is directly exposed to the outer surface of the ovary. This is the area of ultimate rupture of the follicle. There is no loss of blood at ovulation, apparently owing to the fact that blood vessels are practically absent from the rupture area or stigma. The remaining portion of the follicle is well supplied with blood vessels. Though vascular connections are not essential for the completion of ovulation in frogs and other amphibians, it is noteworthy that the emission of eggs from a lobe of the ovary is retarded by poor circulation.

The Fish Ovary

Among viviparous fishes the ovaries are not only structures for the production of ova and hormones, but they are somewhat similar to uteri, inasmuch as they provide housing and nourishment for the developing young. The eggs may be fertilized within the ovarian follicle and retained there to continue their development; in such cases, ovulation either does not occur or it is synonymous with the birth of young. In other species, the eggs are ovulated into a special chamber of the ovary where fertilization occurs and in which the young are retained and nourished. Sperm often live for prolonged periods within the ovaries of such fishes. The teleost fishes are a very versatile group, and one may find among them almost every reproductive device characteristic of the higher vertebrates.

THE MALE ACCESSORY SEX ORGANS

The accessory ducts and glands of the male are specializations for the storage of spermatozoa and for their conveyance, in an adequate vehicle, to the exterior at the proper time. These structures in the human male include multiple ductuli efferentes, paired epididymides, vasa deferentia, seminal vesicles, ejaculatory ducts, Cowper's glands, a prostate gland, the urethra with its multiple glands of Littré, and the copulatory organ itself (Fig. 12–4). The urethra of the male serves to convey seminal products as well as urine. There are a large number of anatomic and functional variations among the different mammalian species.

The epididymis is an extremely convoluted tube that, in some domestic animals, measures around twenty feet in length when straightened out. The epididymis is a storage place for spermatozoa, which have been shown to improve in their capacity for motility and fertilization after a period of residence in this organ.

The vas deferens ascends through the inguinal canal, arches over the ureter, and continues medially to the base of the urinary bladder where it receives the duct from the seminal vesicle. It then becomes known as the ejaculatory duct, which courses through the substance of the prostate and enters the prostatic portion of the urethra. The vas deferens contains well-developed muscle layers and is largely responsible for the movement of sperm along the tract. In a number of species, including the human, sperm storage may occur in the proximal end of the vas deferens, as well as in the epididymis. The spermatozoa are believed to be nonmotile in these storage structures but become motile when mixed with the accessory gland secretions. All of these accessory elements depend on androgenic hormones for full functional development and are quite inactive until the advent of puberty.

The seminal fluid, emanating from the accessory glands, is quite variable among mammals, both with respect to volume and chemical composition. It furnishes a vehicle for the conveyance of germ cells and perhaps provides an environment in which they can retain their greatest fertilizing capacity. It appears that the accessory gland secretions may not be absolutely necessary for fertilizing ability: sperms taken directly from the testis or epididymis have some capacity to fertilize eggs. Sperms become motile when exposed to the air and mixed with any physiologic fluid; motility, however, is not necessarily an index of fertilizing capacity. Some species (*e.g.,* cat and dog) have no seminal vesicles. Fertility in the rat and boar is not appreciably affected by removing both the seminal vesicles and prostate.

The semen of rats coagulates promptly upon ejaculation, and this forms the vaginal plug present in the female tract after mating. An enzyme contained in the secretion from the coagulating gland causes the semen to harden. This plug sometimes drops out of the vagina shortly after mating, but it is gradually resorbed if it remains in the vagina. The finding of a vaginal plug is frequently used as a means of obtaining timed copulations. A similar plug is formed in guinea pigs and squirrels, but not in the majority of mammals. Human semen coagulates shortly after ejaculation but soon liquefies owing to the action of a proteolytic enzyme presumably derived from the prostate.

The male accessory structures of certain passerine birds undergo modifications during the breeding season to form seminal vesicles, or glomera, for the storage of sperms at temperatures lower than those of the body cavity. The glomera arise through the growth and coiling of the vasa deferentia, eventually forming storage organs which protrude from the cloacal wall.[53]

THE FEMALE ACCESSORY SEX ORGANS

The female accessories include the oviducts, or fallopian tubes as they are generally termed in the human subject, the uterus, the vagina, and the external genitalia. The functional status of these organs is conditioned by the ovarian hormones.

Mammals

The oviduct provides a passageway between the ovary and uterus. The ovarian end of this tube is expanded into a funnel, having a fimbriated margin, and is usually closely applied to the ovary. Some of the epithelial cells lining the tube possess cilia that beat inwardly. This, together with the increased activity of the fimbria at the time of ovulation, probably assists in the apprehension of the ovum and its movement toward the uterus. By removing one ovary and ligating the oviduct on the contralateral side, it has been shown in laboratory animals that some of the eggs that are freed into the body cavity can traverse the patent oviduct. In some species the oviduct forms a bursa, or periovarial sac, that encapsulates the ovary.[47] In the dog and fox, the bursa contains a slitlike opening through which the ovary may be expressed, but in the rat and mouse the bursa is completely closed except for a very minute pore.

Fertilization typically occurs in the oviducts. In the human being this generally occurs in the upper end of the tube, usually within 24 hours after the egg has been freed from the ovary (Fig. 12–5). Secretions from the tubal mucosa are thought to be important in denudation of the ovum and its penetration by the spermatozoon. The early embryo arrives in the uterus about three days after ovulation and implants in the wall of the uterus four to six days after arriving there. Experiments on rabbits and rats indicate that the spermatozoa must be exposed to the secretions of the female tract for a certain period before they acquire the capacity to fertilize eggs. This phenomenon is called capacitation, and it is not known how extensively it applies to other species.[12]

The primate uterus is a pear-shaped muscular organ suspended in the broad ligament. The uterine wall is composed of a serous covering (perimetrium), a thick mass of interwoven smooth muscle cells (myometrium), and a glandular lining (endometrium). The *body*, or corpus uteri, bends forward and rests against the urinary bladder. The *fundus* is the portion of the body that extends cranially above the entrance of the fallopian tubes. The narrow caudal end of the uterus is the *cervix*, which communicates with the vagina by means of the *external os uteri*. The surface of the endometrium is sloughed during each menstruation, but during pregnancy, it becomes highly modified to facilitate implantation of the blastocyst and its subsequent development.

The female accessory organs are derived mostly from the paired müllerian ducts of the embryo, but the evolutionary tendency has been to produce unpaired structures in the adult. The primitive mammals (*e.g.*, opossum) have two vaginae, two cervices, and two separate and unconnected uterine bodies. The cleft penis of the male marsupial correlates functionally with the existence of paired vaginae in the female. All of the higher mammals have single vaginae. Many gradations may be found between *duplex* and *simplex* types of uteri. In rats and rabbits each uterus is completely separated from the other and has its own cervix. In such forms as the pig the cervix has become single and the caudal ends of the uteri have fused a little to produce a small body. In the cow, ewe, dog, cat, etc., the uterine body remains small, but the two uterine horns are separated by a conspicuous septum. Fusion has become more extensive in the mare, giving rise to a large uterine body with small horns. Among primates the fusion is complete and the horns are absent.

The anatomy of the *cervix* varies among the different species of mammals, but it contains dense fibrous tissue, as well as muscle cells, and functions as a sphincter. The cervical glands produce a large amount of thin, alkaline mucus during the preovulatory period of the primate cycle, and this may favor sperm migration, motility, and longevity. The cervix is kept rather tightly closed at all times except during parturition when it softens and undergoes marked dilatation. In many species the cervical mucus hardens during pregnancy and forms a plug that seals off the uterus from the vagina. The cervical plug liquefies shortly before parturition. Breaking the seal in cattle apparently exposes the uterus to bacterial invasion and generally leads to the loss of the fetus.

In most mammals many more eggs are shed than are implanted. An extreme case is the elephant shrew (*Elephantus*), which may release more than a hundred eggs from the ovaries, but only one or two implant in the uterus. The opposite condition is found in the armadillo: only one egg is shed and fertilized; then it divides and produces identical quadruplets. Furthermore, *delayed implantation* occurs normally in the Texas armadillo. The blastocyst is formed in the tube and then passes into the uterus where it becomes lodged in a pocket and remains unattached for a period of three or four months. Blastocysts of the grey seal remain in the uterus for about 100 days before becoming implanted.[4] Delayed implantation also occurs in the badger, marten, and roe deer, and probably in bears and mink.

Under certain conditions, delayed implantation occurs in such laboratory mammals as the rat and mouse. These species come into estrus and ovulate after delivering a litter. If copulation is permitted at this postpartum heat, the female carries a litter *in utero* while she is suckling the first litter. However, the gestation period for the second litter appears to be significantly longer than the normal 21 days; the second litter may not be delivered until 30, 40, or even 50 days after the postpartum mating. In these cases the eggs fertilized at the postpartum heat have been found to develop normally in the oviducts, but float free in the uterus without implanting. They eventually implant when the proper endocrine situation prevails and have a gestation period of 21 days just as in other pregnancies.

A progestational endometrium suitable for the reception of the blastocyst may develop only in localized areas of the endometrium. In mammals that have cotyledonary placentas (*e.g.*, cattle and sheep) no glands are found below the cotyledons; these areas are set aside as special sites for placental attachment. In the giant fruit bat (*Pteropus giganteus* B.) a progestational endometrium develops only in a localized area of one uterus. This asymmetric implantation area appears at the extreme distal end of the uterus and is in close anatomic contact with the single corpus luteum of that ovary. It is possible that progesterone from the corpus luteum is delivered directly to this implantation area, without being distributed by the general circulation. The pregnant females spend much of their time hanging head downward, and it has been suggested that this implantation area may serve the purpose of letting the large fetus rest against the diaphragm, thus preventing strain and injury to the uterus and its attachments.[27]

The human vagina is an unpaired, dilatable tube, approximately 4 inches in length, extending from the caudal end of the uterus to the vestibule. The lining of the vagina is a stratified squamous epithelium devoid of glands; the muscle layers are thin. Before coition the external vaginal orifice is more or less occluded by a membranous *hymen.* This membrane generally becomes perforate during fetal life, but in some instances it may persist until adolescence and interfere with the elimination of menstrual discharge.

In rats, mice, and guinea pigs the caudal vagina is a solid cord of epithelial cells until ovarian functions become well established during postnatal life. The vaginal introitus in these species is controlled by estrogenic hormones, although it may be influenced by environmental factors such as temperature. In the hamster, however, perforation of the vagina occurs eight to nine days after birth in both intact and ovariectomized females, suggesting that the process may not be under hormonal control in this species. A membrane closes the vagina of the guinea pig during the diestrous periods of the cycle.

The vagina does not provide a satisfactory environment for the survival of spermatozoa. In the human, they die within a few hours, whereas they may remain viable for two or three days in the uterus and fallopian tubes. In bats and certain other species the spermatozoa may remain viable in the female tract for many months.

The external genitalia of the female consist of the clitoris, the labia majora and minora, and certain glands that open into the vestibule (Fig. 12–5). The latter groove is bounded laterally by the labia. The clitoris is an erectile organ homologous with the penis; it consists of small cavernous bodies ending in the rudimentary glans clitoridis. The glands of Bartholin, homologous to Cowper's glands in the male, open by ducts into the vestibule.

Birds

At the time of ovulation the egg cytoplasm contains large stores of proteins, fats, vitamins, and minerals. As it traverses the oviduct it receives additional supplies of water and protein in the form of an albumenous coating (egg white) and acquires the shell membranes and shell.

In the great majority of birds only the left oviduct grows to functional size; the right is lost entirely or persists as a rudiment.

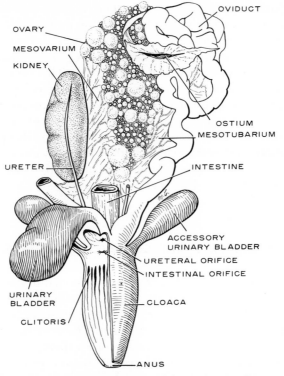

OVIDUCT

OVARY

MESOVARIUM

KIDNEY

OSTIUM
MESOTUBARIUM

URETER

INTESTINE

ACCESSORY
URINARY BLADDER

URETERAL ORIFICE

INTESTINAL ORIFICE

URINARY
BLADDER

CLOACA

CLITORIS

ANUS

Figure 12–10. Female urogenital system of the turtle, *Pseudemys scripta*, ventral view. The ventral surface of the cloaca has been removed on one side to disclose the various openings into it; the urinary bladder is retracted to the right; only the left ovary is shown.

The avian oviduct is a rather sizable tube extending from the region of the ovary to the cloaca. From craniad to caudad, the main regions are infundibulum, magnum, isthmus, shell gland (uterus), and vagina.

The ovulated egg falls into the body cavity and is fertilized there or after it is taken up by the funnel-shaped infundibulum. The hen's egg remains in the infundibulum for about 15 minutes and while there acquires the chalazae, the springlike cords that extend through the albumen from the yolk to the poles of the egg. The magnum is the longest portion of the oviduct and contains many large albumen-secreting glands. The next region is the isthmus, the beginning of which is marked externally by the magnum-isthmus junction. The egg spends a little more than an hour here and acquires the shell membranes. The egg is retained longest in the shell gland (about 20 hours) where a porous shell is formed by the deposition of calcium carbonate. After the shell is formed, the egg spends about one minute in the vagina. Here it receives a thin coat of mucus, presumably to seal the pores and thus prevent rapid evaporation of water and to protect against bacterial invasion. The normal interval between ovulation and laying is 25 to 26 hours in the domestic fowl.

When foreign bodies such as glass beads are introduced into the avian oviduct, the various glandular regions deposit their secretions around them just as if they were living ova. The endocrine factors involved in control of the avian oviduct are reasonably well known, but the physical mechanisms involved in the deposition of albumen, membranes, and shell are largely obscure. For example, the egg normally traverses the oviduct with the pointed end directed caudad, and this definitive shape becomes apparent shortly after the ovum has entered the magnum and acquired a very meager coating of albumen.

The genital organs of oviparous reptiles are very similar to those of birds (Fig. 12–10).

THE SECONDARY SEXUAL CHARACTERS

The secondary sexual characters are physical differences between the sexes that have nothing to do with the production and movement of gametes, but that may serve to bring the sexes together for courtship, to provide for the protection or nutrition of the young, or to facilitate amplexus.[44] In the human species there are sexual differences in body build, distribution of fat, degree of development of the mammary glands, distribution of hair and pigment, and physical differences in the larynx. It is well established that some of these characters are under the control of hormones. That genetic influences also operate is attested by the fact that there are marked differences in the amount and distribution of body and facial hair among the different ethnic groups. Thus males of the Mongoloid and Caucasian groups are generally very different in this respect. The hormonal control of secondary characters has not been so carefully studied in the human as in birds.

The pattern of control of these sex differences may be very complex and frequently varies from group to group. The immediate expression of the characters may be genetic or hormonal, but it is always basically genetic, since the type of regulation is determined by the genetic complex inherent in the species.

In some breeds of sheep the ram possesses horns, whereas the ewe does not. Orchiectomy suppresses growth of the horns and they are retained in the same condition as they were at the time of the operation. In breeds in which both sexes have horns, the heavy growth characteristic of the ram is prevented by orchiectomy, ovariectomy having no effect on horn growth. In other breeds, both sexes are hornless, and horns do not develop after gonadectomy.

Antlers are typical secondary sexual characters in Virginia deer and are present in males but not in females. Their development is regulated by a complicated interplay of genetic factors and of hormones from the gonads and hypophysis.

Many birds undergo very striking seasonal and sexual variations in the pigmentation of their bills.[49] The bill pigments are mainly brown and black melanins and red, orange, and yellow carotenoids. The melanins are synthesized by melanophores, located in the basal layer of the epidermis, and the pigments are transferred to epidermal cells which move toward the cornified outer layers of the bill. The carotenoids are derived from food, instead of being synthesized by the bird.

In the house sparrow (*Passer domesticus*), the bills of both sexes are light brown during the nonbreeding season (eclipse) and become jet black as the breeding season begins. Gonadectomy of either sex stops the deposition of melanin and the bills become light ivory in color. Melanin deposition, resulting in black bills, is reinstated by injecting androgens, but estrogens and progesterone have no effect. This is very strong evidence that the avian ovary, as well as the testis, is capable of secreting androgens. The bills of male and female starlings (*Sturnus vulgaris*) are bright orange during the breeding season and black during the eclipse. After gonadectomy, the bills of both sexes become black; androgens restore the orange color (carotenoids) of the bills, but estrogens and progesterone do not have this effect.

There is much variability among birds in the extent of dependence of secondary sex characters upon genetic and hormonal factors. The plumages of the house sparrow and certain other species are neither modified by gonadectomy nor by the administration of gonadal and pituitary hormones. The normal plumage dimorphism seems to be genetic and autogenous instead of hormonal.

Plumage changes have been extensively studied in the Brown Leghorn fowl. The cock plumage is generally considered to be the neutral form, the hen plumage requiring estrogen for its differentiation. Orchiectomy has no effect on the plumage, but total ovariectomy causes the appearance of cock plumage. Exogenous androgens have no effect on the plumage, but estrogens or ovarian transplants induce the "henny" plumage in both sexes.

In the Sebright Bantam both cocks and hens are normally hen feathered, and both sexes assume the cock plumage following gonadectomy. Treatment of the castrates with either estrogens or androgens induces the reappearance of hen feathering. The failure of cock plumage to develop in normal males of this breed is due to the appearance of a mutant gene which prevents the feather germs from developing cock feathering in response to androgens.

The *syrinx* is an organ of voice production in birds, and its development is regulated by gonadal hormones. The syrinx of the male duck is asymmetrical and well developed; that of the female

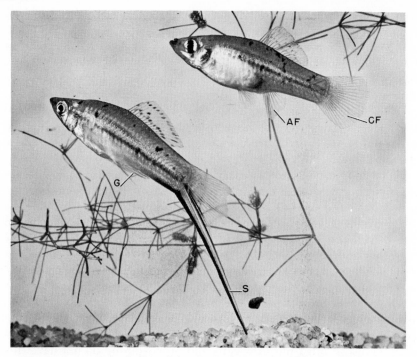

Figure 12–11. Male (left) and female (right) specimens of *Xipophorus hellerii.* Notice that the anal fin (AF) of the male is modified into an intromittent organ, the gonopodium (G): the caudal fin (CF) of the male is modified to form a sword (S). These fin specializations in the male are conditioned by testicular hormones and may be induced in the female by proper treatment with androgens. (Courtesy of James W. Atz, The American Museum of Natural History, New York, N. Y.)

is small and symmetrical. Castration of the duck embryo leads to the development of a male type syrinx. It has been shown that ovarian steroids normally operate to inhibit the development of the male type syrinx in females.[51]

The middle foreclaws of the slider turtle (*Pseudemys scripta troostii*) become modified as secondary characters employed in courtship. Growth of the claws in the juvenile animal may be accelerated by male sex hormone or prevented from developing by removing the testes.[15] The male toad (*Bufo arenarum*) normally croaks and develops a black callosity on the thumb during the breeding season. Both may be eliminated by castration or reinstated by the administration of testosterone propionate. In these cases it is obvious that the testicular hormone is the immediate conditioning agent.

Many kinds of secondary sex characters, signaling a state of sexual readiness, are found among fishes, and some of these are conditioned by gonadal steroids. Nuptial pigmentation and modifications of the various fins, as well as behavioral patterns, are often very striking. In the swordtail, *Xiphophorus hellerii*, the anal fin of the male becomes modified into an intromittent organ (the gonopodium), and the caudal fin develops the characteristic sword (Fig. 12–11). These fin modifications occurring in the male are dependent upon testicular androgens.

AMBISEXUAL ORGANIZATION OF THE AMNIOTE EMBRYO

The Origin of Germ Cells

It is now well established that the gonocytes, or primordial germ cells, originate extragonadally in the vicinity of the yolk-sac entoderm. Gonocytes are first recognizable in very young human embryos near the caudal end of the primitive streak and are seen in the hindgut entoderm in embryos of only a few millimeters in length. In mammals, these early germ cells move through the tissues and reach the genital ridges largely as a consequence of their own ameboid movements, possibly aided by their capacity for histiolytic destruction of cells and membranes that block their way. Living gonocytes of the mouse have been followed from the yolk sac to the genital ridges, and their ameboid movements recorded cinematographically.[6] In reptiles and birds, the gonocytes first become segregated in the area pellucida, migrate into the blood islands of the area vasculosa, and are carried to the genital ridge area by the peripheral circulation. It is generally believed that the gonocytes are unable to differentiate into somatic elements, and those that fail to reach the gonadal primordia degenerate and disappear.

Embryologic studies clearly indicate that the primitive genital ridges are unable to differentiate into anything resembling gonads unless adequate numbers of gonocytes are incorporated into them. Upon arriving at the gonadal blastema, the germ cells lose many of their characteristic features and are difficult to distinguish from nongerminal elements. Many of the germ cells present in the early gonads die off without accomplishing their transformation into oögonia or spermatogonia. Some workers have held that all the gonocytes degenerate after reaching the gonadal primordia, definitive germ cells being derived from later proliferations of the gonadal epithelium. Others have vigorously insisted that some of the gonocytes do survive and give rise to all definitive germ cells of the testis and ovary, thus constituting a continuous germ line, or Keimbahn. Evidence for the latter point of view has been strengthened by the introduction of new techniques and methods.

Embryogenesis of the Gonads and Accessory Sex Organs

The Gonads

The genital ridges first appear as bilateral thickenings along the mesial edges of the mesonephric kidneys. The gonocytes accumulate in the mid-portions of the ridges, and only these areas contribute to the gonads; the sterile cranial region becomes the suspensory ligament, and the caudal portion contributes to the utero-ovarian ligament. The thickened coelomic epithelium, covering the genital ridge, is at first separated from the underlying mesenchyme by a basement membrane; this soon disappears and cells are actively proliferated from the epithelial surface into the underlying mesenchyme (Fig. 12–12, A and B). This forms a *gonadal blastema* which contains gonocytes and is obviously constructed from mesenchyme and proliferations from the coelomic epithelium. The basement

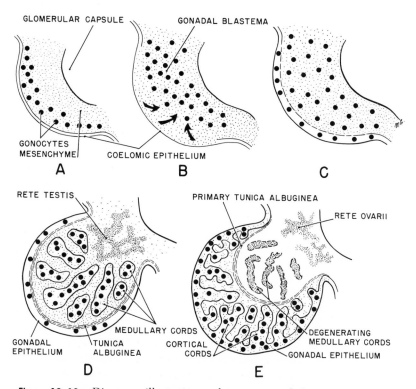

Figure 12–12. Diagrams illustrating embryogenesis of the mammalian gonad. Gonocytes are indicated as blackened circles. *A*, Basement membrane separates coelomic epithelium from underlying mesenchyme. *B*, Basement membrane is lost and coelomic epithelium proliferates actively to form gonad blastema. *C*, Basement membrane is restored and gonocytes are present in the gonadal epithelium. *D*, Medullary cords arise from the gonadal blastema and differentiate into a testis. *E*, Medullary cords regress and cortical proliferations form an ovary. (From Turner, C. D.: Amer. J. Obst. & Gynec., *90*:1208, 1964; modified from figures by R. K. Burns.)

membrane reappears and gonocytes have been incorporated into the epithelial layer (Fig. 12–12, C). The medullary (primary) sex cords arise directly from the gonadal blastema; they incorporate gonocytes together with somatic elements. The rete cords arise from the blastema at a deeper level, and a delicate layer of connective tissue forms below the surface epithelium. This is the presumptive tunica albuginea. In the testis (Fig. 12–12, D), the medullary cords continue their differentiation; the gonocytes eventually form spermatozoa and the somatic elements within the cords become the sustentacular cells of Sertoli. The interstitial cells of Leydig arise from intertubular elements, and the tunica becomes markedly thickened. The surface epithelium, with its gonocytes, typically disappears early, thus removing all potentiality for cortical development. Cortical (secondary) cords may start to form in the human testis, and in certain other species, but such proliferations are normally abortive.

In ovarian differentiation (Fig. 12–12, E) the medullary cords, corresponding to the seminiferous tubules, involute, and a conspicuous system of cortical (secondary) cords arises from the gonadal epithelium. The gonocytes which are entrapped within the cortical cords give rise to ova, whereas the somatic elements of the cords become follicle cells. It is important to note that the somatic elements within the medullary and cortical cords differentiate into Sertoli cells and follicle cells, respectively, and that these constituents of the testis and ovary are homologous. The interstitial cells of the ovary, as well as the thecal layers of the follicles, arise from intertubular components. The medullary part of the ovary may normally undergo considerable development and hypertrophy in some mammalian species as the mole, certain shrews, and the fetal ovary of the horse.

The sex-determining mechanism which is established at fertilization directs and controls all of the later ontogenetic processes (postgenetic differentiation) involved in the formation of testes or ovaries and corresponding accessory genitalia. The somatic cells of the embryo, as well as the primordial germ cells, carry sex-determining genes. It appears that the primordial germ cells are dependent upon the cortical and medullary components of the early gonad for the special influences that direct their differentiation into sperms or eggs. Gonocytes which lodge in the cortex typically become eggs; those of the medulla become sperms. The cortex and medulla are, of course, genetically determined, and they appear to exert contrasting influences upon the early germ cells. The basic problem is how the sex-determining genes act upon the genital primordia to condition their differentiation into male or female organs.

The Accessory Ducts and Glands

The Wolffian and Müllerian ducts are discrete primordia which temporarily coexist during the ambisexual period of development

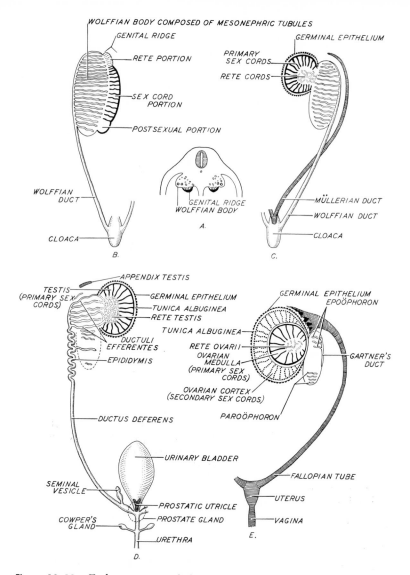

Figure 12–13. Embryogenesis of the genital system in amniotes. *A*, Section through the dorsal region of an early embryo, showing the Wolffian bodies (mesonephric kidneys) and the genital ridges on their mediolateral surfaces. *B*, The Wolffian body and genital ridge in sagittal section. With respect to the fate of its parts the genital ridge is divisible into three general regions. The Wolffian (mesonephric) ducts drain the kidneys, but genital ducts as such are not present. *C*, The indifferent (ambisexual) stage. The rete cords have become enclosed by the primary sex cords. The Müllerian ducts appear and temporarily coexist with the Wolffian ducts in both genetic males and females. *D*, Differentiation of the male genitalia. *E*, Differentiation of the female genitalia.

The primary sex cords are shown in solid black, whereas the secondary sex cords are represented by large stipples. The Müllerian ducts and their derivatives are heavily cross hatched; the Wolffian ducts are relatively unshaded.

in all amniotes, regardless of genetic sex determination (Fig. 12–13). One type of duct persists normally and gives rise to accessory ducts and glands, whereas the heterologous system disappears except for unimportant vestiges. Though genetic sex determination is present from the time of fertilization, regression of the heterologous duct system does not occur until the postgenetic differentiation of the gonad is well advanced.

Neutral Primordia

The urogenital sinus and genital tubercle are neutral primordia which are present in the embryos of both sexes. Whether they differentiate in the male or female direction depends upon whether the gonad becomes a testis or an ovary. Male and female genitalia originating from primordia of this type are homologous.

MODIFICATIONS OF POSTGENETIC SEXUAL DEVELOPMENT

Theories of Sexual Differentiation

Hormone Theory

Lillie attempted to account for cattle freemartins on the basis of androgenic hormones arising from the fetal testes of the male co-twin.[26] The freemartin is an intersexed female, always associated *in utero* with a male co-twin. The condition results only in those cases where there is an early fusion of the two placentae and a consequent intermingling of blood between the two fetuses. The external genitalia of the freemartin are generally female in type, but the clitoris is often enlarged. Although there are many gradations in severity, the accessory sex organs usually consist of both Wolffian and Müllerian duct derivatives. The gonads are hypoplastic and may contain sterile seminiferous tubules with practically no cortical development; in other instances, both cortical and medullary components may be present to form the equivalent of an ovotestis. Similar anomalies have been reported in sheep, goats, and pigs. Placental fusion may occur in cats, rabbits, marmosets, and human beings without resulting in any sexual anomaly. These negative findings do not necessarily invalidate the hormone theory; they do suggest that the vascular anastomoses must occur at a very early age in order to modify the sexual development of the female fetus. It is also possible that in certain species effective amounts of testicular hormones are absent from the blood at the critical period, or that the masculinizing agents are counterbalanced in some manner by the female recipient. There may also be species variations with respect to the androgen production by the fetal testis. Since the availability of pure steroid hormones, there have been repeated failures to duplicate the gonadal impairments experimentally.

Corticomedullary Inductor Theory

This concept is based on the fact that the early gonads of vertebrates are composed of discrete primordia (medulla and cortex) which are genetically determined to form testes or ovaries, respectively. There is no transformation of one primordium into the other, but rather a development of one accompanied by the recession of the other. Witschi theorized, largely on the basis of his amphibian studies, that the medulla and cortex might be the source of special substances (medullarin and corticin) which act after the manner of embryonic inductors. According to this view, corticin would have the over-all effect of inhibiting the medulla, and medullarin would inhibit the cortex.[48]

Several facts should be kept in mind with respect to the hypothetical gonadal inductors: (1) there is necessarily much vagueness in the use of the term "inductor"; (2) such materials have never been isolated and chemically identified; and (3) there is no information on the biochemical mechanisms which intervene between the sex genes and the characters they determine. There is no doubt that steroid hormones and gonadal grafts can modify or completely reverse gonadal differentiation in certain vertebrates. It is not known whether steroid hormones act directly, in these instances, as "inductors," or produce their effects secondarily by modifying some kind of an inductor system.

Spontaneous and Experimental Sexual Transformations

Intersexuality occurs spontaneously in all classes of vertebrates, and may be produced experimentally by a variety of procedures, particularly when these are applied during the ambisexual period of development. Hermaphroditism occurs in many of the lower vertebrates, and this may be considered a normal aspect of their life cycles. The experimental procedures include gonad grafting, administration of hormones, surgical ablations, parabiosis, tissue culture, and the creation of various unfavorable states. The literature in this area is voluminous, and space does not permit more than a brief account of current concepts and the description of only a few examples.

Fishes

The gonads of the lamprey and other cyclostomes are unpaired structures extending almost the entire length of the body cavity. The accessory sex organs of the cyclostome are simple (Fig. 12–14). The mature germ cells are freed into the body cavity and are passed through peritoneal funnels and abdominal pores into a urogenital sinus which opens to the exterior. The sinus of the male opens to the outside through a small orifice at the tip of a penis-like structure. Although both ovarian and testicular tissues are generally present in the same gonad, the individuals of most species function either as males or as females throughout their lives.

Reproductive processes are more varied among bony fishes than in any other vertebrate class.[3] Some species function first as males and later as females (protandry); others function first as females and become males later in life (protogyny). *Rivulus marmoratus* is the only teleost definitely known to reproduce regularly by fertilizing its own eggs. Self-fertilization apparently occurs in the ovarian cavity, and nearly all of the young are females.[20] Many gradations are found between species characterized by hermaphroditism and those that are highly gonochoristic.

The developing gonads of cyclostomes and teleosts do not possess cortical and medullary components, and, in this respect, differ from all other vertebrates. The gonad primordium arises from the coelomic epithelium, without the participation of a mesonephric blastema. Some have argued that this unique character of the gonad primordium might correlate with the relatively high

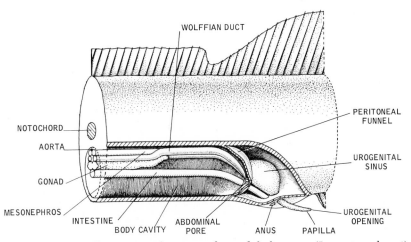

Figure 12–14. The urogenital system of an adult lamprey *(Lampetra planeri)*. Mature germ cells are freed into the body cavity and reach the exterior by passing through abdominal pores and the urogenital sinus. (From a dissection by Dr. S. Ishii.)

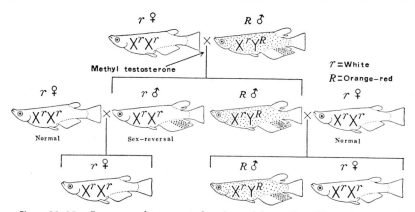

Figure 12–15. Sex reversal in genetic female medaka produced by androgen. When reversed genetic females are mated with normal genetic females, all-female progenies result. (From Yamamoto, T.: J. Exp. Zool., *137*, 1958.)

frequency of hermaphroditism in these groups, but this remains uncertain.

The medaka (*Oryzias latipes*) is an oviparous cyprinodont fish in which complete sex reversals have been obtained by the administration of gonadal hormones to genetically analyzed breeds. The newly hatched young have sexually indifferent gonads, and there is no tendency for the juvenile males to undergo a temporary female-like stage of gonadal development. In the medaka the sex determining mechanism is XX for female and XY for male, the genes for skin color (R = orange-red; r = white) being present in the sex chromosomes (Fig. 12–15).

Through the use of proper mating types, it has been shown that intersexes and complete sex reversals can be produced in *Oryzias* by administering estrone to genetic males (XY). Sex-reversed orange-red males, functioning as females (X^rY^R), were mated with normal orange-red males (X^rY^R) and progeny testings made on F_1 sons. A single orange-red son among the F_1 offspring was identified as the Y^RY^R male, which had sired all-male offspring.[54]

When genetic females of *Oryzias* are treated with methyltestosterone, they become completely reversed and develop the sex equipment and reproductive capacity of normal males. Progenies consisting only of females resulted when sex reversed males of the female genetic constitution (X^rX^r) were crossed with normal females (X^rX^r) either by natural mating or by artificial fertilization (Fig. 12–15). When excessive amounts of the androgen are given, both genetic males and females differentiate into males with rudimentary testes and later become neuters because of the complete destruction of germ cells.[55, 56]

Studies on *Oryzias* illustrate two important principles: (1) the early gonads, as well as the accessory system, have the ability to differentiate in a direction opposite to their own genetic constitution, and (2) the early germ cells are bipotential and, in spite of their genetic constitution, can become functional eggs or sperms. The breeding experiments show that the genome, or genetic complement, of the germ cells is not altered by the procedures employed in producing the reversal of sex.

The experiments on these fishes indicate that there is a critical period in development during which the hormones are effective. Sex differentiation in genetic males of *Oryzias* has been reversed by injecting estrone or stilbestrol into the eggs, the estrogens apparently being retained until sex differentiation begins.[21]

Amphibians[16, 18]

It is well known that many physiologic alterations, such as nutritional level, disease, and factors in the physical environment, can result in sex reversals in certain animals. Among certain Amphibia low temperatures, prevailing during larval life, have been found to encourage the differentiation of females and higher temperatures to be productive of males. Histologic studies indicate that low temperatures retard the medullary component of the gonad, whereas high temperatures retard or completely destroy the cortex. Thus at high temperatures the ovaries are gradually changed into testes. A comparable effect of temperature on the differentiation of gonads from embryonic rats has been reported. Over-ripeness of the amphibian egg before fertilization occurs is harmful to the germ cells. If anuran eggs are inseminated after being retained within the ovisac for an extended time, a high preponderance of males results therefrom. The cortical portion of the gonad is impaired in the young that develop from these stale eggs. It is not known whether such environmental factors influence sex differentiation in the human, but they may well do so.

It is apparent from our previous discussion of embryology that sex differentiation is a competitive process between genital primordia. It would be instructive to remove the dominant portion of a gonad surgically and determine how the suppressed portion differentiates, but this can be accomplished only in certain species. The male toad has a cortical deposit, or rudimentary ovary, at the cranial end of each testis. This is called *Bidder's organ*. When the testes are removed, this organ enlarges and slowly develops into a functional ovary capable of producing fertile eggs (Fig. 12–16).

Among amphibians it is relatively easy to graft gonad primordia and to unite animals parabiotically. When heterosexual combinations

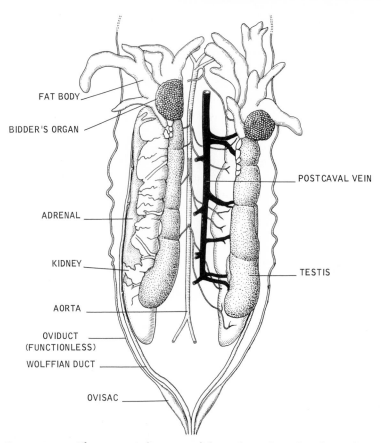

FAT BODY

BIDDER'S ORGAN

ADRENAL

KIDNEY

AORTA

OVIDUCT
(FUNCTIONLESS)

WOLFFIAN DUCT

OVISAC

POSTCAVAL VEIN

TESTIS

Figure 12–16. The urogenital system of the male toad, *Bufo vulgaris formosus.*
(From a dissection by Dr. H. Kobayashi.)

are made, one sex is suppressed and partial or complete sex reversals
result. The male gonad is typically dominant but, in rapidly differentiating species, the ovary may predominate. In heterosexual
combinations complete functional transformations may result or,
if there is incomplete dominance, a prolonged period of intersexuality
prevails. Removal of the dominant gonad graft, or separation of the
parabionts, may permit the transformed individual to return to the
type of sexual development typical for its genetic constitution.

The African frog *Xenopus* has been extensively employed in
experiments on sex reversal. When young larvae are raised in aquarium water containing 50 μg of estradiol per liter, the genetic males
differentiate completely and permanently as functional females.
This exposure to hormone must be made at a critical period of development, and does not need to prevail for more than three days.
Exogenous androgenic steroids do not interfere with normal gonadal
development in *Xenopus*, but testicular grafts do produce functional

sex reversal in female hosts. Complete reversal of the ovaries into testes has been accomplished by Mikamo and Witschi by transplanting testes into the body cavities of larval recipients prior to the onset of gonad differentiation. The females of *Xenopus* are normally heterozygous (ZW) and the males are homozygous (ZZ). When reversed males (ZZ) are mated with normal males (ZZ), they yield only male offspring. Crossing a normal female (ZW) with a reversed female (ZW) gives 25 per cent WW females, 50 per cent ZW females, and 25 per cent ZZ males. Only ZW females are produced when an estradiol feminized male (ZZ) is mated with a testis-graft masculinized WW female. Breeding experiments have shown that all three possible chromosome-gene combinations (ZZ, ZW, WW) can develop either into fertile males or females.[10, 11, 30, 31]

These studies on *Xenopus* are important because they provide unequivocal evidence that the differentiation of primordial germ cells can be reversed without altering their constitution. They clearly indicate that the final "decision" on maleness or femaleness is made at the level of the gonad (postgenetic differentiation), and not at the time of fertilization. Unless environmental factors intervene, sex determination and sex differentiation are harmonious.

Birds

The *in vitro* culture of amphibian and avian gonads by Wolff and his collaborators indicates that gonad differentiation is an autonomous process which can occur quite independently of the whole organism.[52] Among birds, in contrast to mammals, it is the ovary that plays the dominant role in determining genital development.[19, 40] When heterosexual pairs of chick or duck gonads are placed contiguous to each other in culture dishes, the ovary stimulates the testis to proliferate cortical tissue until it becomes an ovotestis. The transformation may go far enough to make it indistinguishable from a normal ovary of the same age. Estradiol benzoate, added to the culture medium, modifies the testis in the same manner as living ovarian tissue.

Castrations of chick and duck embryos have been accomplished by localized irradiation of the genital ridges as early as the third day of incubation. In castrate male embryos, the Müllerian ducts, instead of regressing as they normally do, continue to develop. In castrate female chicks the right oviduct, which normally is lost in intact birds, likewise continues to develop. The Wolffian ducts serve as nephric ducts and remain after castration in an undifferentiated state. The genital tubercle of the male duck forms a prominent intromittent organ, whereas it becomes a rudimentary clitoris in the female. The administration of estrogen to young embryos suppresses development of the penis in the male, and, at hatching, it appears equivalent to the clitoris of the female. After castration of **early** embryos, both sexes develop genital tubercles of the male type. It is apparent that the ovary determines this sexual dimorphism by inhibiting the differentiation of the genital tubercle into a penis.

The exposure of chick embryos to estrogens has profound effects upon the differentiation of male gonads and sex accessory organs. Such steroids convert the left testis into an ovotestis; the epithelium of the right testis can form cortex only to a limited extent and consequently responds less markedly to estrogens. This treatment causes both oviducts of genetic males to persist. The chorioallantoic grafting of ovaries into male embryos produces genital anomalies which are quite comparable to those resulting from treatment with exogenous estrogens. All of the experiments are consistent with the concept that genital differentiation in birds is controlled by factors from the ovary. Although these factors have not been identified conclusively, they appear to be sex steroids, or to resemble the sex steroids very closely.

The right ovary of the chicken remains rudimentary and retains its medullary component. When the left functional ovary is removed from a young bird, the right rudiment may form a testis-like structure or an ovotestis. After sinistral ovariectomy of older chickens, the right rudiment generally develops into a functional ovary.

Mammals

Many degrees of intersexuality appear spontaneously in laboratory and domesticated mammals, and others may be produced experimentally. Some of these are remarkably similar to sexual anomalies known to occur in man. For example, a type of hereditary tubular dysgenesis has been found in King-Holtzmann hybrid rats, and the defect is associated with a color marker which makes it possible to identify the abnormal offspring at birth. Spermatogenesis fails at an early age, and parts of the accessory system are missing. The animals are chromatin negative, and the karyotype is normal. The mutant genes act in some manner to mask the male potential in these rats and, in many respects, the syndrome resembles a type of pseudohermaphroditism occurring in the human male.[1]

After purified androgens and estrogens became available for experimental purposes, many workers tried to simulate the freemartin condition in ambisexual young by introducing the steroids into the maternal circulation. The hormones apparently can traverse the placenta and cause anomalous sexual development of the young *in utero*. Androgens are known to induce female intersexuality when administered in this manner to rats, mice, guinea pigs, hamsters, rabbits, monkeys, and human beings. A wide range of genital defects results from this treatment, depending in severity upon the species, the developmental stage of the embryo, the kind of androgen used, the quantity administered, and the route of administration. When synthetic androgens are administered to the pregnant mother, Wolffian ducts are retained in genetic female embryos, but the Müllerian ducts are not caused to involute. Furthermore, the ovaries of the intersexed young are not conspicuously impaired in structure. The highly modified ovaries of cattle freemartins contain sterile seminiferous tubules, but this anomaly has not been simulated in any mammalian species through the administration of exogenous hormones.

The administration of estrogens to gravid rats and mice produces sexual maldevelopments in both male and female offspring. There is often persistence and hypertrophy of the Müllerian ducts in genetic males, shortening of the anogenital distance, and arrested development of accessory sex glands. The treatment may cause isolated segments of the Wolffian ducts to be retained in genetic females.

Two mg. of testosterone propionate, administered subcutaneously to the mouse on the 12th day of pregnancy, are sufficient to masculinize all of the female fetuses, thus resulting in permanent sterility. The female intersexes possess ovaries and derivatives of both Müllerian and Wolffian systems: oviducts, uteri and cranial vagina persist together with epididymides, ducti deferentes, seminal vesicles, prostate lobes, bulbourethral glands, and a clitoris modified in the direction of a penis (Fig. 12–17). The anogenital distance in the newborn females is increased, and they cannot be distinguished externally from normal males in the same litter, until penile development and testicular descent occur in the latter. As the intersexed females mature, the perineal region appears somewhat like an empty scrotum, and this is more pronounced if androgen treatment is continued postnatally. The short cranial vagina opens by a minute orifice into the urethra, the caudal vagina being absent. The uteri become extremely distended with fluid, and this usually causes death by the end of the second month.[42]

The young of the opossum are born in a very immature state, after a brief gestation period of about 13 days, and complete their development in the marsupial pouch. The young are sexually undifferentiated at birth, and hormones may be administered directly while they are within the marsupium and attached to nipples of the mammary glands. Burns was able to induce cortical development in the testes of neonatal opossums by giving minute amounts of extradiol from the day of birth. The testes continued to proliferate cortex until they became ovotestes, or, in some cases, until they were equivalent to normal ovaries of the same age. The gonocytes present in the proliferating cortex of the testis differentiated as oöcytes, and early follicles were observed in some cases. This is

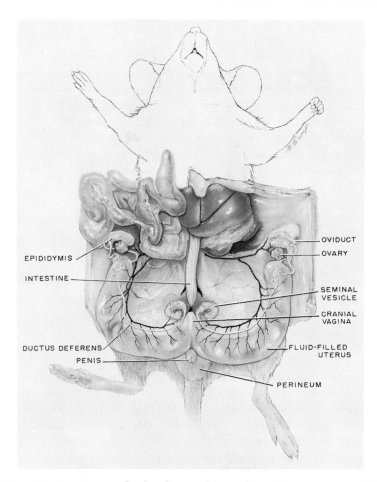

Figure 12–17. Viscera of a female pseudohermaphroditic mouse (age, 60 days) whose mother received a single injection of testosterone propionate (2 mg.) on the twelfth day of gestation. Note bilateral persistence of Wolffian and Müllerian duct derivatives and the distention of the uteri with fluid. (From Turner, C. D.: Amer. J. Obst. & Gynec., *90*:1208, 1964.)

the only report of gonadal reversal in a mammalian species being accomplished through the administration of steroid hormones.[7-9]

Germ-cell reversal has been accomplished in mice by homotransplanting fetal ovaries (11½ days) next to fetal testes of the same age, below the kidney capsules of adult castrated hosts. The testes developed normally for this site, whereas the ovaries became ovotestes. The cortical component was weakly represented, whereas the medullary portion of the grafted ovaries contained dilated seminiferous tubules in which spermatogenesis progressed to the point at which secondary spermatocytes were produced. Under these conditions, gonocytes, genetically determined as ova, differentiated in the direction of spermatozoa. The fetal testis is the source of a morphogenetic factor(s) which masculinizes the fetal ovary; it acts only over short distances, and its chemical identity remains obscure. Attempts to duplicate these effects of fetal testicular grafts by administering androgenic steroids have not been successful.[43]

Studies on mammalian fetuses, gonadectomized during the ambisexual stage, indicate that normal differentiation of the male accessory ducts and glands depends upon the presence of a testis, rather than upon the ovary.[24, 25] In genetic male rabbit fetuses, orchiectomized *in utero* at the fetal age of 19 days, when the Müllerian and Wolffian systems are still sexually indifferent, the Wolffian ducts degenerate and no ducti deferentes or seminal vesicles are formed. The Müllerian ducts persist and differentiate into oviducts, uterine horns, and a large segment of the vagina; the urogenital sinus and external genitalia become of the female type. Female organogenesis progresses normally after the fetal ovaries are removed. Thus, in the absence of the gonads, both genetic males and females acquire the female type of accessory system. It appears that the fetal testis exerts two effects: (1) stimulation of the masculine differentiation of the Wolffian ducts, urogenital sinus, and genital tubercle, and (2) an inhibitory influence leading to the rapid loss of the Müllerian ducts. Similar results have been obtained in mice and rats following removal of fetal gonads.

There are many advantages in being able to excise genital complexes and culture them apart from the body. In this way it is possible to observe the organs differentiate on culture media which are known to be free from hormones arising from other endocrine glands of the mother or fetus, such as the adrenal cortices, placenta, and pituitary gland. Moreover, the genital complex is removed from the influence of the liver, an organ known to inactivate steroid hormones. Under these circumstances the effects exerted by endogenous gonadal hormones or exogenous hormones added to the culture are known to be direct rather than mediated through other glands.

Rat fetuses at 17 days of age are in the ambisexual stage, and the genital tracts may be removed *in toto* and allowed to develop on a proper culture medium. The explanted tracts may be observed under different experimental conditions: with both gonads present; with one gonad absent; with both gonads absent; with gonads of the opposite sex; or with both gonads absent and exogenous hormones added to the medium (Fig. 12–18). A and B are male and female tracts at 17 days, the age of explantation. When male tracts are cultured for 4 days, the Müllerian ducts disappear except for vestiges, whereas the Wolffian ducts persist and seminal vesicles begin to arise from their caudal ends (A1). In the absence of both testes (A2), the Wolffian ducts regress and seminal vesicles do not form. The addition of testosterone micropellets to the culture medium substitutes for

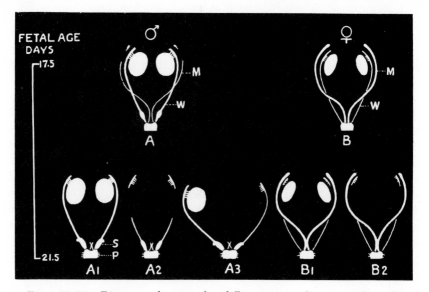

Figure 12–18. Diagrams showing the differentiation of rat genitalia cultured *in vitro*. M, Müllerian ducts; P, prostate gland; S, seminal vesicle; W, Wolffian duct. (From Price, D., and Pannabecker, R., 1958. After Watterson [ed.]: Endocrines in Development. Chicago, University of Chicago Press.)

a testis; the gonadless male tracts develop normally as in A1. One testis can promote normal differentiation of the male tract. When one testis is removed, and the two sides of the tract are widely separated (A3), the side of the tract possessing the testis develops normally, but the contralateral side tends to regress. Removal of the ovaries (B2) has no effect on the Müllerian ducts; they persist as in B1, and the Wolffian ducts regress. These experiments show that the Wolffian ducts depend upon morphogenetic agents from the testis for their maintenance and development, whereas the Müllerian ducts seem to be independent of gonadal control.[35, 36]

PATTERNS OF REPRODUCTIVE BEHAVIOR

There are two categories of vertebrates: those that breed continuously throughout the year (continuous breeders) and those that restrict reproductive events to a particular season (seasonal breeders). There is a tendency for animals in the wild to reproduce at those seasons when environmental factors such as food supply, temperatures, and shelter are most propitious for the pregnant or incubating mother and for survival of the young. Domestic animals are removed from many of the natural environmental exigencies, thus making it possible for the breeding periods to be prolonged or even for the animals to become continuous breeders.

The wild Norway rat is anatomically and physiologically very different from its domesticated prototype. The laboratory rat reproduces continuously, whereas the wild rat is definitely more seasonal, the high peak of reproductive efficiency extending from December through June. Reproduction may occur sporadically at other periods, but estrous cycles are irregular and the litters are small. Gonadectomy greatly reduces the spontaneous running activity of laboratory rats but has little effect on the activity of wild Norways. The adrenal cortices are much heavier in the wild rat than in the laboratory rat. It has been suggested that during the process of domestication the gonads of the domesticated rat have taken over the control of certain functions that are largely controlled by the adrenal in the wild Norway.

Wild cattle show a definite tendency to reproduce during the fall, spring, and early summer, but domesticated forms may conceive at any time. Horses of the North American continent usually breed during the spring and early summer, and although they may conceive at other periods, the heats become irregular and unpredictable. Domestic rabbits are continuous breeders, but, under North American climatic conditions, the wild form shows a low peak of reproductive activity during the summer months. Among domesticated chickens there are annual variations in the rates of egg production, and the high and low levels of fecundity correlate with daily light periods and other environmental conditions. In man there are variations in reproductive proficiency that correlate with the latitude.

Among seasonal breeders the gonads of both sexes may involute and become practically quiescent during the nonbreeding periods; in other species the male may retain reproductive competence at all seasons, only the female becoming sexually impotent at certain periods.

The seasonal release of eggs or embryos is the most prevalent reproductive pattern among the fishes but, under laboratory conditions, successive broods may be produced throughout the year.[22, 23] In some species the period of sexual inactivity is very brief or does not exist at all, the production of eggs being almost as continuous as the production of spermatozoa. *Oryzias latipes* may ovulate and spawn every day for prolonged periods, but the process eventually becomes irregular. At the other extreme are some fishes (*e.g.*, genus *Oncorhynchus*) in which the gonads become mature only once during a lifetime, death being an inevitable consequence of spawning.

A seasonal wave of reproductive activity occurs in the majority of Amphibia, mating and oviposition taking place during the spring. In some of the Urodela pairing occurs in the early autumn and ovulation does not take place until spring. In these cases the sperm are stored during the winter in the receptaculum of the female. Most reptiles are seasonal breeders, though certain tropical species extend their reproductive activities throughout the year, without any evidence of a seasonal rhythm.

In the tropics, apparently both continuous and seasonal patterns are found among birds. Though most domestic birds are continuous breeders, the turkey and goose retain their seasonal rhythmicity even in captivity. Migratory birds provide the clearest example of seasonally breeding forms. The breeding season is a very labile characteristic of animals as is shown by removing eggs from the nests of birds as they are laid, the parent being given no chance to incubate them. The sparrow generally lays three to five eggs and then incubates them, but if the eggs are removed daily the female can be induced to lay 50 to 80 eggs. Broodiness is linked with cessation of egg production and does not appear unless a characteristic number of eggs is in the nest.

The common breeds of sheep confine their reproductive periods to the autumn or winter months, but this can be modified by genetic selection. The Merinos and Dorset Horn breeds have prolonged breeding seasons, and at least two strains have been produced that are continuous breeders. This provides another example of the lability of reproductive rhythms.

The Estrous Cycle

In most vertebrates, with the exception of the primates, sexual receptivity is restricted to recurring periods called *estrus*. During heat, or estrus, the female is physiologically and psychologically conditioned to receive the male, and structural changes occur in the female sex accessories. *Monestrous* animals complete a single estrous cycle annually, a long anestrous period separating the heats. *Polyestrous* forms complete two or more cycles annually if not interrupted by pregnancy.

Ovulation is the dominant event in the estrous cycle and usually occurs during estrus, but in a few species (*e.g.*, cow) it occurs shortly after the end of estrus. In most mammalian species ovulation occurs *spontaneously* and is ushered in by a short period of very rapid follicular growth; in other species (*e.g.*, rabbit, cat, ferret) ovulations do not occur spontaneously but are *induced* by the act of coitus or some comparable stimulation of the uterine cervix. The induced ovulators generally remain in continuous heat, the ovary being characterized by large follicles for long periods, and preovulatory growth of the follicles and ovulation occur after coitus. In the latter animals there are occasional diestrous intervals during which the female is not receptive to the male; these periods correlate with massive atresia of the vesicular follicles. Careful studies of vaginal smears and histology of the reproductive tract of the rabbit suggest that there is a latent tendency for cyclic alterations to occur at four- to six-day intervals.

Ovulation is dependent upon the release of gonadotrophins from the anterior pituitary, and there is much evidence that this release is mediated by a hypothalamic mechanism. Possibly in all forms the central nervous system is involved in the ovulatory process. In many fishes, amphibians, reptiles, and birds it is very probable that court-ship encounters have a bearing upon ovulation and that it would not occur in their absence. Among induced ovulators, the intensity and duration of coitus is also variable. In the rabbit, squirrel, and cat, coitus is relatively brief; but in the ferret it is protracted and violent. Copulations must be repeated frequently in the short-tailed shrew to induce the release of eggs from the ovary, approximately 20 copulations in one day being necessary to cause ovulation. Me-chanical (glass rod) stimulation of the cervices of the estrous rabbit generally does not produce ovulation unless the threshold of pituitary activation is lowered by giving exogenous progesterone. It thus appears that the act of coitus has an effect which is not completely duplicated by the artificial means. These observations suggest that ovulation is consummated by a neurohumoral or neurohormonal stimulation of the anterior hypophysis.

Some domestic animals, particularly cows and mares, occasion-ally exhibit so-called *quiet heat*. These animals may show all the anatomic and physiologic alterations of typical estrus, including ovulation, but sexual receptivity is lacking. It may be that such animals are not receiving sufficient estrogen or that there is not a proper balance between estrogen and progesterone, to bring them into psychologic heat.

The Menstrual Cycle

The menstrual cycle, characteristic of primates, is fundamentally comparable to the estrous cycle, but there are two important differ-ences: in primates there are no unequivocal peaks of heightened sexual receptivity and the breakdown of the endometrium at the end of the cycle is accompanied by a loss of blood. The primate cycle is approximately 28 days in length, and ovulation ordinarily occurs about midway between the two menstrual periods. Anovu-latory cycles are frequent in otherwise normal women. In most estrous mammals, excepting the mouse and rat, the uterus thickens appreciably under the influence of ovarian hormones, and deteriora-tion and sloughing of the uterine lining occur at the end of the cycle. These changes are quite comparable to those that occur in the primate uterus. Although estrous mammals do not menstruate, the lining of the uterus is periodically lost and renewed. In ewes, cows, and swine, large plaques of tissue are often peeled off from the lining of the uterus during the end of the luteal phase or the beginning of the follicular phase. All mammalian uteri respond in much the same manner to the presence of ovarian hormones, or to their absence.

REFERENCES

1. Allison, J. E., Stanley, A. J., and Gumbreck, L. G.: Idiograms from rats exhibiting anomalous conditions associated with the reproductive organs. Amer. Zool., *4*:401, 1964.
2. Amoroso, E. C., Hancock, J. L., and Rowlands, I. W.: Ovarian activity in the pregnant mare. Nature, *161*:355, 1948.
3. Atz, J. W.: Intersexuality in fishes. *In* C. N. Armstrong and A. J. Marshall (eds.): Intersexuality in Vertebrates Including Man. New York, Academic Press, 1964, p. 145.
4. Backhouse, K. M., and Hewer, H. R.: Features of reproduction in the grey seal. Med. & Biol. Illustration, *14*:144, 1964.
5. Barr, M. L.: Sex chromatin and phenotype in man. Science, *130*:679, 1959.
6. Blandau, R. J., White, B. J., and Rumery, R. E.: Observations on the movements of the living primordial germ cells in the mouse. Fertil. & Steril., *14*:482, 1963.
7. Burns, R. K.: Experimental reversal of sex in the gonads of the opossum, *Didelphys virginina*. Proc. Nat. Acad. Sci., *41*:669, 1955.
8. Burns, R. K.: Urogenital system. *In* B. H. Willier, P. A. Weiss, and V. Hamburger (eds.): Analysis of Development. Philadelphia, W. B. Saunders Co., 1955, p. 462.
9. Burns, R. K.: Role of hormones in the differentiation of sex. *In* W. C. Young (ed.): Sex and Internal Secretions, Vol. 1. Baltimore, The Williams & Wilkins Co., 1961, p. 76.
10. Chang, C. Y., and Witschi, E.: Breeding of sex-reversed males of *Xenopus laevis* Daùdin. Proc. Soc. Exp. Biol. & Med., *89*:150, 1955.
11. Chang, C. Y., and Witschi, E.: Genetic control and hormonal reversal of sex differentiation in *Xenopus*. Proc. Soc. Exp. Biol. & Med., *93*:140, 1956.
12. Chang, M. C.: Capacitation of rabbit spermatozoa in the uterus with special reference to the reproductive phases of the female. Endocrinol., *63*:619, 1958.
13. Clermont, Y.: Contractile elements in the limiting membrane of the seminiferous tubules of the rat. Exp. Cell. Res., *15*:438, 1958.
14. Davidson, W. M.: The nuclear sex of leucocytes. *In* C. Overzier (ed.): Intersexuality. New York, Academic Press, 1963, p. 72.
15. Evans, L. T.: Endocrine relations in turtles: claw growth in the slider, *Pseudemys scripta troostii*. Anat. Rec., *112*:251, 1952.
16. Foote, C. L.: Intersexuality in amphibians. *In* C. N. Armstrong and A. J. Marshall (eds.): Intersexuality in Vertebrates Including Man: New York, Academic Press, 1964, p. 233.
17. Franchi, L. L., Mandl, A. M., and Zuckerman, S.: The development of the ovary and the process of oogenesis. *In* S. Zuckerman (ed.): The Ovary, Vol. 1. New York, Academic Press, 1962, p. 1.
18. Gallien, L.: Comparative activity of sexual steroids and genetic constitution in sexual differentiation of amphibian embryos. Gen. & Comp. Endocrinol., Suppl. 1:346, 1962.
19. Gardner, W. A., Jr., Wood, H. A., Jr., and Taber, E.: Demonstration of a nonestrogenic gonadal inhibitor produced by the ovary of the brown leghorn. Gen. & Comp. Endocrinol., *4*:673, 1964.
20. Harrington, R. W., Jr.: Twenty-four-hour rhythms of internal self-fertilization and of oviposition by hermaphrodites of *Rivulus marmoratus*, a cyprinodontid fish. Physiol. Zool., *36*:325, 1963.

21. Hishida, T.: Reversal of sex-differentiation in genetic males of the medaka (*Oryzias latipes*) by injecting estrone-16-C^{14} and diethylstilbestrol (monoethyl-1-C^{14}) into the egg. Embryologica, 8:234, 1964.
22. Hoar, W. S.: Reproduction in teleost fish. Memoirs Soc. Endocrinol., No. 4:5, 1955.
23. Hoar, W. S.: Hormones and reproductive behavior of the poikilothermous vertebrates. *In* F. L. Hisaw, Jr. (ed.): Physiology of Reproduction. Corvallis, Oregon State University Press, 1963, p. 17.
24. Jost, A.: Hormonal factors in development of the fetus. Cold Spring Harbor Symp. Quant. Biol., 19:167, 1954.
25. Lederberg, J.: Bacterial reproduction. Harvey Lectures, 52:69, 1959.
26. Lillie, F. R.: The free-martin: a study of the action of sex hormones in the fetal life of cattle. J. Exp. Zool., 23:371, 1917.
27. Marshall, A. J.: The unilateral endometrial reaction in the giant fruit-bat (*Pteropus giganteus* Brünnich). J. Endocrinol., 9:42, 1953.
28. Marshall, A. J., and Coombs, C. J. F.: Lipoid changes in the gonads of wild birds: their possible bearing on hormone production, sexual display and the breeding season. Nature, 169:261, 1952.
29. Marshall, A. J., and Lofts, B.: The Leydig-cell homologue in certain teleost fishes. Nature, 177:704, 1956.
30. Mikamo, K., and Witschi, E.: Functional sex-reversal in genetic females of *Xenopus laevis*, induced by implanted testes. Genetics, 48:1411, 1963.
31. Mikamo, K., and Witschi, E.: Masculinization and breeding of the WW *Xenopus*. Experientia, 20:622, 1964.
32. Miller, M. R.: The seasonal histological changes occurring in the ovary, corpus luteum, and testis of the viviparous lizard, *Xantusia vigilis*. Univ. Calif. Pub. Zool., 47:197, 1948.
33. Moore, J. G., Van Campenhout, J. L., and Brandkamp, W. W.: Chromosome analysis in abnormal sexual differentiation and gonadal dysfunction. Internat. J. Fertil., 9:469, 1964.
34. Nalbandov, A. V.: Reproductive Physiology, 2nd ed. San Francisco, W. H. Freeman & Company, 1964.
35. Price, D.: Influence of hormones on sex differentiation in explanted fetal reproductive tracts. *In* Gestation, 3rd conf. New York, Josiah Macy Jr. Foundation, 1957, p. 173.
36. Price, D., Pannabecker, R.: Organ culture studies on foetal rat reproductive tracts. Ciba Found. Colloq. on Ageing, 2:3, 1956.
37. Russell, L. B.: Genetics of mammalian sex chromosomes. Science, 133:1795, 1961.
38. Segal, S. J., and Nelson, W. O.: Initiation and maintenance of testicular function. *In* C. W. Lloyd (ed.): Endocrinology of Reproduction. New York, Academic Press, 1959, p. 107.
39. Sohval, A. R.: Chromosomes and sex chromatin in normal and anomalous sexual development. Physiol. Revs., 43:306, 1963.
40. Taber, E.: Intersexuality in birds. *In* C. N. Armstrong and A. J. Marshall (eds.): Intersexuality in Vertebrates Including Man. New York, Academic Press, 1964, p. 285.
41. Talmage, R. V., and Buchanan, G. D.: The armadillo: A review of its natural history, ecology, anatomy and reproductive physiology. The Rice Institute Pamphlet, 41:No. 2, 1954.
42. Turner, C. D.: Special mechanisms in anomalies of sex differentiation. Amer. J. Obst. & Gynecol., 90:1208, 1964.
43. Turner, C. D., and Asakawa, H.: Experimental reversal of germ cells in ovaries of fetal mice. Science, 143:1344, 1964.
44. Vandenbergh, J. G.: Hormonal basis of sex skin in male Rhesus monkeys. Gen. & Comp. Endocrinol., 5:31, 1965.
45. Wells, L. J.: Effect of fetal endocrines on fetal growth. *In* Gestation, 3rd conf. New York, Josiah Macy Jr. Foundation, 1957, p. 187.
46. Wimsatt, W. A., and Kallen, F. C.: The unique maturation response of the graafian follicles of hibernating vespertilionid bats and the question of its significance. Anat. Rec., 129:115, 1957.
47. Wimsatt, W. A., and Waldo, C. M.: The normal occurrence of a peritoneal opening in the bursa ovarii of the mouse. Anat. Rec., 93:47, 1945.

48. Witschi, E.: The inductor theory of sex differentiation. J. Fac. Sci., Hokkaido University, Series VI, Zoology, *13*:428, 1957.
49. Witschi, E.: Sex and secondary sexual characters. *In* A. J. Marshall (ed.): Biology and Comparative Physiology of Birds, Vol. 2. New York, Academic Press, 1961, p. 115.
50. Witschi, E., and Opitz, J. M.: Fundamental aspects of intersexuality. *In* C. Overzier (ed.): Intersexuality. New York, Academic Press, 1963, p. 16.
51. Wolff, E.: Endocrine function of the gonad in developing vertebrates. *In* A. Gorbman (ed.): Comparative Endocrinology. New York, John Wiley & Sons, 1959, p. 568.
52. Wolff, E., and Haffen, K.: Sur l'intersexualité expérimentale des gonades embryonnaires de canard cultivées *in vitro*. Arch. Anat. Microscop. Morphol. Exper., *41*:184, 1952.
53. Wolfson, A.: The ejaculate and the nature of coition in some passerine birds. Ibis, *102*:124, 1960.
54. Yamamoto, T.: A further study on induction of functional sex reversal in genotypic males of the medaka (*Oryzias latipes*) and progenies of sex reversals. Genetics, *44*:739, 1959.
55. Yamamoto, T.: Hormonic factors affecting gonadal sex differentiation in fish. Gen. & Comp. Endocrinol., Suppl. 1:341, 1962.
56. Yamamoto, T.: The problem of viability of XY zygotes in the medaka *Oryzias latipes*. Genetics, *50*:45, 1964.

13 _____

ENDOCRINOLOGY
OF THE TESTIS

The testis performs two functions that are to a large extent complementary: the proliferation of spermatozoa and the secretion of steroid hormones. The latter determine the physiologic state of the accessory ducts and glands and usually condition the appearance of the secondary sex characters. Phylogenetically, the older function of the gonad seems to be the proliferation of gametes. In the proto-chordates (*e.g.*, amphioxus) accessory sex organs are absent; the ripe gonads free the germ cells into the atrial cavity, and these are conveyed to the exterior by the water leaving the atriopore. The gonads of the protochordates are not known to secrete sex hormones. The genital system of the cyclostome is poorly developed, and the urinary ducts are not employed for the conveyance of genital products as in teleost fishes and higher forms (Fig. 12–14). In aquatic verte-brates, such as fishes and amphibians, the gonadal hormones become indispensable adjuncts for reproduction. In general, the accessory sex mechanism increases in complexity with the advent of terrestrial or aerial life, and the hormones of the gonads assume even broader functions than in the lower aquatic species.

HISTOPHYSIOLOGY OF THE TESTIS

The testis is composed of seminiferous tubules and the inter-stitial cells of Leydig which are present in the angular spaces be-tween the tubules (Fig. 13–1). The lining of the tubules constitutes

423

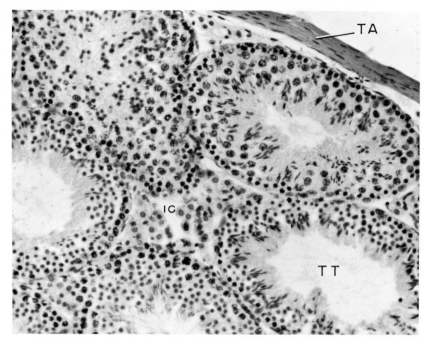

Figure 13–1. Normal testis of an adult mouse. IC, Interstitial cells of Leydig; TT, testis tubule; TA, tunica albuginea.

a seminiferous epithelium which rests on the inner surface of a basement membrane. Externally, the basement membrane is strengthened by a thin lamina propria. The germinal epithelium contains nongerminal, nutrient, and supporting elements, the cells of Sertoli, and the germ cells, which, through proliferation and complex transformations, give rise to spermatozoa. The least differentiated germ cells are nearest the basement membrane, whereas the most advanced are near the lumen. Two essential processes are involved in the transformation of spermatogonia into spermatozoa: (a) reduction of the number of chromosomes (meiotic divisions), and (b) the transformation of haploid cells into spermatozoa (spermiogenesis). The spermatids form the inner layers of the epithelium. They are found in rather discrete aggregations, all cells of the group having originated from a single spermatogonium. As the spermatids transform into spermatozoa, they lose cytoplasm and are temporarily connected to the Sertoli cells. In man, as in other mammals, the cells derived from a spermatogonium tend to remain together and to differentiate synchronously, thus forming cellular associations of fixed composition.

Radioautographic techniques have been employed in several mammalian species in attempts to determine the time required for the completion of spermatogenesis. Thymidine-H^3, a specific precursor of deoxyribonucleic acid (DNA), is an excellent tracer substance since it is incorporated into the nuclei of spermatogonia preparing for mitosis and into spermatocytes preparing for meiosis. By preserving the testes at different intervals after injection of the radioactive tracer, it is possible to determine how rapidly the labeled germ cells develop. Germ cells which are in the process of synthesizing DNA may also be labeled with P^{32}. Spermatogenesis in the mouse extends over a period of 4 cycles and requires about 33.5 days for completion. Four cycles are also identifiable in rats, and the duration of spermatogenesis in the Sherman strain has been estimated as 48 days. Sprague-Dawley rats have slightly longer cycles and require about 51.6 days to complete the process. Studies on testicular biopsies of the human testis, taken at frequent intervals after the intratesticular administration of thymidine-H^3, indicate that there are 4.6 cycles, each cycle of the epithelium lasting 16 days. These studies on man indicate that it requires about 74 days for a spermatogonium to transform into functional spermatozoa.[35, 36] The indications are that the rate of germ-cell development is constant for given species and strains of mammals, and that this rate cannot be accelerated by hormones such as gonadotrophins and androgens. Cytologic observations suggest that germ cells must move forward in their differentiation; if unfavorable environments make it impossible for them to pursue their differentiation at the normal rate, they degenerate and are eliminated from the system. Although hormones do not accelerate the *rate* of germ-cell differentiation, they must contribute to the creation of favorable environments for their transformation into spermatozoa.[14, 16, 17]

There is general agreement that the interstitial cells of Leydig are the main source of testicular androgens, but it has been difficult to show that the constituents of the seminiferous tubule play no role in the biosynthesis of steroid hormones. Leydig cells are often difficult to distinguish from intertubular connective-tissue elements, and variations in size and number cannot be quantitated with much accuracy. Consequently, the evidence derived from seasonal changes and breeding behavior is largely indirect and circumstantial. The enzyme 3β-hydroxysteroid dehydrogenase is important in androgen biosynthesis since it catalyzes the conversion of pregnenolone to progesterone. Histochemical tests have demonstrated that this enzyme is present in the interstitial tissue of several mammalian species.[64]

The testes of the rat lack septa, and the interstitial tissue is very loosely attached to the seminiferous tubules. It is possible, by using a dissecting microscope, to pull out the tubules from the interstitial tissue. Tubules can be obtained which are virtually free of interstitial cells, the latter remaining in a coherent web of connective tissue. The biosynthetic competence of these two testicular components may be tested by incubating them separately with a labeled androgen precursor.[11] Both tubular and interstitial-cell fractions are capable of transforming progesterone to 17-hydroxyprogesterone, androstenedione, and testosterone, but the interstitial tissue is much more efficient in this respect than the seminiferous tubules. These results indicate that androgens can be synthesized to a minimum extent by the tubules, but it is not known whether they emanate from Sertoli cells, cells of the lamina propria, or the germinal cells. There is no evidence that germinal cell tumors (seminomas) can synthesize steroids, but Sertoli cell tumors have been reported to secrete estrogens. If Sertoli cells can synthesize estrogens, it is probable that they would also produce androgens as intermediates.

Washed microsomes, obtained from homogenates of testicular tissue, contain certain enzymes which are essential for androgen biosynthesis. Electron microscopic studies on several mammalian species have shown that the cells of Leydig are characterized by a highly-developed agranular endoplasmic reticulum. There are strong indications that this organelle is the site of at least part of the steroid biosynthesis occurring in these cells. Smooth or agranular endoplasmic reticula are also found in Sertoli cells and germinal cells; this suggests, but does not prove, that these tubular elements may have some capacity to participate in steroid biosynthesis. Solution of the problem awaits further refinements in histochemical techniques. The exact cellular source of testicular estrogens remains to be determined.[11]

HORMONES OF THE TESTIS

Androgens are masculinizing compounds that are produced chiefly by the testis under normal conditions. They also arise from the adrenal cortices and ovaries and are very probably present in the placenta. Such compounds are found in the urine of males, females, and castrates: androsterone is the principal androgen of human urine and was isolated in 1931. A yield of 15 mg. of crystalline androsterone was obtained from 15,000 liters of normal male urine. Testosterone was isolated from testicular tissue in 1935. A significant portion of the androgen present in the mammalian organism arises from the adrenal cortex. These compounds are formed from adrenocortical steroids such as cortisol and are released into the blood as biologically active material. Certain types of ovarian and testicular tumors may produce and release tremendous amounts of androgen. It is probable that androgenic steroids perform significant roles in the reproductive processes of female birds.[8, 9]

It is certain that a number of organs possess the necessary enzymatic equipment to produce androgenic steroids. It is reasonably well established that all of the steroid hormones, whether adreno-cortical, testicular, or ovarian, are produced by biosynthetic pathways common to all these organs. Thus the endocrine differences between testis, ovary, and adrenal cortex are quantitative rather than qualitative. This accounts for the fact that the adrenal cortex, for example, may function abnormally and liberate an excess of gonadal steroids.

The common pathways employed by different organs in the synthesis and degradation of steroids accounts for the interconvertibility of these compounds. *Proandrogens* are compounds which are not androgenic when applied locally, but acquire androgenic activity during their metabolism within the organism. 17α-Hydroxyprogesterone produces no growth of the chick's comb when applied by inunction, but when it is given orally a pronounced growth of the comb occurs. Cortisone and cortisol are adrenal glucocorticoids and are not androgenic, but the organism may convert them into androgens such as 11-hydroxyandrosterone, adrenosterone, 11-ketoandrosterone, and 11β-hydroxyandrostenedione. 17-Hydroxyprogesterone and 11-deoxycortisol may also serve as proandrogens and yield androsterone and androstenedione.

Testosterone and androstenedione are the main androgens produced by the testis.[21, 38] Sensitive and reliable procedures are available for determining the quantity of testosterone in the blood plasma. The plasma of normal men contains about 0.5 μg. of testosterone per 100 ml. of plasma; in normal women, the value is about 0.1 μg. per 100 ml. of plasma. Certain estrogens, particularly estradiol-17β and estrone, have been identified in extracts of normal human testis as well as in blood from the spermatic vein. The total estrogen content of male urine is the equivalent of about 40 I.U. of estrone per day; this is less than one-tenth the quantity excreted by women at the time of ovulation.

When steroids are administered orally or intraperitoneally, they enter the portal veins and are carried to the liver where they are promptly inactivated. Greater activity is generally observed following subcutaneous or intramuscular administrations; the compounds are released slowly from the site of injection and absorbed into the systemic circulation, thus avoiding liver inactivation.[55]

It is always important to recognize that hormones are ineffective unless the targets are capable of responding to them. The clinical syndrome called "feminizing testis" is a very good example of this. The individuals are genetic males as is indicated by the absence of Barr chromatin and the presence of an XY karyotype, but they are phenotypic females. The blood plasma of these patients contains normal male levels of testosterone; even when large quantities of exogenous testosterone are administered there is no hair growth or other virilizing manifestations. The target tissues and organs seem to be insensitive to androgens, even though they are genetic males. *In vitro* studies on testicular tissue from these subjects have shown that it is capable of synthesizing testosterone from progesterone and androstenedione, and of producing estrogens from testosterone and androstenedione.[65]

Chemistry of the Androgens

For purposes of terminology, the androgens may be regarded as derivatives of androstane; they contain nineteen carbon atoms and possess methyl groups at C-10 and C-13. Biologic activity is altered by making relatively small additions or substitutions at the various carbon positions. The natural androgens vary greatly in their potencies even when bioassayed by the same end points; they also differ in their capacities to stimulate different end points. For example, testosterone and androstenedione possess a high degree of androgenicity when tested by the ordinary fowl and mammalian parameters, but they have little capacity to maintain spermatogenesis in the testis of the hypophysectomized rat. Pregnenolone, on the other hand, is not androgenic by the usual tests but is extremely potent in maintaining testicular weight and spermatogenesis in the hypophysectomized rat. Biochemists have tried, with some measure of success, to produce steroid compounds which have mild or no masculinizing actions but have marked protein anabolic actions.

Several interrelated routes to the biosynthesis of androgens have been demonstrated, and some of these are shown in Fig. 13-2. The degradation products of the steroid hormones are not salvaged by the organism and used again for the synthesis of new compounds. Hence there is little or no feedback, and the level of hormones in the blood depends upon the availability of precursors and the capacity of the cells to produce new hormones. It has been shown that androgens may be synthesized from acetate, and that cholesterol is not an obligatory intermediate. Since acetate is a precursor to cholesterol, however, it should not be concluded that the organism never uses the latter as a precursor for the androgens.[19, 32]

Testosterone in the circulation is bound to the blood proteins and hence does not normally filter through the kidney glomeruli. It is not stored in the body but is quickly utilized, or degraded into relatively inactive androgens which are excreted through the urine or through the bile and feces. The androgens of the urine are present as water-soluble sulfates and glucuronides and are not biologically active.

The testis of the stallion contains large quantities of estrogenic material, and the urine contains high titers of estrogen metabolites. After removal of the testes the urinary estrogens diminish to very low levels. The administration of chorionic gonadotrophin to adult

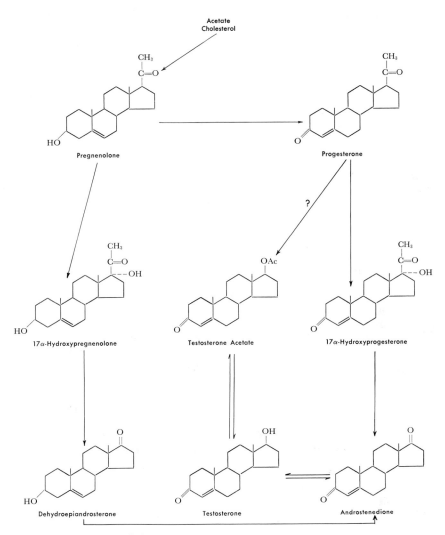

Figure 13–2. Probable pathways of androgen biosynthesis in the gonads.

men stimulates the testes and increases the output of both androgen and estrogen. When testosterone and other androgens are administered to human subjects, there is an accelerated excretion of estrogenic material, which has been identified as estrone, estradiol, and estriol. Slices of human ovaries, incubated with C^{14}-labeled testosterone, release labeled estradiol-17β. The *in vitro* conversion of testosterone to estrogens can also be accomplished by the placenta. Testosterone and related 19-carbon compounds apparently serve as precursors for testicular estrogens, as they do in the ovary and adrenal cortex.

Urinary 17-Ketosteroids

The common bioassay methods for androgens include growth of the capon's comb, enlargement of various muscles, increased weight of the ventral prostate or seminal vesicles of the castrate rat, or increased quantities of fructose and citric acid in the sex accessories of the castrate mammal after treatment with such compounds. Several chemical methods are available for assessing the levels of androgens in the organism and, in clinical work, these are more practical than the biologic tests. The determination of neutral 17-ketosteroids in the urine is commonly practiced. These are the catabolic end products of the androgens formed by the testes and the adrenal cortices.

These 17-ketosteroids (*e.g.*, androsterone) have a keto group at position 17 of the steroid nucleus. Because of this feature they give characteristic color reactions with *m*-dinitrobenzene (Zimmermann reaction) and antimony trichloride (Pincus reaction). Since estrone, an ovarian hormone, contains a phenolic ring, it is acidic, but it may be removed from the neutral fraction by washing with alkali. The neutral 17-ketosteroids, freed of estrone, represent the androgens produced by the adrenal cortex and the testis. During the first two years of life, children excrete only small amounts of 17-ketosteroids, and there are no significant sexual differences in normal subjects before puberty. Normal adult women excrete 5 to 15 mg. daily, and the amount may increase during late pregnancy. The values for normal adult men, during the reproductive years, usually range from 7 to 20 mg. daily. Very high values are obtained in diseases characterized by adrenal or testicular hyperplasia. Hypofunctions of the anterior hypophysis, testes, or adrenal cortices produce low 17-ketosteroid values.

EFFECTS OF TESTICULAR HORMONES

The androgens are essential for the control of secondary sex characters of the male and for the functional competence of the accessory reproductive ducts and glands. The most profound metabolic action of these steroids is the promotion of protein anabolism. At the human level, androgens are involved in the control of hair patterns, voice changes, skeletal configurations, and the regulation of sebaceous-gland activity.[68] Androgens also exert effects upon the germinal epithelium of the testis tubules and thus influence sperm production; chemistry of the seminal fluid is determined through their actions upon the accessory glands.

Regulation of Male Accessory Organs

The accessory system of male ducts and glands are, morphologically and physiologically, dependent upon the production of androgens (Figs. 13–3 and 13–4). In the prepuberal animal, as in seasonal breeders during the anestrus, all of these structures are small and relatively nonfunctional. Castration of the adult functional male likewise causes these organs to involute until they approximate the same structures of juvenile animals. Androgens completely restore all of these organs in the castrate or cause them to surpass the normal conditions.[33] Since the degree of restoration of the accessory glands is, within limits, proportional to the amounts of androgen administered, these end organs have been employed for the bioassay of androgens. Secondary sex characters such as the capon's comb may also be used for the assay of androgens (Fig. 13–5). When testosterone is applied to the capon's comb by inunction, the amount required to produce a significant enlargement of the comb is about one-hundredth the amount required by injection.

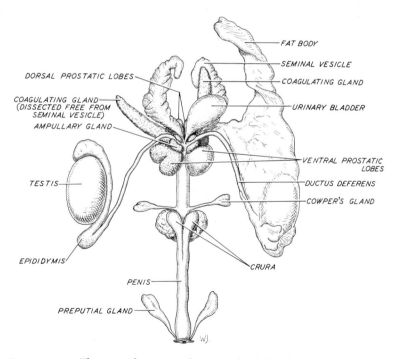

Figure 13–3. The genital system of a normal adult dissected out *in toto* and drawn from ventral view. The urinary bladder was pulled slightly toward the animal's left. The fat body was removed on the right side, and the coagulating gland dissected free from the seminal vesicle. The membranous covering was removed from the right lobe of the ventral prostate. The coagulating glands may be regarded as anterior prostatic lobes.

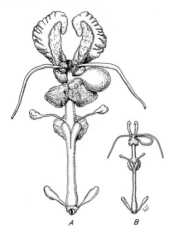

Figure 13–4. The effect of male sex hormone upon the genital tract of the castrate rat. Both littermate animals were bilaterally orchiectomized at 30 days of age and autopsied six months later. *A,* This animal received daily injections of testosterone propionate for 20 days before autopsy. *B,* This castrate littermate received no replacement therapy. It is apparent that male sex hormone builds up the accessory organs of the castrate until they approximate the normal. (Both tracts were dissected *in toto* and drawn to scale from ventral view. See Figure 13–3 for the identity of parts.)

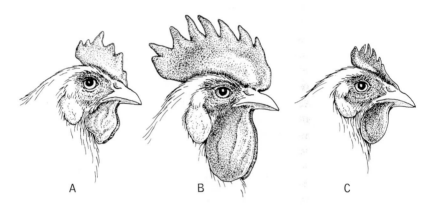

Figure 13–5. *A,* White Leghorn capon; *B,* normal cock; *C,* normal hen.

Structural Changes

Androgens have been shown to prolong the life of epididymal spermatozoa in the castrate guinea pig, and this provides a sensitive mammalian test. If the epididymis is surgically disconnected from the testis, some of the spermatozoa stored in the epididymis, when diluted with saline solution, are capable of motility for a period of 65 to 70 days after epididymal section. In the bilaterally castrated animal the epididymal sperms usually lose their capacity for motility within 30 days after removing the source of male sex hormone.

In the guinea pig, as in the rat, the male ejaculate hardens rapidly after emission from the male and is responsible for the copulation plug that forms within the vagina of the female. The hardening is due to the action of a prostatic enzyme upon the secretion of the seminal vesicles. An alternating current of 30 volts passed through the head of the guinea pig elicits an ejaculation from the genital tract, feces and urine not being voided. The ejaculation hardens within a few minutes after leaving the male tract, and its firm rubbery consistency permits it to be weighed with ease and accuracy. After castration, the seminal vesicles and prostate become atrophic, and a coagulable ejaculation cannot be obtained. The administration of androgens rehabilitates the accessory glands and coagulable ejaculates are obtainable within a few days.[20]

The ventral lobes of the rat's prostate shrink markedly in gross size after castration.[3, 34] Histologically, the epithelial cells decrease in height from tall columnar in the normal animal to low cuboidal in the castrate. Within four or five days after removal of the testes the characteristic light areas disappear from the luminal ends of these cells. The light areas occupy approximately the same position in the cells as the Golgi bodies. After castration the Golgi bodies in these secretory cells are reduced quickly. The administration of androgen to the castrate rat restores the light areas and the Golgi bodies and increases the height of the epithelial cells (Fig. 13–6).

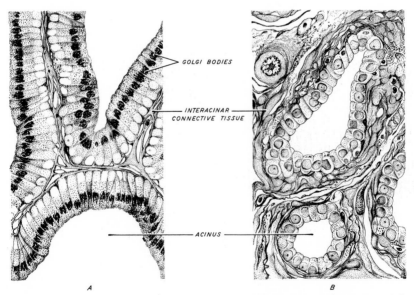

GOLGI BODIES

INTERACINAR CONNECTIVE TISSUE

ACINUS

A *B*

Figure 13–6. The effect of castration on the cytology of the ventral prostatic lobes of the adult rat. *A*, Normal gland. The secretory cells lining the acini are high columnar in shape and have conspicuous Golgi bodies (blackened filaments in the supranuclear ends of the cells). *B*, The ventral prostate from a littermate which had been orchiectomized for six months. Notice the shrinkage of the acini, diminished height of the epithelial cells, and absence of the Golgi bodies. (Both were prepared according to the technique of Mann-Kopsch and drawn to scale.)

The seminal vesicle appears to be a more sensitive indicator of androgen than is the ventral prostate. Cytological changes become apparent in the seminal vesicle epithelium in approximately two days after castration; it requires about four days for decisive changes to occur in the prostatic epithelium. In the castrate rat, however, smaller daily doses of androgen are required to maintain the prostatic epithelium in a normal condition than are required to maintain the seminal vesicle epithelium.

After castration the seminal vesicles diminish in size and lose their ability to secrete normally. Within 20 days the epithelial cells of the seminal vesicles have changed from a tall columnar to a low cuboidal shape. By two or three days after castration the epithelial cells have lost the secretory granules normally present in the distal ends of these cells. Both macroscopic and microscopic features are brought back to normal by the administration of androgens.

Since the production of androgen by the testis depends on pituitary gonadotrophin, the sex accessories of the hypophysecto-

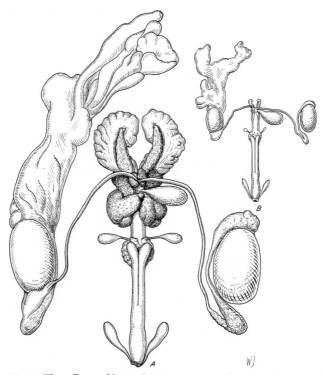

Figure 13–7. The effects of hypophysectomy upon the genital system of the male rat. *A*, Genital tract from a normal male rat 7 months of age. *B*, Genital tract from a littermate brother which was hypophysectomized when 30 days old and autopsied at 7 months of age. Observe the juvenile condition of the tract from the hypophysectomized littermate. (Both tracts were dissected *in toto* and drawn to scale from ventral view. See Figure 13–3 for identity of parts.)

mized animal are equivalent to those of the castrate (Fig. 13–7). By use of hypophysectomized-orchiectomized rats, it is possible to administer adrenocorticotrophin and stimulate the adrenal cortices to produce enough androgen to restore the male accessory organs partially. Somatotrophin facilitates this response to ACTH by producing general improvement of the secretory epithelium and connective tissue stroma of the accessory glands. Ovaries or adrenals, implanted directly into the seminal vesicles of castrated rats, produce local androgenic effects on the seminal vesicle epithelium. These observations suggest that androgens, like other hormones, do not normally produce their effects in isolation but act in concert with other hormones present in the organism.

Most of the androgen tests described above require killing the animal and making histologic observations. Androgenic activity may be assessed more quickly and conveniently by determining changes in the secretory capacity of the male accessory glands as reflected by changes in the chemical composition of the seminal plasma.

Chemical Changes

The seminal plasma originates almost entirely from the accessory sex glands, the prostate and seminal vesicles generally being the most important. There is a close interdependence between the chemical composition of the seminal plasma and the quantity of androgen present in the organism.[46, 60] In most mammals fructose is the only sugar present in the semen, although glucose may be present in the semen of cocks and rabbits. The sugar is an important source of energy for the spermatozoa and its rate of breakdown (fructolysis) correlates with the number of motile sperms present in the semen. The fructose arises through the enzymic conversion of blood glucose to fructose in the accessory organs. In pancreatic diabetes both blood glucose and seminal fructose are increased and both can be reduced by the administration of insulin.

The semen contains several dephosphorylating enzymes that are produced by the accessory glands. Human semen and prostatic tissue contain much acid phosphatase and small amounts of alkaline phosphatase. In bull semen the proportions are reversed. The level of the enzyme in the human prostate is low in children but increases markedly at puberty. Like fructose, the level of these enzymes in the seminal plasma depends on the androgen titers of the blood.

Citric acid occurs in the semen of many species. In the bull, stallion, boar, and ram, most of the fructose and citric acid are produced by the seminal vesicles. In the rat, citric acid is formed by the ventral prostate and seminal vesicle, but most of the fructose arises in the dorsal prostate and coagulating glands.

The functional state of the male accessory sex organs may be accurately evaluated by determining the fructose, citric acid, and phosphatase activity of the seminal plasma. These chemical methods for assessing androgen production are especially useful in following progressive changes that may result from age, nutritional states, etc. By these methods androgen production may be determined in the living animal, at desired intervals, and over extended periods. There are, however, many factors other than male sex hormone that can influence the presence of these materials in the semen. Frequency of ejaculation, sexual excitation, storage capacity of the glands, nutritional state, the level of blood glucose, and other factors may cause marked variations.

The Protein Anabolic Action of Androgens

The most profound general metabolic action of androgens is the promotion of protein anabolism. Testosterone or similar androgens decrease the urinary loss of nitrogen without increasing the non-protein nitrogen of the blood, and produce at least a temporary increase in body weight. This suggests that the hormone causes a true storage of nitrogen in the form of tissue protein. In the dog, androgens have been reported to increase the synthesis of proteins and decrease the rate of catabolism of amino acids. Testosterone or methyltestosterone, administered to orchiectomized men whose diet and exercise are controlled, produces nitrogen retention and progressive gains in weight. The protein anabolic response to androgens may be materially altered by the state of the protein stores at the time the treatments are begun. When the androgen treatment is withdrawn, the level of urinary nitrogen increases and, for a limited time, surpasses that of the untreated castrate. Androgens produce nitrogen retention less effectively in normal males than in hypogonadal or castrate subjects. Since androgens increase the protein matrix of bone, they have been used in the clinical treatment of certain skeletal defects.

Since the male accessories of starved and fed animals respond to equivalent extents when androgens are given, it appears that these sexual structures accumulate protein in advance of other tissues such as skeletal muscles. In general, however, the quantity of nitrogen retained is too great to be accounted for by an effect on the sex accessories alone; body muscles, bones, kidneys, and other tissues are generally increased owing to protein accumulation. Experiments have clearly shown that androgens can induce protein anabolic effects in animals deprived of their gonads, pituitary, pancreas, or adrenals.

Testosterone has no significant effect on the body length of the hypophysectomized rat unless somatotrophin is given jointly with it.

Although androgens increase the body weights of young hypophysectomized rats, most of this gain is accounted for by the increased mass of the genital complex, apparently consequent upon protein retention.

Castration has a variable effect on the skeletal muscles: some cease growing immediately, others continue to grow at a reduced rate, and certain ones show no significant effect. Androgens also selectively stimulate certain muscles (myotrophic effect) more than others. The masticating muscles of the guinea pig undergo the greatest atrophy after castration, and these are the ones that increase most after androgen injections. The levator ani muscles of the rat respond similarly. It is significant, however, that such hormones cannot stimulate any of the castrate-atrophied muscles to exceed normal proportions by increasing the dosage or prolonging the treatment. It is interesting that testosterone and methyltestosterone, both equally potent in stimulating the male accessory organs, promote the growth of different muscles in the guinea pig.

The changes in body weight produced by testosterone vary with the species and also depend on the nutritional status of the animals. Growth is markedly inhibited in young chicks by large doses of this hormone, whereas it produces little effect in the male guinea pig. In normal and castrated young rats, low doses of androgen produce increases in body weight, but continued treatment, especially with higher doses, prevents body weight gains. The initial stimulation is very brief in the intact rat, but is more marked and prolonged in castrated animals. The loss of body weight in the rat, after excessive androgen, may result from reduced food intake and an accelerated utilization of body fat. These metabolic adjustments probably represent fat-catabolic, as well as protein-anabolic, effects of the androgen.

Although androgens can suppress testicular functions through the pituitary, a direct supportive effect on the seminiferous tubules has been demonstrated. The androgens differ in their capacity to maintain spermatogenesis in hypophysectomized animals. They can maintain the testicular tubules of hypophysectomized rats fed protein-free diets, but the hormones are less effective in this respect if the animals are given no protein prior to hypophysectomy. When rats are deprived of dietary protein for one month, the seminal vesicles shrink in size and the gonadotrophin content of the pituitary is reduced, but it requires prolonged protein deprivation to reduce the protein stores of the testis. The role of androgen in the spermatogenic function of the testis remains obscure, but it may correlate in some manner with the protein-anabolic action of these steroids.

After the administration of androgen the volume of urine diminishes and the loss of sodium, chloride, potassium, and inorganic phosphorus, as well as nitrogen, is reduced. There is no conspicuous increase in any of these materials in the blood plasma. The retention of nitrogen, potassium, and phosphorus is probably related to the increased anabolism of tissue protein. The protein concentration of the plasma generally remains normal. The capacity of the androgens to promote retention of sodium and chloride resembles that of the adrenal cortical steroids; however, androgens are much weaker in this respect than the adrenal steroids and are unable to maintain the lives of adrenalectomized animals.

Mechanism of Action of Androgens

There is increasing evidence that androgens affect protein synthesis by influencing gene-controlled mechanisms.[70] Since nucleic acids are intimately associated with the synthesis of proteins, the growth processes initiated by androgens in various target tissues could be mediated at the level of the gene. When mice are given 1.0 mg. of testosterone propionate for two days, the rate of incorporation of glycine-1-C^{14} into kidney protein is increased 30 to 50% *in vitro.*[27] Adrenocortical steroids such as cortisol have inhibitory effects under the same conditions. It has been demonstrated that microsomes obtained from the prostate gland of testosterone-treated rats have a greater ability to incorporate valine-C^{14} into protein than microsomes from castrated subjects.[39, 47]

Growth of the mouse kidney is enhanced by androgens, and this is accompanied by a marked increase in ribonucleic acid (RNA), principally in the microsomal fraction. In both rats and mice, testosterone increases the protein, RNA, and deoxyribonucleic acid (DNA) content of the ventral prostate and seminal vesicles. Hypophysectomy or castration diminishes the levels of these materials in the accessory sex glands. Castration of the guinea pig causes a rapid loss of total RNA and DNA from the seminal vesicles and prostate, but both are rapidly and progressively increased above normal values by giving testosterone.[40, 50]

It is known that the temporal and masseter muscles of the guinea pig are dependent upon androgens for growth, whereas the oblique and gastrocnemius are relatively unresponsive. The weight, RNA, and DNA of the oblique and gastrocnemius muscles are not changed by castration or androgen administration. Treatment of castrated males with testosterone causes a rapid increase in the RNA of both temporal and masseter muscles, accompanied by increased weight, but does not produce significant changes in the total DNA.[41, 42]

Electrophoretic studies have shown that enzymes acting upon the same substrate may assume different molecular forms (isoenzymes) even within a particular tissue. A hormone-dependent enzyme, called male kidney esterase, has been found in the mouse. This esterase is absent from the kidneys of immature mice; it is typically absent in adult females, but traces of it may be found in some individuals. Orchiectomy reduces the concentration of this enzyme, but it can be restored by administering testosterone. It can be induced in young animals and in adult females by the same treatment. Estrogens and progesterone are ineffective. Testosterone is ineffective *in vitro*, and this implies that it operates through an indirect route. The function of male kidney esterase is not known, but it is possible that it may function in the excretion of androgen metabolites. Since enzymes are proteins, it is apparent that testosterone acts in some manner upon the kidney of the mouse to facilitate the synthesis of a particular protein.[63]

THE REGULATION OF TESTICULAR FUNCTIONS

Pituitary Gonadotrophins[10]

The production of spermatozoa is known to be under the influence of pituitary hormones and of androgens derived from the testis itself. Within a few days after hypophysectomy, the epithelial lining of the seminiferous tubules becomes disorganized and spermatozoa are not produced thereafter (Figs. 13–8 and 13–9). The testes decrease in size, become soft, and regress into the abdominal cavity in certain species. The testicular alterations are not attributable to the movement of the gonad out of the scrotum, since the experimental retention of the testis in the scrotum does not prevent the impairments. Furthermore, the testes do not become intra-abdominal until several weeks after the removal of the hypophysis. The accessory sex organs become quite atrophic following removal of the pituitary, and this indicates that the cells of Leydig secrete little, if any, androgen.

Testicular tissue from neonatal rats has been maintained *in vitro* for long periods. The seminiferous tubules retain their configurations and Sertoli cells persist, but the primordial germ cells do not go far in their differentiation toward spermatozoa. The interstitial cells of Leydig do not differentiate under these circumstances. The addition of follicle-stimulating hormone (FSH) or human chorionic gonadotrophin (HCG) to the culture medium does not stimulate the primordial germ cells to undergo maturational changes; these hormones do cause the nongerminal elements of the tubules to assume the morphologic characteristics of mature Sertoli cells. Early germ cells, in these cultures, can advance to the stage of primary spermatocytes, in the absence of gonadotrophins, if vitamins A, E, and C are added.[67]

Some residual spermatogenesis occurs in the tubules of hypophysectomized rats, all adenohypophysial hormones being absent. A few spermatogonia divide to give rise to primary and secondary

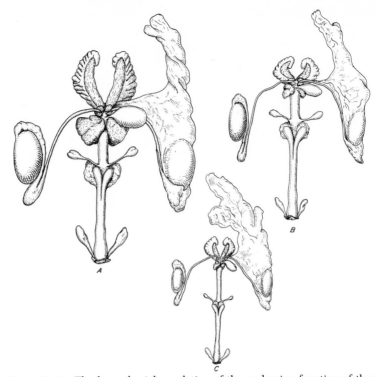

Figure 13–8. The hypophysial regulation of the endocrine function of the testis. *A*, Genital system of a normal adult rat. *B*, Genital tract of a littermate brother which had been hypophysectomized for 30 days. In the absence of the hypophysial gonadotrophins the testes shrink and do not secrete sufficient male sex hormone to maintain the sex accessories. Compare the sizes of the testes and accessory glands in this animal with corresponding organs of the normal littermate (*A*). *C*, Genital complex of a third littermate which had received heavy doses of estrogen at frequent intervals for six months. Note the pronounced atrophy of the testes and sex accessories. Large amounts of estrogens or androgens, injected for long periods, apparently injure the adenohypophysis to such an extent that it becomes unable to release sufficient gonadotrophin to maintain the gonads. The result of such treatment is an impaired genital system which simulates that present in an animal that has been deprived of its hypophysis for an extended period. (The three tracts were dissected *in toto* and drawn to scale from ventral view. See Figure 13–3 for the identity of the genital organs.)

spermatocytes, and the latter may form a few spermatids.[15] The spermatids never give rise to spermatozoa in the untreated hypophysectomized animal. The prompt injection of appropriate gonadotrophins or of androgens into hypophysectomized subjects prevents degeneration of the germ cells. These hormones have some capacity to restore the seminiferous epithelium and the interstitial tissue, if hypophysectomy has not prevailed too long. After prolonged posthypophysectomy regression of the testis, some of the tubules apparently lose their ability to respond to these hormones. Restoration of the Leydig cells is generally possible if the replacement therapy is continued for sufficient periods. Though testosterone alone can

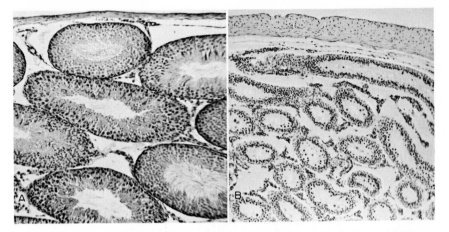

Figure 13-9. The effects of hypophysectomy upon the testis of the rat. *A,* Testis of a normal adult rat. *B,* Testis of a rat hypophysectomized at 4 months of age and killed six months later. Observe atrophy of the seminiferous tubules and thickening of the tunica albuginea (tunica albuginea is at the top of each figure). The testes shrink markedly in size after removal of the pituitary gland, and this is reflected in the thickening of the tunica and the small size of the seminiferous tubules. Both figures are of the same magnification.

restore spermatogenesis to a limited extent in adult rats, 70 days after hypophysectomy, the androgen is much more effective if pituitary growth hormone (STH) is given in conjunction with it.[7, 52]

The hypophysis of the male liberates the same gonadotrophins as that of the female, i.e., follicle-stimulating hormone (FSH), luteinizing hormone (LH or ICSH), and prolactin. As with the other hormones involved in sexual processes, the differences between male and female individuals are quantitative rather than qualitative. Current research indicates that FSH, LH, and androgens are all involved in the normal development and function of the testis. The action of LH is to stimulate the cells of Leydig to produce androgen, and the latter hormone acts directly upon the germinal epithelium. Although purified LH alone is effective in maintaining spermatogenesis for relatively short periods in hypophysectomized rats and mice, if given immediately after the operation, definitive experiments show that both LH and FSH are required for sperm production over long periods.[51, 71, 74]

Leydig cell stimulation has been produced in the immature hypophysectomized rat by injecting ovine or human LH (ICSH) directly into the testis. With low doses (0.025 μg), the effect was localized, that is, it did not spread to the contralateral testis.[66] The intratesticular injection of FSH in adult hypophysectomized rats does not stimulate or maintain either the Leydig cells or the germinal cells, but it does induce secretory hypertrophy of the Sertoli cells.[57]

Hormones and Spermatogenesis

Recent studies indicate that it is necessary to distinguish two aspects of the spermatogenic process, namely, the *rate* at which it progresses and the *yield* in terms of the number of spermatozoa produced per spermatogonial stem cell. Studies employing the technique of radioautography indicate that the time required for the spermatogonia to differentiate into spermatozoa is a biologic constant, varying with the species and strain, but which is not altered by hormones and other factors. On the other hand, observations on many species of vertebrates leave no doubt that the number of spermatozoa produced is dependent upon pituitary gonadotrophins, androgens, nutritional factors, temperatures, light, etc.

It is well known that spermatogenesis in rams is influenced by photoperiods and temperatures. Short periods of daily illumination increase the output of pituitary gonadotrophin and increase the number of spermatozoa produced by the testis; long daily photoperiods have the reverse effect. Ortavant labeled the germ cells with P^{32} and found that the time required for the completion of spermatogenesis was the same in animals exposed to long days and those exposed to short days. He concluded that gonadotrophins have no effect on the rate of spermatogenesis, but increase the yield of spermatozoa from the seminiferous epithelium.[15, 59]

Studies on the rat have shown that the duration of the cycle of the seminiferous epithelium is the same in normal animals, hypophysectomized animals, hypophysectomized animals receiving testosterone, and hypophysectomized animals receiving chorionic gonadotrophin. Furthermore, the rates of spermatogenesis in human subjects receiving norethandrolone (known to depress sperm formation) and in those receiving chorionic gonadotrophin (known to promote sperm formation) were found to be identical with that of normal men. These observations indicate that differentiating germ cells die and are removed if their tissue environment becomes unfavorable; in other words, they cannot stop their differentiation at any stage of the cycle and resume from that point when the milieu becomes favorable. Maximal sperm counts mean that a high percentage of the derivatives of the spermatogonial stem cells have had environments favorable to their progressive differentiation. The stem cells may persist for long periods in the tubules, without differentiating.[15]

Experiments on the intratesticular transplantation of embryonic testes of the mouse have shown that the early germ cells are capable of beginning the spermatogenic process about seven days earlier than they normally do (Fig. 13–10). In normal mice of this strain, advanced spermatids (stage 16 of Oakberg[58]) appear in the normal scrotal testes 35 days after birth. If testes are removed from embryos on the eleventh day of gestation (seven days before parturition) and transplanted into the scrotal testis of a normal host, late spermatids

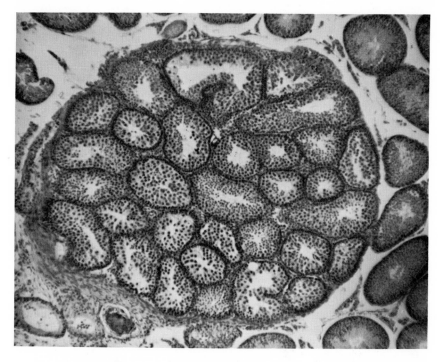

Figure 13–10. The testis of an 11-day-old mouse embryo after being grafted into the scrotal testis of an adult host for 30 days. The tubules of the graft are approximately the same size as those of the host testis. Interstitial tissue is well developed and most of the tubules contain many spermatids. Mature spermatozoa appear in such grafts after about 35 days. (Courtesy of H. Asakawa, Duquesne University; unpublished photograph.)

appear in the grafts 33 to 35 days later. The time required for the completion of spermatogenesis apparently is not shortened but, under the favorable adult environment, the primordial germ cells are stimulated to begin the process earlier than they would in the normally developing individual.[2]

Cryptorchism, Scrotum and Pampiniform Plexus

In the human species the testes normally descend into the scrotum shortly before birth and remain permanently in that position. Scrotal sacs are absent in all vertebrates below mammals, the testes remaining abdominal throughout life. Though most mammals have scrota, the rhinoceros, seal, elephant, and whale are notable exceptions. In most rodents the inguinal canals remain open, and the testes occupy the scrota only during the breeding season. Although typical scrotal sacs are not present in the Insectivora and the Chiroptera, the testes distend the caudal abdominal wall during the breeding season and assume positions close to the exterior of the body.

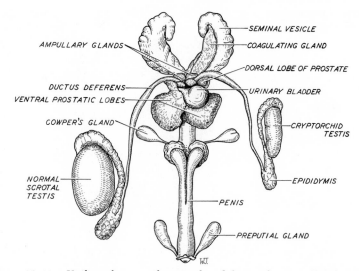

Figure 13–11. Unilateral cryptorchism in the adult rat. The animal's left testis was confined within the abdominal cavity for six months, whereas the right testis was permitted to occupy its normal scrotal position. Note the shrunken condition of the cryptorchid testis as compared with the scrotal testis. Spermatozoa were absent from the left epididymis, but abundantly present in the right epididymis. The accessory sex organs are normal. (The tract was dissected *in toto* and drawn from ventral view.)

In man and domesticated mammals it is not uncommon for the testes to be retained in the abdominal cavity rather than to descend normally into the scrotum. This condition is called cryptorchism (Greek *kryptos*, hidden; *orchis*, testis); when it occurs bilaterally, complete sterility results. Cryptorchism in the human being may result from obstruction of the inguinal canals and possibly from certain hypophysial dysfunctions. Laboratory rodents in which the inguinal canals remain open have been used extensively as subjects for experimentally testing the effects of confining one or both testes to the abdominal cavity. In the rat and guinea pig it is a simple surgical procedure to open the abdomen, lift the testes from the scrotum into the abdominal cavity, section the gubernaculum, and ligate the inguinal canals in such a manner that the gonad cannot push back into the scrotum.

After the testis of the adult rat has been surgically confined to the abdominal cavity, a rapid decrease in size and turgidity of the organ ensues (Fig. 13–11). Histologically, severe disorganization of the seminiferous tubules becomes apparent within a week after the operation. The germinal epithelium deteriorates quickly, and the seminiferous tubules shrink in diameter. After one or two months practically all germinal elements of the tubule have been lost, and little remains except a single layer of Sertoli-like cells next to the basement membrane of the tubule. The most highly differentiated cells disappear first, the order being spermatozoa, spermatids, spermatocytes, and lastly spermatogonia. If all the spermatogonia have not degenerated, replacement of the cryptorchid testis into the scrotum permits the germinal epithelium to recover and again proliferate spermatozoa. Similar results are obtained in the guinea pig and other mammals in which the testes normally occupy scrotal sacs.

The capacity of the cryptorchid testis to renew spermatogenesis after being returned to a scrotal position is directly related to the number of tubules still possessing spermatogonia. In the rat irreparable damage to all tubules occurs within seven months; hence such testes cannot again proliferate sperms even though they are replaced in the scrotum. It appears that in the rat irreparable damage occurs more slowly than in other mammalian species that have been studied. There is no agreement as to how long the human testis can remain in ectopic positions without irreparable damage to the seminiferous epithelium.

An extensive sequence of experiments demonstrates that cryptorchism impairs testicular functions because the temperature of the abdomen is higher than that of the scrotum. Simultaneous measurements indicate that the temperature of the abdomen is approximately 4° C. higher than that of the scrotum. Insulation of the scrotum of the ram by encasing the organ with nonconductive materials elevates the temperature of the scrotum and produces testicular damage that is in all respects similar to that prevailing during cryptorchidy. The same effect is produced by the artificial application of warmth to the exterior of the normal scrotum. A convincing experiment has been performed with the dog. Both testes were confined to the abdomen. Immediately after the operation one abdominal testis was artificially cooled by circulating water of a known temperature through a system of coils. The uncooled testis showed typical heat effects, whereas the other did not. Febrile conditions in man and other mammals contribute to testicular impairment, one of the factors involved being the high temperatures to which the testes are subjected. Testicular homotransplants persisting in the anterior chamber of the eye and in the scrotum are capable of proliferating spermatozoa, since the temperatures of these two sites are relatively lower than that of most other parts of the mammalian body. These considerations convincingly demonstrate that the scrotum is a thermoregulator for the testis and is indispensable for sperm proliferation in the majority of mammals.

The effect of high body temperature on the cells of Leydig and their ability to secrete androgens has not been clarified to the satisfaction of most workers. Studies on the rat indicate that artificial cryptorchism results in a temporary increase in androgen production as evidenced by changes in the accessory reproductive organs; this is followed by a fall in androgen secretion which continues at a fairly constant level.[13] It has been shown that temperature is an important factor in determining the rate of incorporation of acetate-1-C^{14} into testosterone-C^{14} by slices of rabbit testis *in vitro*. Both androgen biosynthesis and lysine incorporation were significantly lower at 40° C than at 38° C, temperatures which are comparable to those of the abdomen and scrotum, respectively, of the rabbit.[31] There are numerous reports in recent literature indicating that nonscrotal temperatures impair certain enzyme systems of the mammalian testis. It is beginning to appear that the interstitial cells of Leydig share with the germinal epithelium a dependence upon lower temperatures for maximal activity.

The pampiniform plexus is a second mechanism which operates in mammals to keep the temperatures of the testis lower than those of the body cavity. This is a plexus of veins from the testis and epididymis, forming part of the spermatic cord. The plexus is supplied by the spermatic artery, and the venous blood empties into the spermatic vein. The plexus functions to cool the blood from the body before it enters the testis and also to warm the blood from the testis before it is returned to the systemic circulation. The cellular and biochemical mechanisms employed in temperature regulation by the pampiniform plexus are obscure, and little is known about its importance in mammals other than the ram and rat. An interesting type of estrogen-secreting tumor of the testis has been produced experimentally in the rat by injuring the pampiniform plexus and ligating the ducti deferentes.[69]

Minute amounts of cadmium, administered to the male rat, produce testicular impairments which are exactly the same as those resulting from cryptorchism. The initial effect of cadmium is upon the cells that line the blood vessels of the pampiniform plexus; other blood vessels seem not to be vulnerable to its actions. Since the damaged plexus cannot cool the blood before it enters the testis, the seminiferous tubules promptly become permanently aspermic and the cells of Leydig are probably impaired. Male rats may be protected from cadmium by pretreating them with zinc, or by giving the zinc simultaneously with the cadmium. The latter metal is without effect in female rats, since they do not develop a pampiniform plexus.

Vasectomy and Testicular Function

It has long been known that ligation of the pancreatic duct causes the acinar portion of the organ to degenerate more rapidly than the islets of Langerhans. Without adequate experimental evidence many workers have assumed that ligation or section of the excurrent ducts of the testis would destroy the germinal epithelium and halt the proliferation of spermatozoa.

The experimental evidence indicates that vasectomy does not destroy completely the gametogenic function of the testis, and there are no quantitative studies indicating that the operation results in any actual hypertrophy of the cells of Leydig. The testis of the dog may proliferate mature spermatozoa for as long as five years after the closure of the excurrent passages. Vasoligation of laboratory rodents, *e.g.*, rats, rabbits, and guinea pigs, does not preclude the proliferation of mature germ cells. Since the sperms cannot be passed to the exterior, they degenerate and are resorbed. Histologic examination of testes subjected to vasoligation for long periods has shown that some of the seminiferous tubules contain cells in all stages of spermatogenesis. A certain percentage of the seminiferous tubules are degenerate, and it is probable that the tubules alternately degenerate and repair.

It was reported in 1903 that vasoligation destroys the spermiogenic tissue of the testis and leads to hypertrophy of the interstitial cells of Leydig. In 1920 the hypothesis was advocated and vigorously contended (1) that vasoligation of domestic animals and man destroys the germinal epithelium of the testis and increases the cells of Leydig, (2) that the hypertrophied cells of Leydig yield an increased amount of male sex hormone, and (3) that the augmented release of androgen serves to "rejuvenate" the senescent male. These claims have been held in disrepute by most testicular physiologists. However, the problem of the effects of vasectomy on androgen secretion and libido remains unresolved.

It has been reported that vasectomy of the bull results in the loss of certain amino acids from the semen and that they may be restored by the administration of testosterone; they disappear from the semen again after the androgen injections are discontinued. Extremely high levels of fructose and citric acid are said to appear in the ejaculates of bulls and rams after vasoligation. The semen of the vasectomized animal would be more concentrated than normal owing to the absence of spermatozoa and fluids from the testis and epididymis, but the reduced volume of the semen after vasoligation is said to be too small to account for the higher levels of fructose in it. Prolonged studies on vasectomized bulls have shown that seminal fructose reaches a high level about one year after vasoligation and, concomitant with the rise in fructose, libido and aggressiveness are increased. The administration of exogenous androgen to the bull does not produce these striking changes in fructose levels and sex drive. Variations in libido occur in human subjects after vasectomy, but since so many psychic factors are involved, it is difficult to evaluate the reported changes.[53]

We must conclude that vasectomy is an effective method of sterilizing the male and that it does not completely prevent spermatogenesis, but its effect, if any, on the endocrine functions of the testis remains obscure.

Castration

Prepuberal castration of the human male prevents the functional differentiation of the accessory sex ducts and glands and also the appearance of certain secondary sexual characters. The larynx remains small and the voice high-pitched. Hair fails to appear on the face and body, but its abundance on the scalp is not modified. The penis remains infantile, and sexual libido is usually suppressed. Frequently, but not invariably, castration of the prepuberal human male seems to retard the closure of the epiphyses. This may result in an enlargement of the stature, especially a disproportioned lengthening of the paired appendages. As to a tendency toward obesity, there seems to be extreme individual variation among eunuchoid human beings; some become obese, whereas others remain lean. Contrary to popular belief, mental attitudes, initiative, and industry are variable among human castrates.

Castration of human males after the attainment of sexual maturity produces regression of all accessory sex organs of reproduction. The urinary excretion of 17-ketosteroids is generally reduced to about one-half the normal value, although it may remain within normal limits. Mental processes are not modified so extensively as in the prepuberal castrate. Clinical literature indicates that orchiectomized males may retain sexual libido for long periods. Male rats castrated during adulthood may copulate with estrous females for eight months or longer after the withdrawal of male sex hormone.

Nutrition and Testicular Functions

It is a well-established fact that malnutrition has an adverse effect on the reproductive organs of both sexes.[45] Inanition, vitamin deficiencies, caloric restriction, or insufficient quantities of specific food substances such as proteins are capable of impairing testicular functions. Hypofunctioning of the Leydig cells is indicated by atrophy of the accessory sex organs, which is followed by disorganization of the seminiferous epithelium and the cessation of spermatogenesis. Inadequate diets may impair the endocrine function of the testis without producing any appreciable defects in the seminiferous tubules. Vitamin B deficiency in the rat causes the male accessory organs to involute until they resemble those of castrated or hypophysectomized animals. This accessory gland atrophy can be repaired either by the administration of androgen or pituitary gonadotrophins. Since the gonads respond to exogenous gonadotrophins and the sex accessories respond to androgen, it becomes apparent that the primary defect is in the release of pituitary gonadotrophins. Various types of underfeeding produce the same general syndrome in man and experimental animals as vitamin B deficiency. For example, if dietary proteins are inadequate to maintain a normal nitrogen balance, the male accessories atrophy as in vitamin deficiency and their repair is effected by small doses of gonadotrophins. This syndrome resulting from undernutrition is related to diminished pituitary gonadotrophins in the circulation and is often called pseudohypophysectomy.[43, 44]

In chronically undernourished rats, the levels of fructose in the coagulating glands and of citric acid in the seminal vesicles fall until they are quite comparable to those prevailing in total castrates. Both constituents of the accessory gland secretions may be raised to normal levels by exogenous androgen or gonadotrophins. It seems reasonably certain that the primary lesion is in the hypophysial mechanism that is needed for the normal functioning of the testis. In some species, such as the bull, the testicular effects of underfeeding develop more slowly than in the rat; recovery is also slower.

In studies of identical-twin calves, it has been found that underfeeding of the young animal greatly delays the appearance of fructose and citric acid in the ejaculates. This indicates that nutrition is an important factor in establishing testicular functions in the prepuberal animal.[53]

Gonadal functions may be impaired by diets deficient in proteins or specific amino acids. Chronic starvation or protein-free diets prevent testicular maturation in young rats. Diets lacking only protein are less effective than starvation in abolishing spermatogenesis in the adult rat. Diets containing 6 per cent casein are not adequate for body growth in the young rat, but such diets do permit some degree of spermatogenesis. This suggests that the reproductive system may be given some priority to proteins when their dietary intake is limited. Many types of experiments indicate that adequate nutrition is especially important in the young animal for proper gonadal maturation, and it is not improbable that some types of adult infertility are the consequences of malnutrition during fetal or prepuberal periods.

THE BIOLOGY OF SPERMATOZOA

The spermatozoa of different species show extraordinary diversity of shape and structure (Fig. 13–12). Many of the finer structural details of these cells have been revealed by electron microscopic studies. The axial filament extends the entire length of the mid-piece and tail. It consists of a number of fine fibers that are probably the contractile elements of the cell, responsible for the whiplike undulations of the tail. The axial filament of the mammalian sperm cell is surrounded by an axial sheath; the enzymes responsible for sperm motility are probably located in the mid-piece region of this sheath. The cytoplasmic sheath contains lipoprotein and forms a protective

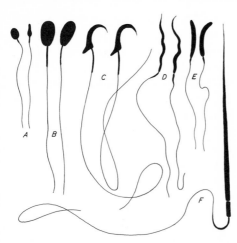

Figure 13–12.   Spermatozoa from different species of vertebrates. *A*, Human; *B*, sheep; *C*, rat; *D*, chicken; *E*, frog; *F*, *Ambystoma* (a salamander). All drawn to scale from stained smears.

capsule surrounding the mid-piece and tail. The sperm nucleus is present in the head and a caplike structure, called the *acrosome,* fits over the anterior part of the head. The spermatozoa are mature cells and do not undergo mitotic divisions, though various types of morphologically abnormal spermatozoa may be observed.

Cytochemical tests indicate abundant glycogen in the Sertoli cells and spermatogonia, progressively less in the primary and secondary spermatocytes and spermatids, and practically none in the mature spermatozoa. In mammals at least, the ripening of the spermatozoa continues during their storage in the epididymis. The spermatozoa in the epididymis are immotile but are capable of long survival. The development of motility coincides with their movement along the male tract at ejaculation and mixing with the seminal plasma.

Though the spermatozoa possess meager intracellular reserves of nutrients, they can metabolize a wide range of extracellular substrates which are present in seminal plasma and in the secretions of the female reproductive tract. The semen, consisting of spermatozoa and seminal plasma, is somewhat similar to a suspension of motile microörganisms existing in a nutrient medium. Much progress has been made in the biochemical elucidation of sperm cell metabolism.[5, 6]

The Biochemistry of Semen[54]

Although some fluid accompanies the spermatozoa as they move through the testis and epididymis, most of the seminal plasma is derived from the seminal vesicles, prostate, and Cowper's glands. In the epididymis the sperms are immotile at a pH of around 7. The seminal plasma is approximately isotonic and generally has a pH of 7 or slightly above. The quiescence of the epididymal sperms seems to correlate better with the lack of carbohydrate, low oxygen tension, and crowding than it does with hydrogen ion concentration. The spermatozoa of most species tolerate alkalinity better than acidity; increasing the pH to 8 or higher may enhance motility but excessive acidity renders them immotile. Most workers agree that pH 7, or slightly higher, is optimum for motility and survival of the sperm cells of most species.

As already mentioned, the accessory gland products contain fructose and citric acid. Fructose occurs in the semen of virtually all mammals, but its concentration varies with the volume of semen ejaculated. Cock semen contains no fructose; that of the rabbit contains both glucose and fructose.

Although there are many species variations, calcium, sodium, magnesium, potassium, phosphate, and chloride ions are present in the seminal plasma. Human seminal fluid contains about 14 mg. per 100 ml. of zinc, a higher concentration than is found in any other human tissue. The calcium content of human semen is several times higher than that of the blood. Heavy metals and calcium have been found to reduce the viability of mammalian spermatozoa. Spermatozoa of the ram and bull rapidly become immotile in the absence of potassium. It may be that one function of citric acid in the seminal fluid is to combine with calcium and thus prevent the precipitation of insoluble calcium salts.

Polypeptides and proteins of low molecular weight are present in mammalian semen. The proteins present in human seminal plasma are atypical inasmuch as they are not coagulated by heat and pass through cellulose membranes. Free amino acids are also present; some of these probably arise through the breakdown of proteins after the semen is ejaculated. Bull semen contains five free amino acids: glutamic acid, alanine, glycine, serine, and aspartic acid. These disappear after castration and, with the exception of glutamic acid, are restored in part by exogenous androgens. Since glutamic acid comes mainly from the testis and epididymis, it is absent in castrated and vasectomized bulls.[29] There are suggestions that the seminal amino acids may protect the spermatozoa by combining with heavy metals which may become toxic or, in the case of proteins, by preventing agglutination and the loss of intracellular material as the spermatozoa are diluted. The mammalian prostate releases an anti-agglutinic factor, containing sugar, sulfuric acid residues, and a vitamin E derivative, and this acts to prevent the clumping of·sperm heads.

Most mammalian semens contain ascorbic acid and traces of B vitamins. The seminal vesicles of the boar produce high concentrations of inositol, and smaller amounts are found in other species. There is no evidence that inositol is utilized by mammalian semen.

Human semen coagulates at first but later liquefies, the

liquefaction being brought about by one of the proteolytic enzymes contained in the prostatic secretion. This secretion is rich in acid phosphatase, its natural substrate (phosphorylcholine) being contributed by the seminal vesicles. Seminal fluids of the bull and ram, on the other hand, contain little acid phosphatase but high amounts of the alkaline enzyme.

Hyaluronidase is another enzyme present in semen, but its functional role is far from clear. This enzyme is actually contained within the sperm cell, but is very quickly released into the seminal plasma; thus it is not a product of the accessory glands. Because of its ability to depolymerize hyaluronic acid, it was thought that it might perform a role in facilitating penetration of the ovum by the sperm. This hypothesis has not received much experimental support.

Human semen contains high concentrations of choline and spermine, the latter apparently occurring only in the human species. Both of these substances can be easily detected chemically, and they form the basis of various tests employed in medicolegal investigations.

Sperm Metabolism

Mammalian spermatozoa are capable of metabolizing a wide range of materials, such as various sugars, organic acids, and alcohols, found in the seminal plasma, in the fluids of the female tract, or in the artificial media in which they are stored. Under anaerobic conditions, the spermatozoa rely upon the metabolism of carbohydrate as the chief source of energy. When sperms are incubated anaerobically, the fructose concentration of the seminal plasma decreases and lactic acid accumulates. Additional energy is obtained under aerobic conditions by the oxidation of lactic acid to carbon dioxide and water.

The first phase of fructolysis involves the enzymatic conversion of phosphotriose to phosphoglyceric acid, and the simultaneous reduction of nicotinamide adenine dinucleotide (NAD) to NADH. The oxidation of phosphotriose is coupled with the esterification of inorganic phosphate and the synthesis of ATP. The conversion of phosphoglyceric acid to phosphopyruvic acid results in the production of pyruvic acid and ATP. In the second oxidoreduction, NADH is oxidized to NAD and pyruvic acid is reduced to lactic acid (Fig. 13–13).

ATP is the cardinal link between carbohydrate metabolism and sperm motility. The breakdown of ATP apparently provides the energy for the contraction of the sperm fibrils, the replenishment of ATP being dependent on the normal metabolism of fructose. The ATP content of spermatozoa correlates closely with their motility. For example, if spermatozoa are maintained under anaerobic con-

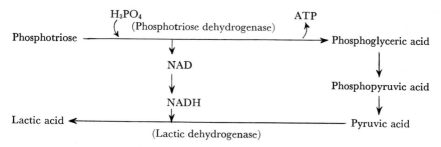

Figure 13-13. Fructolysis in semen. Adapted from Mann, T.: The Biochemistry of Semen and of the Male Reproductive Tract. New York, John Wiley & Sons, 1964.)

ditions and without a glycolyzable sugar, motility becomes very low. Motility is restored by adding fructose or some other glycolyzable sugar. The highest motility results when oxygen and fructose are present together.

It is not clear why mammalian spermatozoa normally utilize fructose anaerobically, whereas other tissues employ glucose instead of fructose. This special sugar for the sperm cells is localized in the accessory glands and is dependent upon androgen control. It is an arrangement that enables the spermatozoa to derive their energy from fructose without competing with other tissues for glucose which is so widely distributed within the organism.

The *in Vitro* Storage of Spermatozoa

Artificial insemination is widely practiced in the breeding of domestic animals. This procedure involves the collection of viable spermatozoa, the retention of these cells *in vitro,* and the proper introduction of them into the female tract. The optimal temperature for the storage of most sperms is approximately 12° C; body temperature is most favorable for maximal motility. Human spermatozoa are unique inasmuch as they survive freezing to very low temperatures moderately well.[37] Human spermatozoa have survived and shown motility after freezing in liquid nitrogen at −195° C.; some have survived after existing in a frozen state for 70 days. Diluents containing glycerol or other polyalcohols offer some protection for bull, goat, horse, and rabbit sperms against the harmful effects of freezing, but the rate of thawing must be slow.

Sperm survive best when they are stored in an isotonic medium of about neutral pH that contains fructose or glucose as a source of energy. Under anaerobic conditions fructolysis produces large quantities of lactic acid, so it is necessary that the diluent contain a satisfactory buffer. In the presence of oxygen some of the lactic acid can be oxidized and buffer is not so much needed. The phosphate content of the diluent has a marked effect on the amount of lactic acid that can be oxidized. Calcium and high levels of phosphate are harmful to sperm motility. Potassium, on the other hand, promotes motility and glycolysis of washed ram and bull sperms. The egg yolk-citrate medium has been found moderately satisfactory for artificial insemination procedures, although more complex physiologic diluents might give better results.

Experience indicates that mammalian spermatozoa survive best if they are stored at as high a concentration as possible; in other words, dilution has a harmful effect on the germ cells. Small numbers of sperm do not survive well, even when stored in large quantities of an isotonic diluent containing glycolyzable sugars. The depression occurring during storage at low cell concentration seems to be due largely to the loss of substances from the sperms, though little is known about the nature of these substances. It is known, however, that materials of high molecular weight, such as proteins and starch, protect against the dilution effect. Egg yolk is commonly used for this purpose, and the active constituent is probably a lipoprotein.

It is desirable to store semen at a low temperature in order to retard bacterial growth, but if it is cooled to temperatures below 10° C., the temperatures must be reduced slowly in order to avoid cold shock. This causes a rapid reduction of ATP and the loss of intracellular proteins into the medium. Egg yolk and other materials provide some protection against cold shock. It is a common practice to add antibiotics to the diluent because of the harmful effect of bacteria on the sperms and the possibility of spreading genital infections.

ENVIRONMENT AND SEXUAL PERIODICITY

A wealth of information indicates that various external environmental agencies intervene to adjust reproductive activities to particular seasons of the year. The precise factors that operate appear to vary with the species, and perhaps in all species a multitude of coordinated physical and social factors are involved. It is widely held that the environment acts through the intermediation of the hypothalamus and the anterior pituitary gland, the latter serving as a liaison organ between the nervous system and the target glands, which are regulated by its trophic hormones. The main gap in our knowledge is how the nervous impulses impinging on the hypothalamus trigger the release of pituitary trophic hormones. A few typical examples will now be mentioned to illustrate the manner in which some environmental situations affect breeding states.[1, 30, 61, 72, 73]

Food

The African weaver-finch (*Quelea quelea*) has reproduced so successfully in its native habitat that it is considered a major pest because of its damage to small grain crops. The breeding colonies may consist of more than a million birds. The male uses fresh green grass to construct a perpendicular nest-ring upon which he displays himself in nuptial plumage. Copulation occurs on or near this ring, and the nest is completed by weaving additional green grass into it. The young are fed on insects for the first five days of life and then on green grass seeds. Vast quantities of insects and green grass are necessary for successful reproduction, and breeding sites are frequently abandoned if these requirements are not met. Breeding in this species occurs only after a rainy period. It is probable that environmental conditions prevailing after rainfall, operating in conjunction with the internal sexual rhythm, are the critical factors determining the time of reproduction in this species.[18]

Light

There is overwhelming evidence that light is an important environmental stimulus influencing reproductive rhythms. The onset of the breeding season is controlled in some species by increasing light periods, whereas in other species diminishing periods of light constitute the effective stimulus. It has been known for many years that egg production in domestic hens may be encouraged by subjecting the animals to increasing periods of light. Rowan in 1926 was the first to show that lengthening the day by providing additional illumination would bring the involuted gonads of the junco into a breeding state.[62] He thought that the increased exercise or activity of the birds incident to increased daily photoperiods was the essential stimulus that induced gonadal recrudescence, but this hypothesis has not been confirmed.

The ferret is sexually dormant during autumn and winter, the long anestrus extending from August to March. Ferrets do not breed during this period, but they can be brought into breeding condition by keeping them in artificial light for a few hours after sunset each day. The female is more easily controlled in this way than the male. The ferret does not respond to increasing photoperiods if it is blind or if either the hypophysis or gonads are removed. The chain of reactions involved seems to be: transmission of impulses along the optic nerve to the brain (probably hypothalamus); stimulation of the adenohypophysis to release gonadotrophins and perhaps other hormones; activation of the gonads by the pituitary gonadotrophins; stimulation of the accessory sex organs; and the induction of psychological heat by the gonadal hormones.

In some species the onset of the breeding season may be hastened by *diminishing* the daily amounts of light and ended by *increasing* the photoperiods. Sheep, for example, start to breed earlier if the amount of light normally available in the spring is reduced. The majority of birds and many mammals (*e.g.*, horse, ferret) tend to have breeding periods in the spring (long-day breeders), whereas other mammals (*e.g.*, deer, sheep) breed during the fall (short-day breeders). Again, in the guinea pig, ground squirrel, rabbit, and cow, light periods seem to be without effect on reproductive processes.

Female rats receiving additional rations of light remain in heat, or estrus, for several weeks instead of the normal period of 14 hours. Young female rats kept in continuous light from birth attain sexual maturity about a week earlier than normal; constant darkness from the time of birth delays the onset of sexual maturity by two or three weeks.[24] The gestation period of the American marten is about nine months, but there is a period of delayed implantation of seven months. Increasing photoperiods hasten the implantation of the blastocysts, and the young are born about four months earlier than usual.

Long photoperiods cause pronounced testicular growth in domestic ducks, but this does not occur after hypophysectomy or after the pathway from the hypothalamus to the pituitary is experimentally blocked. On the other hand, the domestic fowl, parakeet, and house sparrow can attain sexual maturity when kept in complete darkness.

The foregoing examples are sufficient to indicate that light has a pronounced effect upon the production of pituitary gonadotrophins in birds and mammals. There is general agreement now that the effects of light and other environmental stimuli on gonadal activities are mediated by the central nervous system (hypothalamus), the hypophysial portal veins, and the adenohypophysis.

The Mode of Action of Light

After Rowan's interpretation, many workers have felt that the effects of light on reproductive phenomena might result secondarily from metabolic alterations consequent upon lengthened periods of wakefulness and physical exercise. However, egg production in the domestic hen can be increased by subjecting them to 20-second shocks of intense light at 4:00 A.M. and 4:45 A.M., while the birds are sleeping. Since the birds remain on the roosts and show little if any activity after these shocks, it would seem that increased exercise does not explain the phenomenon.

During midwinter the gonads of white-crowned sparrows (*Zonotrichia*) are small and inactive. When the animals are caged and subjected to elevated environmental temperatures, they develop periods of nocturnal activity. This provides a convenient and natural way to increase physical activity without lengthening the daily photo-period. Increasing the daily activity in this species, without an accompanying increase in light, does not produce gonadal recrudes-cence. Although exercise may be an essential element in certain species, or a factor of some importance in maintaining reproductive behavior once it is begun, a direct action of light *per se* upon the central nervous system seems to provide a more adequate explanation than the wakefulness-activity hypothesis.[22, 23]

Extensive studies on the duck have shown that gonadal recrudes-cence, even after removal of the eyes, can be achieved by focusing light directly on the pituitary, hypothalamus, or rhinencephalon.[4] By stereotaxically implanting small, light-sensitive, photovoltaic cells into the hypothalamic regions of sheep, dogs, rabbits, and rats, it has been shown that sunlight can penetrate deeply into the mam-malian brain.[28] This observation indicates that the capacity of light to penetrate the brain directly must be taken into account when studying the effects of light upon the hypothalami and pituitary glands of vertebrates.

Exposure of female rats to constant light causes them to enter periods of prolonged estrus, as is indicated by large numbers of keratinized scales in the vaginal smear, and this response normally depends in large measure upon the eyes as light receptors. If rats are blinded and small glass fibers are implanted into regions of the hypothalamus, the opposite ends of the fibers projecting above the skull surface, exposure to light induces constant estrus. It thus appears that light falling directly upon hypothalamic neurons can evoke the release of pituitary gonadotrophins which produce func-tional changes in the gonads. Light appears to act upon the same areas of the hypothalamus which have been shown to respond to implanted sex steroids and influence the estrous cycle and behavior of the rat.[48, 49]

The *pineal gland* may possibly be involved in the mediation of the gonadal changes effected by continuous light or darkness in the rat.[25, 75] The theory is that melatonin, a specific product of the pineal gland, exerts an inhibitory effect upon gonad functions. The capacity of the pineal to produce melatonin is regulated by light; it is syn-thesized largely in the absence of light. Accordingly, the increased ovarian weight and constant estrus, produced by continuous illumina-tion, might be a consequence of the reduced output of melatonin by the pineal under these conditions. The effects of the pineal gland on gonadal functions will be discussed more fully in Chapter 14.

Temperature

It is well known that breeding efficiency among cattle declines during the hot summer months and also that the yields of both milk and butter fat are usually reduced during these periods. In the male ground squirrel testicular involution is correlated with rising summer temperatures and testicular reactivation with the falling temperatures of autumn and winter. Males of this species remain in a constant breeding condition when maintained at 40° F. for one year, the anestrous phase of the normal cycle not appearing. Light appears not to be important in the ground squirrel. Neither light nor temperature seems to have decisive effects in the male prairie dog.

Social Impact

Most people are aware that many species of birds and mammals, although perfectly healthy and in a comfortable environment, fail to exhibit seasonal reproductive changes and never produce young in captivity. Something seems to be lacking in the psychological atmosphere that is essential for activation of the pituitary gland and the initiation of reproductive functions.

Certain sea birds nest in colonies, and studies have indicated that the total number of birds present in the colony is an important factor in reproductive efficiency. Within limits the larger colonies produce more eggs and hatch more young: the period of egg laying becomes more prolonged if the size of the colony is reduced; if it becomes too small, there is no reproductive success. In certain species a small colony may arrive at the breeding grounds but neither produce eggs nor rear any young, and this may continue for several years until the colony has increased its numbers to an essential minimum.

Many species of seal practice a harem system on the breeding grounds; a male takes over a number of females and guards them against the attention of rival males. In these carnivores there is typically a postpartum estrus during which copulations are permitted. It is probable that this social arrangement is an important factor in providing the necessary psychological stimulus for reproduction and the maintenance of adequate numbers.

After surgical removal of the olfactory bulbs of mature mice, the ovaries and uteri become significantly smaller than those of the controls.[72] Corpora lutea are absent or atrophic and the vagina remains small. In males, similarly operated, the testes appear normal but the accessory sex glands are smaller and lighter than usual. The estrous cycle is modified by the presence of a male or his excreta.

A very rigid social hierarchy is established in male chickens as they become sexually mature. Studies have shown that the weights of the adrenal glands of cocks correlate reciprocally with social rank. The testes of subordinate grouped cocks gain weight more slowly than those of dominant grouped males; furthermore, the onset of spermatogenesis is delayed, and degenerative changes occur in the testis tubules. These studies show that grouping and social position are important factors in conditioning the production of pituitary gonadotrophins and hence fertility in male birds.[26] Extensive observations of this type have been made on mammalian species.[12]

The Refractory Period

Although light, temperature, rainfall, food supply, social impact, and other environmental factors are important in conditioning seasonal periodicity, it should be pointed out that the reproductive state cannot be prolonged indefinitely even by the most favorable external environment. Neither can another sexual cycle be reinstated immediately after the close of one. This is referred to as the *refractory period*.[56]

The factors responsible for the onset of this period are largely obscure. It may be that the pituitary gland becomes exhausted and cannot supply the necessary gonadotrophins, or that the gonads no longer possess the necessary structure to respond to the gonadotrophins. As mentioned earlier, the cells of Leydig in the bird's testis become exhausted at the end of the reproductive period and another generation of such cells must be regenerated from connective tissue elements. It may be that the onset of the refractory period in the case of the male bird coincides with the interval required to build up another generation of Leydig cells.

REFERENCES

1. Amoroso, E. C., and Matthews, L. H.: The effect of external stimuli on the breeding-cycle of birds and mammals. Brit. M. Bull., *11*:87, 1955.
2. Asakawa, H.: Precocious spermatogenesis in intratesticular homotransplants of fetal mouse testes. Amer. Zool., *3*:493, 1963.
3. Bengmark, S., Ingemanson, B., and Källén, B.: Endocrine dependence of rat prostatic tissue *in vitro*. Acta Endocrinol., *30*:459, 1959.
4. Benoit, J., and Assenmacher, I.: The control by visible radiations of the gonadotropic activity of the duck hypophysis. Recent Prog. Hormone Research, *15*:143, 1959.
5. Bishop, D. W.: Sperm motility. Physiol. Rev., *42*:1, 1962.
6. Bishop, D. W. (ed.): Spermatozoan Motility. Washington, D.C., American Association for the Advancement of Science, (Publ. No. 72), 1962.
7. Boccabella, A. V.: Reinitiation and restoration of spermatogenesis with testosterone propionate and other hormones after a long-term post-hypophysectomy regression period. Endocrinol., *72*:787, 1963.
8. Breneman, W. R.: Reproduction in birds: the female. Memoirs Soc. Endocrinol., No. 4, 94, 1955.
9. Breneman, W. R.: Steroid hormones and the development of the reproductive system in the pullet. Endocrinol., *58*:262, 1956.
10. Breneman, W. R., Zeller, F. J., and Creek, R. O.: Radioactive phosphorus uptake by chick testes as an end-point for gonadotropin assay. Endocrinol., *71*:790, 1962.

11. Christensen, A. K., and Mason, N. R.: Comparative ability of seminiferous tubules and interstitial tissue of rat testes to synthesize androgens from progesterone-4-^{14}C *in vitro*. Endocrinol., 76:646, 1965.

12. Christian, J. J., Lloyd, J. A., and Davis, D. E.: The role of endocrines in the self-regulation of mammalian populations. Recent Prog. Hormone Research, 21:501, 1965.

13. Clegg, E. J.: Some effects of artificial cryptorchidism on the accessory reproductive organs of the rat. J. Endocrinol., 20:210, 1960.

14. Clermont, Y.: Quantitative analysis of spermatogenesis of the rat: a revised model for the renewal of spermatozoa. Amer. J. Anat., 111:111, 1962.

15. Clermont, Y., and Harvey, S. C.: Duration of the cycle of the seminiferous epithelium of normal, hypophysectomized and hypophysectomized-hormone treated albino rats. Endocrinol., 76:80, 1965.

16. Clermont, Y., Leblond, C. P., and Messier, B.: Durée du cycle de l'épithelium séminal du rat. Arch. Anat. Microscop. Morphol. Expér., 48:37, 1959.

17. Clermont, Y., and Perey, B.: The stages of the cycle of the seminiferous epithelium of the rat: practical definitions in PA-Schiff-hematoxylin and hematoxylin-eosin stained sections. Rev. Canad. de Biol., 16:451, 1957.

18. Disney, H. J. de S., and Marshall, A. J.: A contribution to the breeding biology of the weaver-finch *Quelea quelea* (Linnaeus) in East Africa. Proc. Zool. Soc. London, 127:379, 1956.

19. Dorfman, R. I., Forchielli, E., and Gut, M.: Androgen biosynthesis and related studies. Recent Prog. Hormone Research, 19:251, 1963.

20. Dugal, L. P., and Dunnigan, J.: Les poids de l'électro-éjaculat chez le cobaye soumis à une exposition chronique au froid. Canadian J. Biochem. & Physiol., 40:407, 1962.

21. Ellis, LeG. C., and Berliner, D. L.: Sequential biotransformation of 5-pregnenolone-7α-^{3}H and progesterone-4-^{14}C into androgens by mouse testes. Endocrinol., 76:591, 1965.

22. Farner, D. S., and Mewaldt, L. R.: Is increased activity of wakefulness an essential element in the mechanism of the photoperiodic responses of avian gonads? Northwest Sci., 29:53, 1955.

23. Farner, D. S., and Wilson, A. C.: A quantitative estimation of testicular growth in the white-crowned sparrow. Biol. Bull., 113:254, 1957.

24. Fiske, V. M., and Greep, R. O.: Neurosecretory activity in rats under conditions of continuous light and darkness. Endocrinol., 64:175, 1959.

25. Fiske, V. M., Pound, J., and Putnam, J.: Effect of light on the weight of the pineal organ in hypophysectomized, gonadectomized, adrenalectomized or thiouracil-fed rats. Endocrinol., 71:130, 1962.

26. Flickinger, G. L.: Effect of grouping on adrenals and gonads of chickens. Gen. & Comp. Endocrinol., 1:332, 1961.

27. Frieden, E. H., Cohen, E. H., and Harper, A. A.: The effects of steroid hormones upon amino acid incorporation into mouse kidney homogenates. Endocrinol., 68:862, 1961.

28. Ganong, W. F., Shepherd, M. D., Wall, J. R., Van Brunt, E. E., and Clegg, M. T.: Penetration of light into the brain of mammals. Endocrinol., 72:962, 1963.

29. Gassner, F. X., and Hopwood, M. L.: Seminal amino acid and carbohydrate pattern of bulls with normal and abnormal testes function. Proc. Soc. Exp. Biol. & Med., 81:37, 1952.

30. Hafez, E. S. E.: Environment and reproduction in domesticated species. *In* W. J. L. Lefts and R. J. Harrison (eds.): Internat. Rev. Gen. & Exp. Zool., Vol. 1. New York, Academic Press, 1964, p. 113.

31. Hall, P. F.: Influence of temperature upon the biosynthesis of testosterone by rabbit testis *in vitro*. Endocrinol., 76:396, 1965.

32. Hall, P. F., Sozer, C. C., and Eik-Nes, K. B.: Formation of dehydroepiandrosterone during *in vivo* and *in vitro* biosynthesis of testosterone by testicular tissue. Endocrinol., 74:35, 1964.

33. Harding, B. W., and Samuels, L. T.: The uptake and subcellular distribution of C^{14}-labeled steroid in rat ventral prostate following *in vivo* administration of testosterone-4-C^{14}. Endocrinol., 70:109, 1962.

34. Harkin, J. C.: An electron microscopic study of the castration changes in the rat prostate. Endocrinol., 60:185, 1957.

35. Heller, C. G., and Clermont, Y.: Spermatogenesis in man: an estimate of its duration. Science, *140*:184, 1963.
36. Heller, C. G., and Clermont, Y.: Kinetics of the germinal epithelium in man. Recent Prog. Hormone Research, *20*:545, 1964.
37. Hoagland, H., and Pincus, G.: Revival of mammalian sperm after immersion in liquid nitrogen. J. Gen. Physiol., 25:337, 1942.
38. Ibayashi, H., Nakamura, M., Uchikawa, T., Murakawa, S., Yoshida, S., Nakao, K., and Okinaka, S.: C_{19} steroids in canine spermatic venous blood following gonadotropin administration. Endocrinol., 76:347, 1965.
39. Karlson, P. (ed.): Mechanisms of Hormone Action. New York, Academic Press, 1965.
40. Kochakian, C. D., Hill, J., and Aonuma, S.: Regulation of protein biosynthesis in mouse kidney by androgens. Endocrinol., 72:354, 1963.
41. Kochakian, C. D., Hill, J., and Harrison, D. G.: Regulation of nucleic acids of muscles and accessory sex organs of guinea pigs by androgens. Endocrinol., 74:635, 1964.
42. Kochakian, C. D., Tillotson, C. T., Austin, J., Dougherty, E., Haag, V., and Coalson, R.: The effect of castration on the weight and composition of the muscles of the guinea pig. Endocrinol., 58:315, 1956.
43. Leathem, J. H.: Nutritional and hormonal influences upon testis function. Proc. III Intern. Congr. Animal Reprod., Cambridge, 11, 1956.
44. Leathem, J. H.: Hormones and protein nutrition. Recent Prog. Hormone Research, *14*:141, 1958.
45. Leathem, J. H.: Nutritional effects on endocrine secretions. *In* W. C. Young (ed.): Sex and Internal Secretions, Vol. 1. Baltimore, Williams & Wilkins Co., 1961, p. 666.
46. Levey, H. A., and Szego, C. M.: The effect of androgens on fructose production by the sex accessories of male guinea pigs and rats. Endocrinol., 56:404, 1955.
47. Liao, S., and Williams-Ashman, H. G.: An effect of testosterone on amino acid incorporation by prostatic ribonucleoprotein particles. Proc. Nat. Acad. Sci., 48:1956, 1962.
48. Lisk, R. D., and Kannwischer, L. R.: Light: evidence for its direct effect on hypothalamic neurons. Science, *146*:272, 1964.
49. Lisk, R. D., and Newlon, M.: Estradiol: evidence for its direct effect on hypothalamic neurons. Science, *139*:223, 1963.
50. Lostroh, A. J.: Effect of testosterone and growth hormone on nucleic acid and protein in the sex accessory glands of Long-Evans and Sprague-Dawley rats. Endocrinol., 70:747, 1962.
51. Lostroh, A. J.: Parameters in the biology of spermatogenesis. *In* R. F. Escamilla (ed.): Laboratory Tests of Endocrine Functions. Philadelphia, F. A. Davis Co., 1962, p. 326.
52. Lostroh, A. J., and Li, C. H.: Stimulation of the sex accessories of hypophysectomized male rats by non-gonadotrophic hormones of the pituitary gland. Acta Endocrinol., 25:1, 1957.
53. Mann, T.: Male sex hormone and its role in reproduction. Recent Prog. Hormone Research, *12*:353, 1956.
54. Mann, T.: The Biochemistry of Semen and of the Male Reproductive Tract. New York, John Wiley & Sons, 1964.
55. Meli, A.: Route of administration as a factor influencing the biological activity of certain androgens and their corresponding 3-cyclopentyl enol ethers. Endocrinol., 72:715, 1963.
56. Miller, A. H.: The occurrence and maintenance of the refractory period in crowned sparrows. Condor, 56:13, 1954.
57. Murphy, H. D.: Sertoli cell stimulation following intratesticular injections of FSH in the hypophysectomized rat. Proc. Soc. Exp. Biol. & Med., *118*:1202, 1965.
58. Oakberg, E. F.: A description of spermiogenesis in the mouse and its use in analysis of the cycle of the seminiferous epithelium and germ cell renewal. Amer. J. Anat., 99:391, 1956.
59. Ortavant, R.: Thèse, Faculté des Sciences, l'Université de Paris, 1958. (Quoted from Clermont and Harvey, 1965.)

60. Ortiz, E., Price, D., Williams-Ashman, H. G., and Banks, J.: The influence of androgens on the male accessory reproductive glands of the guinea pig: studies on growth, histological structure and fructose and citric acid secretion. Endocrinol., 59:479, 1956.
61. Parkes, A. S., and Bruce, H. M.: Olfactory stimuli in mammalian reproduction. Science, 134:1049, 1961.
62. Rowan, W.: Experiments in bird migration. Manipulation of the reproductive cycle: seasonal histological changes in the gonads. Proc. Boston Soc. Nat. Hist., 39:151, 1929.
63. Shaw, C. R., and Koen, A. L.: Hormone-induced esterase in mouse kidney. Science, 140:70, 1963.
64. Shikita, M., and Tamaoki, B-I.: Testosterone formation by subcellular particles of rat testes. Endocrinol., 76:563, 1965.
65. Southren, A. L., Ross, H., Sharma, D. C., Gordon, G., Weingold, A. B., and Dorfman, R. I.: Plasma concentration and biosynthesis of testosterone in the syndrome of feminizing testes. J. Clin. Endocrinol., 25:518, 1965.
66. Squire, P. G., Johnston, R. E., and Lyons, W. R.: Intratesticular injections of interstitial cell-stimulating hormones in hypophysectomized rats. Internat. J. Fertil., 8:531, 1963.
67. Steinberger, E., Steinberger, A., and Perloff, W. H.: Initiation of spermatogenesis *in vitro.* Endocrinol., 74:788, 1964.
68. Strauss, J. S., and Pochi, P. E.: The human sebaceous gland: its regulation by steroid hormones and its use as an end organ for assaying androgenicity *in vivo.* Recent Prog. Hormone Research, 19:385, 1963.
69. Takewaki, K.: Estrogen-secreting tumor produced experimentally in the rat. Factors involved in tumorigenesis and endocrine activity of the tumors. J. Fac. Sci., Tokyo University, 10:205, 1963.
70. Talwar, G. P., and Segal, S. J.: Prevention of hormone action by local application of actinomycin D. Proc. Nat. Acad. Sci., 50:226, 1963.
71. Van Rees, G. P.: Influence of steroid sex hormones on the FSH-release by hypophyses *in vitro.* Acta Endocrinol., 36:485, 1961.
72. Whitten, W. K.: The effect of removal of the olfactory bulbs on the gonads of mice. J. Endocrinol., 14:160, 1956.
73. Wolfson, A.: Regulation of annual periodicity in the migration and reproduction in birds. Cold Spring Harbor Symp. on Quan. Biol., 25:507, 1960.
74. Woods, M. C., and Simpson, M. E.: Pituitary control of the testis of the hypophysectomized rat. Endocrinol., 69:91, 1961.
75. Wurtman, R. J., Axelrod, J., Chu, E. W., and Fischer, J. E.: Mediation of some effects of illumination on the rat estrous cycle by the sympathetic nervous system. Endocrinol., 75:266, 1964.

14_____

ENDOCRINOLOGY
OF THE OVARY

The ovary functions chiefly in the production of mature eggs and in the elaboration of hormones that regulate the reproductive tract and secondary sex characters, condition the mating reactions, and exert other metabolic effects. Neither the gametogenic nor endocrine functions are continuous processes; they fluctuate rhythmically during the life of the individual. The periodic changes in the female tract are determined by cyclic variations in the pituitary gland and ovaries. The intervals are called *estrous cycles* in subprimate species and *menstrual cycles* in man and other primates. Although both kinds of cycles are regulated by the same or similar pituitary and ovarian hormones, they differ in important details and will be discussed later.

Another type of cycle corresponds to the life span of the individual: the period of prepuberal development is followed by a period of sexually active life, after which the ovaries grow old and reproduction gradually ceases. Menopausal symptoms generally occur in women between the ages of 40 and 50 years, the ovaries involute, and the menstrual cycles gradually cease. Egg production in birds gradually diminishes with age and ceases entirely in the aged animal. Studies on a variety of species indicate that the mammalian ovary usually cannot increase its store of oöcytes after the age of puberty. There are some exceptions to this general rule, and it may well be that oögenesis ceases in some species earlier than in others. Generally speaking, however, the mammalian ovary is a transient structure and has little capacity for replenishing the supply of oöcytes after the age of puberty. The ovary becomes senescent much earlier than the testis, and no hormones are known that can restore its capacity to proliferate germ cells.

Although reproductive functions and behavioral patterns are clearly influenced by endocrine secretions, it must not be assumed that these are the only factors involved. The secretion of certain interacting hormones is mediated, at least in part, by the nervous system, and the whole reproductive mechanism may be stimulated or inhibited by factors arising in the external environment. Nutritional factors can be extremely important conditioning agents. For example, the onset of puberty in mice is delayed by reducing the caloric intake, but such animals live longer than well-fed controls. These females develop reproductive competence after being given full caloric intake and may bear young at a time when their littermate controls are infertile or already dead.[60]

HISTOLOGY OF THE MAMMALIAN OVARY

In addition to the surface epithelium, the three functional subunits of the ovary are follicle, corpus luteum, and stroma. The primary follicle consists of an oöcyte surrounded by a single layer of flattened epithelial cells. These follicles lack a connective tissue

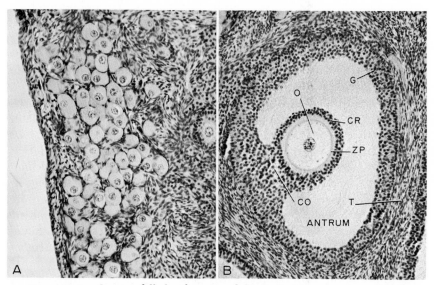

Figure 14–1. Ovarian follicles from an adult cat. *A*, Large numbers of primary follicles (single layer of flattened cells around the oöcyte) near the edge of the ovary. *B*, A graafian follicle located more deeply in the same ovary. CO, cumulus oöphorus; CR, corona radiata; G, granulosa; O, ovum; T, thecal layers; ZP, zona pellucida. *A* and *B* are of the same magnification.

or thecal investment and are most numerous immediately beneath the tunica albuginea (Fig. 14–1). Occasionally, more than one oöcyte may be present in a primordial follicle; these may result from the division of a single germ cell, or, more probably, from the failure of early germ cells to become separated as they are invested by nongerminal elements. As the follicles mature, they move away from the tunica and assume a deeper position in the stroma. The egg increases in size, and the follicular cells proliferate mitotically. The squamous cells of the primary follicle first turn into a single layer of columnar epithelium but, as proliferation continues, this becomes a stratified epithelium. When the cell membrane of the ovum has transformed into a zona pellucida, and the follicular investment has become multilayered, it is designated a secondary follicle.

The growing follicle is soon encapsulated by a sheath of tissue derived from the stroma. This is the theca which promptly becomes divided into a well-vascularized theca interna and a theca externa, which is composed of connective tissue. The theca interna is separated from the granulosa layer by a thin membrana propria. Blood vessels and lymphatics penetrate the theca externa and form a rather extensive plexus of fine vessels in the theca interna. These blood vessels do not penetrate the membrana propria; thus the cells comprising the granulosa are without direct blood supply until after ovulation. Cavities appear in the multilayered granulosa, and these coalesce to form an antrum which contains fluid. After establishment of the antrum, the follicle is said to be vesicular or graafian. The granulosa cells surrounding the ovum are destined to become the corona radiata, and those which attach it to the wall of the antrum are the cumulus oöphorus. The cumulus is generally found on the wall of the antrum opposite to the surface which will rupture at ovulation. In many species, the corona cells remain around the egg after it is ovulated, but, in others, the eggs are ovulated without it (Fig. 14–1).

After ovulation, the collapsed follicle transforms into a new endocrine structure, the corpus luteum. The histogenesis of the corpus luteum seems to vary among different species, but, in the human being and many other mammals, it appears to be derived from proliferations of both the granulosa and theca interna. There is no doubt that the cells of the theca interna perform important roles before, during, and immediately after ovulation.

Atresia is a degenerative process whereby eggs are lost from the ovary other than through ovulation. It has been estimated that 99.9% of the 500,000 oöcytes present in the human ovaries at birth are destined to be lost by atresia at some stage of their development. The earliest signs of retrogression appear in the ovum itself and then spread to other components of the follicle. The ova in atretic follicles may give off polar bodies and undergo mitotic or amitotic divisions, thus producing several cells within the zona pellucida. Some workers have considered this to be an attempt of the egg to undergo partheno-genetic development. The incidence of atresia may be affected by age, season, nutrition, stage of the reproductive cycle, pregnancy and lactation, hypophysectomy, unilateral ovariectomy, exogenous hor-mones, and impairments of the blood supply to the ovaries.

Corpora lutea atretica are commonly seen in certain species dur-ing pregnancy, pseudopregnancy, and lactation. In these cases, the theca interna and granulosa begin to form thick layers of lutein tis-sue before ovulation has occurred; the egg may survive for some time near the center of what appears to be a well-formed corpus luteum (Fig. 14–2). It is probable that not all of the corpora lutea which contain oöcytes are the consequence of atresia; an egg may fail to escape from its antrum at ovulation and be trapped within the center of a normal corpus luteum.

Atresia may also be associated with the formation of enlarged, cystic follicles. The ovum degenerates and the antrum is distended with liquor folliculi. The antrum of cystic follicles is generally lined by a single layer of granulosa cells, or the granulosal lining may prac-tically disappear, the enlarged follicle being supported by heavy thecal tissue. Hemorrhagic cysts result from ruptured blood vessels and the extravasation of blood into the antrum. Follicles of this type

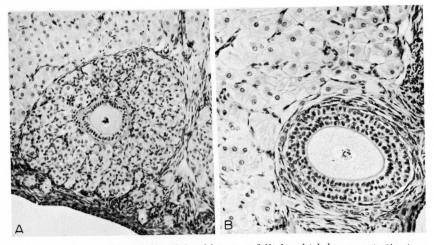

Figure 14–2. Ovary of the adult rabbit. *A*, A follicle which became atretic at an early age. Notice that the granulosa consists of a single layer of columnar cells, in-dicating that it is quite young, and that thecal tissue is not present immediately exterior to the granulosa. The follicle is completely surrounded by lutein tissue, and hence could never ovulate. This appears to be a case of precocious luteinization; it is probable that the theca interna of this follicle began to proliferate lutein tissue at a very early age, resulting in a structure which has the appearance of a small corpus luteum. This animal was never sexually receptive and was more than 5 years of age when killed. *B*, An apparently normal multilaminar follicle from the same ovary. Notice the large volume of interstitial tissue in the rabbit's ovary.

are frequently found in unmated rabbits; these become dark brown and are eventually resorbed.

The stroma of the ovary contains connective tissue and variable numbers of interstitial cells. These take the form of cords or irregular clusters of large polyhedral cells. Various interpretations have been expressed as to the origin of these cells. Some have maintained that they originate directly from connective tissue cells; others feel that they arise, in part at least, from the theca interna of atretic follicles. In some mammals (*e.g.*, rabbit), the interstitial tissue is very conspicuous and occupies nearly all of the space not taken up by follicles and corpora lutea (Fig. 14–2). Recent evidence indicates that the interstitial cells of the ovary may be capable of producing both androgens and estrogens, and hence constitute an endocrine tissue. *In vitro* studies of human stromal tissue have demonstrated that it can synthesize radioactive steroids from acetate-1-C^{14}. This study showed that the greatest incorporation of radioactivity was in three androgens (androstenedione, dehydroepiandrosterone, and testosterone), and lesser amounts were in two estrogens (estradiol-17β and estrone).

CYSTIC FOLLICLES OF THE OVARY

It frequently happens that ovarian follicles enlarge beyond the stage of ovulation and remain permanently or for long periods in the ovaries (Fig. 14–3). Cysts are often encountered among women and domesticated and laboratory mammals and are a common cause of abnormal reproductive cycles and sterility. These are the consequences of endocrine imbalances, often impairments in the release of pituitary gonadotrophins, but the specific causes and methods of prevention and treatment remain to be worked out. The multiple cysts of swine ovaries may attain a diameter of 10 cm., and are associated with a long history of sterility. These cysts secrete less estrogen than normal follicles; the estrous cycles are abnormal and the animals tend to remain in anestrus for exceptionally long periods. Smaller cysts often show patches of lutein tissue in their walls, and bioassays indicate that they produce progesterone. After prolonged distention with fluid, all components of the follicle degenerate. In cattle, but not in other species, cystic ovaries are often associated with intense psychologic heat (nymphomania), enlargement of the clitoris, and other signs of masculinization.[41] This syndrome is poorly understood, but experimental observations indicate that it is *not* due to an excessive production of estrogen by the cystic follicles, as is often assumed. Hypertrophy of the adrenal cortices has been reported in cattle with cystic ovaries and nymphomania, and this suggests that glands other than the ovaries may be involved. Some amelioration

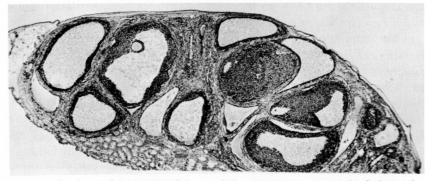

Figure 14–3. A fetal ovary of the rat following persistence in the kidney of a normal male rat for 60 days. The male pituitary does not release FSH and LH cyclically, as in the female; consequently, the graft consists of vesicular and cystic follicles. Ovulation does not occur, and corpora lutea are seldom found. Notice that the cystic follicles have lost their ova, and, in some cases, the granulosa is reduced to a single layer of flattened cells. Kidney tissue is present below the graft, at the lower left.

of the symptoms, during early stages of the disease, may be obtained by the administration of gonadotrophins which exert LH actions.

Polycystic ovaries may be induced in rats by giving human chorionic gonadotrophin (HCG) after inducing a state of hypothyroidism.[35] The animals are fed thiouracil (0.5 per cent) in a 20 per cent casein diet for ten days, and then given HCG (10 IU daily) for 20 days. Ovaries weighing 800 to 1000 mg. may result from this dual treatment; neither hypothyroidism nor HCG alone is capable of producing cysts. Once formed, the ovarian cysts do not regress even though the hypothyroidism is corrected and the HCG injections are discontinued. An anti-estrogen, ethamoxytriphetol (MER-25), prevents this type of cyst formation when it is administered together with the HCG.[36] The tremendous increase in ovarian weight is due to increased lutein tissue and the retention of fluid in the cysts. Histologically, the large cysts are lined with a simple squamous epithelium, and granulosa cells and lutein tissue are absent. *In vitro* studies on the capacity of this type of cystic ovary to synthesize steroids have demonstrated that they produce excessive progesterone (20α-hydroxypregn-4-en-3-one), but subnormal quantities of estrogens.[9]

It is well known that a single injection of testosterone to 5-day-old rats impairs the hypothalamus and prevents the pituitary gland from secreting adequate quantities of LH.[4, 5] When the treated animals mature, they remain in constant vaginal estrus, and, histologically, the ovaries lack corpora lutea, but contain many enlarged follicles (polyvesicular or polycystic) which do not ovulate. Consequently, the animals are permanently sterilized.[57] Progesterone, administered in conjunction with the androgen, protects the neonatal rat against this type of steroid-induced sterility.[33a] *In vitro* tests show that the ovaries of these androgen-sterilized rats produce several times more testosterone, estrone, and estradiol than do the ovaries of untreated controls.[61] Analyses of human and bovine cystic ovaries, using both *in vivo* and *in vitro* tests, suggest that there may be an enzymatic defect which prevents the normal conversion of androgens (C_{19} intermediates) into estrogens, the result being an excessive accumulation of androgens.

BIOCHEMISTRY OF THE OVARIAN HORMONES

The ovary elaborates estrogens, progestogens (a general term for any substance producing progestational changes in the uterus), androgens, and a nonsteroid hormone called relaxin. Most workers agree that the mature ovarian follicle is an important source of estrogen, but the exact component of the follicle that produces it has never been unequivocally settled; most of the evidence implicates either the membrana granulosa or theca interna as the source. The corpus luteum elaborates both estrogenic and progestational steroids. The cellular source of relaxin and ovarian androgens remains unknown. These hormones stimulate growth and differentiation of the female reproductive tract and associated structures and also exert a multitude of systemic effects.

We have emphasized that steroid hormones are produced by testes, ovaries, adrenal cortices, and placenta, and that the same general route of biosynthesis seems to be employed by all of these organs. In the presence of enzymes from these various tissues, a common precursor such as pregnenolone can be converted into any one of the known steroid hormones. Although there is some relationship between biologic activity and chemical configuration of the molecule, it is known that a particular steroid hormone may exert multiple actions. There is no hard and fast dividing line between estrogens, androgens, progestogens, and adrenal corticoids. Some degree of functional overlap is often observed when the dosage of a particular steroid is increased to unphysiologic levels. Thus, steroids generally regarded as "estrogens" because they stimulate the female accessories may also be "androgens" because they stimulate the male tract. Some hormones thought of primarily as adrenal corticoids may be "progestogens," since they have slight ability to produce progestational changes in the endometrium. While progesterone is a natural progestogen, it can stimulate the prostates and seminal vesicles of castrated animals. Women who receive massive doses of natural or synthetic progestogens during pregnancy sometimes give birth to mildly masculinized female infants. An appreciable degree of steroid hormone interconversion may occur within the system after purified hormones are administered.

The Estrogens*

The predominant natural estrogens of the human are estradiol-17β, estrone, and estriol. Several other estrogens, representing estrogen metabolites, have been isolated in significant amounts from normal urine. All of the estrogens contain eighteen carbon atoms and, for terminological purposes, may be considered as derivatives of the theoretical parent substance, "estrane." They are characterized by the aromatic nature of ring A (three double bonds), the absence of a methyl group at C-10, and the presence of a phenolic hydroxyl group at C-3.

Estrogens are present in various animal tissues, such as ovaries, testes, adrenals, and placentae, and small amounts have been found in spermatozoa themselves. Estrogenic activity has been demonstrated in about 50 species of plants. The subterranean clover of Western Australia was found to contain sufficient estrogen to affect the reproductive performance of grazing sheep adversely.[7]

It appears that the human ovary elaborates only estradiol-17β and estrone; estriol is thought to be a degradation product of the former steroids in nonpregnant women. During human pregnancy both estriol and 16-epiestriol are probably produced by the placenta. Estriol has been believed characteristic of the human species and is found primarily in the urine. In the cow, as in numerous other mammalian species, the placenta seems to be the principal source of estrogens during pregnancy. Estrone, estradiol-17β, and estradiol-17α have been isolated from bovine placental extracts. A large group of nonsteroidal estrogens have been produced synthetically and used for clinical purposes (Fig. 14–4). They possess the same biologic characteristics as the naturally occurring estrogens; diethylstilbestrol and hexestrol are examples.

It has been established that both acetate and cholesterol may serve as precursors for the synthesis of estrogens. It is interesting that estrogens in the ovaries, testes, adrenal cortices, and placenta arise from androgens. The biosynthetic pathway proceeds through the 19-hydroxylated intermediates of androstenedione and testosterone. This is followed by elimination of the C_{19} side chain and the aromatization of the A ring (Fig. 14–5). Estradiol-17β and estrone are interconvertible, and estriol is the predominant urinary end product of estrogen metabolism.[13]

The circulating estrogens are bound to plasma proteins, and the

---

*Much progress has been made in elucidating the mechanisms whereby estrogens may act at the cellular level. Investigations have been made from such a variety of angles that the situation has become too complex to treat in a general textbook and do justice with it. The reader is referred to an excellent treatment of the topic by O. Hechter and I. D. K. Halkerston: *In* G. Pincus, K. V. Thimann, and E. B. Astwood (eds.): The Hormones, Vol. 5. New York, Academic Press, 1964, p. 786.

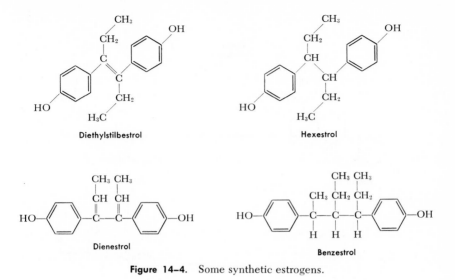

Figure 14-4. Some synthetic estrogens.

binding process is accomplished in the liver. It has been proposed that the liver performs a dual role in estrogen metabolism, inactivating these steroids and also exerting an "activating" influence through the formation of estroproteins.[54] About 50 per cent of the blood estrogen is conjugated with glucuronide or sulfate. This conjugation occurs in the liver and the excreted compounds in the urine are in this form. An enterohepatic circulation occurs, and some animals (rat, dog) excrete estrogen mainly through the feces. Ligation of the bile duct may lead to an increased excretion of metabolites through the urine.

Estrogens in human urine increase twice during the menstrual cycle: the first coincides with ovulation and the rise in basal body temperature, the second occurs during the luteal phase of the cycle. Pregnancy urine is a very rich source of estrogen, which appears to be produced by the placenta. This is indicated by the fact that ovarietomy of the pregnant woman or pregnant mare does not cause the urinary estrogens to disappear. The type of estrogen in the urine during pregnancy varies with the species: human pregnancy urine contains mostly estriol, whereas that of the mare is mostly estrone. Equilin and equilenin are weak estrogens that have been found only in the pregnant mare. Ring B of these compounds is either partially or totally converted to the aromatic form. During human pregnancy all of the estrogens increase rapidly in the urine. Just before parturition estrone and estradiol have increased a hundredfold and estriol a thousandfold. The estrone and estradiol are usually excreted in a constant ratio of about 3:1. The urinary estrogens diminish rapidly after parturition and the loss of the placenta.

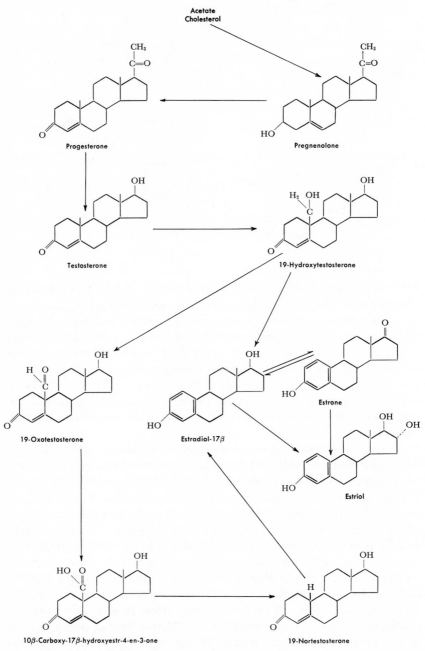

Figure 14–5. Probable pathways in the biosynthesis and metabolism of estrogens. (Based on Dorfman, R. I.: Obst. & Gynec. Survey, *18*:65, 1963.)

The vaginal cornification technique has been used extensively for the bioassay of estrogens. The test material is administered systemically to the ovariectomized rodents, the full-blown estrous reaction being indicated by vaginal smears that contain mostly cornified epithelial cells (Fig. 14–13). A more sensitive bioassay is to introduce the test material directly into the vagina, care being taken not to traumatize the vaginal mucosa. The most sensitive and accurate method is based on the fact that estrogens cause a striking increase in uterine weight when administered to ovariectomized animals. Six hours after the subcutaneous injection of a dose of estrogen to a castrate rat the uterus increases in weight by imbibition of water; another weight increase occurs 21 to 30 hours after the single injection owing to hypertrophy and hyperplasia of the uterine tissues.[2]

Physicochemical procedures are available for the determination of estrogenic potency, but they require a rather high degree of sample purity. The bioassay and chemical techniques are too laborious and expensive to be applicable for routine clinical diagnosis. Estrogenic activity can usually be satisfactorily assessed by proper examination of the exfoliated cells of the patient's vagina. The Greenstein method of staining vaginal smears and endometrial biopsies has been found suitable for office practice and the clinical laboratory.[26]

The Progestogens

These compounds have varied actions upon the female reproductive organs and, under physiologic conditions, often act synergistically with estrogens. The progestogens and estrogens are also capable of inhibiting the actions of each other and, under these conditions, are considered to act antagonistically. These steroids are of special importance in preparing the uterus for the implantation of blastocysts, in maintaining pregnancy, and in regulating the accessory organs during the reproductive cycle. Progesterone is present in the ovary, the testis, the adrenal cortex, and the placenta; in addition to being an intermediate in the biosynthesis of other steroid hormones, it is an important hormone in its own right. The progestogens are C_{21} steroids, having the basic structure of the pregnane nucleus. Compared with the estrogens, it may be noted that ring A of the progesterone molecule is more saturated, a methyl group is present at C-10, and a two-carbon side chain is present on C-17. At least two steroids, in addition to progesterone, are known to occur naturally in mammals and to have progestational effects. These are 20α-hydroxypregn-4-en-3-one and 20β-hydroxypregn-4-en-3-one (Fig. 14–6). These are present in ovarian follicles, corpora lutea, placenta, and blood. A variety of progestogens that are highly potent and orally effective have been produced synthetically (Fig. 14–7).

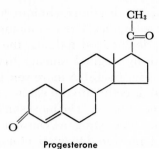

Progesterone

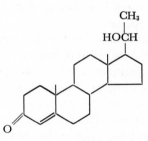

20β-Hydroxypregn-4-en-3-one

20α-Hydroxypregn-4-en-3-one

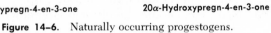

Figure 14–6. Naturally occurring progestogens.

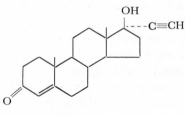

Ethisterone

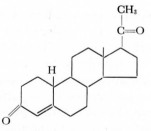

19-Norprogesterone

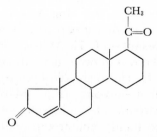

A-Norprogesterone

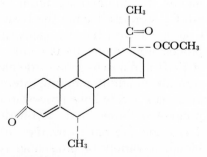

6α-Methyl-17α-acetoxyprogesterone

Figure 14–7. Some analogs of progesterone.

The principal urinary metabolites of the progestogens are pregnanediol and pregnanetriol, and these are eliminated chiefly as glucuronides. It was formerly supposed that the synthesis of progesterone by the system could be precisely gauged by the quantities of pregnanediol excreted in the urine, but it is now known that this metabolite may also be derived from deoxycorticosterone of the adrenal cortex. Nevertheless, pregnanediol determinations are useful in studying the progesterone output in abnormalities of menstruation and pregnancy. Pregnanetriol is the urinary metabolite of 17α-hydroxyprogesterone, and may be derived to a minor extent from 11-deoxycortisol and 17α-hydroxypregnenolone.

The bioassays for progesterone are complicated by the fact that the responding tissues require preliminary or auxiliary treatment with estrogen. Decidual responses and progestational changes in the endometrium are used as end points in certain tests. Chemical and physicochemical procedures are available, but these require a high degree of sample purity, may necessitate large amounts of starting material, and are usually not entirely specific.

Ovarian Androgens

In view of the evidence indicating that testosterone is an intermediate in the biosynthesis of estrogen, it is not surprising to find that ovaries secrete androgens. Ovarian extracts have long been known to produce androgenic effects when tested on laboratory rodents, but it has been difficult to determine whether the activity is due to progesterone or to some definitive androgen characteristic of the testis. Ovarian homografts persisting in the ears of orchiectomized mice and rats prevent atrophy of the seminal vesicles and prostates (Fig. 14–8). Certain cells have been described in the hilus of the

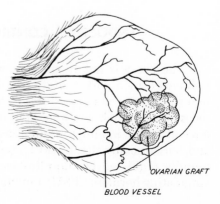

Figure 14–8. An ovarian homograft persisting in the ear of an orchiectomized male rat. Such ovarian grafts become capable of secreting enough androgen to maintain secretion in the male accessory glands. Thus the two ovarian grafts in the ears provide an endocrine substitute for the intact testes of the host. (The graft and blood vessels were sketched from the transilluminated ear.)

OVARIAN GRAFT

BLOOD VESSEL

human ovary that are similar to testicular Leydig cells, and these are thought to secrete androgen.

In vitro studies on human polycystic ovaries have suggested that there may be enzymatic defects in the synthesis of estrogens. These defects could accelerate the production of androgen precursors and result in the virilization which is frequently seen in patients with polycystic ovaries. Although there is no doubt that pathologic ovaries may release tremendous amounts of androgen, there is no absolute proof that the normal ovary secretes significant amounts of such steroids.

Relaxin

This is a water-soluble hormone present in the ovaries, placentae, and uteri of various mammalian species during pregnancy. Four peptides having relaxin activity have been isolated from aqueous ovarian extracts and partially purified. Relaxin was discovered at about the same time as the ovarian steroids, but it bears no structural relationship to them whatever. It is definitely a hormone of pregnancy and has not been found in the blood of men or nonpregnant women. Substances having relaxin-like activity have been obtained from the ovaries of elasmobranchs and from the testes of birds. Relaxin levels in the blood reach a high peak during the terminal stages of human pregnancy and disappear within one day after delivery.

The bioassay of relaxin is made difficult because of its functional interrelations with estrogens and progestogens. Three bioassay methods are commonly used: (1) manual palpation or x-ray photographs of the innominate bones of the estrogen-primed guinea pig after relaxin injections; (2) measurement of the length of the interpubic ligament in mice by means of a transilluminating device and ocular micrometer; (3) inhibition of motility in mouse uterine segments *in vitro*.[70]

ENDOCRINE CONTROL OF THE OVARY

The ovary is not an autonomous organ; its functional capacity is influenced by a wide variety of external stimuli which are funneled into the central nervous system and then "translated" into chemical messengers which act directly upon it. Perhaps all endocrine glands have at least a modulating influence upon the production of gametes and hormones by the gonads. The ovary, like the testis, is most profoundly regulated by the pituitary gonadotrophins, namely, follicle-stimulating hormone (FSH) and luteinizing hormone (LH).

Anterior Hypophysis

Hypophysectomy of adult mammals causes prompt deterioration of the ovary and female accessory reproductive organs. The animals become irresponsive to many environmental stimuli, and the reproductive cycles are terminated. Young ovarian follicles start to differentiate, but become atretic before ovulation and luteinization occur. Total hypophysectomy of the laying hen causes rapid regression of the ovary, the oviduct, and comb. Oviposition, however, continues after the posterior lobe alone is removed.[42]

The growth and development of ovarian follicles of mammals depend upon FSH, but LH is required for their final maturation. The latter gonadotrophin acts upon the FSH-primed follicle to promote preovulatory growth and the secretion of estrogen. Further release of LH results in ovulation and the transformation of the emptied follicle into a corpus luteum. FSH and LH are both necessary for the production of estrogen by the maturing follicle. It is probable that the circulating estrogen, acting via the hypothalamus, serves to suppress the release of FSH and to facilitate the release of LH. Purified LH alone, administered to hypophysectomized subjects, has no conspicuous effect upon the ovarian follicles. The progestogens of the blood also appear to condition the release of gonadotrophins through effects on the hypothalamus.

Some workers have considered prolactin to be a gonadotrophin since it seems to be necessary for the maintenance of corpora lutea and for the secretion of progestogens by these structures in rats and mice. Thus, prolactin is sometimes called "luteotrophin" because of its action in these species. However, prolactin is not *luteotrophic* in the majority of mammals. In fact, the administration of prolactin to many species of adult birds and mammals causes regression of the testes and ovaries, thus exerting what could be considered an antigonadotrophic effect. Studies on the *in vitro* synthesis of progesterone by human and bovine corpora lutea indicate that LH is the only pituitary hormone capable of stimulating this steroid pathway. Prolactin is completely inert in these systems. A large body of evidence supports the view that prolactin does not stimulate progesterone synthesis by corpora lutea from women, monkeys, sows, ewes, rabbits, and guinea pigs.[40, 49, 50]

Ovarian Hormones

Large amounts of estrogen, given to intact animals, inhibit the gonads by altering the release of pituitary gonadotrophins. Permanent sterility may be produced in neonatal rats of either sex by the administration of exogenous estrogens. For example, if female rats are given estrogen from the day of birth until they are 30 days old, the mature animals remain in a state of persistent diestrus and are permanently sterile. The ovaries contain only small follicles; corpora lutea are absent and the uteri remain threadlike and are equivalent to those of animals ovariectomized during prepuberal life.[33]

In addition to systemic effects by way of the pituitary, there are indications that estrogens can exert direct, local effects upon the ovary.[8] When immature hypophysectomized rats are given a single large dose of estrogen, ovarian weights are increased by the third day and many follicles have advanced to the antrum stage. These follicles show thecal hypertrophy and active proliferation of the granulosa. If estradiol or stilbestrol is applied directly to one ovary of the immature rat, leaving the contralateral ovary untreated, the treated ovary increases in weight due to follicular growth and luteinization. It was formerly thought that hormones could not act directly upon the glands that produce them, but there are strong indications that androgens affect the testis directly and that estrogens exert some direct influences upon the ovaries.

Factors from the Uterus

Removal of the uterus (hysterectomy) in certain mammals markedly prolongs the functional life of the corpora lutea, just as would occur during pregnancy and pseudopregnancy. Total hysterectomy of the guinea pig, for instance, causes the corpora lutea to persist and secrete progesterone for a period approximately equal to that of normal gestation. Subtotal hysterectomy results in more limited maintenance. Similar results have been reported for the sow, sheep, and cow, but the effect is not observed in primates. After unilateral hysterectomy of swine and guinea pigs, the cycles are lengthened and striking histologic asymmetry develops in the ovaries. The corpora lutea are maintained in the ovary on the operated side, whereas they undergo usual regression on the unoperated side. Removal of the ovary on the operated side (with persistent corpora) permits the contralateral ovary to become cyclic and to undergo ovulation and subsequent luteinization.[18] These experiments might suggest that the uterus exerts a direct inhibitory effect on the corpora lutea, mediated locally, but they do not rule out the possibility that neural and hormonal mechanisms of a systemic nature are also operating.

If young corpora lutea are maintained *in vitro* and provided with proper substrates, they can synthesize progesterone. Their capacity to produce this steroid is greatly increased by adding LH to the medium. When corpora lutea of the sow are maintained *in vitro* and scrapings from the uterine lining (in early luteal phase) are added to the medium, the production of progesterone is significantly enhanced.

Endometrial scrapings taken during the end of the luteal phase have an inhibitory effect on steroidogenesis.[1, 14, 32]

Hypophysectomy of hysterectomized animals, removing all endogenous pituitary gonadotrophins, does not prevent the persistence of existent corpora lutea. This indicates that the uterus has an ovarian effect which is not mediated through the pituitary gland. Denervation of the sow's uterus does not prevent estrous cycles. Autotransplanted uteri or pieces of the endometrium into totally hysterectomized guinea pigs prevent the persistence of corpora lutea. This is evidence that the uterine stimulus is not neural.

A small-granule fraction of the guinea pig ovary contains the necessary enzymes for the conversion of pregnenolone to progesterone. The addition of an extract of the guinea pig uterus to this system produces a dramatic inhibition of progesterone biosynthesis. When similar fractions of the rat's ovary are used as an enzyme source, the uterine extracts have no effect on the conversion of pregnenolone to progesterone.[12]

There seems to be no doubt that the uteri of certain mammals are the source of a "luteolytic" substance that functions during the estrous cycle, but its nature remains obscure. The persistence of corpora lutea during pregnancy and pseudopregnancy clearly involves neural mechanisms that alter the rate of release of pituitary gonadotrophins. Uterine influences on the ovary during pregnancy and during the estrous cycle seem to be contradictory, and the dilemma cannot be resolved until further information is available.

The Pineal Gland

The discovery that bovine pineal extracts cause melanophore contraction (blanching) of the frog's skin *in vitro* provided a bioassay that led to the isolation of melatonin. Biochemical studies have shown that melatonin, found only in the pineal gland, is synthesized from serotonin through the catalytic action of hydroxyindole-O-methyl transferase (HIOMT). Although serotonin is found in many tissues, HIOMT is present only in the pineal gland.[20, 47, 67]

Data have accumulated during recent years suggesting that the mammalian pineal gland exerts important actions in regulating photoperiodic influences on the gonads. It is too early to make final evaluation of these studies, but the theory is that the pineal gland serves as a kind of transducer in the mediation of environmental stimuli. Light perceived by the retina is believed to set up impulses which travel through unknown pathways to the superior cervical ganglia and then to the pineal gland. The discharge of impulses in this end organ alters the rate of synthesis and release of melatonin, a blood-borne agent which is regarded as a hormone. The site of melatonin action is not known; it might act directly on the gonad or indirectly through the central nervous system and anterior hypophysis.[19, 46, 66]

The reported observations on the rat may be summarized as follows: (1) When normal rats are maintained in constant light, the ovaries increase in weight and the animals tend to remain in persistent estrus. Constant darkness has the reverse effect. (2) Pinealectomy of 28-day-old female rats causes the ovaries to increase in weight; although these animals show a high incidence of estrous smears, they ovulate and reproduce normally. (3) Removal of the pineal gland in neonatal female rats has no effect on body weight, ovarian weight, time of vaginal openings, or the estrous cycles.[63] (4) The administration of pineal extracts or pure melatonin to immature rats reduces the weight of the ovaries and decreases the incidence of estrus.[11] (5) Darkness promotes the synthesis and release of melatonin from the pineal, whereas light inhibits its production and release. Rats maintained in constant light have small pineals, and these contain much less HIOMT and less melatonin than those kept in darkness. There is a diurnal variation in the pineal content of HIOMT, more enzyme and more melatonin being present at night than during the day. Removal of the pituitary gland or the ovaries does not impair the normal responses of the pineal gland to changing illumination. (6) After destruction of the retina, photoperiods have no effect on the pineal enzymes and the quantities of melatonin synthesized. (7) The pineal gland contains a very high content of serotonin, an amine from which melatonin is synthesized. (8) There is a diurnal variation in the amount of serotonin present in the pineal; a peak occurs at noon (light) and a trough at midnight (darkness).[46] In rats kept in constant light, the pineal content of serotonin is low, but, in these animals, the content of serotonin-forming enzyme, 5-hydroxytryptophan decarboxylase (5-HTD), is increased. This suggests that the enzyme is not rate limiting in the production of serotonin by the pineal. Removal of the eyes blocks the effect of light on 5-HTD. (9) The pineal gland of the rat is innervated largely by sympathetic fibers originating in the superior cervical ganglia. Bilateral removal of these ganglia blocks the effects of illumination on both the serotonin-forming enzyme (5-HTD) and the melatonin-forming enzyme (HIOMT).[45, 65]

If male hamsters are exposed for 30 days to 1 hour of light and 23 hours of darkness, regression of the testes ensues. The same type of testicular atrophy can be produced by the removal of both eyes. The testicular involution resulting from either procedure can be prevented by pinealectomy. Here, as in the female rat, it is believed that darkness causes the pineal to release excessive melatonin, a hormone which affects the gonads adversely. Long periods of light act by way of the nervous system to inhibit the production of melatonin by the pineal gland.[30]

In an earlier discussion of vertebrate chromatophores, it was mentioned that pinealectomy of amphibian larvae modifies their pigmentary responses to light. Studies on several species indicate that a substance of pineal origin, probably melatonin, acts directly upon the melanophores, and not indirectly by modifying the release of MSH peptides from the pars intermedia.[3]

The participation of the pineal gland in the mediation of light stimuli seems to be a fruitful area of investigation. Some reservation, however, seems justifiable until certain aspects of the theory are clarified, and until observations have been extended to a wider variety of vertebrates.

BIOLOGIC EFFECTS OF THE OVARIAN HORMONES

The estrogens act directly, or in cooperation with other hormones, to produce a great variety of effects on specific target organs and on the chemistry of the body as a whole. Some of these actions will be discussed more specifically in connection with the estrous and menstrual cycles, in this chapter, and in connection with pregnancy and lactation in Chapter 15. Scarcely a tissue in the organism remains unaffected by estrogens, and no attempt is made to discuss all of them.

The Actions of Estrogens

Carcinogenesis

Perhaps the most general effect of the estrogens is to promote tissue growth. This is most pronounced in the accessory sex tissues, but it occurs in other tissues as well. By stimulating cell divisions in the deeper layers of the skin, estrogens cause a more rapid replacement of the outer cornified layers. There is some evidence that the estrogens may be potentially dangerous inasmuch as they may encourage the formation of cancer in certain individuals. This may correlate with the concept that a continued high rate of cell division is one factor predisposing a tissue to become cancerous.

Among the many carcinogenic hydrocarbons that have been studied, 1, 2-benzpyrene, 1, 2, 5, 6-dibenzanthracene, and methylcholanthrene are representative. These compounds typically produce epitheliomas when applied to the skins of susceptible rodents and sarcomas when administered subcutaneously. Some of the synthetic carcinogens are chemically related to the estrogens and initiate estrous changes in test animals. That cancer in experimental animals may follow treatment with estrogens has been proved under special circumstances. The estrogens are the only steroid hormones that have been shown to be carcinogenic.

The Vagina

Ovariectomy causes a marked involution of the vagina. The vaginal lining becomes thin and mitotic divisions are seldom encountered. The administration of estrogen to the castrate causes rapid growth of the vagina as is indicated by the many mitotic figures in the epithelium and cornification of the superficial layers. Characteristic changes take place in the vaginal epithelium of the rodent during pregnancy and pseudopregnancy (Fig. 14–9). Growth of the vaginal epithelium occurs during the follicular phase of the menstrual cycle, accompanied by the deposition of glycogen and mucopolysaccharides in this tissue. The vaginal smear of the estrous rodent contains large numbers of cornified epithelial cells with degenerate nuclei. Similar epithelial cells are exfoliated into the human vagina and are a reliable index of estrogenic action.

The Uterus

A striking effect of estrogens is the promotion of uterine growth. The frequency of endometrial mitoses during the follicular phase of the primate cycle can be correlated with the action of estrogens. Moreover, it is certain that estrogens have an effect on the tonicity of the uterine muscles. The uterus of the rat is highly contractile

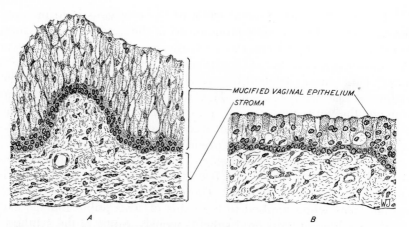

MUCIFIED VAGINAL EPITHELIUM

STROMA

A   *B*

Figure 14–9. Vaginal mucification in the rat. *A,* Section through the vaginal wall taken on the seventeenth day of a normal pregnancy. *B,* Milder degree of mucification in a pseudopregnant rat.

during estrus, whereas that of the untreated castrate is practically quiescent.

The uterus of the castrate rodent is an excellent target organ for determining the metabolic effects of estrogens (Fig. 14–10). It is believed that the primary effect of a hormone is to trigger some physicochemical mechanism within the target cells and, after this, a series of rather nonspecific changes occurs in the target tissue as a consequence of the original hormone action. Many experiments have been designed to determine the sequence of biochemical changes in the uterus of the castrate rodent after the administration of estrogen. The end effect of estrogen treatment is increased weight and growth (hypertrophy and hyperplasia) of all uterine tissues, but these effects are preceded by various alterations in tissue composition and enzymatic activity. The first observable change in the uterus, occurring within an hour or so after estrogen administration, is an increased blood supply (hyperemia) associated with increased permeability of the uterine capillaries. There are indications that this expansion of the microcirculation may result from the endogenous release of histamine by the tissues.[10, 55, 56] The hyperemia is accompanied by an augmented uptake of water and electrolytes by the uterine tissues. Within four hours both aerobic and anaerobic glycolysis are elevated. The weight of the uterus reaches a peak four to six hours after administration of the estrogen, but this is due almost entirely to the imbibition of water by the tissues.

The dry weight of the estrogen-treated uterus begins to increase by 12 hours, and there is a second wave of water imbibition occurring 20 to 24 hours after the injection. At this time, there is an accelerated incorporation of radioactivity from C^{14}-amino acids into the uterine tissues.[55] This second weight increase is correlated with cellular proliferation and the accumulation of uterine solids. The first increase in uterine weight can be prevented by administering adreno-

Figure 14–10. Photographs of female tracts of the rat dissected out *in toto. Left,* Tract from a normal animal killed at 20 days of age; *middle,* tract from an animal which was oöphorectomized at 18 days of age and autopsied six months later; *right,* a littermate control which was made castrate at 18 days of age, and killed six months later after receiving estrogen for ten days before autopsy.

corticotrophic hormone (ACTH) concurrently with the estrogen. Cortisol and cortisone have the same effect as ACTH. It is thus apparent that certain adrenal steroids antagonize the effects of estrogen on the uterus, possibly by counteracting the effect of estrogen on capillary permeability.[53]

The ribonucleic acid (RNA) content of the uterus rises from 6 to 24 hours after the initial estrogen treatment, and in its wake there is accumulation of protein. Respiration, as well as glycolysis, is substantially increased by 20 hours. No increase in deoxyribonucleic acid (DNA) occurs during the first 24 hours but, if the hormonal stimulus is repeated, increases do occur between 40 and 72 hours. During the first six hours there is an increase in phosphorylase *a* owing to the conversion of inactive phosphorylase *b* to *a*, but total phosphorylase remains practically unchanged. The total phosphorylase content of the uterus has increased substantially by 24 hours after the hormone stimulus, and by 48 hours the total phosphorylase has increased about 146 per cent, more phosphorylase *a* being formed. Correlated with these enzymic changes, a single injection of estrogen produces the highest concentration of uterine glycogen about 46 hours later.[37, 48, 52]

There has been much interest in trying to account for the simultaneous occurrence of two or more estrogens within the body of an individual. Although no conclusive answer has been found, it is probable that the effects observed after the administration of a steroid hormone are not due solely to that compound but also to the metabolites that may be formed from it within the system. Some estrogens are more effective than others in promoting the imbibition of fluid into the uterus; others are especially active in promoting true tissue growth. Estriol is the most effective natural estrogen in encouraging the uptake of water by the uterus after a single injection. It is especially effective in this respect when given in saline rather than oil; the activity of estrone and estradiol does not seem to be so dependent on the type of vehicle. For promoting the uptake of water by the rat's uterus the order of effectiveness is: estriol→estradiol-17β→estrone.[29]

Small amounts of estriol, having little or no effect on uterine weight when administered alone, inhibit the growth-promoting effect of estradiol and estrone when the estrogens are given simultaneously. The three natural estrogens differ greatly in their effectiveness in activating the various enzyme systems of the uterus. For example, a transhydrogenase of the placenta, presumed to be present also in the endometrium, is activated *in vitro* by estradiol-17β and estrone, whereas estriol has little or no such effect.[59]

In the normal organism the uterine response probably depends upon the combined actions of several estrogens working in concert; some are particularly effective in promoting specific regulations, and the action of one may be limited by that of another. Regulation of the female tract during the estrous and menstrual cycles, and during pregnancy, involves a multitude of intricate endocrine adjustments. The abundance of estriol in pregnant women and of equilin and equilenin in the pregnant mare strongly suggests that they are hormones of pregnancy and probably perform special roles during the course of gestation.[15]

The Mammary Gland

The ovarian hormones are essential for the anatomic preparation of the mammary glands for milk secretion. There are many species variations in the effects of estrogen and progesterone on mammary development. In some species, estrogen alone produces only a lengthening and branching of the duct system; if given in large doses and over long periods, it may also induce the differentiation of mammary alveoli. In many species, progesterone alone produces only alveolar growth without having much effect on the duct system. As a general rule, the mammary glands require pretreatment with estrogen before the progestogens are effective.

Sexual Receptivity or Heat

In mammals exhibiting an estrous cycle, sexual receptivity typically coincides with estrus, a period during which the ovaries are secreting large amounts of estrogen. The ovarian hormones probably act through the central nervous system (hypothalamus) to condition the psychic manifestations such as increased spontaneous activity, lordosis, sexual receptivity, etc. Ovulation is the most important event of the female cycle, but it may occur without any manifestation of sexual receptivity. On the other hand, sexual receptivity may be induced at almost any period of the estrous cycle by giving exogenous estrogen, but this does not mean that ovulation has occurred. Ovulation is a consequence of the effects of pituitary gonadotrophins, whereas heat is the result of ovarian hormones acting upon the nervous system.

Full mating behavior generally depends upon both estrogen and progesterone. Estrogen injections alone induce sexual receptivity in the rat, but smaller quantities of estrogen are required if the female is pretreated with small amounts of progesterone. Psychic heat in the guinea pig, sheep, and many other species requires a trace of progesterone together with the estrogen.

The Actions of Relaxin

Marked *pelvic relaxation* occurs during late pregnancy in a number of mammals including the human subject. At this time there is a separation of the symphysis pubis and, in some species, a loosening of the sacroiliac union. The pelvic bones become less rigid and the birth canal is enlarged, thus facilitating parturition. These pelvic modifications are brought about by relaxin operating in conjunction with other hormones, especially estrogens. The connective tissue of the symphysis increases in vascularity, and this is followed by the imbibition of water, disaggregation of the fibers, and depolymerization of the mucoproteins in the ground substance.

The mechanisms of softening and relaxation of the reproductive structures in preparation for parturition are complex phenomena and involve more than an effect of relaxin on connective tissue polymers. Some have postulated that estrogens act on the symphysis to convert cartilage into connective tissue, after which relaxin acts to depolymerize the connective tissue ground substance. More recent studies indicate that the biochemical mechanisms are quite involved and probably cannot be accounted for by such a simple hypothesis. In the guinea pig, without prior estrogen priming, relaxin has been found to stimulate the incorporation of glycine into the proteins of the symphyseal connective tissue. This protein anabolic effect of relaxin is probably independent of the relaxation process.[27, 34]

Relaxin exerts profound effects on the morphology, physiology, and biochemistry of the uterus. In ovariectomized, estrogen-primed rats, relaxin increases the glycogen concentration and water content of the uterus, as well as the dry weight and total nitrogen. Relaxin promotes water imbibition by the rat's uterus, and this response does not require pretreatment with estrogen. Like estradiol, relaxin produces a high peak of water imbibition at six hours, but no secondary peak occurs later. Additive effects on water content of the uterus are obtained when both estradiol and relaxin are administered. Relaxin inhibits uterine motility both *in vivo* and *in vitro*. It also potentiates the action of progesterone in causing progestational proliferation in the rabbit's uterus.

A marked dilatation of the uterine cervix of the sow occurs after relaxin administration.[69] As with the relaxation of the pubic symphysis of the guinea pig, the response requires pretreatment with estrogen. The dilatation and softening of the cervix facilitates parturition. The cervical response involves depolymerization of the ground substance and increased water content of the connective tissue. Relaxin also increases cervical dilatability in the spayed estrogen-primed rat. There are indications that relaxin may be useful in conditioning the uterine cervix of women prior to the induction of labor.

THE REPRODUCTIVE CYCLES

The cyclic alterations of the reproductive system are regulated by hormones from the anterior pituitary-gonadal axis. The hypothalamic portion of the brain appears to be the source of factors which pass through the portal veins to the adenohypophysis where they act to promote the differential release of hormones. Hypothalamic activity is conditioned to a large extent by external environmental stimuli and by the levels of steroid hormones in the circulation. The accessory sex organs and most of the secondary sex characters, as well as breeding behavior, are under the direct control of the gonadal hormones and the latter, in turn, are conditioned by the pituitary gonadotrophins.

The Estrous Cycle

The structural aspects of the estrous cycle have been very carefully determined for the common laboratory rodents and domestic mammals.[39] The effects of pituitary gonadotrophins on the ovaries and the effects of ovarian hormones on the accessory genitalia are fairly well established. The manner in which the various hormones interact to determine the cyclic events remains poorly understood. The gonadal and hypophysial hormones are most directly involved, but there is no doubt that the adrenal, thyroid, and other glands concerned with general metabolism exert indirect though important influences.

Laboratory rats, mice, hamsters, and guinea pigs are polyestrous species that repeat their cycles throughout the year without much variation, unless interrupted by pregnancy or pseudopregnancy. Although ovulation is governed by a hypothalamic-pituitary mechanism whose final link to the pars distalis is neurohormonal the process is "spontaneous" in these species. It is not dependent upon mating or some overt nervous stimulation as in reflexly ovulating species such as the rabbit. Eggs are normally released from the ovaries of these species during heat (estrus). Since the rat is used so extensively for the study of reproductive processes, it will be described as exemplifying a simple estrous cycle (Fig. 14–11).

Rats

The estrous cycle of the rat is completed in four to five days, although the timing of the cycle may be influenced by exteroceptive factors such as light, temperature, nutritional status, and social relationships. In species having such short cycles, the ovaries contain follicles in various stages of formation, as well as corpora lutea of several past estrous cycles. The cycle is roughly divisible into four stages:

1. ESTRUS. This is the period of heat, and copulation is permitted only at this time. This condition lasts from 9 to 15 hours and is characterized by a high rate of running activity. Under the influence of follicle-stimulating hormone (FSH) a dozen or more ovarian follicles grow rapidly; estrus is thus a period of heightened estrogen

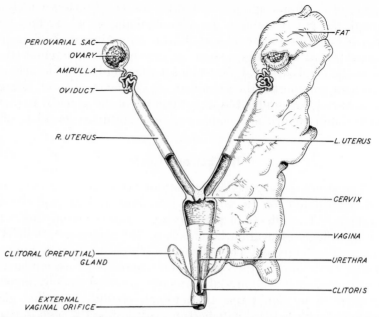

Figure 14-11. Female genital tract of a normal rat dissected out *in toto* and drawn from ventral view. The fat is removed from the right side. Portions of the uterine and vaginal walls are cut away in order to expose the cervices.

secretion. Behavioral changes include quivering of the ears and lordosis, or arching of the back in response to handling or to approaches by the male. The uteri undergo progressive enlargement and become distended owing to the accumulation of luminal fluid (Fig. 14–12). Many mitoses occur in the vaginal mucosa and, as new cells accumulate, the superficial layers become squamous and cornified. The latter

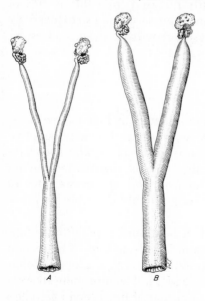

Figure 14-12. Normal female genitalia of adult rats dissected out *in toto* during diestrus *(A)* and proestrus *(B)*. Compare the sizes of the uteri and vaginas in the two instances. (The drawings are to scale.)

cells are exfoliated into the vaginal lumen, and their presence in *vaginal smears* is indicative of estrus (Fig. 14–13). During late estrus there are cheesy masses of cornified cells with degenerate nuclei present in the vaginal lumen, but few if any leukocytes are found during estrus. Ovulation occurs during estrus and is preceded by histologic changes in the follicle suggestive of early luteinization. Much of the luminal fluid in the uteri is lost before ovulation.

2. METESTRUS. This occurs shortly after ovulation and is intermediate between estrus and diestrus. The period lasts for 10 to 14 hours and mating is usually not permitted. The ovaries contain corpora lutea and small follicles, and the uteri have diminished in

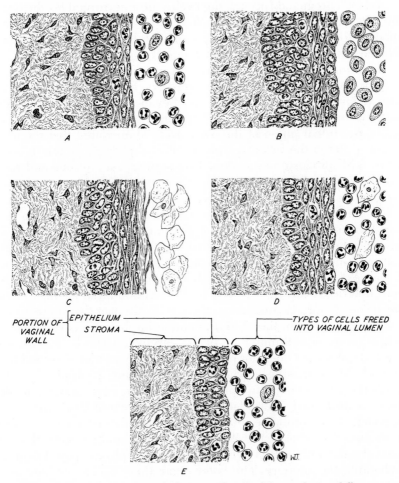

Figure 14–13. Sections through the vaginal wall of the rat during different stages of the estrous cycle, showing the corresponding types of cells which appear in smears obtained from the vaginal lumen. *A,* Diestrus; *B,* proestrus; *C,* estrus; *D,* metestrus; *E,* adult animal which had been oöphorectomized for six months.

vascularity and contractility. Many leukocytes appear in the vaginal lumen along with a few cornified cells.

3. DIESTRUS.   This lasts 60 to 70 hours during which functional regression of the corpora lutea occurs. The uteri are small, anemic, and only slightly contractile. The vaginal mucosa is thin, and leukocytes migrate through it, giving a vaginal smear consisting almost entirely of these cells (Fig. 14–13).

4. PROESTRUS.   This heralds the next heat and is characterized by functional involution of the corpora lutea and preovulatory swelling of the follicles. Fluid collects in the uteri and they become highly contractile. The vaginal smear is dominated by nucleated epithelial cells, which occur singly or in sheets. Copulation is not permitted by the female.

In case pregnancy occurs, the cycles are interrupted for the duration of gestation, which lasts for 20 to 22 days in the rat. The animal comes into estrus at the end of pregnancy, but the cycles are again delayed until the termination of lactation.[31]

Pseudopregnancy may be induced in many laboratory mammals by procedures that prolong the secretory function of the corpora lutea of ovulation, thus holding in abeyance the onset of the next estrus. In mammals such as rats and mice, which have short estrous cycles, the luteal phase of the ovary is so abbreviated that the uteri do not undergo the extensive progestational changes generally associated with progesterone action. Pseudopregnancy in rats and mice may be induced by stimulating the cervix of the estrous animal with a glass rod or other mechanical means, by electrical stimulation, or by mating with a sterile male. The condition has also been produced in rodents by stimulation of the nipples, by adrenalectomy, by irritating the nasal mucosa with silver nitrate, and by experimentally manipulating the steroid hormone balance of the organism. The onset of the next estrus is delayed for about 13 days; the corpora lutea remain functional during this time and the endometrial changes simulate those of normal pregnancy. Except for the fact that there are no developing young in the uteri, the endocrine balance is very similar to true pregnancy. Stimulation of the cervix at estrus by mechanical or electrical means does not result in pseudopregnancy if the animals are under deep anesthesia when these procedures are applied. Neither do they become pseudopregnant after the nerve supply to the uterus is destroyed. These facts indicate that neural mechanisms are involved. It is probable that cervical stimulation elicits afferent nerve impulses that reach the hypothalamus and promote the release of agents that are conveyed via the hypophysial portal venules to the anterior pituitary. The latter organ then discharges hormones that are essential for prolonging the functional life of the corpora lutea. These neuroendocrine adjustments cause the corpora lutea of the last ovulation to persist and function well beyond the time when they would ordinarily have regressed.

In most species, pseudopregnancy lasts for about half the length of time required for a normal pregnancy. The pseudopregnant state may be prolonged by administering estrogens or by traumatizing the uterus to produce deciduomas. The latter are growths that develop in the estrogen-progesterone conditioned uterus in response to trauma and represent an attempt of the uterus to form the maternal placenta in the absence of implanting blastocysts (Fig. 14–14). The corpora lutea of pseudopregnancy maintain the uterus in a state capable of receiving blastocysts, and conspicuous proliferation of the mammary glands occurs. The mammary glands of the pseudopregnant bitch may actually lactate. Nest building and retrieving of foster young are often noted in pseudopregnant rats and mice.

ENDOCRINE REGULATION OF THE CYCLE. Although the reproductive cycles are governed by the interplay of pituitary and gonadal hormones, the picture is far from complete and only a general outline

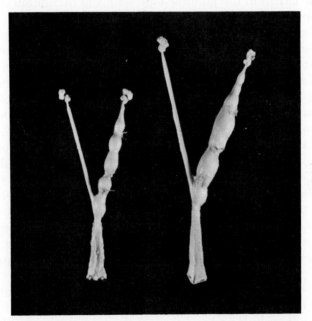

Figure 14–14. Deciduomas in the rat. Trauma of the guinea pig's uterus during the luteal phase of the normal cycle results in the formation of the maternal aspect of the placenta (deciduoma). In the rat, however, the luteal phase is short, and pseudopregnant animals are used for producing the same reaction. Pseudopregnancy in the rat is induced by mechanical stimulation of the cervix at estrus; two or three days later, the uterus is traumatized by sutures or otherwise. The tract on the left was removed three days after uterine trauma; the one on the right was removed four days after trauma. Only the left uteri were traumatized. The deciduomas are the swellings around the sutures.

can be given here. According to current concepts, a feedback mechanism operates whereby the pituitary release of FSH and LH is controlled by the levels of estrogen and progesterone in the circulation. It is not known what factors are originally responsible for the activation of the pituitary-ovarian axis, but it has been postulated that very low levels of estrogens, coming from the immature follicles or extragonadal sources, may stimulate the pituitary to augment its release of FSH. Significant production of estrogen by the follicle apparently requires both FSH and LH. When the level of estrogen in the blood becomes high, indicating that the ovarian follicles are full-grown, it acts to prevent a greater release of FSH by the hypophysis and to promote an augmented release of LH. Under the influence of rising titers of LH, preovulatory swelling ensues and definite lutein changes occur in the walls of the mature follicles. The preovulatory follicle undoubtedly secretes some progesterone as well as large quantities of estrogens. Ovulation occurs while LH is in ascendancy, and there is an immediate fall in the circulating estrogens after ovulation. The ruptured follicle becomes transformed into a corpus luteum, which becomes functional under the influence of prolactin. The discharge of LH from the anterior lobe seems to be inhibited by rising titers of progesterone.

The corpora lutea remain functional for only a short period unless pregnancy or pseudopregnancy supervenes, but the ovaries of cyclic rats always contain several sets of corpora lutea in different stages of disintegration. Changes in the ovaries must be regarded as resulting from the interaction of the gonadotrophins and changes in the sex accessories as consequences of the interaction of the various ovarian hormones.

There is ample evidence that in many mammalian species the secretion of progesterone by the follicle begins before ovulation has occurred, during the period of preovulatory swelling. Even in species that ovulate spontaneously, it is interesting that sexual receptivity precedes ovulation. In the cow ovulation is spontaneous, but it does not occur until 13 to 15 hours after the end of heat. The secretion of progesterone by the ovarian follicles of the rat, guinea pig, and perhaps other species probably coincides with the onset of sexual receptivity.

The uteri of the rat become quite small and anemic during diestrus, indicating that while the corpora lutea persist they secrete progesterone only for a brief time in the cyclic animal. When pregnancy or pseudopregnancy follows a period of estrus, the corpora lutea remain functional much longer, probably due to the action of prolactin. The progestational changes in rats and mice are much less extensive than those that occur in the uteri of such forms as the rabbit. However, the progestational uteri, conditioned by estrogen plus progesterone, are equally sensitive to implanting blastocysts or to endometrial trauma.

Dogs

Another type of estrous cycle is illustrated by the dog. Ovulation is spontaneous, and there are generally two estrous periods per year; in smaller breeds it may occur more frequently. Proestrus lasts for about ten days, and this is followed by estrus which lasts from six to ten days. Ovulation typically occurs during early estrus, and copulations may be permitted for six to eight days thereafter. Loss of blood occurs through the vagina during proestrus and not infrequently extends throughout estrus. This blood arises from the uterus by diapedesis, rather than through disintegration of the endometrial surface, and is in no way comparable to menstruation. Each estrus is followed by a functional luteal phase lasting approximately 60 days: a fertile mating leads to pregnancy; an infertile mating, or no mating, is followed by pseudopregnancy. During pseudopregnancy the reproductive tract and mammary glands are developed much as in normal pregnancy. A brief period of milk secretion may be noted, even though the animal is not pregnant.

Rabbits

Certain species, such as rabbits, ferrets, cats, etc., are often called "induced ovulators" because eggs are not released from the ovaries except after coitus or some comparable cervical stimulation. Although there may be slight fluctuations in the degree of sexual receptivity, the adult nonpregnant rabbit is in a constant state of estrus. The ovaries contain follicles in all stages of development and atresia, but corpora lutea of ovulation are absent. Full development (progestational proliferation) of the uterus, characteristic of pregnancy and pseudopregnancy, requires both estrogen and progesterone (Figs. 14–15 and 14–16). Pseudopregnancy, lasting about 18 days, may be induced by sterile matings. Although estrous cats may be caused to ovulate by stimulating the cervices with a glass rod, this procedure is generally ineffective in the rabbit unless the animals are given special hormone treatments. The duration of pregnancy in the rabbit is 31 to 32 days. Comparable mechanisms operate in both spontaneous and induced ovulators: rupture of the follicles is conditioned by the action of ovarian steroids and also by a discharge from sex centers in the hypothalamus. Coital stimulation does not induce ovulation in the hypophysectomized animal. If the pituitary is removed within one hour after coitus, or if the pituitary stalk is sectioned during this time, ovulations do not occur. Ovulations pro-

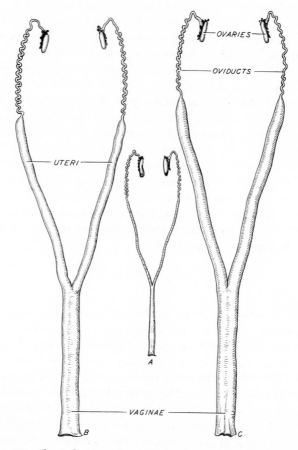

Figure 14–15. The influence of ovarian hormones upon the female tract of the sexually immature rabbit. *A*, Tract of an untreated juvenile rabbit; *B*, tract from a juvenile rabbit after receiving six daily doses of estrogen; *C*, tract from a juvenile animal after receiving six daily doses of estrogen followed by four daily doses of progesterone. The three animals were littermates and were the same age at autopsy. See Figure 14–16 for the histologic changes in the uteri of similar animals. (The tracts were dissected out *in toto* and drawn to scale.)

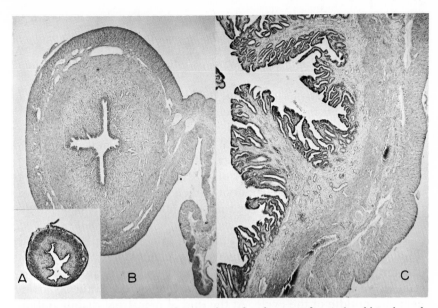

Figure 14-16. Microscopic changes elicited in the uteri of juvenile rabbits through the administration of ovarian hormones. *A,* Section through the uterus of the untreated control; *B,* comparable section through the uterus of a littermate which had received six daily doses of estrogen; *C,* a portion of the uterine wall of a third littermate which had received six daily doses of estrogen plus six daily doses of progesterone. The type of uterus shown in *B* is identical with that which prevails in the normal estrous adult. The progestational condition shown in *C,* requiring progesterone subsequent to estrogen, simulates that which normally prevails during pregnancy and pseudopregnancy. See Figure 14-15 for the macroscopic appearance of similar tracts. *A, B,* and *C* are of the same magnification.

ceed normally if the pituitary is removed later than one hour after the mating stimulus. The mechanism of ovulation is discussed later in this chapter.

The Menstrual Cycle

Menstrual cycles are characteristic of primates and do not occur in other vertebrate groups. The length of the cycle is highly variable, though 28 days is generally regarded as typical for women. The cycle in the chimpanzee requires about 35 days. Both estrous and menstrual cycles are regulated by the same interplay of pituitary and ovarian hormones, and the effects of the ovarian hormones on the reproductive tract are comparable in most respects. The chief differences between the two types of cycles are the presence of a menstrual phase in primates and the spreading of sexual receptivity throughout the cycle, rather than the limitation of it to a definite period. During the menstrual phase the superficial layers of the endometrium are sloughed with accompanying bleeding; this type of bleeding does not occur in nonprimates. Spiral arteries are absent from the uteri of estrous mammals but are present in primates with the exception of the New World monkeys. The latter animals menstruate, but the loss of blood is greatly reduced.

The menstrual phase, lasting four to seven days, is regarded as the beginning of the primate cycle. This arrangement is sanctioned because menstruation is the easiest period of the cycle to recognize and because it corresponds with the formation of new follicles in the ovaries (Fig. 14–17). However, if the uterus alone is considered, menstruation represents the terminal event: with subsidence of the corpus luteum and a consequent deficiency of ovarian hormones, the endometrium cannot maintain itself and hence regresses and the surface disintegrates.

Four phases of the menstrual cycle are usually distinguished: the menstrual, proliferative (follicular), ovulatory, and progestational (luteal). The *proliferative phase* is conditioned by estrogen and extends from the end of menstruation to ovulation, the latter occurring near the middle of the cycle. At the end of menstrual disintegration, the endometrium is thin and poorly vascularized, and only the basal parts of the endometrial glands remain. The endometrium thickens as the estrogen titers rise, and the glandular and vascular patterns are restored.

No conspicuous changes occur in the endometrium during the

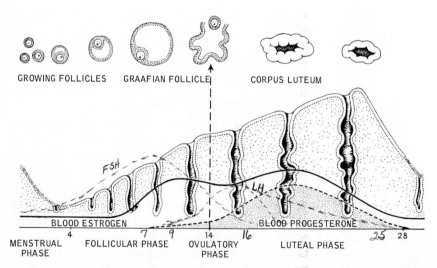

Figure 14–17. Diagram showing changes in the endometrium, the ovaries, and the circulating ovarian hormones during the menstrual cycle.

ovulatory process. Cyclic variations in the body temperature of the human female correlate with menstrual changes. A distinct rise in basal body temperature occurs at ovulation and remains high until the onset of the next menstrual period. The changing titers of hormones during the menstrual cycle apparently account for the temperature fluctuations.

During the *progestational phase* the uterus is under the influence of both estrogens and progestogens, and the endometrium differentiates into a tissue that can fulfill the requirements of an embryo ready to implant. The stroma becomes highly vascularized and edematous, the mucosa is thicker, and the glands develop corkscrew and serrate features. The progestational endometrium, normally requiring both estrogens and progesterone, is the only type of structure in which blastocysts can readily implant and develop normally. If implantation has not occurred, the corpus luteum diminishes in function, and degenerative changes are observable in the endometrium. Predecidual cells form solid sheaths below the surface epithelium, leukocytes invade the tissue, necrotic changes occur in the stroma, and the uterine glands involute. With menstruation, the outer portion of the endometrium is lost, and there is bleeding into the uterine cavity.

Endocrine Interactions

At the beginning of menstruation the inhibitory influence of the corpus luteum on the pituitary is removed and FSH is secreted in increasing amounts. This stimulates the growth of the young follicles and, as they grow, they release increasing quantities of estrogens. The high estrogen content of the blood causes the pituitary to diminish its production of FSH and increase the output of LH. Ovulation occurs when the balance between FSH and LH has swung sufficiently in favor of the latter hormone. There is evidence that small amounts of progesterone are produced by the preovulatory follicle, and this hormone may be involved in the ovulatory process, perhaps through its action on the brain or the anterior hypophysis. After ovulation, the corpus luteum begins to form in the ruptured follicle under the influence of LH.

Gonadotrophins activate the corpus luteum and cause it to secrete progesterone and small amounts of estrogen. If a fertilized egg is not produced, functional degeneration of the corpus luteum begins eight to ten days after ovulation. The onset of menstrual bleeding correlates with the withdrawal of progesterone and, to a lesser extent, of estrogen from the circulation (Fig. 14–17). The factors immediately involved in the breakdown of the endometrial blood vessels with subsequent bleeding remain largely unknown.

If the egg is fertilized, the pituitary continues to release luteinizing hormone, and the corpus luteum increases in size and augments its output of hormones. Secretory competence of the corpus luteum diminishes slowly after the fourth month of pregnancy, although it remains structurally intact until the end of pregnancy. The placenta, rather than the ovary, is the principal source of progesterone and estrogen during the latter half of pregnancy. Removal of the ovaries after midpregnancy neither terminates pregnancy nor diminishes the levels of the two types of steroid hormones in the circulation.

The Mechanism of Ovulation

Ovulation has been observed and studied in a variety of mammals, birds, and amphibians. The indications are that the process is initiated by a neural mechanism in the hypothalamus that releases pituitary gonadotrophins at the proper time. The ovulation-inducing hormone is thought to be principally LH, but the exact manner in which it brings about rupture of the ovarian follicle is not understood. The administration of a combination of highly purified FSH and LH to immature rats 7 to 100 days after hypophysectomy induces ovulation and the formation of corpora lutea.[58] Neither hormone is effective when given alone, and this is strong evidence that both FSH and LH are involved in ovulation and luteinization. All of the available evidence indicates that the pituitary starts to release LH very quickly, in a matter of minutes, after application of the neurogenic stimulus. Furthermore, it seems that LH does not need to act on the ovarian follicle for long periods. It probably acts on the follicular wall rather quickly, producing subtle changes that remain microscopically hidden until just before rupture. If the frog is pretreated with pituitary gonadotrophins, the excised ovaries ovulate in the absence of vascular and nervous connections. The ovarian follicle of the hen, previously subjected to pituitary gonadotrophins, ovulates normally even after the stalk that attaches it to the ovary is sectioned or clamped off in such a manner as to eliminate nervous and vascular supplies.

It does not appear likely that increased intrafollicular tension, arising through the accumulation of fluid in the antrum, is the immediate cause of rupture of the mammalian follicle. Ovarian cysts occur commonly in pathologic ovaries, and in these follicles there is a tremendous increase in liquor folliculi, yet they do not rupture. In all species that have been studied, ovulation is found to be a slow oozing rather than an explosive process. The preovulatory follicles of swine, cattle, and sheep lose follicular fluid before any break in the follicular wall can be detected. In certain species of bats there is a tremendous hypertrophy of the cumulus oöphorus and, just before ovulation, the antrum is reduced to a mere slit.

Since the fimbriated ends of the oviducts become very active at the time of ovulation, it was formerly believed that they might promote ovulation by a massaging action on the ovaries. It has been shown that ovulations occur normally in the pig, fowl, and other species after surgical removal of the oviducts. Ovulation in several species may be accomplished when the ovaries are maintained *in vitro.* The modern view is that certain hypothalamic areas signal the anterior hypophysis in some manner and promote the release of LH, which initiates a series of changes in the follicular wall leading to its eventual rupture.

Ovulation in Mammals

Induced ovulators, such as the rabbit, ferret, cat, and mink, require coitus or some comparable stimulus for ovulation to occur. There are strong indications that participation in coitus leads to a reflexive stimulation of the pituitary gland and a consequent discharge of LH. The rabbit's hypophysis releases enough LH within one hour after coitus to cause ovulation. A similar neural mechanism appears to be involved in the rat when it is induced to become pseudopregnant by artificial stimulation of the cervices. Although this species ovulates spontaneously, the corpora lutea of ovulation do not remain functional in the absence of pregnancy unless a cervical stimulus is applied before the corpora lutea become nonfunctional. Segregated female rats of certain strains show a tendency to exhibit persistent estrus. If such females accept coitus or receive small injections of progesterone, ovulation and the recurrence of cycles may follow. These procedures apparently act directly or indirectly via the nervous system to cause the pituitary release of LH.

Direct electrical stimulation of the pituitary gland of the anesthetized rabbit does not induce ovulation unless there are indications that the stimulus has spread to the hypothalamic region. Lower voltages applied directly to the hypothalamus do induce ovulation. Stimulation of the hypothalamus of the unanesthetized rabbit, for only three minutes by the remote control method, results in ovulation; similar stimuli applied directly to the anterior pituitary for periods up to seven hours do not result in ovulation. These and other studies make it apparent that the hypothalamic portion of the brain is intimately involved in the pituitary release of LH.[16, 28]

Very careful studies have been made on inbred strains of rats kept under strictly controlled environments.[16] Some strains ovulate at four-day intervals and others at five-day intervals. Under these controlled conditions ovulations occur between 1 and 2 o'clock in the morning. The five-day cycle may be shortened to four days by injecting estrogen on the second day or progesterone on the third day of diestrus. In other words, these treatments advance the time of ovulation by 24 hours. The capacity of progesterone to cause early ovulation can be blocked by the administration of either dibenamine (antiadrenergic) or atropine (anticholinergic). A study of the effects of atropine blockade at intervals after the administration of progesterone on the third day of diestrus has shown that pituitary release of LH does not occur until 2 P.M. no matter how early the progesterone is administered. Furthermore, ovulation in normal cyclic animals may be blocked by dibenamine or atropine if administered before 2 P.M. on the day of proestrus. If the drugs are administered after 4 P.M. on this day, ovulations occur as usual early the next morning. The conclusion is that in rats, under controlled conditions, the release of pituitary LH is triggered by a neurohumoral mechanism on the day of proestrus between 2 and 4 P.M., 10 to 12 hours before ovulation occurs.

If the rats are kept under moderate barbiturate anesthesia during the critical hours (2 to 4 P.M.) on the day of proestrus, ovulation is prevented and activation of the pituitary is delayed for a full day. The graafian follicles persist when this treatment is applied for several days at the same hours, but, if the anesthesia is withheld until 4 P.M. on any day, ovulations will occur during the night. The follicles that are prevented from ovulating by barbiturate anesthesia for several days undergo atresia about two days before the beginning of the next proestrus.

Some workers find that ovulation in the estrous rabbit may be induced by injecting epinephrine or norepinephrine directly into the substance of the anterior lobe or into the third ventricle of the brain. Adrenergic and cholinergic blocking agents prevent ovulation in the rabbit only if they are administered during the first minute after mating. Although it was postulated that coitus might rapidly activate hypothalamic nerve terminals to release an adrenergic substance into the hypophysial portal system, recent evidence indicates that the adrenergic mechanism is not the final link or mediator that activates the anterior pituitary gland. Ovulation resulting from direct electrical stimulation of the hypothalamus is not blocked by antiadrenergic agents, although ovulation after the intraventricular administration of norepinephrine is prevented by prior treatment with atropine or pentobarbital. Both adrenergic and cholinergic components now appear to be central nervous phenomena.[51]

In both the rat and rabbit, ovulations occur about 10 hours after the anterior pituitary releases LH. It thus appears that in both spontaneous ovulators (rat) and induced ovulators (rabbit) the ovulatory process involves the action of ovarian hormones and the release of a transmitter substance from certain centers in the hypothalamus. In the rabbit, the hypothalamic center is apparently stimulated by the act of copulation or, in some instances, by psychic stimuli without actual mating. In the rat, on the other hand, the hypothalamic center either discharges at a particular time of the day because of its own inherent rhythmicity or is regulated by some nervous mechanism that has a diurnal rhythm.

In summary, most workers who have studied ovulation in mammals feel that a neuroendocrine mechanism is involved in species that ovulate spontaneously (rat), as well as in those that ovulate reflexively (rabbit). Current concepts may be summarized as follows: (1) Ovulation is controlled by both the hypothalamus and the pituitary gland; hence the mechanism is both neural and hormonal. The final link to the adenohypophysis involves a neurohormonal agent which travels via the hypophysial portal vessels, causing the pituitary to release luteinizing hormone. (2) The hypothalamus contains one or more centers that are stimulated or inhibited by circulating estrogens and progestogens, as well as by afferent nerve impulses of various kinds. (3) The ovarian steroids may influence the ovulatory process by modifying thresholds in the nervous system. (4) Some, if not all, mammalian species possess potential mechanisms which subserve both reflexive and spontaneous ovulation.

Ovulation in Birds

The domestic fowl is a very suitable form for studying the ovulatory process.[21] The hen's ovary produces eggs in clutches, and a single egg is oviposited at daily intervals. Under conditions of natural illumination, ovulation usually occurs in the morning and seldom takes place after 3 P.M. It requires 25 to 26 hours for the egg to traverse the oviduct, most of this time being spent in the shell gland. Ovulation of the next egg occurs 30 to 60 minutes after the previous one is laid. Since the time required for egg formation is greater than 24 hours, oviposition will occur a little later each day. When this lag brings the time of oviposition to late afternoon, laying is held in abeyance for several days after which ovulations begin anew from the early morning.

Multiple steroid hormones are required for the functional development of the avian oviduct. Full development of the magnum, the region of the oviduct that secretes the albumen around the ovum, can be produced by estrogen followed by either androgen or progesterone. Estrogen alone causes growth of the glands of the magnum, but does not induce the formation of albumen antecedents in the glands; the latter requires either an androgen or progesterone. When the organ has been built up by the proper steroid hormones, the actual secretion of albumen occurs in response to any foreign body in the oviduct. Ovulation does not generally occur while there is an egg in any part of the oviduct. The presence of an irritant in the magnum, such as a loop of thread, completely prevents ovulation in the great majority of laying hens. It is probable that the suture in the magnum neurogenically inhibits the release of ovulating hormone from the hen's anterior pituitary, and ovulation of the next ovum in the series cannot occur.

For hens to lay 365 eggs in a year, as they sometimes do, must require a rather vigorous metabolism of calcium. The shell gland differs from the other parts of the oviduct inasmuch as estrogen alone is sufficient for its development. Hypercalcemia and lipemia are characteristic of laying hens and may be produced in males or nonlaying females by the administration of estrogens. The medullary bone of laying birds undergoes sequences of deposition and destruction that correlate with the storage and liberation of calcium. Laying soon ceases when calcium is withheld from the diet. It is not known how estrogen acts to promote both the deposition of calcium in bone and its withdrawal from bone.

The process of ovulation in the bird is easily observed. During the period of rapid growth, the future site of follicular rupture, the stigma, may be observed as a light band extending across the hemisphere opposite to the stalked attachment (Figs. 12–9 and 14–18). Just before rupture of the follicle, the stigma appears to widen owing to the blurring of blood vessels that extend into it. Rupture usually begins at one pole of the stigma and extends rapidly to the opposite pole, freeing the ovum almost immediately. The ruptured follicle, or calyx, persists and, together with the most mature follicle, performs a role in the timing of oviposition. If the calyx is surgically removed, the egg that originated from it is held in the shell gland for an abnormally long period.

Figure 14–18. Mature follicles of the domestic fowl, treated to show the stigma, or cicatrix. (From Fraps, R. M.: *In* J. Hammond, (ed.): Progress in Physiology of Farm Animals, vol. 2. London, Butterworth & Co., 1955.)

The pituitary principle responsible for ovulation in birds is believed to be LH, or a gonadotrophin similar to it, and this is released some six to eight hours before the next ovulation. The administration of mammalian LH to intact laying hens hastens the release of the mature follicle destined to ovulate next, but this treatment never provokes the ovulation of any of the smaller follicles in the ovary. Ovulation does not occur in the laying hen if the pituitary is removed 10 hours before the expected event. If a laying hen is hypophysectomized and injected promptly with LH, not only the largest follicle but several of the smaller ones are ovulated and passed into the oviduct. Since this cannot be duplicated in animals with intact hypophyses, it appears that the pituitary is the source of a substance which inhibits the ovulation of immature ova. If the hypophysectomized hen is first given FSH, immediately after the operation, the subsequent administration of LH causes only the largest follicle to ovulate. Thus, it appears that FSH inhibits the ovulation of all follicles except the one which is largest and most mature.[42, 43]

Ovulation in Amphibians

The homoimplantation of pituitary glands in various species of amphibians causes ovulation in the female and spermiation in the male. These two processes are quite comparable, since the sustentacular cells (Sertoli cells) of the testis are homologous with the granulosa cells of the ovary. Spermiation may also be induced in *Bufo, Xenopus,* and certain common frogs by small amounts of pregnancy urine, a reaction that is frequently used as a test for pregnancy. Ovulation may be induced by human pregnancy urine, but it is a much less sensitive reaction than spermiation.

Most of the evidence suggests that luteinizing hormone (LH) is the chief ovulation hormone, but FSH and ACTH, as well as gonadal hormones, probably cooperate with it in the intact animal. Hypophysectomized frogs and toads do not ovulate, though they may be caused to do so by homoimplanting pituitaries into the coelomic cavity or under the skin shortly after the pituitary is removed. Some workers have found that hypophysectomy has a sensitizing effect, a smaller dose of pituitary extract being required to bring about ovulation than is required in intact animals. This effect is probably explained by the escape of hypophysial hormones into the circulation during surgical manipulation of the hypophysis. Ovulation may be induced in nonbreeding *Rana temporaria* by merely exposing the hypophysis and crushing it *in situ.* This indicates that the pituitary contains sufficient LH during the nonbreeding season but does not release it. Pieces of ovaries from mature animals ovulate *in vitro* when treated with dilute suspensions of pituitary tissue.

Ovulation has been observed to occur in the following manner. It is a dual process involving rupture of the follicle and emergence of the egg. Follicular rupture is not a cataclysmic process but is completed in approximately a minute at laboratory temperatures. Under similar conditions the emergence of the egg requires from four to ten minutes. The initial break in the follicular wall is small at first, but rapidly enlarges until the whole rupture area is involved. After rupture there is no leakage of follicular fluid, as in mammals. There is no preovulatory growth or any other visible change within the follicle that can be regarded as signifying an impending rupture. After the rupture area has given way, the smooth musculature of the cyst wall contracts and gradually squeezes the egg through the relatively small opening. After the egg has been discharged, the follicle closes and the original rupture is drawn together. The follicle cells lying next to the vitelline membrane do not escape with the ovum but remain within the collapsed follicle. Around the postovulatory follicle may be observed an accumulation of spindle-shaped cells, presumably relaxed smooth muscle cells derived from the cyst wall of the follicle.

In sexually inactive frogs slitting of the rupture area by a lancet leads only to incomplete ovulation; the follicular muscles are able to force the egg only partially through the aperture. Electrical and mechanical stimuli applied directly to the musculature of the follicle do not cause a breaking away of the rupture area. However, after rupture has occurred, the application of these stimuli does cause the egg to emerge more rapidly than normally. Escape of the egg through the open rupture area is clearly due to the hormonal activation of the smooth musculature in the wall of the follicle itself. The breaking of the rupture area is likewise conditioned by hormonal agents.

The ovulation of frogs' eggs *in vitro* in response to pituitary extracts may be enhanced by the addition of certain steroids, including androgens, progestogens, and adrenal corticoids. Some of the nonestrogenic steroids induce ovulation *in vitro* in the absence of pituitary factors. Progesterone is one of the most effective steroids tested. It has been suggested that in amphibians the pituitary gonadotrophins may stimulate the ovaries to produce steroidal hormones, the latter acting directly on the ovarian follicles to induce ovulation.[6, 64]

The Progestogens and Decidual Reactions

The classical experiments of Leo Loeb demonstrated that decidual responses in the uterus could be elicited experimentally only after luteinization of the ovary. Loeb's work provided the first experimental evidence that the corpora lutea perform a secretory function.

He permitted estrous guinea pigs to copulate with vasectomized males. Several days later, when implantation would have occurred normally, glass beads were inserted into the uteri. He observed that overgrowths of uterine cells occurred around the beads and recognized that the beads, by simulating implanting blastocysts, had induced the uterus to begin the differentiation of the maternal portion of the placenta. These tumorous responses of the progestational endometrium to trauma are called *deciduomas* or placentomas (Fig. 14–14). In the guinea pig the luteal phase of the normal cycle is long enough to permit the production of deciduomas without bringing the animal into a state of pseudopregnancy.

It is interesting to note that in normal cyclic animals the period when deciduomas can be elicited corresponds to the time when nidation of the blastocysts would occur. The reaction results also from traumatization of the uterus during early pregnancy and the first half of lactation. In the intact animal the essential requisite is the production of traumatic injury to a uterus that has been acted upon first by estrogen and subsequently by progesterone. Extremely large doses of progesterone administered to the ovariectomized animal sensitize the uterus for the production of deciduomas, but much smaller amounts of the luteal hormone are effective in this respect if pretreatment with estrogen is made. Endometrial proliferations have been produced in the monkey by mechanically traumatizing the progestational uterus at the proper time. These traumatic responses in the primate differ from Loeb's decidual reactions, inasmuch as the growths originate from the epithelium rather than from the stroma.

Though it is impossible to produce deciduomas during the normal four- or five-day cycle of the rat, it becomes possible to do so when the functional life of the corpora lutea is prolonged by pseudopregnancy resulting from either sterile copulation or mechanical stimulation of the cervices, or from the application of suckling stimuli to the nipples. Although pseudopregnancy in the rat normally lasts about 13 days, it can be extended to the length of a normal pregnancy (20 to 22 days) by inducing deciduomas in the uterus. Furthermore, the extended length of the pseudopregnancy is proportional to the number of deciduomas induced in the uteri.

After traumatization of the endometrium the first reaction is the proliferation of decidual cells in the subepithelial region of the stroma. These cells grow and multiply rapidly and soon form a tumorous growth that practically occludes the uterine lumen and distends its walls. The deciduomatous cells lying next to the mesometrium become packed with glycogen granules. The storage of glycogen invariably occurs in the decidual cells that occupy the mesometrial side of the uterus, irrespective of the site of the trauma. The position of these glycogen-storing cells corresponds to that of

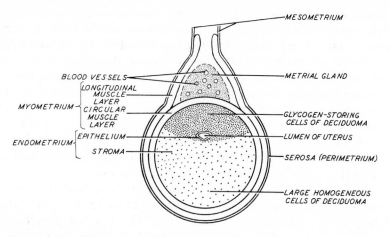

Figure 14–19. Diagrammatic section through a rat's uterus in which a deciduoma has been caused to differentiate.

similar cells that appear below the fetal placenta during normal pregnancies. In rodents the placentae invariably form on the mesometrial side of the uterus, and this site seems to be determined by factors operating in the uterus rather than in the implanting blastocysts. The deciduomas attain maximal differentiation about five days after uterine trauma; after this they undergo necrosis and gradually disappear. The glandular cells at the point of mesometrial attachment are the last to disappear.

During the involution of each deciduoma a *metrial gland* develops on the mesometrial side of the uterus (Fig. 14–19). The gland consists of large cells of epithelial appearance arranged in thick sheaths around certain blood vessels in this area of the uterus. In most mammals these cells appear to be scattered throughout the uterine tissue, but in the rat they form a circumscribed, macroscopically visible organ that seems to be glandular in nature. This structure develops below the insertion of each placenta during normal pregnancy and at the mesometrial edge of each deteriorating deciduoma. It has been suggested that the protein granules of the metrial gland may be related to the presence of relaxin.[62]

A problem of great importance is how uterine trauma or blastocysts in the lumen of the uterus signal the anterior hypophysis to release the necessary hormones for prolonging the secretory function of the corpora lutea. Experiments on sheep have shown that blastocysts fail to implant normally after surgical section of the uterine nerves or partial resection of the pituitary stalk. After either operation the estrous cycles remain normal in length; ovulation and fertilization occur normally, but most of the blastocysts do not implant. One operation interrupts the nervous connection between the uterus and pituitary and the other, the connection between the hypothalamus and pituitary. Under these conditions, it appears that the pituitary gland does not continue to release gonadotrophin and maintain functional corpora lutea. Consequently, the progesterone titers fall too early and the uterus involutes before the blastocysts can implant.

GONADAL HORMONES AND SEXUAL BEHAVIOR IN MAMMALS

There is a vast amount of information indicating that hormones perform important roles in determining and regulating the patterns of sexual behavior. It is important to recognize that the gonads begin to secrete hormones during early stages of development, though maximal production of hormones and the release of mature germ cells occur much later. Since behavior relates to the nervous system, the implication is that hormones influence neural tissues, and there is ample documentation of this concept. We have repeatedly emphasized that the relationship between the nervous and endocrine systems is one of reciprocity. The problem of reproductive behavior is extremely complex and may be influenced by a multitude of factors such as genetic constitution, social contacts, the kinds of hormones present, and the age at which they act. Only a few salient aspects can be considered here, and the discussion will be limited to mammals.

Gonadal Hormones and the Control of Neural Function

Adult Mammals

The production and release of ovarian and testicular steroids are determined by the pituitary gonadotrophins. The gonadal steroids in the blood stream operate through a feed back mechanism to adjust the kinds and amounts of gonadotrophins released by the anterior pituitary. The circulating steroids act upon the hypothalamus, and this portion of the brain regulates pituitary functions through the production of neurohormonal, releasing factors. This seems to be a stabilizing and self-balancing system which makes it possible for environmental stimuli and various neural factors to affect gonadal functions. The gonadal hormones, and perhaps others, appear to act directly upon the central nervous system to initiate the behavioral responses characteristic of the species during the breeding periods. In certain species, the gonads of both sexes are quiescent for long periods during which reproductive behavior is entirely absent. In polyestrous forms, there are recurring periods of heat or sexual receptiveness in the female, the male being in a state of sexual readiness at all times.

Reproductive processes in the female are definitely rhythmic, whereas testicular functions lack this high degree of cyclicity. The female hypothalamus is rhythmic and this causes a rhythmic ripening of the ovarian follicles (FSH secretion), ovulation, and luteinization (LH secretion). The hypothalamus of the male, on the other hand, maintains a steady state output of FSH and LH which keeps the testis functional at all times, thus making it possible for environmental stimuli to elicit sexual behavior at any time.

The beginning of heat in such animals as the rat and guinea pig coincides with preovulatory growth of the graafian follicle, when large amounts of estrogen and some progesterone are being secreted. There can be no doubt that the change from diestrous to estrous behavior is due to the action of these hormones on the nervous system. The females of infraprimate mammals are never sexually receptive after castration or hypophysectomy, though they may be brought into heat by the administration of estrogen and progesterone. Males generally do not copulate if castrated during prepuberal life; copulations may continue for weeks or months in certain mammals following removal of the adult testes. Though exogenous gonadal hormones have an effect on the strength of the sex drive in adult mammals, including man, they do not determine the direction it will take or the means by which it is expressed.

Fetal or Neonatal Mammals

Since there is a difference in the release of gonadotrophins by adult male and female pituitaries, it follows that the hypothalami must be different. One could speak of a "male" brain and a "female" brain, thinking largely in terms of the hypothalamus. Current studies indicate that there is a critical period in development during which the undifferentiated hypothalamus is sensitive to the gonadal hormones in the circulation. In animals with long gestation periods (guinea pig, monkey), this period of hypothalamic sensitivity ensues in the fetus; in species having relatively short gestation periods (rat and mouse), the sensitive period is not ended until about 8 days after birth. Briefly stated, the indications are that the immature hypothalamus differentiates in the male direction when it is exposed to the influence of a testis or to exogenous androgens; if an ovary is present, or if gonads are absent, during this critical period, the hypothalamus differentiates into that of the female type.[23, 24, 44, 68]

We mentioned earlier that if rabbit and mouse fetuses are gonadectomized while the reproductive tracts are undifferentiated, female genital organs develop regardless of genotypic sex. This indicates that secretions of the fetal testis are essential for the differentiation of male genitalia, whereas the female genitalia develop independently of the ovarian hormones. This concept seems to be applicable to the differentiation of neural tissues which mediate mating behavior. It has been shown that the administration of testosterone to pregnant guinea pigs and monkeys, while the neural and genital tissues of the genetic female fetuses are immature, results in intersexuality. Objective studies on female intersexes of this type have shown that there is a permanent suppression of the capacity to display female behavior and an intensification of the capacity to display male behavior.

If male rats are castrated at birth, while the hypothalamus is still undifferentiated, they display feminine mating behavior as adults.[25] Two criteria have been employed in assessing male and female type hypothalami: first, the type of sexual behavior displayed by the adult and, secondly, the type of ovarian development. The latter reflects the pattern of release of the pituitary gonadotrophins. If female rats are given a single dose of testosterone before the eighth day after birth, the adult ovaries contain only vesicular follicles and these do not ovulate or luteinize. This indicates that the hypothalamus is not releasing FSH and LH cyclically and hence is of the male type. Ovarian grafts, persisting in male hosts, typically contain vesicular follicles which do not ovulate or form corpora lutea. Studies of the adult sexual behavior of these androgen-sterilized female rats reveal that they are incapable of female mating behavior, but show marked patterns of male behavior.[17, 22, 38]

These various studies suggest that androgens, acting during fetal or neonatal life, have an organizing effect on the neural tissues which mediate mating behavior after the attainment of adulthood. In the adult, both ovarian and testicular hormones serve to activate a pattern which is latent within the central nervous system. In other words, androgens or the absence of androgens exerts a fundamental influence upon the brain during ontogenesis, and this determines whether the sexual reactions brought to expression by the gonadal hormones of the adult will be masculine or feminine in character. Once the definitive organization of the hypothalamus has been accomplished, it cannot be changed by gonadal hormones or any other procedure.

REFERENCES

1. Anderson, L. L., Bowerman, A. M., and Melampy, R. M.: Neuro-utero-ovarian relationships. *In* A. V. Nalbandov, (ed.): Advances in Neuroendocrinology. Urbana, University of Illinois Press, 1963, p. 345.
2. Astwood, E. B.: A six-hour assay for the quantitative determination of estrogen. Endocrinol., 23:25, 1938.

3. Bagnara, J. T.: Independent actions of pineal and hypophysis in the regulation of chromatophores of anuran larvae. Gen. & Comp. Endocrinol., 4:299, 1964.

4. Barraclough, C. A.: Production of anovulatory, sterile rats by single injections of testosterone propionate. Endocrinol., 68:62, 1961.

5. Barraclough, C. A., and Gorski, R. A.: Evidence that the hypothalamus is responsible for androgen-induced sterility in the female rat. Endocrinol., 68:68, 1961.

6. Bergers, A. C. J., and Li, C. H.: Amphibian ovulation *in vitro* induced by mammalian pituitary hormones and progesterone. Endocrinol., 66:255, 1960.

7. Biggers, J. D., and Curnow, D. H.: Oestrogenic activity of subterranean clover. Biochem. J., 58:278, 1954.

8. Bradbury, J. T.: Direct action of estrogen on the ovary of the immature rat. Endocrinol., 68:115, 1961.

9. Callard, G. V., and Leathem, J. H.: *In vitro* synthesis of steroids by experimentally induced cystic ovaries. Proc. Soc. Exp. Biol. & Med., 118:996, 1965.

10. Cecil, H. C., Bitman, J., and Wrenn, T. R.: Effect of histamine and estrogen on the glycogen content of the rat uterus. Endocrinol., 74:701, 1964.

11. Chu, E. W., Wurtman, R. J., and Axelrod, J.: An inhibitory effect of melatonin on the estrous phase of the estrous cycle of the rodent. Endocrinol., 75:238, 1964.

12. Cooper, E., and Hess, M.: Uterine inhibition of ovarian progesterone biosynthesis. Anat. Record, 151:338, 1965.

13. Dorfman, R. I.: Steroid hormones in gynecology. Obst. & Gynecol. Survey, 18:65, 1963.

14. Duncan, G. W., Bowerman, A. M., Anderson, L. L., Hearn, W. R., and Melampy, R. M.: Factors influencing the *in vitro* synthesis of progesterone. Endocrinol., 68:199, 1961.

15. Edgren, R. A., Elton, R. L., and Calhoun, D. W.: Studies on the interactions of oestriol and progesterone. J. Reprod. Fertil., 2:98, 1961.

16. Everett, J. W.: Neuroendocrine mechanisms in control of the mammalian ovary. *In* A. Gorbman (ed.): Comparative Endocrinology. New York, John Wiley & Sons, 1959, p. 174.

17. Feder, H. H., and Whalen, R. E.: Feminine behavior in neonatally castrated and estrogen-treated male rats. Science, 147:306, 1965.

18. Fischer, T. V.: Local uterine inhibition of the corpus luteum in the guinea pig. Anat. Record, 151:350, 1965.

19. Fiske, V. M.: Serotonin rhythm in the pineal organ: control by the sympathetic nervous system. Science, 146:253, 1964.

20. Fiske, V. M., Bryant, G. K., and Putnam, J.: Effect of light on the weight of the pineal in the rat. Endocrinol., 66:489, 1960.

21. Fraps, R. M.: Twenty-four periodicity in the mechanism of pituitary gonadotrophin release for follicular maturation and ovulation in the chicken. Endocrinol., 77:5, 1965.

22. Gorski, R. A., and Barraclough, C. A.: Effects of low dosage of androgen on the differentiation of hypothalamic regulatory control of ovulation in the rat. Endocrinol., 73:210, 1963.

23. Gorski, R. A., and Wagner, J. W.: Gonadal activity and sexual differentiation of the hypothalamus. Endocrinol., 76:226, 1965.

24. Goy, R. W.: Reproductive behavior in mammals. *In* C. W. Lloyd (ed.): Human Reproduction and Sexual Behavior. Philadelphia, Lea & Febiger, 1964, p. 409.

25. Grady, K. L., and Phoenix, G. H.: Hormonal determinants of mating behavior; the display of feminine behavior by adult male rats castrated neonatally. Amer. Zoologist, 3:482, 1963.

26. Greenstein, J. S.: A new diagnostic method of staining vaginal smears and endometrial biopsies for office practice and clinical laboratory. Internat. J. Fertil., 9:493, 1964.

27. Hall, K.: Relaxin: a review. J. Reprod. Fertil., 1:368, 1960.

28. Harris, G. W.: Follicle ripening, ovulation, and estrous behavior. *In* C. W. Lloyd (ed.): Endocrinology of Reproduction. New York, Academic Press, 1959, p. 21.

29. Hisaw, F. L., Jr.: Comparative effectiveness of estrogens on fluid imbibition and growth of the rat's uterus. Endocrinol., *64*:276, 1959.
30. Hoffman, R. A., and Reiter, R. J.: Pineal gland: influence on gonads of male hamsters. Science, *148*:1609, 1965.
31. Hoffmann, J. C., and Schwartz, N. B.: Timing of post-partum ovulation in the rat. Endocrinol., 76:620, 1965.
32. Howe, G. R.: Influence of the uterus upon cyclic ovarian activity in the guinea pig. Endocrinol., 77:412, 1965.
33. Kikuyama, S.: Secretion of luteotrophic hormone by the anterior hypophysis in persistent-estrous and -diestrous rats. J. Fac. Sci., University of Tokyo, *10*: 231, 1963.
33a. Kincl, F. A., and Maqueo, M.: Prevention by progesterone of steroid-induced sterility in neonatal male and female rats. Endocrinol., 77:859, 1965.
34. Kroc, R. L., Steinetz, B. G., and Beach, V. L.: The effects of estrogens, progestogens, and relaxin in pregnant and nonpregnant laboratory rodents. Ann. N. Y. Acad. Sci., 75:942, 1959.
35. Leathem, J. H.: Biochemistry of cystic ovaries. Ciba Found. Colloquia on Endocrinol., *12*:173, 1958.
36. Leathem, J. H., and Adams, W. C.: Prevention of ovarian cyst formation by ethamoxytriphetol (MER-25). Proc. Soc. Exp. Biol. & Med., *113*:240, 1963.
37. Leonard, S. L.: Hormonal effects on phosphorylase activity in the rat uterus. Endocrinol., *63*:853, 1958.
38. Levine, S., and Mullins, R., Jr.: Estrogen administered neonatally affects adult sexual behavior in male and female rats. Science, *144*:185, 1964.
39. Long, J. A., and Evans, H. M.: The estrous cycle of the rat and its associated phenomena. Mem. Univ. California, 6:1, 1922.
40. Nalbandov, A. V.: Comparative physiology and endocrinology of domestic animals. Rec. Progress Hormone Research, *17*:119, 1961.
41. Nalbandov, A. V.: Reproductive Physiology, 2nd ed. San Francisco, W. H. Freeman & Co., 1964.
42. Opel, H.: Oviposition in chickens after removal of the posterior lobe of the pituitary by an improved method. Endocrinol., 76:673, 1965.
43. Opel, H., and Nalbandov, A. V.: Ovulability of ovarian follicles in the hypophysectomized hen. Endocrinol., 69:1029, 1961.
44. Phoenix, C. H.: Hypothalamic regulation of sexual behavior in male guinea pigs. J. Comp. Physiol. Psychol., *54*:72, 1961.
45. Quay, W. B.: Reduction of mammalian pineal weight and lipid during continuous light. Gen. & Comp. Endocrinol., *1*:211, 1961.
46. Quay, W. B.: Circadian rhythm in rat pineal serotonin and its modifications by estrous cycle and photoperiod. Gen. & Comp. Endocrinol., *3*:473, 1963.
47. Quay, W. B., and Halevy, A.: Experimental modification of the rat pineal's content of serotonin and related indole amines. Physiol. Zool., *35*:1, 1962.
48. Robertson, G. L., Hagerman, D. D., Richardson, G. S., and Villee, C. A.: Estradiol stimulation of glycine incorporation by human endometrium in tissue culture. Science, *134*:1986, 1961.
49. Savard, K., and Casey, P. J.: Effects of pituitary hormones and NADPH on acetate utilization in ovarian and adrenocortical tissues. Endocrinol., *74*:599, 1964.
50. Savard, K., Marsh, J. M., and Rice, B. F.: Gonadotropins and ovarian steroidogenesis. Rec. Progress Hormone Research, *21*:285, 1965.
51. Sawyer, C. H.: Nervous control of ovulation. *In* C. W. Lloyd (ed.): Endocrinology of Reproduction. New York, Academic Press, 1959, p. 1.
52. Schane, H. P., and Leonard, S. L.: Rate of glycogenolysis in the estrogen-primed rat uterus *in vitro*. Endocrinol., 76:686, 1965.
53. Szego, C. M.: Pituitary-adrenal cortical antagonism to estrogenic stimulation of the uterus of the ovariectomized rat. Endocrinol., *50*:429, 1952.
54. Szego, C. M.: The influence of the liver upon estrogen-protein binding *in vitro*. Endocrinol., *52*:669, 1953.
55. Szego, C. M., and Lawson, D. A.: Influence of histamine on uterine metabolism: stimulation of incorporation of radioactivity from amino acids into protein, lipid and purines. Endocrinol., *74*:372, 1964.

56. Szego, C. M., and Sloan, S. H.: The influence of histamine and serotonin in promoting early uterine growth in the rat. Gen. & Comp. Endocrinol., *1*:295, 1961.
57. Takewaki, K.: Hormone-independent persistent changes in reproductive organs in female rats induced by early postnatal treatment with androgen. Proc. Japan Acad., *41*:310, 1965.
58. Velardo, J. T.: Induction of ovulation in immature hypophysectomized rats. Science, *131*:357, 1960.
59. Villee, C. A., and Hagerman, D. D.: Hormonal effects on pyridine nucleotide metabolism in human placenta. Gen. & Comp. Endocrinol., *1*:317, 1961.
60. Visscher, M. B., King, J. T., and Lee, Y. C. P.: Further studies on influence of age and diet upon reproductive senescence in strain A female mice. Amer. J. Physiol., *170*:72, 1952.
61. Weisz, J., and Lloyd, C. W.: Estrogen and androgen production *in vitro* from 7-^{3}H-progesterone by normal and polycystic rat ovaries. Endocrinol., *77*:735, 1965.
62. Wislocki, G. B., Weiss, L. P., Burgos, M. H., and Ellis, R. A.: The cytology, histochemistry and electron microscopy of the granular cells of the metrial gland of the gravid rat. J. Anat., *91*:131, 1957.
63. Wragg, L. E.: Effects of pinealectomy in newborn female rats. Anat. Record, *151*: 435, 1965.
64. Wright, P. A.: Induction of ovulation *in vitro* in *Rana pipiens* with steroids. Gen. & Comp. Endocrinol., *1*:20, 1961.
65. Wurtman, R. J., Axelrod, J., Chu, E. W., and Fischer, J. E.: Mediation of some effects of illumination on the rat estrous cycle by the sympathetic nervous system. Endocrinol., *75*:266, 1964.
66. Wurtman, R. J., Axelrod, J., and Fischer, J. E.: Melatonin synthesis in the pineal gland: effect of light mediated by the sympathetic nervous system. Science, *143*:1328, 1964.
67. Wurtman, R. J., Axelrod, J., and Phillips, L. S.: Melatonin synthesis in the pineal gland: control by light. Science, *142*:1071, 1963.
68. Young, W. C., Goy, R. W., and Phoenix, C. H.: Hormones and sexual behavior. Science, *143*:212, 1964.
69. Zarrow, M. X., Neher, G. M., Sikes, D., Brennan, D. M., and Bullard, J. F.: Dilatation of the uterine cervix of the sow following treatment with relaxin. Amer. J. Obst. & Gynec., *72*:260, 1956.
70. Zarrow, M. X., Yochim, J. M., and McCarthy, J. L.: Experimental Endocrinology. New York, Academic Press, 1964, p. 109.

15 _____

THE HORMONES
OF PREGNANCY
AND LACTATION

The hormones that are most directly involved in pregnancy and lactation originate from the pituitary gland, the ovary, the placenta, and probably, in certain species, from the uterine endometrium. Like many other physiologic processes, these events involve a whole train of balanced forces and cannot be accounted for on the basis of hormones acting in isolation. Other endocrine glands, whose products are more directly concerned with systemic metabolism, exert indirect but important influences on pregnancy, parturition, and lactation.

THE EVOLUTION OF VIVIPARITY

With the evolutionary movement of organisms from aqueous to terrestrial habitats, many changes have occurred in the nature of the egg and in the structure and function of the genital system. Although widely separated taxonomic groups have exploited different devices for retaining the developing young on or within the body of a parent, there are suggestions that endocrine mechanisms have played an important role in making these adaptations possible. Evolutionary innovations are difficult to prove, and no unifying concept has emerged that accounts for all the facts. Although many specific exceptions can be found, the following evolutionary trends

513

seem to be apparent: (1) a reduction in the number of eggs produced; (2) a closer association of the sexes and internal fertilization; (3) the addition of reserve food materials to the egg and compression of the larval stages into the embryonic period; (4) retention of embryos within the female tract and parental protection of the young; (5) reduction in size of the egg and the development of a placenta; and (6) endocrine regulation of the mammary glands for early nutrition of the newborn.[3, 31, 37]

The most primitive method of sexual reproduction is that of discharging innumerable gametes into the surrounding water, fertilization occurring without any participation of the parents. Such eggs generally contain little yolk and are largely devoid of protective coverings. A closer association between the sexes became established, and in many fishes and amphibians the spermatozoa are discharged in close proximity to the eggs. In the salamander *Ambystoma punctatum*, the males discharge packets of sperms, which the females insert into their reproductive tracts. Thus fertilization is internal but there is no association of the sexes. With the production of fewer eggs, various kinds of mechanisms have arisen to assure the survival of the embryos. One finds among teleost fishes many kinds of parental care, nest building, and brooding. Male pipefishes and sea horses, for example, have specialized brood pouches on the ventral body wall. In other species, either the males or females take up the fertilized eggs and incubate them in their mouths. In the primitive ovoviviparous condition the eggs contained tremendous quantities of yolk and they were retained within the oviducts to provide greater protection and more uniform environments for development.

In most salamanders and a few reptiles, the zygotes only begin to cleave before leaving the female tract. The eggs of birds are in the early gastrula stage when they leave the oviduct, but reptilian eggs may be retained much longer. Almost all amphibians are oviparous and return to water for breeding, but there are a few exceptions. Adaptive viviparity has been described in a small toad, *Nectophrynoides occidentalis*, which breeds in arid mountainous environments. After a gestation period of nine months the young are born in a fully metamorphosed condition and do not require an aqueous habitat. Parturition is accomplished by inflation of the lung sacs and contraction of thoracic muscles, but delivery cannot occur unless the animal finds suitable mechanical support in the environment.[23]

The oviducts secrete a great variety of materials for the protection and nutrition of the eggs. The aquatic eggs of fishes and amphibians are provided with jelly envelopes, membranes, and shells. In reptiles and birds, the albumenous covering of the egg contains large quantities of water, which are absorbed by the yolk before or after laying. In ovoviviparous selachians, with no intimate apposition of fetal and maternal vascular structures, the secretory products of the uterus provide an important source of nourishment. The viviparous selachians develop circulatory structures as an additional source of nourishment to supplement a reduced supply of yolk in the egg.

Corpora lutea have been identified in the ovaries of a number of vertebrates and they are not invariably associated with viviparity.[17] They have been found in oviparous and ovoviviparous selachians, teleosts, amphibians, and reptiles, as well as in the oviparous monotremes and all higher mammals. They correlate with the retention of eggs in the oviducts in ovipara and with the retention of embryos in the uteri in the vivipara. The luteal structures of certain teleost fishes have been shown to release progesterone-like agents that control the growth of the ovipositor. The ovaries of some ovoviviparous snakes appear to contain progesterone, and similar materials are found in the blood plasma.[7] It is clear that progesterone is not exclusively a mammalian hormone and this is another indication that there have been evolutionary changes in hormone emphasis rather than changes in the types of hormones.

The monotremes (*Ornithorhynchus, Echidna*) are the only mammals that lay eggs. The eggs are relatively small but contain enough nutriment to support development up to an advanced stage, though not to the level of self-sufficiency. In all other mammals, methods of uterine feeding have been perfected and the size of the egg is radically reduced. Mammalian eggs are typically fertilized in the oviducts and undergo early development while retained there. The cleaving eggs of many species are coated with albumenous secretions from the oviducts, but the nutritional requirements are met largely by the limited stores contained within the developing egg. During oviducal development, lasting from 4 to 10 days, the bulk of the embryo shrinks rapidly, indicating that there has not been any appreciable absorption of materials from the fluids of the oviduct. The embryotroph elaborated by the uterine glands is of great importance in many species for nourishment of the blastocyst before the placenta has been established. It is probable that in the Artiodactyla and Perissodactyla the uterine secretions are an important source of nourishment for the embryo and fetus, from the beginning to the end of pregnancy. In cases of delayed implantation, the uterine secretions apparently maintain the blastocysts for weeks or months.

The first step toward viviparity in mammals has been the retention of embryos within the uterus, nothing more than a primitive yolk-sac placenta being established. The gestation period of the opossum (*Didelphis virginiana*) is only 12 or 13 days, the young being born as soon as the metamorphic changes have been completed. The luteal phase of the estrous cycle is prolonged and parturition correlates with the involution of the corpora lutea. Pregnancy may be terminated at any stage by removal of the ovaries, which suggests that in this species pregnancy does not involve any hormones other than those that regulate the estrous cycle. Extraovarian mechanisms operate in higher mammals and produce hormones that make it possible for embryos to be retained in the uterus for periods longer than the limits of the estrous cycle.[2, 30]

HORMONES IN PREGNANCY AND PARTURITION

The Hypophysis

We have seen that the anterior pituitary gonadotrophins are essential for the periodic release of eggs from the ovary and for the secretion of ovarian hormones that build up the type of uterus most suitable for the reception of the blastocysts. After the animal has become pregnant, the effects of hypophysectomy vary with the species and in accordance with the stage of gestation at which the operation is performed. In the rabbit, cat, and dog, hypophysectomy produces abortion no matter at what stage of pregnancy it is performed. In other species, such as the mouse, rat, guinea pig, and monkey, hypophysectomy at approximately midterm or later may not interrupt gestation or interfere appreciably with delivery. Lactation fails to occur or is of short duration. The gestation period of the dogfish *Mustelus canis* is 10 months, and hypophysectomy during the first 5 months does not interfere with embryonic development, the absorption of yolk, or the establishment of the yolk-sac placenta. The pituitary gland is necessary for the maintenance of normal gestation in viviparous snakes.

Rats may be hypophysectomized at midpregnancy and carried to term by the administration of estrogen and progesterone. Since the ovaries of the rat are indispensable throughout the course of pregnancy, it appears that the maintenance of pregnancy after hypophysectomy depends upon the continued function of the corpora lutea brought about by a luteotrophic principle (prolactin), which must be of extrahypophysial origin. The corpora lutea appear to be the main source of progesterone in the rat. Extracts possessing luteotrophic action have been prepared from the rat's placenta. There is circumstantial evidence indicating that in certain mammalian species the placenta functions as an adjunct to the anterior hypophysis and takes over the production of gonadotrophins, which are necessary for the maintenance of gestation.[22, 29, 48]

Studies suggest that maintenance of the corpora lutea of the pregnant rabbit is a function of estrogenic hormones rather than a direct consequence of gonadotrophin action. The corpora lutea of hypophysectomized rabbits may be maintained either by the administration of estrogens or gonadotrophins.[26] It may be that in this species the gonadotrophins do not act directly on the corpora lutea to cause the continued release of progesterone, but prolong luteal secretion by encouraging the production of estrogens. It is probable that the gonadal hormones *per se* have more important direct actions on the gonads than is commonly supposed. It is well known that estrogens have considerable ability to promote growth of the ovarian follicles of hypophysectomized rats. There are apparently many species variations in the relative importance of estrogens and pituitary gonadotrophins in maintaining luteal function.

The Ovary

Full differentiation of the endometrium requires both estrogen and progesterone, and removal of the ovaries while the developing zygotes are in the tubes invariably prevents implantation of the blastocysts and placentation.[9] If pregnant females are ovariectomized while the blastocysts are floating free in the uterine lumen, the blastocysts generally die. However, if the armadillo is bilaterally ovariectomized at about the middle of the four-month period of delayed implantation, implantation occurs about 30 days later and is indistinguishable from normal implantation.[8] Hence, in this species some non-ovarian tissue can assume the function of maintaining the uterus. As with the pituitary gland, the ovary is more essential for the maintenance of pregnancy in some species than in others. The ovaries are indispensable at practically all stages for the maintenance of pregnancy in the opossum, mouse, rat, rabbit, golden hamster, 13-lined ground squirrel, goat, and viviparous snakes. In women, monkeys, and mares ovariectomy during the early months of pregnancy usually does not cause abortion. In the guinea pig, cat, dog, and ewe, the ovaries may be dispensed with during the second half of gestation. The ovaries are not essential during the terminal stages of pregnancy in cows and pigs. Failure of implantation or abortion in castrate animals may be prevented by the administration of progesterone. There is ample evidence that the placenta performs endocrine functions during pregnancy, being capable of secreting both gonadotrophins and steroids of the ovarian type in certain species.[19]

In a variety of mammals the quantity of estrogen excreted through the kidneys is increased strikingly during pregnancy. The total estrogen in the urine of pregnant women increases gradually after the first week, reaches a peak shortly before parturition and drops abruptly a few days after the birth of young (Fig. 15–1). The increased quantities of estrogen in the urine are not the result of a diminished renal threshold, because after the second month of pregnancy such compounds are present in the blood in greater amounts than at any other time. Nonpregnant women excrete about

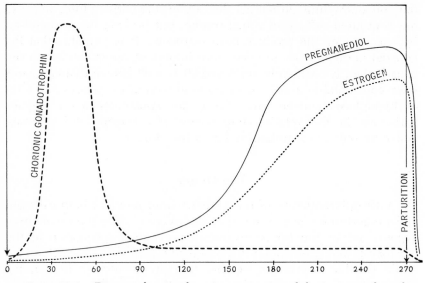

Figure 15–1.   Diagram showing the urinary excretion of chorionic gonadotrophin, total estrogen, and pregnanediol during human pregnancy.

300 M.U. (mouse units) of estrogen per day, whereas during pregnancy the level rises to 20,000 M.U. per day. It is noteworthy that over 99 per cent of the urinary estrogen is in the form of estriol glucuronide and that such conjugated estrogens have little physiologic potency. The total amount of conjugated estrogen begins to fall shortly before parturition, whereas the amount of unconjugated, physiologically active estrogen undergoes a relative increase at this time. This would seem to suggest that estrogen performs some role during parturition that it does not exercise during the preceding months of pregnancy.

The nonpregnant mare excretes around 2,000 M.U. of estrogen daily, but during pregnancy it exceeds one million mouse units per day. Estradiol and estrone are found during the estrous cycle of the mare, but during pregnancy at least three additional steroids appear— equilin, equilenin, and dehydroequilenin, the first two being the most abundant. The abundance of estriol in pregnant women and of equilin and equilenin in pregnant mares supports the concept that these are estrogens of pregnancy and that they probably perform some role peculiar to gestation. Bilateral ovariectomy of pregnant women, monkeys, and mares does not abolish the high excretion of estrogens. The excretion rate of estrogens in pregnant monkeys is not altered by removing the ovaries and fetus, but it falls to nonpregnant levels after removal of the placenta. The development and regression of the fetal gonads of the horse correlate with the rise and fall of the maternal estrogens (Fig. 15–2).

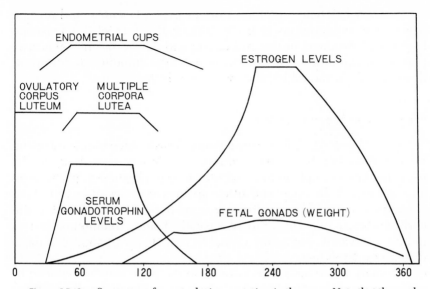

Figure 15–2. Sequence of events during gestation in the mare. Note that the ovulatory corpus luteum wanes and accessory corpora lutea are formed when the serum gonadotrophin levels rise. Urinary estrogens reach a high peak at about 220 days and fall before parturition (After Amoroso, E. C.: Brit. Med. Bull., *11*, 1955.)

Small amounts of progesterone are thought to be secreted by the preovulatory follicle and the titers rise markedly during the course of pregnancy. Pregnanediol excretion in pregnant women rises progressively after the second or third month and falls precipitously after loss of the placenta (Fig. 15–1). The indications are that the corpus luteum of the human ovary produces progesterone during early pregnancy, whereas an additional supply is secreted by the placenta after the second month. The source of the progesterone during pregnancy apparently varies with the species. Since ovariectomy of the ewe around midgestation neither causes abortion nor prevents the rise of blood progesterone, it is clear that the placenta is the major source of the hormone. On the other hand, if the ovaries of the pregnant rabbit are removed seven days before expected delivery, the levels of blood progesterone fall very promptly and this is followed by abortion. The ovaries of the rabbit seem to be the main, if not the exclusive, source of progesterone.

Progesterone disappears very rapidly from the blood stream, and its excretory metabolites seem to vary with the species. Sodium pregnanediol glucuronidate is the chief urinary catabolic product in the human subject. The feces of pregnant cows contain large amounts of androgen, but very insignificant amounts are found in the feces of bulls and nonpregnant animals. It is probable that the placental progesterone of the pregnant cow is converted to androgen and excreted through the feces.

Relaxin has been obtained from ovaries, placentae, and uterine tissue. The ovary seems to be the principal source of this hormone in the sow, whereas in the guinea pig and mouse the placenta may play an important role in its formation. Under suitable conditions all three tissues in the rabbit may produce relaxin.

Pregnancy in Prepuberal Mice

It has been possible to cause young female mice to rear offspring by administering appropriate hormones to induce receptivity to the male, ovulation, implantation, maintenance of pregnancy, parturition, and lactation.[49] In mice and other species it is possible to induce ovulations and to obtain offspring from them by transplanting the early embryos into the uteri of sexually mature recipients, but to induce a sexually immature animal to rear its own young is a more difficult undertaking.

Ovulation and sexual receptivity to the male may be induced in young mice by administering appropriate gonadotrophins. Blastocysts are produced regularly by this procedure, but implantation does not ensue because of improper functioning of the corpora lutea and the consequent absence of a progestational uterus. Viable blastocysts may float free in the uteri for as long as 22 days post coitum without implanting. This shows that blastocysts may survive for relatively long periods in a nonprogestational uterus. In both intact and ovariectomized mice, the blastocysts may be caused to implant by giving small daily injections of progesterone. Larger doses of progesterone are necessary to continue pregnancy.

Progesterone, in the absence of either exogenous or ovarian estrogen, carries pregnancy to completion in mice. The mammary glands of females carrying fetuses to term have developed lobuloalveolar systems that contain secretory products. On the other hand, the mammary glands remain poorly developed in females receiving progesterone treatments in the absence of fetuses and placentae. These facts indicate that endogenous estrogen is being supplied from some source, most likely from the placentae or fetuses.

Parturition in these animals is effected by the administration of relaxin. Although progesterone maintains pregnancy and permits development of the mammary glands, relaxin is required to lengthen the interpubic ligaments and to promote uterine contractility. The pubic symphyses of females not carrying full-term young failed to respond fully to relaxin. This suggests that either the fetuses or the placentae add enough estrogen to act synergistically with relaxin in promoting relaxation of the pubic ligaments. It may be that in these mice relaxin initiates the release of oxytocin from the neurohypophysis and thus encourages uterine motility, progesterone failing to have this effect. Lactation occurs after delivery even in the castrated mothers as a consequence of progesterone and relaxin treatments.

Thus, it is possible through hormone manipulations to induce in young, sexually immature mice all of the events of gestation, parturition, and lactation.

Gonadotrophins Peculiar to Pregnancy

The placenta and, in certain species, the endometrium produce gonad-stimulating hormones that are similar in some respects to those produced by the anterior hypophysis but that differ from the latter both physiologically and chemically. The pregnancy gonadotrophins are present in a variety of mammals but are strikingly different in their physiologic properties.[1, 11, 42]

Chorionic Gonadotrophin

This hormone is a glycoprotein and is characteristic of pregnancy in primates, although hormones similar in activity may be present in lower mammals. It is secreted by the chorionic villi of the placenta and appears in the blood and urine during early pregnancy. Human chorionic gonadotrophin (HCG) appears in the urine shortly after implantation and reaches a high peak about one month after the first missed menstrual period (Fig. 15–1). At this time, around 100,000 R.U. (rat units) may be excreted daily. After this peak the blood and urinary titers of the hormone drop to low levels, which remain fairly constant until a few days after parturition. In the chimpanzee and monkey, chorionic gonadotrophin is produced for a brief period during early pregnancy and disappears thereafter.

HCG resembles luteinizing hormone (LH) from the anterior hypophysis in most of its actions, and in addition it seems to have the properties of a luteotrophin inasmuch as it prolongs the functional status of the corpus luteum. It converts the corpus luteum of the menstrual cycle into the corpus luteum of pregnancy, thereby prolonging the luteal production of hormones until the placenta becomes capable of secreting the high amounts of gonadal steroids required for the continuation of pregnancy. Although HCG has some ability to cause follicle stimulation in hypophysectomized rodents, its main action in the female is on the corpus luteum. Studies have shown that HCG undergoes certain qualitative changes from early to late pregnancy.[34]

Although HCG is found normally only in pregnant women, it produces a great variety of gonadal actions in many other vertebrates. When given to the human male it causes the differentiation of Leydig cells and induces and maintains the production of testicular androgens. When administered to intact animals it produces follicular growth and ovulation, probably by acting synergistically with the circulating endogenous gonadotrophins of pituitary origin.[54] It causes a release of spermatozoa when given to lower vertebrates such as amphibians. Thus HCG may act directly in hypophysectomized animals or indirectly in the presence of pituitary gonadotrophins of intact subjects and affect the follicles and corpora lutea of the ovaries and the cells of Leydig or seminiferous tubules of the testis.

Chorionic gonadotrophin may be found in certain pathologic states associated with pregnancy and in others that have no connection with pregnancy. In such conditions as hydatidiform mole and chorioepithelioma of the female, high titers of HCG may be produced. Some neoplastic diseases of the testis may likewise result in the secretion of this substance.

PREGNANCY TESTS. Since chorionic gonadotrophin is secreted by placental tissue, its presence in the blood or urine forms the basis of many tests for pregnancy. The Aschheim-Zondek test depends on the capacity of pregnancy urine to induce corpora lutea or "blood points" in the ovaries of mice and rats within 96 hours after treatment. The production of vaginal estrus in the immature rat, 72 to 96 hours after injecting the sample of urine, is a sensitive pregnancy test. In the Friedman test, pregnancy urine causes the formation of corpora lutea within 24 hours after being injected into immature or isolated mature rabbits. The amphibian tests are quicker and perhaps more reliable than those done on mammals. Female frogs and toads ovulate within six to eight hours after pregnancy urine has been injected into the dorsal lymph sacs. The Galli-Mainini test depends on the prompt evacuation of sperms from the testes of frogs. If the injected urine contains HCG, sperms can be identified in the cloacal fluid within three hours after the injection. The African frog (*Xenopus laevis*) is about ten times more sensitive to pregnancy urine than the female rat.

A number of immunologic pregnancy tests are now in common use. Most of these are based on the agglutination-inhibition reaction utilizing either erythrocytes or latex particles sensitized with HCG. These methods are accurate and can be completed within an hour or less.[51, 55]

Equine Gonadotrophin

The blood serum of pregnant mares contains a gonadotrophin (PMS) that is apparently constant in composition and is a sugar-containing protein. Its biologic properties are similar to a mixture of pituitary FSH and LH, the predominant effect depending upon dosage. PMS is, however, quite different from human chorionic gonadotrophin and from the hypophysial gonadotrophins. All attempts to split the PMS complex into FSH and LH components have failed so far.[44] Unlike HCG and pituitary FSH and LH, PMS remains in the blood and lymph and is practically absent from the urine. Even when PMS is injected into other animals it remains in the blood for long periods, not being so rapidly metabolized as the other gonadotrophins. If small doses of PMS are given subcutaneously to hypophysectomized rats, growth of the ovarian follicles ensues. When the subcutaneous injection is followed by intravenous injections, ovulation or luteinization occurs. Since the hormone has high FSH activity, cystic follicles are often produced, especially if large doses are given repeatedly.

PMS appears in the blood of the mare on about the fortieth day of pregnancy and remains high until about day 120; then it drops and is absent after day 180 (Fig. 15-2). The corpus luteum of ovulation has begun to wane by the time that PMS appears in the blood. Under the influence of PMS the mare's ovaries form large vesicular follicles. Some of these follicles ovulate and form corpora lutea, whereas others undergo luteinization without ovulating. In this manner a crop of accessory corpora lutea is normally formed during pregnancy. The accessory corpora persist until about the 180th day of gestation, and from this time until the end of pregnancy the ovaries contain neither corpora lutea nor large follicles. It is apparent that the ovaries of the mare do not provide a source of progesterone throughout the whole course of gestation. The placenta apparently secretes both estrogen and progesterone during the second half of pregnancy. It appears significant that the formation and persistence of the accessory corpora lutea coincide with the period of high levels of PMS in the blood. The ovaries of the nilgai and African elephant also contain accessory corpora lutea during pregnancy.[43] The gestation period of the elephant is about two years, and accessory corpora are found only between the sixth and ninth months. It is inferred that these animals produce a pregnancy gonadotrophin similar to that of the mare, but it remains to be determined.

The gonads of equine fetuses also respond to the circulating hormones of the mother (Fig. 15-2). Under the influence of serum gonadotrophin and estrogen, the fetal ovaries become larger than those of the mother. The fetal testes also are larger than the testes of newborn males.

Whereas human chorionic gonadotrophin is produced by the placenta, specifically by the Langhans cells of the fetal chorion, equine gonadotrophin appears to be formed in the endometrial cups (Fig. 15-3) and hence is uterine in origin.[10] The following evidence indicates that the endometrial cups produce PMS: (a) the hormone can be extracted from the cup areas but not from other parts of the endometrium; (b) the hormone appears in the blood coincident with the development of endometrial cups; and (c) when the endometrial cups first appear, they contain higher concentrations of PMS than are present in the blood.

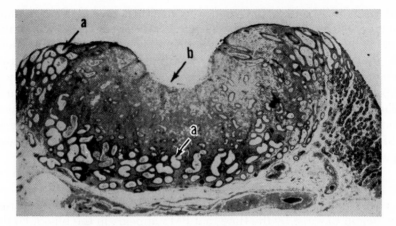

Figure 15–3. Section through an endometrial cup of a pregnant mare. Note the dilated uterine glands *(a)*. The coagulum has been removed from the central region of the cup *(b)*. (From Amoroso, E. C.: Ann. New York Acad. Sci., 75, 1959.)

Mechanisms of Uterine Accommodation

During gestation a new individual develops inside a hollow, muscular organ, the uterus, and it is apparent that the latter must undergo profound modifications in order to accommodate and support the products of conception (Fig. 15–4). Provision must be made for the nutritional, respiratory, and excretory requirements of the retained embryo. As pregnancy progresses there must be gradual enlargement of the uterus to permit growth of the fetus, but at the same time its muscular walls must remain quiescent enough to prevent premature expulsion. At parturition the myometrium must be activated in order to deliver the new individual to the exterior, and in mammals the mammary glands must be called into action for the postpartum nutrition of the young.[46]

The uterus passes through three stages in its adjustments to the products of conception: uterine preparation, growth, and stretching. During the period of *preparation*, before the blastocysts implant, estrogen augments the blood supply to the uterus and causes some increase in the number of cells. With the release of increasing amounts of progesterone there is a decided wave of hyperplasia involving all tissues — particularly the smooth muscle cells. Thus, by the time of implantation the number of cells has increased tremendously. Since the resulting cells are smaller than those from which they arose by mitosis, the marked hyperplasia produces no significant increase in the size and weight of the uterus. The period of uterine *growth* begins immediately after implantation. As the products of conception enlarge sufficiently to constitute an effective physical stimulus, the uterus adapts itself through hypertrophy of the cells

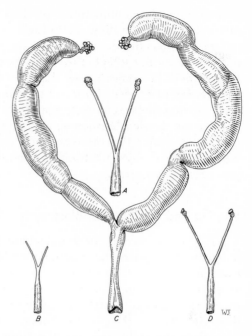

Figure 15–4. Female genitalia of the rat, showing size changes during different natural and experimental conditions. *A*, Tract removed from a normal, adult, virginal animal during diestrus. *B*, Tract from an animal which had been oöphorectomized at thirty days of age and autopsied six months later. *C*, Tract removed on the nineteenth day of normal pregnancy. Observe the large corpora lutea of the ovaries and the marked distention of the uteri produced by the products of conception. Compare with *A*. *D*, Tract from an animal which had been hypophysectomized for six months. (All the tracts were dissected out *in toto* and drawn to scale.)

already present. The tremendous degree of hypertrophy occurring in the smooth muscle cells is sufficient to account for most of the increase in uterine size during middle and late pregnancy. During the period of uterine *stretching*, the products of conception grow at an accelerating rate, whereas uterine growth diminishes. The period of uterine stretching lasts for only a day and a half in the hamster, but it continues for better than three weeks in the guinea pig.

Distention of the uterine lumen is recognized as an important factor conditioning enlargement of this organ. Clinicians have been aware for many years that in advanced ectopic pregnancy the empty uterus remains much smaller than in normal intrauterine pregnancies. Implantations often occur unilaterally in laboratory rodents having a duplex type of uterus, the equivalent uterus remaining empty or sterile. This condition may be produced experimentally by ligating or sectioning the oviduct on one side. In all these instances it has been obvious that the sterile uterus does not enlarge to the same degree as the gravid uterus, even though both are exposed to the same circulating hormones. Moreover, it has not been possible through the administration of hormones to modify the size and structure of a nongravid uterus until it is comparable with a gravid one. These observations, as well as many others, indicate that the tension produced by the growing products of conception constitutes a stimulus that enables the uterus to become structurally adapted to its contents. Tension produced by introducing paraffin pellets or rolled rubber dam into the lumen of the uterus exerts a growth-promoting action comparable to that resulting naturally from the products of conception. Pathologic and surgical conditions that enforce the accumulation of uterine secretions within the lumen produce a similar effect. From the foregoing statements one would be justified in conjecturing that the mature uterus is capable of undergoing two types of normal growth: (1) that which occurs periodically during the sexual cycle mainly as a result of chemical stimulation by the ovarian hormones, and (2) that which takes place during pregnancy under the influence of a complex of hormones together with the added physical stimulus of tension produced by the growing products of conception.

Spacing and Migration of Blastocysts

Little is known about the mechanisms that operate in polytocous mammals to regulate the spacing of embryos in the uterus.[5] In species such as the rabbit, the transplantation sites are approximately the same distance apart. Moreover, in mammals having bicornate uteri, the blastocysts may shift from one horn to the other in order to balance the two sides. In the pig, for example, the left ovary produces more eggs than the right one, but the right and left horns of the uterus accommodate approximately the same number of fetuses. In monotocous species, the fetus may be found in the uterine horn opposite to the ovary that gave rise to the egg.

The spacing and implantation of blastocysts have been carefully studied in the rabbit.[6] The three principal mechanisms are muscle activity, adhesion, and invasion. From three to five days post coitum the blastocysts are moved along the uterus in a random manner and increase rapidly in diameter after this period. It is thought that progesterone conditions the uterus so that muscular contractions arise from both ends and wherever it happens to be stimulated by a blastocyst that has attained a certain size. The contractions emanating from each blastocyst spread in both directions but they lose propulsive strength with increasing distance from the source. In this manner each blastocyst may repel others above or below it, but remain unaffected by the contractions it has produced. Since the repulsions are mutual and become weaker with distance, the blastocysts become separated from each other by about the same distances. At seven days post coitum the blastocysts have become so enlarged that they cannot be moved up or down the uterus. The antimesometrial muscle over each blastocyst loses tone and forms a pocket in which the blastocyst is held. The adjacent circular muscle behaves as an incomplete sphincter and holds the blastocyst in the pocket. The adhesion of the rabbit's blastocyst to the uterus is probably alkali induced. The trophoblast penetrates the uterine lining by both displacement and destruction of cells. Adhesion and invasion occur where the epithelium has an underlying capillary and may result from local elevations of pH attendant upon the transfer of carbon dioxide or similar materials to the maternal circulation.

When a silk suture is placed in the antimesometrial wall of one horn of the rat's uterus before mating, blastocysts do not implant in the sutured horn, though they do implant normally in the unsutured horn. Insertion of the suture before estrus does not induce deciduoma, nor does it interfere with fertilization and tubal transport of the ova. The foreign body may produce an unfavorable intrauterine environment which causes death of the blastocysts, or, by interfering with tone and motility of the uterus, it may allow the blastocysts to escape into the vagina before they have had a chance to implant.[20]

Parturition

The mechanisms involved in the onset of labor are very complex and remain poorly understood. It is certain that we cannot think of parturition as being triggered by any single substance but must regard it as the consequence of many synchronized events that have occurred during the course of gestation. The uterus is relatively quiescent during gestation, but as labor approaches there are signs of increasing myometrial irritability and the development of more efficient patterns of contraction. During the end of gestation actomyosin, the contractile protein of muscle, increases in quantity and improves in quality, and this facilitates the forceful muscle contractions that are required to expel the fetus. There is increased sensitivity of the uterine muscles to hormones and various kinds of mechanical stimuli.

When the fetuses are surgically removed, the placentae and extraembryonic membranes being left *in situ,* gestation continues for the characteristic period. The placentae and empty membranes are carried to term and delivered at the normal time. This shows that hormones or toxic materials released by the fetus do not give the signal for parturition. The length of the gestation period is genetically determined, although it can be modified by many internal or external environmental factors. In certain genetic strains of cattle, the fetus continues to grow *in utero* during a greatly prolonged gestation. The fetuses become so large that normal delivery is impossible, and they must be removed by caesarean section. On the other hand, some strains may carry abnormally small fetuses for prolonged periods. These considerations indicate that fetal size itself does not determine when labor will begin.

The hormones generated from the placenta and ovaries are known to play key roles in determining the onset of labor. In most mammalian species progesterone exerts a pregnancy-stabilizing effect, and labor cannot occur until its influence is effectively diminished. In some species progesterone is produced by the ovary throughout pregnancy but, in others, it arises from both the ovary and placenta. Estrogens promote rhythmic contractility of the uterus. It is probably significant that estrogen increases in amount and effective form as the end of gestation draws near. Oxytocin from the neurohypophysis is also known to have a powerful effect on uterine contractility, and there is circumstantial evidence that it may be involved in the labor mechanism. The fact that totally hypophysectomized animals may deliver young normally does not necessarily prove that oxytocin is not involved in the process; the hypothalamic nuclei that form the hormone may add effective amounts of it to the circulation in the absence of the posterior pituitary. If oxytocin is involved, there is the problem of how it is released at exactly the right time. Relaxin is definitely a hormone of pregnancy and is known to be secreted by the placenta as well as by the ovary.

Without the proper hormonal balance and timing, labor would be abnormal and injure the fetus and mother. For example, it is well known that labor may be precipitated by the administration of large doses of oxytocin. However, if the cervical canal has not been softened and the pubic ligaments relaxed by the action of relaxin and other hormones, the violent uterine contractions would probably kill the fetus and rupture the uterus instead of expelling it through the vagina. Whatever the exact mechanism of labor may be, it is certain that all of the events are nicely synchronized and that no single factor can account for the process.[15] The hormones and other factors that tend to stabilize pregnancy are gradually overcome by forces that act in an opposite direction and tend to end it.

The Theory of Progesterone Blockage[16]

Estrogens encourage the muscles of the uterus to contract, whereas progestogens inhibit uterine contractions and thus prevent premature expulsion of the fetus. As long as progesterone is dominant in the uterus, the myometrium is "blocked" and cannot deliver the fetus. Since progesterone does not affect the actomyosin content of muscle, it must act at a higher level of organization. Progesterone has been found to reduce the excitability of uterine muscle, and no excitation wave spreads from the point of stimulation. Many types of experiments prove that the myometrium is unable to respond effectively to stimulants as long as it is under the influence of progesterone. The concept has been advanced that it is the *progesterone block* that maintains pregnancy, and withdrawal of the block is responsible for the onset of parturition.

Some insight into the mechanism of labor has been gained by studying a rare anomaly of human pregnancy. On very rare occasions a septum divides the human uterus into two horns, and twins, having separate placentae, may develop in the separate chambers. The fetus in one horn of the uterus may be born prematurely, whereas the other may not be born until as much as two months later. Seemingly the onset of labor centers around some local effect of the placenta in these cases. It has been proposed that the placenta discharges its progesterone directly into the uterine tissues rather than into the general circulation. If this is true, the highest levels of progesterone would be found at the implantation site, with a diminishing concentration gradient extending into the myometrium from this area. This would explain why little or no progesterone from the placenta of one twin reaches the myometrium of the opposite horn. If placental progesterone is carried by the blood stream, the failure of one placenta should not cause delivery, since the producing placenta would provide enough progesterone to block myometrial contractions in both horns of the uterus. Experiments on laboratory animals indicate that the concentration of progesterone in the uterus during late pregnancy declines with distance from the placenta.

The postion of the placenta in the uterus appears to be a very important matter (Fig. 15–5). If the placenta is attached at or below the midline of the uterus one would expect, according to the progesterone block concept, that the fundus would recover first from progesterone inhibition after the placenta ceases producing this

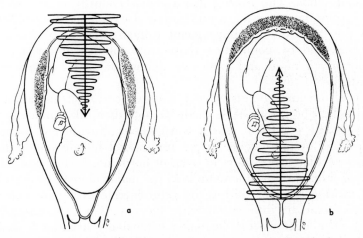

Figure 15–5. Hypothetical illustration of a progesterone gradient in the parturient myometrium determined by the position of the placenta. The normally located placenta (*a*) releases progesterone well down in the uterus. At parturition the corpus of the uterus recovers first from the progesterone block, and uterine contractions push the fetus toward the vagina. When the placental progesterone is concentrated in the upper end of the uterus (*b*), the lower end of the uterus recovers first from the progesterone block and uterine contractions push the fetus in the wrong direction. (From Csapo, A.: Ann. New York Acad. Sci., 75, 1959.)

hormone. Thus myometrial contractions would start at the superior end of the uterus and push the fetus through the cervix. If, on the other hand, the placental attachment is at the upper end of the uterus, the activity gradient would start from the cervical end of the uterus and push the fetus in the wrong direction. These theoretical assumptions strongly imply that a local factor, presumably the progesterone block, performs a decisive role in delivery, but they do not rule out the possibility that substances other than progesterone may be important in conditioning myometrial activity.

THE MAMMARY GLAND AND LACTATION

Anatomy

The mammary glands are regarded as homologous with sweat glands, since they originate as integumentary ingrowths. The manner of embryonic origin is the same in both sexes. Each mammary gland of the human female is composed of 16 to 25 lobes that radiate from the nipple. Each lobe of the gland is drained by a lactiferous duct that extends toward the areola, the pigmented area around the nipple. At this level each lactiferous duct dilates into a sinus, again constricts, and opens at the tip of the nipple. The lactiferous ducts branch repeatedly, producing an extensive arborization within the mammary lobe. The resting gland consists mostly of an extensive duct system; however, a few end buds and alveoli may be proliferated from the ducts in the nonpregnant woman (Fig. 15–6). Each lobe is subdivided by connective tissue into lobules of various sizes. At puberty a rapid and extensive deposition of fat occurs in the breasts.

The immature glands consist of a few short ducts radiating from the nipple. The glands of the male do not differentiate much beyond this infantile condition, but a conspicuous growth and branching of the duct system occurs in the prepuberal female under the influence of increasing titers of ovarian hormone. In the postpuberal virginal female slight fluctuations in the mammae may be correlated with ovarian changes during the reproductive cycle. An extensive and characteristic differentiation of the glands occurs during pregnancy. The duct system becomes extensively arborized, and the terminal twigs end in secretory alveoli. The alveolar lining constitutes a secretory surface from which milk arises. At parturition the secretion of milk is intensified, and the gland gradually involutes until lactation ceases.[4, 32, 33]

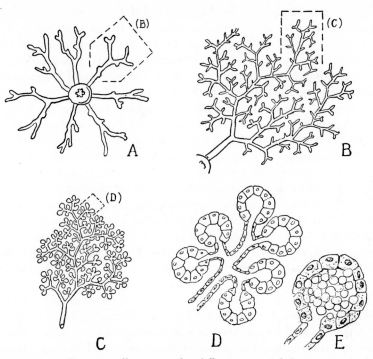

Figure 15–6. Diagrams illustrating the differentiation of the mammary glands. *A*, The gland of prepuberal animals consists of relatively simple ducts radiating from the nipple. *B*, Small segment of *A* enlarged to show the condition of the adult, virginal gland. Under the influence of estrogens the duct system becomes extensively branched. *C*, Small area of *B* enlarged again to show the condition of the gland during pregnancy. Note the great development of terminal alveoli. *D*, Diagram illustrating the cell structure of a few terminal alveoli. *E*, The accumulation of milk globules within an alveolus. (From George W. Corner, 1942.)

Development of the Mammary Glands (Mammogenesis)

Complete functioning of the mammary glands, like pregnancy and parturition, is an exceedingly complex phenomenon involving the interplay of many hormones as well as nervous factors. It is another example of hormones working in concert rather than in isolation. Mammary gland physiology logically falls into two categories; development of the glands to a functional state, and the formation and evacuation of milk.

Early studies involving the administration of ovarian hormones to intact or ovariectomized animals pointed to the conclusion that estrogen is particularly concerned with growth of the duct system and that progesterone, acting in concert with estrogen, is required for full alveolar growth. In species such as the mouse, rat, and monkey, large doses of progesterone, without estrogen priming, have been shown to evoke the development of both the duct and alveolar systems. There are many species variations in the manner in which the mammary rudiment responds to the ovarian steroids. Without discussing the many species differences, it is sufficient to state that there is general agreement that estrogen and progesterone function synergistically and both are needed for the experimental production of glands structurally comparable to those of midpregnancy. Since the anterior pituitary gonadotrophins (*viz.*, FSH, LH, and prolactin) are essential for the production of ovarian hormones during pregnancy, it is obvious that they are indirectly involved in mammary growth. In addition to pituitary effects mediated by the ovary, it has been shown that prolactin and somatotrophin (STH) can act directly on mammary tissue and that ACTH and TSH can influence mammary functions through their respective target organs.[24, 25, 38, 40, 53]

The action of pituitary hormones on the mammary glands has remained a live field of experimentation since Stricker and Grueter (1928) demonstrated that crude extracts of the anterior hypophysis have lactogenic effects.[50] It was soon found that estrogen, alone or in combination with progesterone, fails to induce mammary development in hypophysectomized animals. This finding led to the proposal that estrogen and progesterone acted indirectly on the mammary glands by stimulating the pituitary to secrete specific mammogenic hormones in addition to its six well-authenticated protein hormones. Originally it was suggested that one pituitary "mammogen" stimulated duct growth and the other alveolar growth. The mammogen hypothesis has undergone considerable modification at the hands of its originators, but it must remain highly questionable, since it has not been possible to separate these special substances from pituitary tissue in any state approaching chemical purity. Most workers in the field feel that pituitary-mammary relationships can be accounted for on the basis of the established anterior lobe hormones and that it is not necessary to postulate the existence of other hypophysial factors. With the availability of highly purified anterior pituitary hormones, many aspects of the problem are beginning to be clarified.[18, 35, 52]

Studies on the rat have been systematically pursued by a number of investigators, and, while the results may not be directly applicable to all species, the differences are likely to be in the relative importance of the various hormones rather than in the kinds of hormones required. It appears probable that at least five of the anterior lobe hormones, in addition to ovarian steroids, are involved in the production of a fully developed mammary gland such as is found during late pregnancy. Some of the most pertinent facts may be summarized as follows:

1. When estrogen is administered to castrated male or female rats, it produces mainly growth of the duct system. If larger doses

are given for prolonged periods, some alveolar development may appear. Physiologic doses of estrogen plus progesterone produce full mammary growth (pregnancy type) when administered to castrates. Estrogen alone, given to intact females, produces both ductal and lobuloalveolar development. In the latter instance, it is probable that estrogen encourages the hypophysial release of prolactin and this hormone stimulates the secretion of progesterone by the corpora lutea.

2. In hypophysectomized rats estrogens and progestogens, alone or in combination, fail to induce mammary development. FSH and LH, administered to hypophysectomized subjects, do not stimulate the mammary glands. This indicates that mammary development requires hormones in addition to FSH, LH, estrogens, and progesterone.

3. In immature rats, lacking both pituitaries and gonads, a combination of estrogen and somatotrophin (STH) is necessary to produce growth of the arborescent system of milk ducts. If the adrenal glands, in addition to the pituitaries and ovaries, are removed, ductal growth requires estrogen plus STH plus adrenal corticoids.

4. In order to obtain full lobuloalveolar growth, comparable to that of late pregnancy, prolactin and progesterone are needed in addition to estrogen, STH, and adrenal corticoids. In the presence of the adrenal glands, ACTH may be used instead of the corticoids. Thus, a quintet of hormones is needed to build up the gland to the prolactational stage.

5. Milk secretion (lactogenesis) may be induced in the prolactational gland by withdrawing or diminishing the estrogen and progesterone and continuing the prolactin and adrenal corticoids (or ACTH). Although STH and TSH are not necessary for lactogenesis in the rat, both hormones probably contribute to the normalcy of the process in the intact animal.

Many types of experiments, particularly those involving hypophysectomized animals, suggest that the placenta performs an important role in mammary development during the second half of pregnancy. Ablation of the pituitary gland at midpregnancy does not prevent full mammary growth in the rat and certain other species. There is a tendency to think of milk secretion as beginning at or shortly after parturition but, on the contrary, the transformation from a prolactational to a lactational gland in the rat is very gradual, and there is considerable evidence of secretion during the second half of pregnancy. There is ample evidence that the placenta secretes estrogen, progesterone, and a potent prolactin-like hormone. The latter hormone, like its pituitary counterpart, affects two target organs during pregnancy, namely, the corpora lutea of the ovaries and the mammary glands. It may be supposed that these two targets compete for the prolactin present in the system; but, as the corpora lutea wane during the end of pregnancy, the mammary apparatus gains priority. This ascendancy is retained by the mammary glands after parturition, even though a new crop of corpora lutea is formed as a result of the postpartum estrus.

Milk Secretion (Lactogenesis)

The anterior hypophysis is necessary for the initiation and maintenance of milk secretion. The discovery that crude anterior pituitary extracts are lactogenic was followed by the isolation and purification of prolactin. It was found that minute amounts of purified prolactin, injected into an appropriate teat canal of the rabbit, produced lactation in localized sectors of the mammary gland, neighboring untreated sectors remaining unaffected. Since the rabbits were not hypophysectomized, the possibility that other pituitary hormones participated in the response was not ruled out.

The importance of the adrenal cortex in the initiation of lactation in a variety of mammals has been clearly established. Although animals that are adrenalectomized during pregnancy may deliver normal litters, lactation is so meager that they cannot raise their young. Lactation may be induced in the pseudopregnant rat by prolactin plus adrenal cortical hormone, but purified prolactin alone is ineffective. That lactation can be induced in hypophysectomized rats and guinea pigs by giving either prolactin plus adrenal cortical hormone or prolactin plus ACTH has been shown.

After parturition there is a striking increase in milk secretion. The exact mechanisms that operate at this time have not been fully agreed upon. There is evidence that estrogen and progesterone act synergistically to inhibit lactation. At parturition there is a fall in the circulating titers of ovarian and placental steroids, and this operates in some manner to turn the full force of the pituitary and adrenal cortex upon the mammary apparatus. Low levels of estrogen in the blood stimulate the pituitary to increase its output of prolactin, whereas high levels of estrogen tend to inhibit lactation. It is not known whether this inhibitory action of estrogen is effected through the pituitary or at the level of the mammary gland, or both. It may be that at parturition the fall in the relative ratio of progesterone to estrogen allows the latter hormone to exert its positive effect in promoting the release of prolactin from the anterior hypophysis. Whatever the exact mechanism may be, it is reasonably certain that prolactin and adrenal corticoids are the most essential hormones for the initiation of lactation.

The hormones that are involved in mammogenesis and lactogenesis in the rat may be summarized by reference to Figure 15–7. FSH and LH function synergistically to promote the secretion of estrogen by the ovary. ACTH stimulates the adrenal cortex to secrete

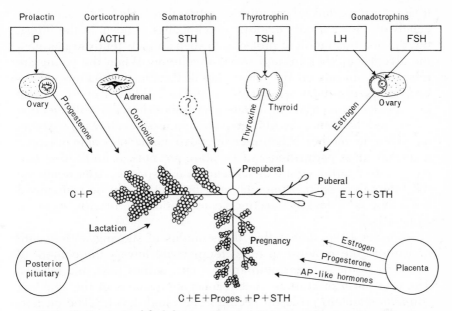

Figure 15–7. A simplified diagram showing the action of hormones on mammary growth and lactation. In the diagram of the gland: upper—rudimentary gland; right—prepuberal to puberal gland; lower—prolactational gland of pregnancy; left—lactating gland. (From Lyons, W. R., Li, C. H., and Johnson, R. E.: Rec. Prog. Horm. Res., *14*, 1958.)

corticoids. Growth of the duct system is produced by the action of estrogen, STH, and adrenal corticoids. Prolactin stimulates the corpora lutea to secrete progesterone. Full lobuloalveolar (prolactational) development requires a combination of prolactin, STH, estrogen, progesterone, and corticoids. Milk secretion by the developed gland ensues when the influence of estrogen and progesterone is diminished and prolactin and adrenal corticoids attain supremacy. It is probable that lactogenesis is facilitated by STH and TSH, although neither is absolutely necessary in the rat.[36, 45]

Maintenance of Lactation (Galactopoiesis)

After delivery of the young, milk yield rises rapidly and then declines slowly until the young are weaned. The hormonal mechanisms involved in galactopoiesis are very similar to those that initiated milk production. Hypophysectomy at any period during lactation terminates the process. The continued production of prolactin is probably essential throughout the period of lactation, and there can be little doubt that ACTH, STH, and TSH are likewise of importance. When milk production begins, pressure develops within the glands and, if it is not relieved by suckling or milking, it rises to the point where milk secretion is retarded. The mammary glands of mice and rats involute quickly after removal of the litters, but the administration of prolactin to such animals tends to maintain the alveolar epithelium and retard involution. When the young are removed from rats on the fourth day of lactation, injections of oxytocin markedly delay mammary involution. Ablation of the neural lobe of the hypophysis of lactating rats abolishes the milk-ejection reflex, and the young die from starvation unless injections of oxytocin are given the mother. When such operated mothers become pregnant a second time, parturition and lactation are normal, indicating that regeneration of the neural lobe occurs in this species. After removing the litters from postpartum rats, milk production can be maintained for as long as 75 days by injecting a combination of prolactin, oxytocin, and cortisol.

Studies have shown that the stimulus of sucking, either with or without the removal of milk, temporarily lowers the content of prolactin in the anterior pituitaries of rats, guinea pigs, and rabbits. There are also indications that regular applications of the suckling stimulus maintain prolactin secretion at a high level.[39] The rat normally lactates for about three weeks, since the young are weaned at this time, but experiments show that the mammary glands are capable of responding for a much longer time. The lactation period has been prolonged for 70 days by providing rats with fresh litters every 10 days.[41] The lobuloalveolar system shows little or no evidence of involution during this extended period, although there is a decline in milk yield as judged by litter weight gains. It is generally agreed that stimulation of the nipple during the act of suckling reflexly prolongs the release of prolactin and other galactopoietic hormones from the animal's hypophysis.

Section of the spinal cord immediately craniad of the first lumbar vertebra in lactating rats completely paralyzes that portion of the body that bears the last three pairs of nipples. If the cranial nipples are covered so as to force the young to suck the denervated nipples, the young rapidly lose weight and succumb from inanition. When other lactating litters are introduced, they die in the same manner. If two of the innervated glands are exposed to suckling litters, lactation continues in all the glands, irrespective of the nerve supply. It may be inferred that this surgical procedure has destroyed nervous pathways that are essential for the stimulus of suckling to prolong the release of galactopoietic hormones from the pituitary gland.

Involution of the mammary glands of mice is delayed when the nipples are irritated by the local application of spirits of turpentine. If this substance is applied to selected nipples, some remaining untreated, lactation from all the glands is prolonged in the absence of nursing litters. Turpentine applied to the skin of the back produces no such effect; such nonirritating materials as water applied to the nipples do not delay mammary involution.

Milk Ejection

For clear thinking about lactation it is necessary to distinguish between milk secretion and milk removal, since the two processes appear to be regulated by different neuroendocrine mechanisms.[12, 27] The former, which we have already discussed, centers around the release of prolactin and other hormones from the anterior hypophysis. Milk removal, on the other hand, involves the reflexive release of oxytocin from the neurohypophysis (Fig. 15–8). Oxytocin is conveyed by the circulation and causes milk evacuation by contracting the myoepithelial cells that surround the mammary alveoli. The act of suckling or milking reflexly stimulates both milk secretion and milk ejection. If a young animal is permitted to nurse an anesthetized mother, only the milk stored in the cistern and larger ducts can be withdrawn without any active participation of the mother. The greater part of the milk in the gland can be obtained only if there is activation of a neurohormonal reflex and a consequent contraction of the mammary alveoli. Within some 30 to 90 seconds after application of the suckling or milking stimulus, intramammary duct pressure suddenly rises and milk begins to flow freely. This results from the onset of the milk-ejection reflex and, in popular language, is called the "let-down" or the "draught."[21, 28]

The afferent component of the reflex arc is nervous, whereas the efferent limb is hormonal. The sensory stimuli associated with suckling excite receptors in the mammary glands and impulses are conveyed over spinal and brain stem tracts to the diencephalon and

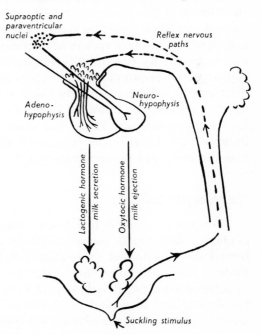

Figure 15–8. Diagram illustrating probable neurohormonal reflexes involved in milk secretion and milk ejection. (From Harris, G. W.: Neural Control of the Pituitary Gland. London, Edward Arnold Publishers, 1955.)

supraoptic nuclei of the hypothalamus. Through the mediation of
the supraoptico-hypophysial tracts, the neural division of the hypophysis discharges oxytocin and probably some vasopressin. Oxytocin
in the blood forms the efferent component of the arc, and the myoepithelial basket cells around the mammary alveoli constitute the
effector tissue. This or a similar mechanism operates in a great
variety of laboratory and domestic animals, and there is much evidence that it functions in lactating women as well. The milk-ejection
reflex may be excited by various kinds of conditioned stimuli, and
it is also subject to inhibition by emotionally stressful situations.

Many factors other than mechanical stimulation of the mammary
glands can induce the milk-ejection reflex. The importance of milking
cows at a set time every day is well recognized. The sound of buckets,
the presence of calves, washing the udder, the sight of food, and so
on may all constitute stimuli to which the animals become conditioned. Manipulation of the external genitalia and other events
associated with mating, rather than with nursing or milking, may
be sufficient to cause the discharge of milk, presumably through
the reflexive release of oxytocin.

It had been known for many years that crude extracts of the
posterior hypophysis facilitate milk evacuation, but the situation
has been clarified since purified and synthetic preparations became
available. Although oxytocin is five to six times more effective than
vasopressin in eliciting milk ejection, the latter hormone possesses
some intrinsic capacity to do so. Milk ejection occurs after the administration of oxytocin to lactating subjects even without mechanical
stimulation of the mammary glands, as well as after the glands have
been denervated. Suckling does not lead to milk ejection after sev-
erance of the pituitary stalk or after certain areas of the hypothalamus
are destroyed by electrolytic lesions. Electrical stimulation of the
supraoptico-hypophysial tract of goats and rabbits causes a copious
discharge of milk. Jugular vein blood drawn from goats thus treated
has the capacity of inducing milk ejection when administered to
lactating test animals. These and many other types of experiments
indicate that the reflexive release of milk is mediated through the
hypothalamus and neurohypophysis.[14]

The Myoepithelial Cells

For many years it had been assumed, on rather inadequate
evidence, that smooth muscle tissue in connection with the alveoli
served the function of squeezing milk from the gland. Histologic
studies, however, failed to reveal the presence of this tissue in
association with the alveoli, except in very meager amounts. Earlier
histologists had identified myoepithelial cells or "basket cells" intimately surrounding the alveoli, but their distribution and structural

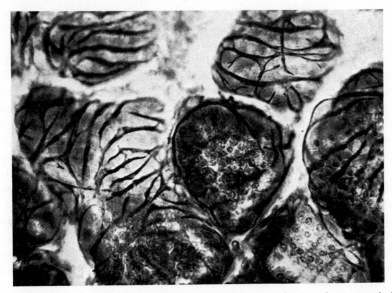

Figure 15–9.   Section of the mammary gland of the goat, showing the myoepithelial cells surrounding the alveoli. (From Harris, G. W.: Proc. Roy. Soc., B, *149*, 1958.)

features remained vague until they were studied after silver impregnation.[47] There is now no reasonable doubt that these cells are the effector contractile tissue of the mammary gland (Fig. 15–9).

Direct microscopic studies of the living gland have shown that the myoepithelial cells are capable of contracting. Direct mechanical or electrical stimulation causes them to contract and evacuate the alveolar contents. They may be caused to contract by the local application of oxytocin or vasopressin. Various drugs, such as histamine, acetylcholine, pilocarpine, and 5-hydroxytryptamine, also contract the myoepithelial cells after local application. Epinephrine and norepinephrine, on the other hand, have no effect on these cells, though they do not prevent oxytocin from exerting its usual effect.

Inhibition of Milk Ejection

Clinicians are aware that worry, fear, embarrassment, sadness, and other strong emotions at the time of nursing may inhibit the flow of milk in women. In human beings as well as in many other mammals, milk ejection may be blocked by the administration of epinephrine. It is probable that the epinephrine blockade is due to vasoconstriction within the mammary gland, since epinephrine does not inhibit the action of oxytocin on mammary alveoli *in vitro.* In the majority of cases, emotional stress seems to block the ejection of milk by preventing the nervous stimulus from reaching the neurohypophysis and causing a discharge of oxytocin. Experiments on laboratory animals have shown that it may also result from a sympatheticoadrenal discharge from the hypothalamus, which produces constriction of the mammary blood vessels.[13]

It is well known that lactation ceases rather promptly if the mammary glands become engorged with milk through absence of suckling or milking or through disturbances in the milk ejection mechanism. Experiments on lactating rats have provided some interesting information on the mechanism of mammary involution after engorgement. On the day after parturition, the teat ducts of some of the mammary glands are ligated subcutaneously, the unoperated teats of the same animal serving as controls. As the animals continue nursing their litters, the operated glands became conspicuously distended by 8 hours and reach a maximum at 24 hours. If the ligatures are loosened at this stage, milk ejection can be elicited by the intravenous injection of oxytocin. If the ducts remain tied for 48 hours, the glands lose their pinkish color and histologic examination reveals that the capillary meshwork of the gland is collapsed and devoid of blood cells. If the sutures are removed at this stage and oxytocin administered intravenously, milk ejection no longer ensues. However, contraction of the myoepithelial cells occurs when minute amounts of oxytocin are topically applied to the surface of the gland. These observations indicate that the failure to eject milk is due to capillary reduction rather than to myoepithelial incompetence. It is not known whether such constriction of the capillary bed occurs naturally in cases of engorgement, although there are suggestions that it does.

REFERENCES

1. Albert, A., and Derner, I.: Studies on the biologic characterization of human gonadotropins. Nature and number of gonadotropins in human pregnancy urine. J. Clin. Endocrinol., *20*:1225, 1960.
2. Amoroso, E. C.: De la signification du placenta dans l'évolution de la gestation chez les animaux vivipares. Ann. d'endocrinol., *16*:435, 1955.
3. Amoroso, E. C.: Comparative anatomy of the placenta. Ann. N. Y. Acad. Sci., 75:885, 1959.
4. Benson, G. K., Cowie, A. T., Folley, S. J., and Tindal, J. S.: Recent developments in endocrine studies on mammary growth and lactation. *In* C. W. Lloyd (ed.): Endocrinology of Reproduction. New York, Academic Press, 1959, p. 457.
5. Blandau, R. J.: Biology of eggs and implantation. *In* W. C. Young (ed.): Sex and Internal Secretions, Vol. 2. Baltimore, Williams and Wilkins Co., 1961, p. 797.
6. Böving, B. G.: Implantation. Ann. New York Acad. Sci., 75:700, 1959.
7. Bragdon, D. E., Lazo-Wassem, E. A., Zarrow, M. X., and Hisaw, F. L.: Progesterone-like activity in the plasma of ovoviviparous snakes. Proc. Soc. Exp. Biol. & Med., 86:477, 1954.
8. Buchanan, G. D., Enders, A. C., and Talmage, R. V.: Implantation in armadillos ovariectomized during the period of delayed implantation. J. Endocrinol., *14*:121, 1956.
9. Chang, M. C.: Maintenance of pregnancy in intact rabbits in the absence of corpora lutea. Endocrinol., *48*:17, 1951.

10. Clegg, M. T., Boda, J. M., and Cole, H. H.: Endometrial cups and allantochorionic pouches in the mare with emphasis on the source of equine gonadotrophin. Endocrinol., *54*:448, 1954.
11. Cole, H. H. (ed.): Gonadotropins: their chemical and biological properties and secretory control. San Francisco, W. H. Freeman & Co., 1964.
12. Cowie, A. T., and Folley, S. J.: Neurohypophysial hormones and the mammary gland. *In* H. Heller (ed.): The Neurohypophysis. London, Butterworth & Co., 1957, p. 183.
13. Cross, B. A.: Neurohormonal mechanisms in emotional inhibition of milk ejection. J. Endocrinol., *12*:29, 1955.
14. Cross, B. A.: The posterior pituitary gland in relation to reproduction and lactation. Brit. M. Bull., *11*:151, 1955.
15. Cross, B. A.: Neurohypophyseal control of parturition. *In* C. W. Lloyd (ed.): Endocrinology of Reproduction. New York, Academic Press, 1959, p. 441.
16. Csapo, A.: Function and regulation of the myometrium. Ann. New York Acad. Sci., 75:790, 1959.
17. Cunningham, J. T., and Smart, W. A. M.: Structure and origin of corpora lutea in some of the lower vertebrates. Proc. Roy. Soc., B, *116*:258, 1934.
18. Damm, H. C., and Turner, C. W.: Evidence for the existence of mammogenic hormone. Proc. Soc. Exp. Biol. & Med., 99:471, 1958.
19. Deanesly, R.: Endocrine activity of the early placenta of the guinea-pig. J. Endocrinol., *21*:235, 1960.
20. Doyle, L. L., and Margolis, A. J.: Intrauterine foreign body: effect on pregnancy in the rat. Science, *139*:833, 1963.
21. Folley, S. J.: The Physiology and Biochemistry of Lactation. London, Oliver & Boyd, 1956.
22. Friesen, H.: Purification of a placental factor with immunological and chemical similarity to human growth hormone. Endocrinol., 76:369, 1965.
23. Gallien, L.: Endocrine basis for reproductive adaptations in Amphibia. *In* A. Gorbman (ed.): Comparative Endocrinology. New York, John Wiley & Sons, 1959, p. 479.
24. Grosvenor, C. E., and Turner, C. W.: Pituitary lactogenic hormone concentration and milk secretion in lactating rats. Endocrinol., 63:535, 1958.
25. Grosvenor, C. E., and Turner, C. W.: Thyroid hormone and lactation in the rat. Proc. Soc. Exp. Biol. & Med., *100*:162, 1959.
26. Hammond, J., Jr.: The rabbit corpus luteum; oestrogen prolongation and the accompanying changes in the genitalia. Acta Endocrinol., *21*:307, 1956.
27. Harris, G. W.: The central nervous system, neurohypophysis and milk ejection. Proc. Roy. Soc. B, *149*:336, 1958.
28. Haun, C. K., and Sawyer, C. H.: Initiation of lactation in rabbits following placement of hypothalamic lesions. Endocrinol., 67:270, 1960.
29. Healy, M. J. R.: Foetal growth in the mouse. Proc. Roy. Soc. B, *153*:367, 1960.
30. Hisaw, F. L.: Endocrine adaptations of the mammalian estrous cycle and gestation. *In* A. Gorbman (ed.): Comparative Endocrinology. New York, John Wiley & Sons, 1959, p. 533.
31. Hisaw, F. L.: Endocrines and the evolution of viviparity among the vertebrates. *In* F. L. Hisaw, Jr. (ed.): Physiology of Reproduction. Proc. of the 22nd Ann. Biol. Colloq. Corvallis, Oregon State University Press, 1963, p. 119.
32. Kon, S. K., and Cowie, A. T. (eds.): Milk: The Mammary Gland and Its Secretion, Vol. 1. New York, Academic Press, 1961.
33. Linzell, J. L.: Physiology of the mammary glands. Physiol. Rev., 39:534, 1959.
34. Lyon, R. A., Simpson, M. E., and Evans, H. M.: Qualitative changes in urinary gonadotrophins in human pregnancy during the period of rapid increase in hormone titer. Endocrinol., 53:674, 1953.
35. Lyons, W. R., Johnson, R. E., and Li, C. H.: Local action of pituitary and ovarian hormones on the mammary glands of hypophysectomized-oöphorectomized rats. Anat. Rec., *127*:432, 1957.
36. Lyons, W. R., Li, C. H., and Johnson, R. E.: The hormonal control of mammary growth and lactation. Rec. Prog. Hormone Research, *14*:219, 1958.
37. Matthews, L. H.: The evolution of viviparity in vertebrates. Memoirs Soc. Endocrinol., No. 4, 129, 1955.

38. Meites, J., and Shelesnyak, M. C.: Effects of prolactin on duration of pregnancy, viability of young and lactation in rats. Proc. Soc. Exp. Biol. & Med., *94*:746, 1957.

39. Meites, J., and Turner, C. W.: Influence of suckling on lactogen content of pituitary of postpartum rabbits. Endocrinol., *31*:340, 1942.

40. Moon, R. C.: Growth hormone and mammary gland lobule-alveolar development. Amer. J. Physiol., *201*:259, 1961.

41. Nicoll, C. S., and Meites, J.: Prolongation of lactation in the rat by litter replacement. Proc. Soc. Exp. Biol. & Med., *101*:81, 1959.

42. Noble, R. L., and Plunkett, E. R.: Biology of the gonadotrophins. Brit. M. Bull., *11*:98, 1955.

43. Perry, J. S.: The reproduction of the African elephant (*Loxodonta africana*). Phil. Trans. Roy. Soc. B, *237*:93, 1953.

44. Raacke, I. D., Lostroh, A. J., Boda, J. M., and Li, C. H.: Some aspects of the characterization of pregnant mare serum gonadotrophin. Acta Endocrinol., *26*:377, 1957.

45. Reece, R. P.: Mammary gland development and function. *In* J. T. Velardo (ed.): The Endocrinology of Reproduction. New York, Oxford University Press, 1958, p. 213.

46. Reynolds, S. R. M.: Gestation mechanisms. Ann. New York Acad. Sci., *75*:691, 1959.

47. Richardson, K. C.: Contractile tissues in the mammary gland, with special reference to myoepithelium in the goat. Proc. Roy. Soc. B, *136*:30, 1949.

48. Smith, P. E.: Continuation of pregnancy in Rhesus monkeys (*Macaca mulatta*) following hypophysectomy. Endocrinol., *55*:655, 1954.

49. Smithberg, M., and Runner, M. N.: The induction and maintenance of pregnancy in prepuberal mice. J. Exp. Zool., *133*:441, 1956.

50. Stricker, P., and Greueter, F.: Action du lobe antérieur de l'hypophyse sur la montée laiteuse. Compt. rend. Soc. de biol., *99*:1978, 1928.

51. Taymor, M. L., Yahia, C., and Goss, D. A.: A three-minute immunologic test for pregnancy. Internat. J. Fertil., *10*:41, 1965.

52. Turner, C. W.: Regulation of lactation. Conf. Radioactive Isotopes in Agric., East Lansing, Michigan, 403, 1956.

53. Turner, C. W., Yamamoto, H., and Ruppert, H. L., Jr.: Endocrine factors influencing the intensity of milk secretion: estrogen, thyroxine and growth hormone. J. Dairy Sci., *40*:37, 1957.

54. Velardo, J. T.: Hormonal actions of chorionic gonadotropin. Ann. New York Acad. Sci., *80*:65, 1959.

55. Wide, L., and Gemzell, C. A.: An immunological pregnancy test. Acta Endocrinol., *35*:261, 1960.

16_____

GASTROINTESTINAL HORMONES: HORMONE-LIKE SUBSTANCES

As pointed out earlier, there is no general agreement as to what constitutes an endocrine gland or as to what cellular products should be accorded hormonal status. Biologists are forced to the conclusion that there are profound gradations within organisms with respect to the degree of differentiation of glands. It appears that cells and tissues may be rather highly differentiated in other directions and still remain capable of releasing special substances into the body fluids. Furthermore, like glands of the exocrine type, it is probable that endocrine glands may be either *unicellular* or *multicellular*. Though the term "hormone" was first applied to secretin, it still is not clear whether all cells of the duodenal mucosa release it or whether its production is restricted to unicellular glands in this portion of the intestine. There is also the problem of how to consider such materials as acetylcholine which are rapidly removed from their sites of action and hence do not reach effective concentrations in the general circulation. It is the purpose of the present chapter to discuss briefly some of the coordinatory agents that are unique in some respects and do not coincide exactly with the classical connotations of the term "hormone."

GASTROINTESTINAL HORMONES

Localized areas of the alimentary tract form a number of hormones that regulate the motor and secretory activities of the digestive

543

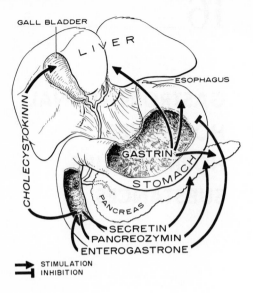

organs (Fig. 16–1). These chemical agents are released into the circulation and their actions supplement those of the autonomic nervous system. One conspicuous feature of the endocrine glands, other than those of the gastrointestinal tract, is that their activities are interrelated in such a manner as to produce a system of checks and balances. No such interrelationship has been clearly demonstrated for the gastrointestinal hormones; they are not known to be influenced by other glands of the endocrine system or to be interrelated among themselves. Their secretion is conditioned largely by the presence or absence of particular food substances in the lumen of the alimentary tract, rather than by other glandular products in the circulation. Little is known about the specific cells responsible for their production. The gastrointestinal hormones produce their effects quickly after the application of appropriate stimuli for their release, and they are quickly destroyed after withdrawal of the stimulus. They appear to be protein or polypeptide in nature.[3, 7, 10]

Secretin

After the ingestion of food there is no appreciable release of pancreatic juice until the partially digested food passes through the pyloric sphincter into the duodenum. The passage of chyme from the stomach causes the duodenal mucosa to release secretin into the blood, and the hormone stimulates the flow of pancreatic juice but not the release of enzymes; the flow of bile and intestinal juices is stimulated to a lesser extent. Secretin continues to be effective after section of the vagus as well as in the atropinized animal, indicating that the hormone acts directly upon the acinar cells of the pancreas. Many materials other than hydrochloric acid stimulate the release of secretin by the duodenal mucosa; water, alcohol, fatty acids, partially hydrolyzed protein, and certain amino acids are all effective. The intravenous administration of acids and secretagogues has no effect upon pancreatic activity.

Hypophysectomy lowers the secretin content of the rat's intestine. Somatotrophin and ACTH preparations, administered to the hypophysectomized rat, maintain normal levels of secretin in the intestinal mucosa.

Secretin has been obtained in crystalline form and is a basic polypeptide. It is most effective when given intravenously, and, since it is inactivated by gastric and pancreatic juices, it is totally ineffective by mouth. The hormone disappears rapidly from the circulation owing to the destructive action of an enzyme called "secretinase." Small amounts of the hormone are excreted in the urine. Although the term "hormone" was first applied to this substance, its cellular site of origin remains obscure, and nothing is known about its mechanism of action on the exocrine pancreas.

Cholecystokinin

Denervation of the gallbladder does not prevent its periodic evacuation, and electrical stimulation of the nerves to this organ produces only mild effects. That an agent conveyed by the general circulation is involved in its regulation is indicated by the fact that a gallbladder transplanted a considerable distance from its normal site (*e.g.,* to the neck) is stimulated to contract when suitable stimulants are installed into the duodenum of the host. There is convincing evidence that fat, fatty acids, dilute acids, and peptones in the duodenum activate cells of the mucosa and cause them to release a substance, called "cholecystokinin," in somewhat the same manner as secretin is liberated. Cholecystokinin is chemically related to secretin, but tests indicate that the two substances are separable. Cholecystokinin is ineffective orally and is destroyed by an enzyme present in the blood. Its chemical structure is unknown.

Pancreozymin

After the administration of secretin, the volume of pancreatic juice released by the gland increases markedly, but this juice is relatively deficient in enzyme activity. Vagal stimulation does not cause any marked increase in the volume of pancreatic juice, but it does enhance its content of digestive enzymes. There is strong evidence that a second hormone, pancreozymin, is liberated by the mucosa of the upper intestine and that it, unlike secretin, stimulates the pancreatic acinar cells to secrete enzymes. The pancreatic juice produced under the stimulus of this hormone is not increased in volume, but it contains a very high content of enzymes and practically no other proteins. This substance has been partially purified from extracts of the duodenal mucosa.

Gastrin

This agent is thought to be produced by the mucosa of the pyloric region of the stomach in response to mechanical distention and the local action of secretagogues contained in the food. Gastrin is supposedly absorbed into the blood and carried to the fundic cells, causing them to secrete hydrochloric acid. Two pure polypeptides have been obtained from pyloric mucosa, and, since they stimulate gastric secretion, are thought to represent gastrin. In addition to stimulating the stomach, these polypeptides also promote pancreatic secretion. It thus appears that the release of pancreatic juice is controlled by three hormones: secretin and pancreozymin from the intestinal mucosa, and gastrin from the stomach mucosa.[6, 22]

There is evidence that histamine may serve as a gastric secretory hormone in the rat.[23] After the administration of aminoguanidine to prevent the destruction of histamine, the consumption of food by the rat releases histamine in quantities sufficient to stimulate gastric secretion.

Enterogastrone

It has been known for many years that the secretion and motility of the stomach are impeded when neutral fat comes in contact with the duodenal mucosa. It is believed that the presence of fat in the duodenum stimulates this region of the intestine to secrete one or more agents, called "enterogastrone," that are conveyed by the circulation and act to quiet the stomach. The intravenous administration of partially purified extracts containing enterogastrone has been shown to produce three types of effects: (1) inhibition of secretion of hydrochloric acid by the parietal cells of the stomach; (2) diminished motility of the stomach when the vagus innervation is intact; (3) prevention of gastrojejunal ulcers in "Mann-Williamson" dogs.

Experimentalists have accumulated a creditable amount of information concerning the etiology of peptic ulcer. The evidence indicates that such gastrointestinal ulceration is correlated with the irritating acid contained in the gastric contents. These lesions are likely to occur at points where the mucosa is exposed to acid gastric juice and are found most frequently where the acid content of the stomach is ejected forcibly against the intestinal wall. Clinicians are aware that duodenal ulcer in man is often accompanied by gastric hyperacidity, and experimentalists have been able to produce intestinal ulcerations by surgical procedures that force the pancreatic

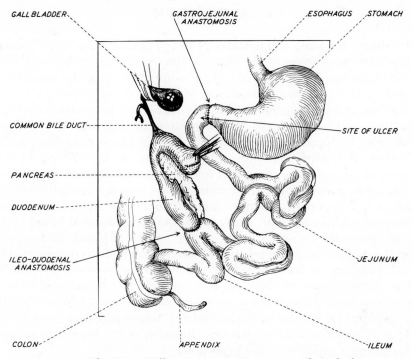

Figure 16-2. The Mann-Williamson gastrojejunostomy. Through this operation the alkaline secretions of the liver and pancreas are drained into the ileum, and the stomach is made to empty into the jejunum. Peptic ulcers, resulting from acid erosion, appear in the unprotected jejunum.

and biliary secretions to drain into the distal region of the intestinal tract (Fig. 16–2).

Approximately 98 per cent of dogs subjected to the Mann-Williamson operation develop chronic peptic ulcers of the jejunum, just distal to the gastric anastomosis and succumb from this condition within nine months unless treated. Since enterogastrone quiets the stomach and diminishes the secretion of acid, it might be suspected that this substance would prove efficacious in the prevention and treatment of experimental ulcer. Partially purified extracts containing enterogastrone have been found to protect Mann-Williamson dogs against ulcer, or to promote healing of the ulcer after it is formed.

Urogastrone

A gastric inhibitory substance, urogastrone, is present in urine. Urogastrone disappears from the urine of dogs after hypophysectomy, indicating that its production is in some manner related to the presence of the pituitary gland.

ANGIOTENSIN

Since the early publications of Bright (1827), it has been known that chronic disease of the human kidney is frequently correlated with high blood pressure, or hypertension. As early as the turn of the century it was shown that extracts of kidney tissue raised the blood pressure of experimental animals. By regulating heart action and the caliber of blood vessels, the nervous system brings about rapid changes in blood pressure and the flow of blood through tissues. Various hormones and other chemical agents, in addition to the nervous system, have important roles in the regulation of blood pressure. For instance, certain tumors of the adrenal medulla, called *pheochromocytomas*, secrete large amounts of epinephrine and norepinephrine and thus cause a profound elevation of blood pressure. Since the kidneys process a large volume of blood and function in the maintenance of a relatively constant internal environment, it is not surprising to find that they are involved in a humoral mechanism that influences blood pressure. Two methods have been found whereby permanent hypertension may be experimentally produced with regularity: (1) section of the modulator nerves produces *neurogenic* hypertension, and (2) mechanical alteration of the hemodynamics of the kidneys produces *renal* hypertension.[14, 19]

Although various workers devised experimental procedures for modifying kidney functions in attempts to produce renal hypertension, Goldblatt and his collaborators were the first to work out a technique that produces permanent hypertension consistently enough to be used in systematic studies.[5] Their method was to produce a deficient flow of blood through the kidneys (ischemia) by applying an adjustable clamp to the renal artery. By this method hypertensive states have been produced in a variety of mammals, *e.g.*, dogs, sheep, goats, rats, and monkeys. There is conclusive proof that localized ischemia of the kidneys produces a persistent hypertension; some workers have followed up such animals for seven years or longer. In dogs having an ischemic kidney on one side only, the contralateral kidney remaining normal, removal of the damaged kidney is followed by a rapid return of blood pressure to normal levels. The same type of hypertension may be produced by ligation of the ureters or the injection of such nephrotoxic substances as mercury, bismuth, and lead. It appears that almost any procedure that results in a deficiency of oxygen in the renal tissues can cause the blood pressure to rise.[12]

Persistent hypertension in a variety of mammals results from procedures that induce perinephritis. For example, when the kidneys are encapsulated by collodion, cellophane, or silk, they react to the foreign substance by forming a fibrocollagenous shell around the organ that compresses the renal parenchyma and does not permit the natural expansion of the kidney while it is functioning. This technique may be used advantageously in small animals in which difficulties would be encountered in applying a clamp to the renal arteries. Renal hypertension results from these procedures after denervation of the kidneys; after bilateral section of the splanchnic nerves; after total sympathectomy, including total denervation of the heart; after subdiaphragmatic splanchnicectomy, the celiac and upper ganglia being removed; after bilateral section of the ventral roots of the spinal nerves; and even after the destruction of the spinal cord below the fifth cervical vertebra.

The hypertensive state is not prevented or modified by ablation of the adrenal medullae. If a kidney is transplanted into the neck by uniting the renal artery with the carotid and the renal vein with the jugular, the intact kidney being removed and the transplanted kidney being made ischemic by clamping the renal artery, typical hypertension ensues. Under these circumstances the ischemic kidney, completely devoid of nervous control, releases a substance that is responsible for the elevation of the blood pressure. Certain types of hypertension in the human subject appear to be due to arteriosclerotic plaques or other obstructions to the flow of blood through the kidneys. In other cases, there appears to be no obstruction of renal blood flow, and the precise mechanism that causes the release of renin by the kidneys remains obscure.

Much progress has been made in defining the mechanism whereby the kidneys influence blood pressure.[2, 20] *Renin* (pronounced ree-nin) is an enzyme produced by the kidney and released into the circulation under certain conditions. It acts on *renin-substrate,* a protein that the liver frees into the blood stream, and produces a substance which is called "angiotensin I." (This substance was originally called "angiotonin" and "hypertensin" by different workers; the hybrid term "angiotensin" is now in general use.) Another blood protein, called "converting enzyme," acts on angiotensin I to split off a pair of amino acids from one end of the peptide chain, thus producing the active substance, angiotensin II. The latter is conveyed to the capillary beds where it causes constriction of the arterioles:

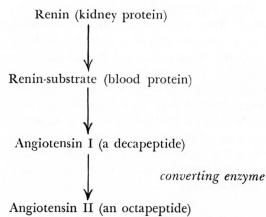

Renin (kidney protein)

Renin-substrate (blood protein)

Angiotensin I (a decapeptide)

converting enzyme

Angiotensin II (an octapeptide)

The amino acid sequence in the angiotensin molecule has been determined and the substance has been produced synthetically.[24] Angiotensin I is a peptide chain consisting of 10 amino acids:

Asp — Arg — Val — Tyr — Iso — His — Pro — Phe — His — Leu.

Angiotensin II, the active form, is identical with the inactive form except for the absence of the terminal amino acids, histidine and leucine. Angiotensins from different species are generally similar, but slight variations are known to occur. Synthetic angiotensin elevates the blood pressure of man and laboratory animals and causes the contraction of uterine muscle. It is probably the most potent vasopressor substance known. Angiotensin I elevates the blood pressure only because it is rapidly converted in the blood stream to angiotensin II; it has no effect on uterine muscle *in vitro*, since the converting enzyme is not present in the tissue. It thus appears that the organism can convert renin-substrate to angiotensin I and store it in this inactive form, converting it to the active octapeptide as the need arises. It is a well-known fact that certain enzymes are similarly stored as inactive proteins. All tissues exhibit some peptidase activity capable of destroying angiotensin II, but kidney and intestine are especially active in this respect.

It is interesting that several other peptides present in the organism exert the same physiologic effects as angiotensin II. For example, vasopressin, a hormone of the neurohypophysis, causes an elevation of blood pressure, and oxytocin has a strong effect on uterine contractility. The neurohypophysial hormones, like angiotensin II, are octapeptides, but no other structural similarities between the two types of substances have been detected. Hydrolysis of blood serum or of certain of its proteins by proteolytic enzymes yields various polypeptides, and some of these exert pharmacologic actions simulating those of vasopressin, oxytocin, and angiotensin II.

Angiotensin II is not found in the blood plasma of normal persons, but it is present in patients suffering from essential hypertension. The renin-angiotensin mechanism has not been accepted by all workers as the dominant factor involved in hypertensive disease of renal origin, and there are indications that other mechanisms may be operative. When kidney slices are incubated under anaerobic conditions, they release into the culture medium a protein having pressor activity. This substance has been called "vasoexcitor material." Several polypeptides having pressor activity have been obtained from the blood of hypertensive patients.

Although angiotensin is a coordinatory material of great importance, there is no general agreement on whether or not it should be regarded as a hormone. Perhaps some unifying concept of what constitutes a true hormone may be forthcoming after more is known of the exact mechanisms whereby hormones and related substances produce their effects.

THE PRODUCTS OF DEAD OR INJURED TISSUES

The Inflammatory Reaction

The functional and structural manifestations of inflammation occur in a definite sequence irrespective of the causative irritant. Although the nature of the causative agent and the anatomic location of the lesion may modify the ultimate appearance of the inflamed area, the inflammatory process develops in accordance with a fundamentally basic pattern. The first manifestation of an inflammatory reaction is an alteration in fluid exchange; the permeability of the capillaries is increased, thus permitting an excessive flow of fluid into the tissues (edema). The capillary endothelium is altered so as to allow the passage of fibrinogen and other plasma proteins into the injured area. Next, there is a series of adjustments that tend to localize or "wall off" the irritant. Fibrinogen is precipitated as a fibrous meshwork in the inflamed area, and the lymphatics that drain the region are occluded by fibrous thrombi. This lymphatic blockade, together with the coagulated plasma at the site of injury, tends to localize the irritant and prevent its spread over the remainder of the organism. This basic mechanism may be reinforced by secondary factors such as the formation of immune bodies.[15]

The next event is the migration of leukocytes into the inflamed region. They are the first cells to arrive at the site of injury, and they function in the phagocytosis of foreign bodies, cellular fragments, and so forth. The polymorphonuclear leukocytes gradually disappear from the area of damaged tissue, their place being taken by macrophages. This shift from polymorphonuclear leukocytes to macrophages seems to be correlated with the local change in pH at the site of injury. The acidosis resulting from increased glycolysis and depletion of alkali reserve proves lethal to the polymorphonuclear leukocytes, whereas the macrophages tolerate the increased acidity much better. Macrophages survive and predominate when the pH of the exudate falls as low as 6.8, but further reduction of pH cannot be tolerated by any type of wandering cell, and suppuration ensues. Pus formation is a consequence of the local acidity developed in the area of inflammation.

The injured tissues at the site of the inflammatory process release several agents that condition these changes. *Leukotaxine* is a nitrogenous substance that escapes from injured cells, and the indications are that it is distinct from histamine. It appears to be a simple polypeptide and probably results from the catabolism of proteins. During initial stages leukotaxine increases capillary permeability and encourages the emigration of polymorphonuclear leukocytes into the region containing damaged tissue. Thus, this product of tissue injury is responsible for two basic adjustments: increased permeability of the capillaries and chemotaxis of phagocytic cells.

In the later stages of an acute inflammation, at about the same time as the exudate attains an acid reaction, another simple polypeptide appears. This one is called *exudin.* Its action is to increase capillary permeability, but, unlike leukotaxine, it does not induce the migration of leukocytes.

Since ACTH and certain adrenocortical steroids inhibit the actions of leukotaxine and exudin, they produce anti-inflammatory effects. The beneficial effects of ACTH and certain adrenocortical steroids in rheumatoid arthritis, various eye diseases, and allergic conditions are probably due to their penetration to the site of injury, where they exert antiphlogistic influences. These compounds are contraindicated in infectious disease, since they inhibit inflammatory mechanisms and hence permit the spread of microorganisms throughout the tissues of the host.

The rise in the level of circulating leukocytes, characteristic of many infectious processes, seems to be referable to the action of a substance called *leukocytosis-promoting factor.* This is a pseudoglobulin and is liberated in the inflamed area (Fig. 16–3).

Another product of tissue injury, called *necrosin,* has been identified. From the foregoing discussion it is apparent that the inflammatory reaction is a manifestation of cellular injury. Leukotaxine, exudin, and leukocytosis-promoting factor produce no detectable cellular injury when injected. Necrosin is contained in the euglobulin fraction of exudates and seems to be the agent responsible for tissue injury *per se.* Although this injury factor is absent from normal blood serums, it can be extracted from the serums of animals suffering acute inflammation. This suggests that necrosin may be absorbed to some extent and lead to certain toxic symptoms. *Pyrexin* is a polypeptide contained in the euglobulin fraction of acid exudates and is thought to be responsible for the high fever that accompanies severe inflam-

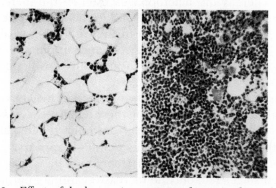

Figure 16–3. Effect of leukocytosis-promoting factor on femoral bone marrow of the dog. *A,* Bone marrow from control animal injected with pseudoglobulin from normal blood. *B,* Bone marrow two days after the injection of leukocytosis-promoting factor. Observe the striking hyperplasia. (From Menkin, V.: Internat. Arch. Allergy, *4,* 1953.)

matory states. Closely associated with pyrexin, but separable from it, is a factor called *leukopenin.* This substance causes a fall in the number of circulating white blood cells. The leukopenia appears to result from a trapping of white blood cells in the alveolar walls of the lungs, liver sinusoids, splenic pulp, and bone marrow.

In summary, inflammation involves a series of reactions that tend to localize and dispose of the irritating substance. The irritant itself directly inflicts injury upon the cells. As a consequence of this injury, cellular metabolism is impaired and a number of by-products (*e.g.,* leukotaxine, exudin, leukocytosis-promoting factor, necrosin, pyrexin, and leukopenin) appear, which are not produced by normal, uninjured cells. Through the interplay of these by-products the inflammatory reaction is initiated, and, if completed properly, the irritant is ultimately disposed of and the damaged area repaired.

HUMORAL CONTROL OF ERYTHROPOIESIS

It is well known that a great variety of factors can influence the rate of formation of blood cells by hematopoietic organs. Any condition that diminishes the quantity of oxygen delivered to the tissues ordinarily promotes the production of red cells. Thus, high altitudes, hemorrhage, induced intravascular hemolysis, nutritional defects, endocrine disturbances, etc., may produce an increase in erythropoiesis. Male sex hormones increase the rate of red blood cell production, whereas female sex hormones have little if any effect. Insufficient quantities of thyroid hormone, adrenocortical steroids, and certain anterior pituitary hormones can depress erythropoiesis.

Strong evidence has accumulated from experiments on different mammalian species that the blood plasma of anemic donors contains a factor that is capable of increasing erythropoiesis when administered to normal subjects. This substance, commonly referred to as "erythropoietin," is thought to be released by some tissue in the body that is sensitive to changes in pO_2. In an attempt to determine the site of origin of erythropoietin, organs have been removed after cobalt treatment, hemorrhage, or hypoxia. The kidneys seem to be the only organs whose removal prevents the stimulated animal from producing erythropoietin. Numerous observations suggest that the kidney is the principal site of erythropoietin production or that it is at least involved in its formation. Some progress has been made in the isolation of this factor, but it has not been chemically characterized.[8, 9]

THE MAST CELLS OF EHRLICH

The mast cells are widely distributed throughout the organism, occurring abundantly in connective tissues and in the walls of blood vessels.[1] These large cells contain basophilic granules that are often so numerous as to obscure the nucleus. They are not phagocytic but may form short pseudopodia and move about freely. The granules of mast cells contain heparin, histamine, and, in certain species, serotonin. Mast cell tumors occur spontaneously in certain species and these, as well as the normal mast cell, contain high concentrations of the materials mentioned above.

Heparin prevents the coagulation of blood plasma. Small amounts of it induce the appearance in the circulation of lipoprotein lipase, an enzyme that may be of importance in regulating the pattern of distribution of blood lipids. Heparin has a retarding effect on various other enzyme systems. Although many effects of heparin have been demonstrated, its physiologic role in the organism remains unclarified. Since the mast cells seem to synthesize and release such important materials as heparin, histamine, and serotonin, it might be possible to regard them as unicellular endocrine glands which migrate through the various tissues of the body.

PHYTOHORMONES

Phytohormones are biologically active materials of plant origin that are effective in minute concentrations at sites remote from the tissues where they are formed.[25] The term includes auxins, wound hormones, flowering hormones, some of the B vitamins, carotenoids, and steroids. The term *auxin* is now used to designate materials that induce the longitudinal growth of shoots; this growth is accomplished by cell elongation rather than by cell division.

Growth Regulators in Plants

The best known auxin is indole-3 acetic acid (IAA); it has been isolated from *Rhizopus* cultures and from a number of different species of higher plants. The auxin is produced most abundantly by regions of active growth, such as coleoptile tips, apical buds, root tips, and young leaves. Proteins containing tryptophan are potential sources of IAA in plants; IAA production, however, appears to be associated with protein synthesis rather than with protein hydrolysis. Spinach leaves contain an enzyme that is capable of converting tryptophan into IAA. It is known that plant tissues contain auxin in both the free and bound form. Some of the IAA is loosely adsorbed on the surface of protein fractions; the auxin is active in this state but is not capable of free movement within the plant. Indoleacetaldehyde has been extracted from plant tissues and is an inactive precursor of IAA. Auxin precursors may form complexes with certain growth inhibitors; this is often found in storage tissues such as seeds and tubers. Plant tissues contain an enzyme system, IAA oxidase, which attacks IAA and converts it into a compound that is without growth-promoting properties. Some tissues contain an inhibitor of IAA oxidase.

Natural auxin promotes the growth of shoots by stimulating both cell enlargement and cell division, but the growth of roots is generally inhibited. However, at extremely low levels of concentration, root growth is usually promoted. If the apical bud is removed from a shoot and a small quantity of IAA is applied to the stump, the lateral buds cease growing. Thus, the same concentration of auxin that promotes growth of the shoot inhibits growth of the lateral buds. As the terminal bud grows away from the lateral buds, the auxin supply is weakened by distance and the lateral buds at a lower level on the stem begin to grow out. A large number of synthetic auxins have been prepared; however, their specific activities vary greatly relative to those of IAA. Some of the synthetic compounds, though not growth-promoting in themselves, may potentiate the action of auxin; they may act as synergists in low concentrations but as inhibitors when present in larger amounts. 2,3,5-Triiodobenzoic acid is an auxin synergist that behaves in this manner. It is possible that the synergistic effect may be associated with a facilitation of auxin transport, whereas the inhibitory effect may be due to competition with auxin for an enzyme system.

Many of the synthetic auxins have become useful tools in plant culture. They have been employed for the rooting of cuttings, induction of flowering and fruit setting, prevention of preharvest dropping of fruits, production of parthenocarpic fruits, and the killing of weeds. All of these varied responses are related to the general function of growth.

WOUND HORMONES. When plant tissues are injured, they tend to produce scar tissue at the site of the wound. This is due to the promotion of cell division in tissues that are already mature and appears to be under the influence of auxin and another substance liberated by the injured cells. A compound, called "traumatic acid," is the best-known wound hormone.

FLOWERING HORMONE. A large body of evidence suggests that leaves are activated by photoperiodic stimuli to produce flowering hormones, or "florigens," which are translocated to apical meristems where they induce reproductive growth. Substances of this nature have not been crystallized and identified.

GIBBERELLINS. A rice disease, called "baka-nae" (foolish seedling), was first reported in Japan in 1898. The disease is due to a fungus, *Gibberella fujikuroi,* which causes the seedlings to grow unusually tall and then to die. Several growth-stimulating compounds, called "gibberellins," have been isolated from the causative fungus.[17, 21] Extracts from certain flowering plants have been found to give gibberellin-like responses. The gibberellins produce a wide variety of growth responses in flowering plants: among these may be mentioned stimulation of shoot growth, root elongation in maize, resumption of nomal growth in certain genetically dwarfed phenotypes of maize, and the transformation of bush beans to the pole type. The gibberellins also promote flowering in certain plants. Gibberellic acid is a tetracyclic dihydroxylactonic acid having the composition of $C_{19}H_{22}O_6$.

KINETIN. This substance is a derivative of adenine, one of the constituents of the vitally important nucleic acids. Kinetin was first obtained from yeast extracts and found to increase the formation of buds in seedlings. It has also been obtained from tobacco plants. When this hormone is added to a tobacco stem grown on a culture medium, it stimulates the formation of a large number of buds. A number of other adenine derivatives have been synthesized and found to be active in stimulating cell division in plant tissues. There is a certain amount of antagonism between the actions of kinetin and indoleacetic acid; minute amounts of indoleacetic acid inhibit bud growth in tobacco, whereas kinetin prevents this inhibition.

ORGANS OF UNCERTAIN ENDOCRINE FUNCTION

The Pineal Body

Clinicians have known for many years that pineal tumors are sometimes associated with precocious puberty, and this aroused the suspicion that some kind of a pineal-gonadal relationship might prevail at the human level. A review of clinical literature, made in 1954, suggests that true parenchymatous pinealomas correlate with depressed gonadal function, whereas tumors resulting in destruction of the pineal are frequently associated with precocious puberty.[11] This suggests that if the pineal is the source of a hormone affecting the gonads, it would probably exert an inhibitory effect. It has been extremely difficult to demonstrate that pinealectomy or the administration of pineal extracts have any significant effects on the gonads of laboratory mammals. Since the pineal of the intact organism functions with a circadian rhythm and hence does not release its products constantly, it is obviously essential to consider the photoperiods to which the experimental and control animals are subjected.

We have noted earlier that the pineal contains a high content of serotonin and an enzyme which converts this compound to melatonin and methoxytryptophol. This enzyme, hydroxyindole-O-methyl transferase (HIOMT), is not known to be present in any tissue other than the pineal body. The activity of HIOMT in the rat follows a circadian rhythm, more melatonin being produced at night than during the day. During the estrous cycle of the rat, HIOMT activity in the pineal is greatest at diestrus and falls appreciably during proestrus and estrus. The methoxyindoles of the pineal have been reported to depress the incidence of vaginal smears showing estrous phases in the rat. Denervation of the rat pineal by superior cervical ganglionectomy, like removal of the eyes, prevents the "early" response of the rat ovary to light.

It has been proposed that one function of the pineal in the rat is to serve as a neuroendocrine transducer, mediating the effects of environmental lighting on the gonads. Accordingly, information about lighting is perceived by the retina and nervous impulses are conveyed to the pineal by way of sympathetic nerves. The pineal responds by altering its production of methoxyindoles; these enter the blood stream and influence the endocrine economy of the body. The methoxyindoles are synthesized by the pineal in the absence of light and exert inhibitory effects on the gonads. It is possible that melatonin and other products of the mammalian pineal play an important role in many nonfeedback processes.[4, 27]

Very little information is available on the biochemistry of the pineal complex of sub-mammalian vertebrates. Bagnara's studies on pinealectomized amphibian larvae indicate that melatonin, or a closely related substance, is present in this class of vertebrates. Since the pineal is the exclusive source of a blood-borne agent (melatonin) which apparently operates as a chemical messenger, the time has probably arrived when it is justifiable to consider it as being an endocrine gland.

The Thymus

It is known that the thymus glands are essential for the establishment and maintenance of immunologic competence in neonatal rodents. When mice are thymectomized soon after birth, their ability to form antibodies in response to particulate antigens and skin homografts is greatly reduced.[16] Thymectomy of adult rodents is accompanied by a fall in lymphocytes, but does not result in any impairment of their immune functions. Two general theories have been advanced to explain the action of the thymus: (1) it may be an essential and exclusive source of immunologically competent cells which leave the organ and populate peripheral lymphoid tissues, and (2) it may be the source of a thymic hormone which conditions the proliferation and maturation of potential immunologically competent cells in many other tissues.

Studies have shown that liver cells from embryonic mice become immunologically competent when passed through the body of a host possessing its thymus gland, but not when passed through thymectomized hosts. The diminished ability of mice to form antibodies after neonatal thymectomy can be restored to normal by implanting into them thymus tissue enclosed in cell-tight Millipore filter chambers. This indicates the presence of a noncellular, diffusible material which is probably conveyed by the blood.[13, 26] If a neonatally thymectomized mouse is allowed to become pregnant when mature, the pregnancy repairs the mother's ability to form antibodies. This has been interpreted as meaning that a hormone or similar substance is produced by the thymus glands of the fetuses *in utero*, and this traverses the placenta and acts to restore immunologic competence to the mother.[18] These and many other experiments suggest that the thymus is the source of a blood-borne factor which induces the differentiation of lymphoid precursor or stem cells, rendering them capable of participating in immune reactions.

Opinions would probably vary on whether or not the thymus qualifies as an endocrine gland; however, there cannot be much doubt that it is the source of one or more hormone-like factors.

REFERENCES

1. Asboe-Hansen, G., and Glick, D.: Influence of various agents on mast cells isolated from rat peritoneal fluid. Proc. Soc. Exp. Biol. & Med., 98:458, 1958.
2. Braun-Menéndez, E.: Pharmacology of renin and hypertensin. Pharmacol. Rev., 8:25, 1956.
3. Code, C. F.: The inhibition of gastric secretion: a review. Pharmacol. Rev., 3:59, 1951.
4. Cohen, R. A., Wurtman, R. J., Axelrod, J., and Snyder, S. H.: Some clinical, biochemical, and physiological actions of the pineal gland. Ann. Int. Med., 61:1144, 1964.
5. Goldblatt, H., Lynch, J., Hanzel, R. F., and Summerville, W. W.: The production of persistent elevation of systolic blood pressure by means of renal ischemia. J. Exp. Med., 59:347, 1934.
6. Gregory, R. A., and Tracy, H. J.: The constitution and properties of two gastrins extracted from hog antral mucosa. Gut, 5:103, 1964.
7. Grossman, M. I.: Gastrointestinal hormones. Physiol. Rev., 30:33, 1950.
8. Jacobson, L. O., Goldwasser, E., and Gurney, C. W.: Control of red cell formation. In F. Stohlman, Jr. (ed.): Kinetics of Cellular Proliferation. New York, Grune & Stratton, 1959, p. 344.
9. Jacobson, L. O., Goldwasser, E., Gurney, C. W., Fried, W., and Plzak, L.: Studies of erythropoietin: the hormone regulating red cell production. Ann. New York Acad. Sci., 77:551, 1959.
10. Jorpes, E., and Mutt, V.: Gastrointestinal hormones. In G. Pincus, K. V. Thimann, and E. B. Astwood (eds.): The Hormones, Vol. 4. New York, Academic Press, 1964, p. 365.
11. Kitay, J. I.: Pineal lesions and precocious puberty: a review. J. Clin. Endocrinol., 14:622, 1954.
12. Langford, H. G.: An explanation of hypertension produced by narrowing the renal artery. Perspectives in Biol. & Med., 6:372, 1963.
13. Law, L. W., Dunn, T. B., Trainin, N., and Levey, R. H.: Studies on thymic function. In V. Defendi and D. Metcalf (eds.): The Thymus: Wistar Institute Symposium Monograph, No. 2. Philadelphia, Wistar Institute Press, 1964, p. 105.
14. McCubbin, J. W., and Page, I. H.: Neurogenic component of chronic renal hypertension. Science, 139:210, 1963.

15. Menkin, V.: Biology of inflammation. Chemical mediators and cellular injury. Science, *123*:527, 1956.
16. Miller, J. F. A. P.: The thymus and the development of immunologic responsiveness. Science, *144*:1544, 1964.
17. Nickell, L. G.: Production of gibberellin-like substances by plant tissue cultures. Science, *128*:88, 1958.
18. Osoba, D.: Immune reactivity in mice thymectomized soon after birth: normal response after pregnancy. Science, *147*:298, 1965.
19. Page, I. H., and Bumpus, F. M.: Angiotensin. Physiol. Rev., *41*:331, 1961.
20. Peart, W. S.: The functions of renin and angiotensin. Rec. Prog. Hormone Research, *21*:73, 1965.
21. Phinney, B. O., West, C. A., Ritzel, M., and Neely, P. M.: Evidence for "gibberellin-like" substances from flowering plants. Proc. Nat. Acad. Sci., *43*:398, 1957.
22. Preshaw, R. M., Cooke, A. R., and Grossman, M. I.: Pancreatic secretion induced by stimulation of the pyloric gland area of the stomach. Science, *148*:1347, 1965.
23. Schayer, R. W., and Ivy, A. C.: Evidence that histamine is a gastric secretory hormone in the rat. Amer. J. Physiol., *189*:369, 1957.
24. Skeggs, L. T., Jr., Lentz, K. E., Kahn, J. R., Shumway, N. P., and Woods, K. R.: The amino acid sequence in hypertensin II. J. Exp. Med., *104*:193, 1956.
25. Thimann, K. V.: Toward an endocrinology of higher plants. Rec. Prog. Hormone Research, *21*:579, 1965.
26. Tyan, M. L.: Thymus: role in maturation of fetal lymphoid precursors. Science, *145*:934, 1964.
27. Wurtman, R. J., Axelrod, J., Snyder, S. H., and Chu, E. W.: Changes in the enzymatic synthesis of melatonin in the pineal during the estrous cycle. Endocrinol., *76*:798, 1965.

Index

Note: Numbers set in *italic* type refer to illustrations.